OXFORD GEOGRAPHY

EARTH MATTERS
Studies in Physical Geography

RON CHASMER

OXFORD
UNIVERSITY PRESS

OXFORD
UNIVERSITY PRESS

70 Wynford Drive, Don Mills, Ontario M3C 1J9
www.oup.com/ca

Oxford University Press is a department of the University of Oxford.

It furthers the University's objective of excellence in research, scholar-
ship, and education by publishing worldwide in

Oxford New York
Auckland Bangkok Buenos Aires Cape Town Chennai
Dar es Salaam Delhi Hong Kong Istanbul Karachi Kolkata
Kuala Lumpur Madrid Melbourne Mexico City Mumbai Nairobi
São Paulo Shanghai Singapore Taipei Tokyo Toronto

and an associated company in *Berlin*

Oxford is a registered trade mark of Oxford University Press
in the UK and in certain other countries

Published in Canada
By Oxford University Press

National Library of Canada Cataloguing in Publication Data
Chasmer, Ron
    Earth matters : studies in physical geography
Includes index.
ISBN 0-19-541555-8
1. Physical geography. 2. Human geography. I. Title.
GB55.C533 2001   910'.02   C2001-930509-5

Printed and bound in Canada
This book is printed on permanent (acid-free) paper ∞

3 4 5 6—04 03 02 01

Acknowledgements
The author wishes to thank Tracey MacDonald,
editor, Oxford University Press, for her guidance on
the development of the manuscript; and Laura
Chasmer, graduate student, University of Waterloo,
for her suggestions during the writing of this book.

Special thanks to ESRI Canada's K-12 Program for
their assistance in developing the GIS lessons
contained in this textbook. For more information
on ESRI Canada, visit their Web site at
www.esricanada.com/k-12

Text design, composition, cartographic art and
illustrations: VISU*TronX*—J & J Loates, R. Sloat,
P. Clayton, C. Hellam

Cover design: Brett Miller

Cover photograph credits:
    Common morpho butterfly: Kevin Schafer/Stone
    Breaking ocean wave: Warren Bolster/Stone
    Lava emerging from Hawaiian spatter cone:
        G. Brad Lewis /Stone
    Tornado striking a Texan town: Alan R. Moller/Stone

Dedicated to Pamela

Contents

Features

UNIT 1

THE EARTH: A VIBRANT PLANET

Human Drama

JAPAN VOLCANO ERUPTS, 15,000 FLEE BILLOWING ASH

April 3, 2000—Japan's snow-capped Mount Usu volcano erupted on Friday, belching forth vast clouds of smoke and ash and forcing 15,000 people to flee their homes.

The 732-metre (2,402-ft) volcano, among Japan's most active, sent rocks hurtling into the air as plumes of dark grey smoke streaked with blue lightning billowed from the conical mountain.

Residents ran for cover, holding towels over their mouths as the smell of sulphur pervaded the air. Onlookers said they could taste grit from the eruption that hurled ash as high as 2,700 metres (8,850 ft) into the sky. A carpet of ash coated cars and houses.

Tremors were jolting the hot spring resort area on the northern island of Hokkaido as the eruption continued, Meteorological Agency official Manabu Komiya told reporters.

Ash, volcanic rocks and mudslides had flowed towards the small town of Abuta and the navy and the Coast Guard were deployed to evacuate the entire population of some 2,000 from homes perched precariously between the mountain and the sea.

Eruption of Mount Usu in Japan, April 2000

Officials said four naval ships, five Coast Guard vessels and two military helicopters had plucked residents to safety. "Depending on developments, the eruption could cause

Continued on next page.

even bigger damage," Prime Minister Keizo Obuchi said.

Officials said there were no reports of casualties. Mount Usu last erupted in 1978 after a series of earthquakes that gave birth to a new and smaller volcano by its side.

Mudslides triggered by that eruption killed three people.

Troops had already helped to evacuate more than 15,000 people from towns around the foot of the volcano and they were being housed in schools and public halls.

Thousands of earthquakes had rumbled through the region since Sunday as the mountain prepared to blow its top. Government experts said another big explosion appeared unlikely but it could take some time until the volcano settled down and more eruptions were possible from new craters.

"The fact that the ash cloud rose so high suggests the force of the eruption was strong. We can't dismiss the chance of other developments, like magma moves," said Yoshiaki Ida, chairman of the government's volcano experts panel.

Snow was falling heavily, further coating the slopes of the volcano still shrouded by billowing smoke from explosions of gases from five craters on the mountain's western slope. "Mount Usu has had seven significant eruptions that we know of, and at no time has it ended quickly with only a small scale eruption", said Yoshio Katsui, a professor at Hokkaido University.

Train services in the area had been disrupted, some flights had been diverted and roads blocked off, officials said. Officials warned residents to beware of mudslides amid predictions of heavy rain later on Friday night because snow on the mountain, believed to be 30 to 80 cm thick, could melt rapidly.

Officials warned there was a chance that an eruption at Mount Usu could mimic the deadly flow of superheated gas and ash from Mount Fugen in southern Japan in 1991, which killed 43 people.

(Story by Toshiyuki Aizawa,
REUTERS NEWS SERVICE)

Unit Focus Questions

1. What is the most widely accepted theory that explains how the Earth was created?

2. Why is the sun the most important energy source for the earth?

3. How did the lithosphere, hydrosphere, atmosphere, and biosphere evolve, and what are the characteristics of each?

INTRODUCTION

Earth is truly an amazing place. It is the only planet in our solar system that has all the necessary ingredients for intelligent life. You just have to look at the earth from space to see how it is different from the other planets in our solar system. Other planets lack the vitality of our planet. The earth is a sparkling jewel of many colours: blue for water, green for forests, sparkling white for ice caps and the swirling clouds, and brown for deserts. All these colours shine from the planet's surface across the vast, black expanse of space.

What we cannot see from space is the enormous range of animals that inhabit the planet, even though the physical evidence of one animal, in particular, is visible. Nondescript blobs of purplish gray interrupt the landscape, smudges of brown mar the crystal blue oceans, and the odd black dot pocks the ground. This animal is, of course, the human species.

Many would argue that humankind is the ultimate creation of the universe. What other creatures have the ability to reason, the genius to create, the capacity to alter the environment to meet their needs? No other creature has ever designed a computer, painted a masterpiece, or built a city of steel and glass. Yet from space, it does not seem that people are part of this incredible planet. The earth is so vast and beautiful that only where people congregate in large numbers is their presence detected on the planet. Unfortunately, people have so dominated and altered the world that much of what makes it remarkable is polluted, destroyed, or changed beyond recognition.

We are part of the biosphere; we are part of planet Earth, and the role of this book is to fill you, the reader, with a sense of wonder about our world. The hope for the future is that humans will no longer be the destroyers of nature but the stewards of the planet—the one species that protects all other species and natural systems. If we do not, the purplish blobs that represent our cities may spread like a cancer, eating up the countryside. The smudges of brown silt running into the oceans from land that has been cleared of its forests will colour more of the oceans, and the black pockmarks of oil spills and pollution will multiply across the landscape.

This book is organized into five units. This, the first unit, examines our beginnings as a planet, as well as the importance of the sun for our energy systems and our ultimate survival. Unit 2 deals with the lithosphere—the first part of our planet to start forming after the solar system was created. The text explores the incredible forces behind plate tectonics and erupting volcanoes, as well as the processes that wear mighty mountains down to flat plains. Unit 3 describes the hydrosphere—the sphere composed of water. Evolving along with the atmosphere from gases emitted from the lithosphere, water takes many forms. The oceans, the incredible movement of glaciers, and the life-giving movements of surface water across the planet are all addressed.

The atmosphere is the focus of Unit 4, in which we find out what we can do to help preserve the chaotic natural systems that swirl over our heads. The last section, Unit 5, deals with the biosphere—the sphere of life on the planet. Plants, animals and soil are not just here to serve people. It is our responsibility to preserve and protect other species as well as to thrive as a species ourselves.

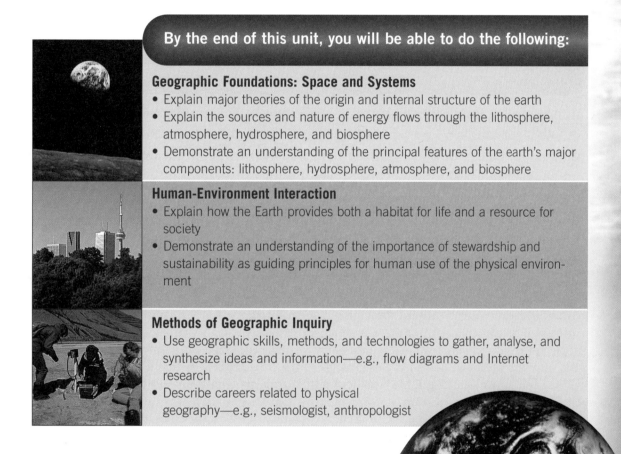

By the end of this unit, you will be able to do the following:

Geographic Foundations: Space and Systems
- Explain major theories of the origin and internal structure of the earth
- Explain the sources and nature of energy flows through the lithosphere, atmosphere, hydrosphere, and biosphere
- Demonstrate an understanding of the principal features of the earth's major components: lithosphere, hydrosphere, atmosphere, and biosphere

Human-Environment Interaction
- Explain how the Earth provides both a habitat for life and a resource for society
- Demonstrate an understanding of the importance of stewardship and sustainability as guiding principles for human use of the physical environment

Methods of Geographic Inquiry
- Use geographic skills, methods, and technologies to gather, analyse, and synthesize ideas and information—e.g., flow diagrams and Internet research
- Describe careers related to physical geography—e.g., seismologist, anthropologist

Contents

Chapter 1

THE BIRTH OF PLANET EARTH

FOCUS QUESTIONS

1. What is the theory most scientists use to explain how planet Earth was created?
2. What technologies are available for mapping and imaging the surface of the earth from space?
3. How can we use the Internet to locate information related to physical geography?

Key Terms

big bang theory

radiogeology

theory

hypothesis

remote sensing

There has been and continues to be a great controversy involving theories of the creation of our planet. Before the twentieth century, many people believed that the earth was a relatively recent creation. During that time, people perceived the world within a human time scale and were not aware of the fact that geological time could be much longer. Medieval Jewish scholars set the date of creation at 3760 BCE (Before the Common Era) and the Jewish calendar is still based on this determination. In 1658, James Ussher, an archbishop of the Church of Ireland, constructed a timeline for creation by interpreting the birth and death dates listed in the Christian Bible. He determined that the earth was created in 4004 BCE. The Greek Orthodox Church calculated creation as occurring in 5508 BCE.

According to Judeo-Christian tradition, God created Earth, all of nature, and humanity in six days and rested on the seventh. Other religions hold similar beliefs about the creation of our planet. Some traditional Pacific Island peoples like the Maoris believed that gods created the world from a great emptiness. According to Maori beliefs, two gods, Rangi and Papa, gave birth to many other gods. There was not enough room for all the gods, so they created the earth and the sky so that life could exist between them. In Africa, the Ashantis believe that a supreme god called Nyame created the universe.

To understand how the earth was created, we must first look at the explanation scientists give for how the universe was born.

Many scientists contributed to the development of the **big bang theory**, which is now the most widely accepted explanation of how the universe came into being. However, this wasn't always so. Today the big bang is thought of as a **theory**, but in the early 1900s it was just a **hypothesis**, lacking much in the way of supporting evidence.

Although the two terms "theory" and "hypothesis" are often used interchangeably, there is a difference in their meanings. Highly creative thinkers are the people who develop hypotheses.

There is no scientific basis for the hypothesis, but the idea comes out of a number of logical assumptions. In other words, the idea seems to make sense. In order for the idea to become a theory, scientists find evidence to support the hypothesis through observation and scientific inquiry. Once enough data supports the hypothesis, it becomes a widely accepted *theory*. We never actually know if the theory really does depict the truth about many geological processes, such as the creation of Earth, because these processes occurred before human observers could document any events. However, other scientific data leads one to believe that a particular theory is the best explanation of an event or process. The theory stands until a new hypothesis is made and factual data disproves the previously held theory. Throughout this book, theories are presented as to why things are the way they are. These ideas and explanations are widely accepted by experts in the field.

Technology was the key that provided evidence in support of the big bang theory. In 1922, astronomer Edwin Hubble observed that the universe was expanding. The most distant galaxies he could see through his telescope were moving away at about 40 000 km per second. More recent telescopes (including the Hubble Space Telescope) can see further into space and determine that more distant galaxies are moving away from Earth at ever-increasing rates. This new information supports **Hubble's law**, which states that the velocity at which a galaxy is moving away from us is proportional to the distance of the galaxy from us. That is, if galaxy B is twice as far away as galaxy A, then it is receding twice as fast as galaxy A. If the universe is expanding, then it is logical to assume that it was once infinitely smaller.

Belgian astronomer Georges Lemaître referred to this state as the "cosmic egg." Albert Einstein hypothesized that this cosmic egg exploded with such violence that its fragments are still flying out from the centre of the explosion billions of years

	Pluto	Neptune	Uranus	Saturn	Jupiter	Mars	Earth	Venus	Mercury
Mean distance from the Sun (million km, not to scale)	5 900	4 497	2 870	1 427	778	228	150	108	58
Time to orbit the Sun (days)	90 502	60 275	30 660	10 767	4 343	687	365	225	88
Diameter (km)	3000	48 400	52 000	120 000	142 800	6 794	12 756	12 104	4 878
Period of rotation (day)	6.38	0.67	0.45	0.42	0.41	1.02	0.99	243.0	58.67

Figure 1.1
The Solar System

later. Russian physicist George Gamow, in the 1940s, first coined the term "big bang" when he hypothesized that the radiation accompanying the explosion would still exist. He speculated that it would now exist as radio-wave radiation coming from all parts of the universe. In 1964, physicists Arno Penzias and Robert Wilson found the radio-wave background radiation. Most astronomers accept that this is sufficient evidence to move the big bang from the category of hypothesis to that of a theory. Today, astronomers and most scientists support the big bang theory as the initiating force that created the universe and eventually all structures contained within it, including Earth.

The big bang theory states that the universe began forming 15 to 20 billion years ago, following an enormous explosion. The dust and gas that were created as a result of this explosion

CHANGING TECHNOLOGY: The Hubble Space Telescope

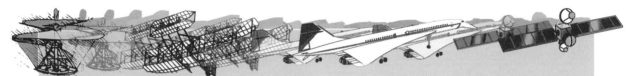

In 1990, the American National Aeronautics and Space Administration (NASA) launched the Hubble space telescope. While the telescope is now over a decade old, it was repaired in 1993, upgraded in 1997, and fitted with a new computer in time for the change of the millennium in 1999. The telescope has literally opened up a whole new universe to explore. It has allowed us to see new stars being born and old ones dying. This technology has increased our knowledge of the universe, and has allowed us to map planets, study moons, and observe asteroids, comets, and meteorites within our solar system.

The space telescope is just one of the many **remote sensing tools** astronomers use. Geographers also rely on remote sensing, but they tend to look at the earth from space, rather than at space from Earth. Earth scientists are very concerned with the relationships that exist among Earth, the sun, the moon, and other extraterrestrial objects. Not only can geographers gain insights into how the earth was created by observing other solar systems, but other aspects of physical geography are enhanced by looking into space. For example, climate change occurs partly because of changes in Earth's orbit and tilt, and the tracking of comets is carefully carried out to foresee collisions that could radically alter Earth's systems.

Question:
Why are remote sensing instruments, of all sorts, so important in the study of physical geography?

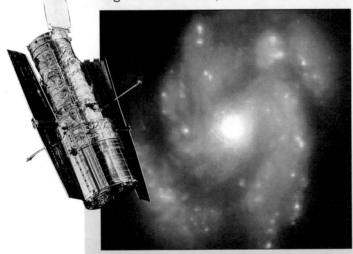

Figure 1.2
The Hubble Space Telescope and One of Its Great Views

Figure 1.3
While other life forms may exist in the universe, we can only satisfy our curiosity about them with our imaginations.

were drawn together by gravitational attraction to form a huge cloud. The debris in this gigantic, swirling cloud began to gather together in circular movements called **eddies**. The largest eddies contained enough matter to form whole galaxies. Smaller sub-eddies formed within the larger eddies. Each of these contained the material that would eventually make up solar systems.

The gravitational pull of the denser material at the centre of each sub-eddy drew matter from the outside inward. As a consequence, the cloud began to shrink and become denser. The increased pressure became so great that radioactive elements—remnants from earlier stars—started to produce huge amounts of energy through thermonuclear fusion. Vast amounts of energy were and still are created as hydrogen is fused into helium. From this nuclear reaction, the sun started to illuminate the newly born solar system. This new star consumed 90 to 95 per cent of the original dust cloud.

The material that was leftover formed a giant, spinning disc 10 billion kilometres in diameter that orbited the new star. Denser matter was drawn closer to the sun. Once enough of the dense matter gathered together, a chunk of rock, or **protoplanet**, was formed. The protoplanets are the terrestrial planets of Mercury, Venus, Earth, and Mars. Using **radiometric dating**, scientists were able to place the date of Earth's formation at approximately 4.6 billion ybp (years

before present). The lighter material flew to the outer margins of the solar system and formed the gaseous planets of Jupiter, Saturn, Neptune, and Uranus. (The question remains as to whether Pluto is gaseous, or is an escaped moon of Uranus.) Eventually all nine planets of our solar system were formed. Some protoplanets remained too small to be captured by the gravitational pull of the sun, but they did start to rotate around planets. These became the moons, and in some cases rings, that circle the planets. Leftover debris formed into asteroids found in the belt between Mars and Jupiter. This extremely complex theory of the big bang evolved over many years from the ideas of a great many scientists.

Seeing the Past

Based on what we have learned about the expanding universe, it is conceivable that we can actually see into the past. Light travels at a speed of 299 792 km per second. A **light year** is the distance light travels in one year (approximately 9.5 trillion kilometres). So, if we were to look at a star one light year away, the light we would see would have been created a year earlier. We would be looking into the past! Of course stars are much further away than one light year. The closest star to our solar system, Proxima Centauri, is 4.3 light years away (40×10^{12} km). How far into the past would you be seeing if you viewed this star? Most stars are much farther away than Proxima Centauri. Stars in our **galaxy**, the Milky Way, are as far as 80 000 light years from the sun. Stars in distant galaxies are billions of light years away. If the universe is 15 billion years old (a figure many scientists agree upon), light created when the universe was born may still be seen today! Theoretically, if astronomers could see to the edge of the universe, they would see the beginning of time and the creation of the universe. However, we can't see that far into the past—yet.

It is a generally accepted fact that humans are the only intelligent life in this solar system; however, that does not mean that we are alone. The chance that other life exists in the universe is not only possible, but it is very likely. World-famous astronomer Carl Sagan estimated

CHANGING TECHNOLOGY:
Radiometric and Radiocarbon Dating

Radiometric dating uses the radioactivity of certain minerals in rocks to determine their ages. It was radiometric dating that ascertained that planet Earth is about 4.6 billion years old. In November 1989, the oldest known rock was discovered in the Canadian Shield. It was formed 3.96 billion ybp, according to the Canadian Geologic Survey. However, meteorites found in ancient sediments are even older. Some have been dated at 4.6 billion ybp. Scientists believe these meteorites were formed at the same time as the earth. This would therefore put Earth's age at approximately 4.6 billion ybp.

Radioactive minerals are fairly ubiquitous and include uranium, thorium, radioactive potassium and radiocarbon, in addition to several other lesser known examples. On average there are about five parts of uranium per million parts of rock. That is an infinitesimal portion but it is enough to make accurate estimations of an object's age. The element emits energy in the form of alpha particles. As each particle is given off, the element gradually becomes less radioactive. A new element called an **isotope** is formed. The isotope has half the radioactivity of the original form of the element. This radioactive decay is not affected by heat, pressure, or any other external force. The length of time it takes the original element to create the isotope is called the isotope's **half-life**.

Uranium-238 is a common radioactive element used in radiometric dating. It is so named because it has an atomic mass of 238. When alpha particles are emitted, the isotope eventually decays until all that is left is lead, a non-radioactive element with an atomic mass of only 206. The half-life of uranium-238 is 4.5 billion years. To establish the absolute date when a rock was formed, geologists compare the amount of uranium-238 in the rock to the amount of lead-206. The more lead there is, the older the rock must be. For example, if a sample contains 2 g of uranium-238 and 2 g of lead-206, then the isotope's half-life has been reached, and the sample is therefore 4.5 billion years old.

Other isotopes have shorter half-lives. Potassium-40, for example, has a half-life of 1.3 billion years. It changes into argon and is commonly found in many rocks. Still, another method is needed for dating even younger material.

Radiocarbon dating enables scientists to date organic substances—that is, those containing carbon. It is accurate from 1000 to 60 000 ybp. Carbon-14 is an isotope found in all things containing carbon. It has an atomic mass of 14, while the atomic mass of non-radioactive carbon is 12. As it has a half-life of only 5700 years, this method is especially useful for dating recent geological events.

Question:
Give some examples of how this dating technology could be used in the study of physical geography?

that there are millions of advanced civilizations in the universe. Other astronomers have made similar assumptions. Given the enormity of the universe, the sheer number of galaxies, and millions of stars, it stands to reason that if even a small fraction of those stars had solar systems, the conditions for life could exist.

Earth: A Living Planet

But let's come back down to Earth. What is it about our planet that makes it so unique, so able to support life? For one thing, planet Earth is the only planet we know of that has large quantities of water in its liquid form. Surface liquid water is needed for complex metabolic processes to occur. Mars appears to have ice caps that increase and decrease with the seasons. It is further away from the sun, so the temperature is colder and liquid water does not form. Mercury is too close to the sun for water to exist in its liquid form since the heat causes the water to evaporate into the atmosphere. Study the chart below to see how the third planet from the sun (Earth) compares to Mars, the planet most like ours.

Another factor that relates to why life exists on Earth has to do with Earth's orbit. Because it is almost circular, Earth's orbit does not result in the

seasonal differences in temperature there would be if the orbit were more **elliptical**. If Earth's orbit were more oval, summers could be so hot that water would boil away, and winters could be so cold that Earth's oceans would freeze solid. These incredible differences in seasonal temperatures would make life as we know it impossible.

It is Earth's size that puts it the best distance from the sun for life to develop. If it had a greater mass, Earth would be closer to the sun and, as a result, the planet would be too hot to sustain life. If it were smaller, it would be too far from the sun and thus too cold. Mass also affects the gravitational pull of the planet. If its mass were smaller, the gravitational pull could be too little to hold essential gasses in the atmosphere, and they would disappear as they did from Mars. In addition to temperature and gravity, the planet's mass also affects tides, ultraviolet radiation, and its rotational period. These are all factors that affect the development of life on Earth.

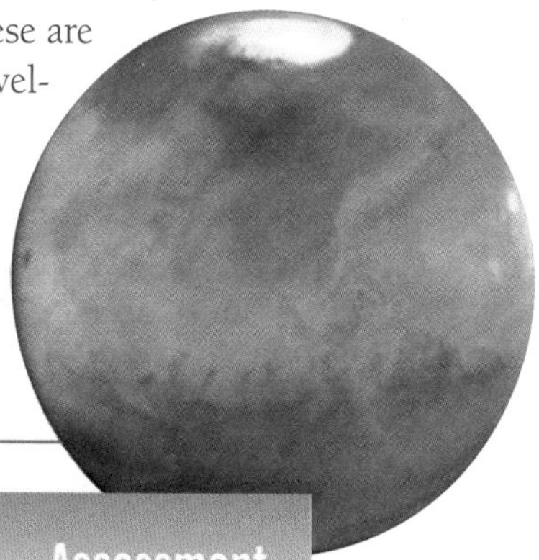

Figure 1.4
Mars, while similar to Earth, cannot support life.

Point of Comparison	Mars	Assessment	Earth	Assessment
Orbit	Almost Circular	Good for life	Almost Circular	Good for life
Length of Year	687 days	Too long	365.25 days	Good for life
Mean distance from Sun	228×10^6 km	Too far away	150×10^6 km	Good for life
Atmosphere	95% CO_2 3% Nitrogen	No O_2 for animals, too little nitrogen for plants	78% Nitrogen 21% Oxygen	Good for life
Diameter	6 794 km	Too small	12 756 km	Good for life
Water	Frozen at poles	Too little, not liquid	Covers about 70% of surface	Good for life

Figure 1.5
Comparing Characteristics of Earth and Mars

Researching on the Internet

The Internet is an incredible invention that allows people access to an enormous amount of information in their homes, workplaces, and schools. Sometimes the amount of information is so overwhelming that it's difficult to know where to start. Fortunately search engines have been designed to help sort information into a manageable system. There are many different search engines, although most are similar in their use of **Boolean strings** to find the requested information.

Traditional search engines may each require slightly different search strategies; however, all work more or less in the following way. Let's say you are looking for theories, other than the big bang theory, to explain the creation of our planet. There are five steps to follow in your search:

1. Log on to the Internet and choose a search engine, such as Yahoo (found at *http://www.yahoo.com*) for example. For a list of the addresses of different search engines, check the web sites *<http://www.ultranet.com/~egrlib/tutor.htm>* and *<http://204.17.98.73/ midlib/tutor.htm>*

2. Type a key word in the search box to describe the information you are looking for. It is vital that you spell the word correctly and use only lower case. Then simply hit the search button and wait. Within a few seconds, the computer will present you with a list of web sites which contain your word. So, if you want to research alternative theories for the creation of Earth, type *earth* in the search box and press the search button.

3. If your topic has a lot of synonyms or associated words, you could include one or two additional words to make your meaning more specific and your search more complete. To do this, use the Boolean search term "OR" between the synonyms. So, your search could become "earth OR world".

The list returned to you at this point will likely be enormous, and although it may contain the information you want, it may take you a very long time to read through all the offerings until you find it. So, you need to narrow your search parameters.

4. In order to reduce the number of sites, make the description of what you are looking for more precise. Since you want to know about creation theories, try adding that phrase to the search. Type the Boolean search term "AND" between the original words and the new phrase. Also, place quotation marks around phrases so that the computer will read those words together. For example, your search instructions could be: earth OR world AND "creation theories".

5. The search is getting better but you keep getting web pages about the big bang theory when what you actually want are alternatives to this theory. How do you think you can eliminate the big bang theory? If you suggested using the linking word "NOT," you are starting to get the hang of Boolean searches. Try the search string: earth OR world AND "creation theories" NOT "big bang". Now you should be well on your way to searching the web for different theories to explain how it all began.

Once the search engine presents you with a list of web sites and you are about to decide which one to check out first, keep in mind that all sites are not created equal. Anyone can set up a web page—you don't have to be an expert in computers or in any other subject to do it. As a result, before you decide to use any information from a web site, you should try to make sure that it has come from a reliable source.

The following tags are found within web site addresses. Recognizing them and knowing what they denote will help you evaluate the reliability and bias of the information contained in it.

.com	business or commercial site
.edu	educational institution site
.org	an organization or group
.ca	Canadian site
~	web page owned by an individual person
.gov	government site

TRY IT!

1. Search the Internet to find:
   - Theories, other than the big bang theory, explaining the creation of our universe
   - Spectacular views of our planet from the Hubble space telescope
   - The discovery of possible signs of life on Mars

ACTIVITIES

UNDERSTANDING CONCEPTS

1. Explain the difference between the terms "hypothesis" and "theory."
2. a) Produce a timeline listing the scientific discoveries that led to the general acceptance of the big bang theory.
   b) Using the big bang theory, explain how each of the following was created: galaxies, solar system, the sun, planets, asteroids, moons.
   c) What is there about the theory that you might find difficult to support?

DEVELOPING AND PRACTISING SKILLS

3. Explain how radiogeology can determine the absolute age of an object.
4. Draw a diagram to show your understanding of how the big bang resulted in the birth of planet Earth. Include labels and a one-paragraph explanation.
5. Conduct a search of the Internet to find out more about why other planets would not be suitable for life to develop. Use an organizer like the one that compares Earth to Mars on page 13.
   a) Assess information to determine each of the criterion in the chart.
   b) Assess why the planet would not have the Earth's capabilities to produce and sustain life.
6. This chapter has a decidedly pro-science bias in its discussion about the creation of planet Earth.
   a) Give evidence to show that there is bias.
   b) Either support the view the text presents or refute the ideas expressed by arguing for the Creationist or another point of view.

LEARNING THROUGH APPLICATION

7. In what ways do geographers use astronomers' tools and techniques to better understand Earth?

Chapter 2

EARTH: FROM CORE TO CRUST

FOCUS QUESTIONS

1. What are the components that make up the internal structure of the earth?
2. How does the science of seismology allow us to study the layers of our planet?
3. What is the principle of uniformitarianism, and how does it allow us to make certain assumptions about the geological features of our planet?

Key Terms

geological record

asthenosphere

uniformitarianism

fossil correlation

seismology

Throughout this book, reference is made to **geology** and **geologists**. Geology is the study of the earth's surface and all the material that lies beneath it. This is an immense field offering many different career opportunities, some of which are explored in subsequent chapters.

Geologists have developed many procedures to help them understand natural systems and structures. For example, in order to determine the internal structure of our planet, geologists used certain established principles, such as those stemming from the **geological record**, in conjunction with technologies such as seismology. These methods and principles allowed scientists to study the layers of the earth from its centre to its surface.

Reading the Geological Record

To historians, history is what people have written over a period of thousands of years. To geologists, history is what nature has recorded in rock over millions and even billions of years. History is literally beneath their feet. A trained geologist can look at the layers of rock in the lithosphere and tell the fascinating story of the changes that occurred in that particular spot. Ancient floods, tectonic uplift, volcanic ash—there is no end to the stories that are told in the geological record.

The time at which each of these geological events occurred can be thought of as either relative or absolute. **Relative time** describes an event as occurring before, after, or at the same time as other events. For example, you ate breakfast before you went to school. If you had a clock, you could describe the **absolute time** when each event occurred. Using the above example to describe absolute time, you could say that you ate breakfast at 8:00 a.m. and went to school at 8:20 a.m.

Geologists use three basic principles to read the geological record using relative time: superposition, uniformitarianism, and fossil correlation. These principles were first put forth by eighteenth-century Scottish naturalist James Hutton. As he was walking along the seashore, he observed that fresh sediments of silt and sand were laid down on top of older ones each day. Each layer was very thin—only a few millimetres thick—but it was obvious that over millions of years the sediments would build up to a considerable thickness. Clearly the sediment on top was newer than the material underneath. This led Hutton to form the principle of **superposition**—that is, the lower the layer of undisturbed rock, the older it is.

Hutton also made the assumption that natural processes occur in the same way today as they did in the past. This concept is known as the principle of **uniformitarianism**. It is an assumption based solely on observations. For example, a river flowing across a plain two billion years ago would have eroded the landscape and deposited silt in exactly the same way as that of a river with the same characteristics flowing through a plain today or a billion years in the future. This is an important discovery because when geologists study layers that were deposited millions of years ago, they make assumptions based on processes occurring on the earth today. So, by studying processes that are occurring today we can understand how geological structures were formed in the past. Processes occur uniformly no matter when they occur. The principle of uniformitarianism can even be applied to other planets. Channels on Mars, for example, indicate that there must have been surface water present at some point in time because they made the same meandering patterns that rivers make on Earth.

The principle of **fossil correlation**, like superposition, is useful in determining the relative age of a layer of rock. Fossils are organic plant and animal matter that has decomposed and been

Figure 2.1
A section of cliff at the Salisbury Crags shows the layers of ancient rock that helped visionary James Hutton develop the theories used by modern scientists to determine the internal structure of Earth.

Figure 2.2
By studying fossils, scientists can determine the relative age of a layer of rock.

removed and replaced by minerals in solution. This process results in the creation of an exact replica of the ancient life form. In different soil deposits that contain the same fossils, the soil and the fossilized animal in both deposits are from the same time period— the time when the animal existed. So, a dinosaur fossil in Saskatchewan would be the same age as a fossil of the same species found in Colorado. If the sediments were deposited before the plant or animal evolved, then its fossilized remains would not be present. Similarly, if the life form were extinct, the remains also would not be there. In this way, sediments with the same fossils can be dated relative to other sediment layers.

If you were to look at the layers of rock in a cliff, you could peel away the pages of geological history one by one. Each layer represents a different time. As you descend into the canyon, you go back further and further until you reach a time when there were no animals and eventually not even any plants. Each layer provides a detailed record of the plants and animals through their fossils.

Climate can also be determined by the kinds of fossils found. For example, if the fossilized remains are of creatures known to live in hot, moist jungles, then you know the climate of the area where the fossils were found. By studying geological processes today, we can make assumptions about what the region was like far into the past. Reading the geological record is fascinating.

CASE STUDY

Finding the Origin of the Human Species in South Africa

Anthropologists are scientists who study the evolution of the human species, among other things. They use the geological record to trace the development of the human species from earlier forms. When fossilized remains are found, field workers are careful not to disturb the rock in which the fossil was found. They want to study the fossil record to establish the rock's relative age. Once the age has been determined, then the fossil can be removed and studied.

In 1992, retired geologist Andre Keyser stumbled on a cave near his home, northwest of Johannesburg, South Africa. Anthropology was his hobby, and he had been looking for fossils when he found several baboon and elephant samples at the edge of the cave. He was excited by his find, but when he went into the cave, he made the discovery of a lifetime. On the floor of the cave, he found what looked like a human tooth. If there was one tooth there, the rest of the skull had to be there too, he figured. He has devoted the rest of his new career to excavating the cave and finding out more about the creatures that inhabited the area in the past.

By May 2000, only 5 per cent of the 1800 square metre site had been excavated. Researchers have to go very slowly so that they don't destroy fossils as they are digging them up. Drimolen, as the study area has come to be called, is one of the richest hominid sites in Africa. It has yielded eighty specimens of early humans so far. But how did all these remains end up in one spot?

Keyser developed the following theory, basing it on his knowledge gained as a geologist: Each year, in the rainy season, water floods into the cave from surrounding fields. As it does, it

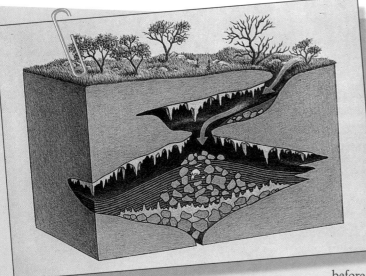

Figure 2.3
This diagram shows the cave in which Keyser discovered the hominid fossils buried under layers of sediment.

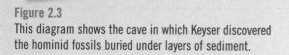

washes sediments, vegetation, bones, and anything else in the surrounding area down into the cave. Using Hutton's principle of uniformitarianism, it is logical to assume that river dynamics were the same a million years ago as they are today. Bones of these chimpanzee-like creatures, along with other objects, were deposited in a lower chamber of the cave. The bones were buried by debris washed in from the surrounding savanna, which also flowed in with the annual flood. So, what you had was a pile of bones, fossils, and soil at the bottom of a cave. Over hundreds of thousands of years, water dripped from the ceiling of the cave onto the accumulation of material. As the water percolated through the limestone above the cave, it dissolved some of the rock. This calcium carbonate was held in solution in the water. When the water evaporated, the calcium was deposited on the mound of fossilized bones and dirt. The calcium carbonate then cemented the different objects in the mound into a sedimentary rock called breccia.

The sediment and the bones were locked for eternity inside rock.

All the researchers have to do is break away the rock very carefully and they find fossils of many animals, including these ancient peoples. Hutton's principle of superposition would not help the researchers establish the age of the fossils since the remains had been disturbed by the annual floods. There was no telling how old the bones were before they were washed into the cave. Fossil correlation could, however provide significant clues as to the age of the hominid remains. By studying the pig fossils, which had also been buried with the hominid bones, Keyser and his researchers could determine the age of the hominids. Pig fossils are particularly useful because they evolved very rapidly at this time. Fossils with certain characteristics have been accurately dated from other fossil finds. Because the age of each different pig species was known, precise estimations of the age of the hominids were now possible. Incredibly, it was determined that these early humans were over 2 million years old! They are the oldest human remains found to date.

QUESTIONS:

1. How did Keyser use Hutton's theories in his discovery?
2. a) Explain how so many bones came to be deposited in the same place.
   b) How does this demonstrate that the world's surface is dynamic, in that it is constantly being reshaped?
3. Identify careers related to the study of early human fossils.

Layers Beneath our Feet

As was explained in Chapter 1, the earth was formed 4.6 billion years ago from a cloud of matter leftover after the formation of the sun. As the matter spun in space, the heavier material gravitated to the centre and the lighter material gathered around the outer side. Thus the layers of the earth were formed. Drilling holes into the earth and using probes to study these layers is impossible because of the huge distances involved. As a result, people did not know much about the internal structure of the planet until the science of **seismology** was developed and used in conjunction with the principle of uniformitarianism to gather information about the layers from the crust to the core.

Seismology evolved as a way of measuring earthquakes. A **seismograph** records the earth's vibrations when there is an earthquake. As the ground shakes, different waves are generated. As different waves move through the layers of rock that make up the planet, different characteristics can be deduced. Two types of waves are produced when there is an earthquake: surface waves and waves that go through the earth.

Two types of compression waves can pass through the internal layers of the planet: primary (P) waves and secondary (S) waves. P waves alternately squeeze and stretch the material they pass through. These compression waves pass through any material—solid rock, water, and even air. They move quickly and arrive first at a seismograph. S waves, by contrast, vibrate at right angles to the P waves and travel only through solids. They result from the compression waves that have passed through the rock before them. If we use the example of driving a car, the forward motion can be thought of as P waves while the vibrations of the car are the S waves.

Laboratory studies have been conducted to determine the properties of the two waves. Using controlled laboratory simulations, scientists were able to determine the speed at which the waves travel through different rock types. Pressure and temperature could similarly be determined. If the

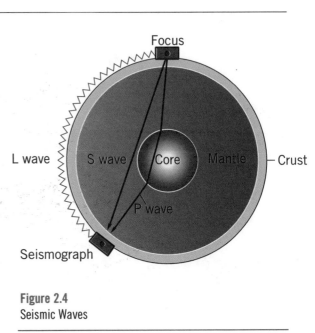

Figure 2.4
Seismic Waves

principle of uniformitarianism holds true, then lab results should be the same as seismic records caused by earthquakes. Therefore, seismic waves can be used as probes to better understand the nature of the internal structure of the planet.

Vibrations move through the layers of the earth differently, depending on temperature—cooler layers are generally more rigid than hot layers. When cool layers vibrate, they send out seismic waves at a higher frequency than the shock waves that travel through hot layers. Rock density also affects how shock waves travel. By determining the difference in velocity between P waves and S waves, the density of each layer of the earth can be determined. In Fig. 2.5, you can see that the speed with which P waves and S waves travel through the layers varies with depth.

At about 2900 km beneath the earth's surface an interesting thing happens. The P waves slow to about the same speed at which they travelled at the surface and the S waves stop completely. From seismic readings he took in 1914, seismologist Beno Gutenberg of the California Institute of Technology deduced that this is the depth at which the earth's liquid core begins. This border between the solid mantle and liquid core is called the **Gutenberg Discontinuity**.

The **core**, located at the centre of the earth, is made up of two parts, the inner core and the outer core. While the core appears quite small compared with the other layers, it actually makes up a third of the planet's total mass. When the earth was formed, the heaviest elements were pulled to the centre of the planet. The inner core is therefore likely made of iron, with some silicon and pockets of oxygen and sulphur. The density of the inner core is estimated to be 12.7 to 13 g/cm^3, about the same density as the metal, mercury.

Estimates of the temperature of the inner core vary from 4000°C to 6650°C. That is even hotter than some estimates of the sun's temperature! This incredible level of heat is the product of decaying radioactive material. Each time an alpha ray is emitted by radioactive matter, **nuclear energy** is given off. So, the same radioactive

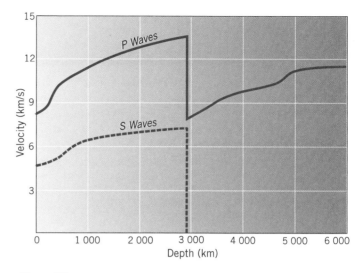

Figure 2.5
This graph shows that at a depth of about 2900 km the P waves slow down and the S waves stop.

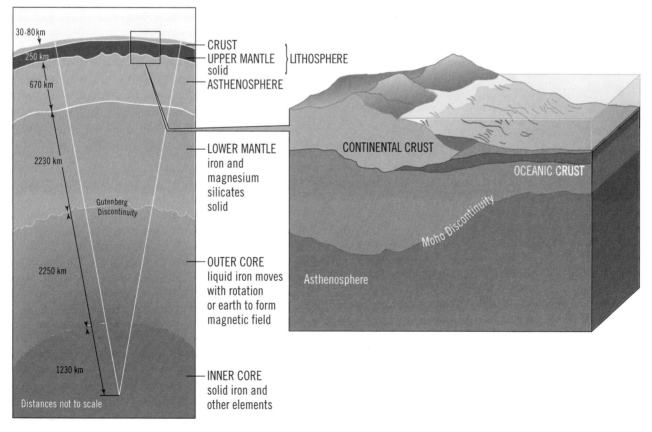

Figure 2.6
The Earth's Interior

Depth km	Oceanic Crust	Assumption	Continental Crust	Assumption
0 – 10 km	6.5 – 7.0 km/sec	Basaltic rock (crust)	1.8 – 5.5 km/sec	Sedimentary rocks (crust)
10 – 20 km	8.0 – 8.2 km/sec	Mantle	5.8 – 6.1 km/sec	Granite rock (crust)
25 – 35 km	8.0 – 8.2 km/sec	Mantle	6.5 – 7.0 km/sec	Basaltic rock (crust)
35 + km	8.0 – 8.2 km/sec	Mantle	8.0 – 8.2 km/sec	Mantle

Figure 2.7
This chart shows that seismic waves moved at different speeds through crust under the ocean and under continents. Assumptions were made about the nature of the rocks under each. Notice that the vibrations moved more slowly through rock layers closer to the surface under oceans than under continents. What differences are therefore inferred regarding the crust under oceans and continents?

isotopes that help geologists date rocks also create the heat of the earth's inner core. All of this heat is held in by the insulating effect of the rock layers that lie above. The enormous pressure of the rock pressing down makes the inner core solid rather than liquid.

Moving to the outer core, the intensity of the heat is still great, but there is less weight pressing down here from the outer layers. The reduced pressure allows the rock of the outer core to exist in a molten state. This liquid rock never reaches the earth's surface, and it should not be confused with the lava we associate with volcanoes. Volcanic eruptions result from much more localized circumstances existing just under the crust. The fluid layer found around the inner core generates about 90 per cent of the earth's magnetic field. Scientists think that this magnetic field is caused by electric currents deep in the outer core, which in turn are caused by the earth's rotation. It also forms the magnetosphere, a force field that protects the planet from cosmic radiation and solar wind. At 10.7 g/cm^3, the outer core is less dense than the inner core even though, like the inner core, it is made up primarily of iron. The transition zone between the

inner and outer core is approximately 5200 km below the earth's surface.

The **mantle** makes up about 80 per cent of the earth's total volume. It is less dense than the core, averaging 4.5 g/cm^3, but denser than the layers above it. Iron, silica, and magnesium are the mantle's main elements. Like the core, the mantle is divided into two parts: the lower mantle and the upper mantle. The lower mantle starts at about 2900 km beneath the earth's surface and extends upward to the much narrower upper mantle at about 500 km below the surface. Moving toward the surface, the temperature of the mantle gradually cools.

A layer in the upper mantle called the **asthenosphere** is thought to affect plate tectonics and mountain building. Decaying radioactive elements create hot spots where the mantle melts, making the rock less dense. Convection currents distribute this heat throughout the asthenosphere. As the material moves through the layers, continents sitting on the crust directly above the asthenosphere also move. This movement causes the crust to be folded or faulted to create mountains. When the hot spots reach the upper limit of the asthenosphere, volcanoes may erupt through the crust, forming new mountains. This is the molten rock that volcanoes bring to the surface. The asthenosphere helps to explain many of the processes that shape the lithosphere.

Above the asthenosphere, a discontinuity was discovered 10 to 35 kilometres from the earth's surface by Croatian seismologist, Andrija Mohorovicic. Below the Mohorovicic (Moho) Discontinuity there is a sharp increase in wave velocity. This has been widely accepted as the dividing line between the asthenosphere and the earth's crust. Interestingly, studies in the 1960s determined that the Moho Discontinuity is not of even thickness throughout the lithosphere. Fig. 2.7 shows the differences in crustal thickness under oceans and continents. This study provided important background knowledge to solve many mysteries about how surface features are formed.

The **crust** is the uppermost layer. It is a very thin covering on the surface of the planet, which makes up only 0.1 per cent of Earth's total volume. The crust is made up of two parts: the **sima**, which lies beneath the oceans, and the **sial**, otherwise known as the continental crust. The sima is made up of basalt rock, which contains mainly iron, magnesium, and silica minerals, and has a density of 2.9 g/cm^3. The sial is differentiated from the oceanic crust by its composition of many different types of elements, including silica, potassium, and aluminum, and by its thickness, which is greater than that of the sima.

The crust is especially important in the study of geography because it is where the natural systems of the four spheres come together. It holds the hydrosphere and supports all life on the planet. Highly complex mixtures of rock and organic matter form from processes in the atmosphere as they work on surface rocks. These complex materials are soils and they form the basis for the biosphere.

Figure 2.8
Seismologists Working at an Oil Site

Beno Gutenberg and Andrija Mohorovicic were both seismologists. This interesting field of study allows scientists to study the nature of objects using the vibrations of shock waves. A form of remote sensing, seismology is used in many fields, but the most common use is related to the monitoring of tectonic activity and oil-well prospecting. Earthquakes are measured by using seismographs. By studying the vibrations, seismologists can determine the location of the **epicentre**, the strength of the tremor, and can even hypothesize why it occurred. Similarly, volcanic activity can often be forecast when there is movement in the earth's crust around a volcano. Seismologists successfully predicted the eruption of Mount Pinatubo in 1991 and many residents were evacuated as a result. While property damage was great, the loss to human life would have been terrible if the people had not been forewarned.

In the oil industry, seismologists determine where deposits of oil or natural gas occur. Variations in shock waves travelling through the rock layers indicate where accumulations of the precious hydrocarbons are likely to be found. With oil wells costing millions of dollars, the seismologist's report can make or break an oil exploration company. A career as a seismologist takes a great deal of specialized training. A university degree in science or geological engineering is followed by post-graduate studies in physics and mathematics. In addition to being skilled in mathematics, physics, and geology, seismologists need to have expertise with computers and be able to function in remote, often dangerous environments.

Life Sprouts from Energy Beneath the Crust

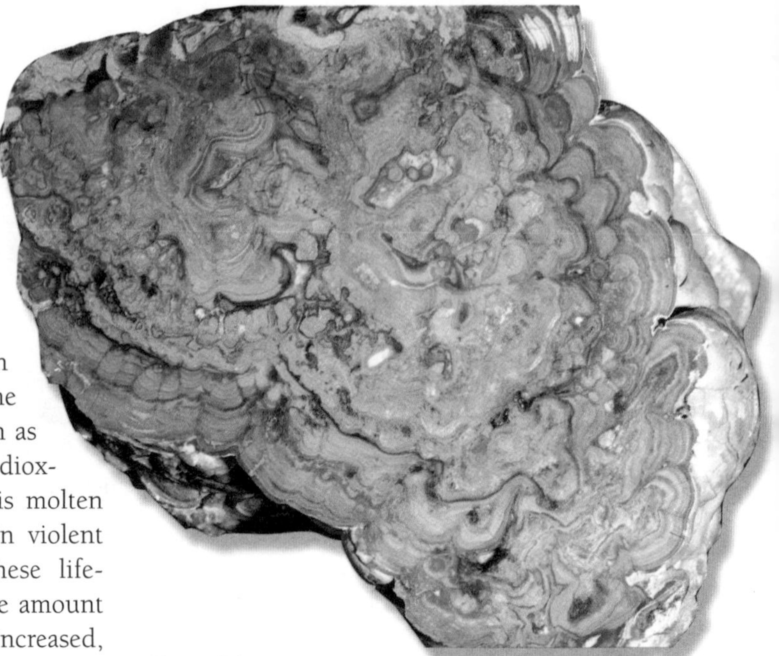

Geothermal energy generated in the layers beneath the crust indirectly contributed to the creation of life on Earth. When the planet was very young, volcanic activity was immense. Volcano cones dotted the landscape, geysers of superheated gases spouted fumes into the thin atmosphere, and lava flowed over the surface of the land. Lighter gases such as ammonia, hydrogen, methane, carbon dioxide, and water vapour trapped in this molten core eventually rose to the surface in violent volcanic eruptions. Gravity held these life-giving gases around the planet. As the amount of carbon dioxide and water vapour increased, the temperature of the planet stabilized. Not only did the air temperature cool, but the **diurnal temperature range** also dropped. No longer were the days boiling hot and the nights freezing cold. Much of the new atmosphere contained water vapour. Surface water started to accumulate at first in streams, then in pools, and eventually in vast oceans. The stage was set for the creation of life.

In the early fifties, American chemists Stanley Miller and Harold Urey conducted experiments simulating processes that likely occurred in the earth's early atmosphere. They sent high-voltage charges of electricity similar to lightning charges through a mixture of ammonia, hydrogen, methane, and water for a one-week period. Amino acids and simple chemical compounds linked to **cellular evolution** were created. Other experiments substituting carbon dioxide for hydrogen yielded similar results. While the links between amino acids and early life is still not understood, most experts in the field believe that amino acids created the building blocks for the earth's first signs of life.

Figure 2.9

This photo shows Proterozoic (1.5 billion-year-old) dolomite bedrock containing stromatolites, an early form of plant life.

Surprisingly, simple plants still exist today, having changed little over millions of years. Blue-green algae is believed to have been the first life form on earth. It accumulated in thin layers of slime on the rocks. As new slime grew on top of old for untold millions of years, layers of organic material created thick mats of organic matter. In time, the thick layers of dead organic material solidified into rock made up of layers of slime and grains of windblown sand. Called **stromatolites**, these rocks are found in many parts of Canada. Blue-green algae was just the beginning. Evolutionary processes transformed this early life into all the plants and animals that exist on the planet today. Without the gases sent into the early atmosphere, neither the atmosphere, nor the hydrosphere, nor the biosphere would have evolved. Our planet is the only place in the universe known to have a biosphere.

ACTIVITIES

UNDERSTANDING CONCEPTS

1. a) Using a relative time scale, prepare a timetable of events that have occurred in your school over the past week.
   b) Revise the list in a) to make it an absolute time scale.
2. a) Prepare fully labelled diagrams explaining the principles of superposition, uniformitarianism, and fossil correlation.
   b) Explain how two of Hutton's geological principles helped determine the age of the South African hominid remains at Drimolen.
   c) Explain how fossilized remains were preserved at Drimolen.
   d) The pig fossils found at Drimolen are called **indicator fossils**. What do you think this term means?
3. a) Explain how seismic waves led to theories about the internal structure of Earth.
   b) How are P waves and S waves different?
4. Why is it important that the outer core is liquid?
5. The magnetic field of the earth has reversed nine times in the past 4 million years. If this were to happen again, what problems could it create?
6. a) In what ways is the asthenosphere different from the other layers?
   b) How were researchers able to determine that the thickness of the crust varies under the ocean and the continents?

DEVELOPING AND PRACTISING SKILLS

7. Prepare an organizer like the one below to compare the different layers that make up the internal structure of the earth.

Name	Inner Core	Outer Core	Inner Mantle	Outer Mantle	Astheno-sphere	Crust
Depth						
Thickness						
Principal Materials						
Solid or Liquid						
Density						
Temperature						
Special Features						

8. a) Explain how the skills of the seismologist can be used for more than just geological research.
    b) What special skills and aptitudes did Andre Keyser carry over from his study of geology that helped him to be a successful amateur anthropologist?

LEARNING THROUGH APPLICATION

9. a) Write a short report on one of the following topics.
    • Explain the role of seismology in the study of geological structures.
    • Outline how Hutton's Geological Principles help anthropologists study fossils.
    b) Self-evaluate your paragraph. Give one mark for each point you believe has been fully explained.
    c) Exchange your work with another student and evaluate each other's work.
    d) Discuss any discrepancies between your mark and the mark that your peer gave you.

Chapter 3

HOW ENERGY GETS THE BALL ROLLING

FOCUS QUESTIONS

1. What are the principal features of the earth's major components: lithosphere, hydrosphere, atmosphere, and biosphere?
2. How does energy from the sun power each of the spheres of a landscape system?
3. How are flow diagrams produced and interpreted?

Key Terms

albedo

solar energy

geothermal energy

landscape system

fossil fuels

The big blue marble that is Earth is evolving and constantly changing. As energy flows through the different spheres, it changes the planet. Most of the energy that powers these changes originates with the sun.

It was no accident that ancient peoples revered the sun as a god. The mighty Ra was credited with growing the grain that made Egypt great. The ancient Greeks believed that their sun god, Apollo, protected their flocks and herds. The Aztecs offered human sacrifices every solstice to make sure the sun would return to produce the golden corn on which their empire depended. These ancient peoples understood the importance of the sun to their very existence. Their beliefs may seem naïve to us today, but in a way, we need to become more aware of how important the sun is to every aspect of our lives on Earth.

Earth is actually made up of four interconnected spheres. The **lithosphere** is the earth's brittle outer layers. It provides the very foundation on which the planet was built. Clouds, bodies of water, and stands of forests hide most of the lithosphere, but it was the first sphere to form and provided the basis for the other three spheres.

The **hydrosphere** is the sphere of water. The oceans cover the largest part of the earth's surface. Of all the known planets, only Earth has vast amounts of surface water. Smaller amounts of water are located underground and in ice caps, glaciers, lakes and rivers.

The **atmosphere** is not visible except for the clouds, which could actually be considered part of the hydrosphere. However, this mostly invisible sphere provides the air that is essential to life. The atmosphere's interaction with the hydrosphere is what makes the planet look alive from space. Swirling weather systems march across the earth's surface, hiding some areas of the surface and exposing others in an intricate dance between the two partners: moisture and air.

The most incredible of the spheres is the **biosphere**. The biosphere includes all life, not just

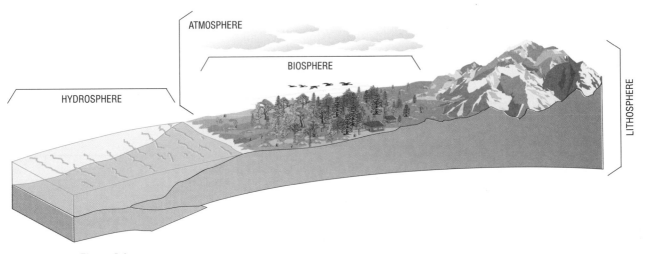

Figure 3.1
The Four Spheres of Earth

the impressive green forests, grasslands, and tundra, but all living creatures, from one-cell organisms to the vast array of more complex animals that roam the planet.

The sun is the largest source of energy flowing through the spheres. It is responsible, either directly or indirectly, for initiating the natural processes that occur all around us.

Solar Energy

Solar radiation travels through space at the speed of light. When it reaches Earth's atmosphere, subtle changes begin to occur. Some of this radiant energy is converted to thermal energy as the sunlight heats dust particles, carbon dioxide, and other greenhouse gases in the atmosphere. Some of the light is reflected back into space as radiant energy by clouds and ice crystals in the upper atmosphere. Much of the ultraviolet radiation is absorbed by the ozone layer. Most visible sunlight, however, makes it to the earth's surface. Once it strikes the earth, it is converted to different forms. Some of the energy is reflected back into the atmosphere as light, some is absorbed by the earth's surface as thermal energy, and some is converted to chemical energy by plants.

The colour of the earth's surface affects how much sunlight is reflected away as light and how

much is absorbed as heat. **Albedo** refers to the amount of solar radiation that is reflected back into the atmosphere as light. When the albedo is high, most of the sun's energy is reflected as radiant energy. Therefore, the air over these surfaces tends to be much cooler than the air over surfaces where the albedo is low. From space, areas with high albedo appear as the brightest parts of the planet during the daylight hours. Ice caps, snowfields, and bare ground all have high

Figure 3.2
The Big Blue Marble: Earth from Space. Of all the planets, Earth stands out as a jewel in a lifeless solar system.

albedos. Many artificial surfaces like parking lots, house roofs and arenas have low albedo because they are dark and dull. Rough surfaces like ploughed soil also have low albedo. Therefore they tend to be hotter than light-coloured, shiny, smooth surfaces.

Nighttime temperatures are a lot lower than daytime ones on the earth's moon and on the sun's other planets, but not on Earth. Why? The fact is that little solar energy comes directly to the earth as thermal energy. The sun provides us with radiant energy that the earth's surface converts to heat. This heat is then re-radiated back into the atmosphere. The atmosphere acts like insulation, trapping the heat close to the earth's surface. It is not surprising that the coolest temperatures are usually just before dawn. This is because the earth has been losing heat all night without receiving any radiant energy from the sun for several hours.

If the earth received more energy than it gave off, the earth's temperature would increase, and this is what many people believe is currently happening at an ever-increasing rate in what is called the "greenhouse effect". Carbon dioxide is being produced as people burn fossil fuels to run their cars, generate electricity, and perform the hundreds of daily tasks that increase carbon dioxide and other greenhouse gases. These gases re-radiate thermal energy back to the earth's surface. If the amount increases, the temperature will rise. This could upset climate systems, raise the sea level, and disrupt human activities all over the world.

If the earth radiated more thermal energy than it received, the situation would be even more disastrous. Temperatures would drop, ice caps would get larger, the growing season would be shortened, and we might not be able to grow the crops needed to support a global population of over 6 billion people.

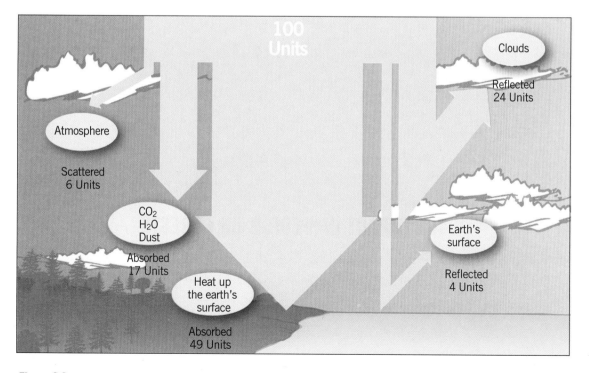

Figure 3.3
Solar Inputs and Global Outputs
For every 100 units of solar energy that enters the atmosphere, only 49 per cent actually heats the earth's surface.

Interpreting Flow Diagrams

Flow diagrams are often used in technical writing. Computer scientists, engineers, other kinds of scientists, and geographers utilize flow diagrams to help explain principles and processes. In order to interpret a flow diagram, follow the steps outlined below.

1. Read the title of the diagram and determine its meaning. In the case of Fig. 3.3, "Solar Inputs and Global Outputs" refers to the energy being received from the sun (solar inputs) and energy being given off by the earth (global outputs).

2. Carefully read the caption and any other text that accompanies the diagram. The caption in Fig. 3.3 explains that only 49 per cent of the solar energy entering the atmosphere actually heats the earth's surface. What is implied but not directly stated in the caption? If 49 per cent of the energy entering the atmosphere reaches the earth's surface, then the other 51 per cent must either be reflected back to space or absorbed by the atmosphere.

3. Determine what is being represented by the symbols and objects shown in the flow diagram. In the example, the picture shows the earth's surface (land and water), the atmosphere, and the sun.

4. Follow the arrows through the diagram to understand the order in which processes are occurring. Make sure to note if the thickness or the length of the arrows change, as this could indicate additional information about the process being illustrated. There are five arrows of varying thickness in the example. It appears that they are drawn to scale to show how much energy is distributed to each of the five different destinations.

5. Note the connection between the labels and the arrows. The labels show in point form what is happening in each situation. For example, 6 per cent of the solar energy received is scattered by the atmosphere.

6. In order to fully understand the implications of the flow diagram it is usually a good idea to restate the idea in a paragraph using your own words.

TRY IT!

1. Using the steps outlined in this feature, analyse the flow diagram on p. 34 (Figure 3.6)

2. Create a flow diagram to illustrate the effects of one human activity on one aspect of the environment. Here's an incomplete example related to forestry. What can you add to it?

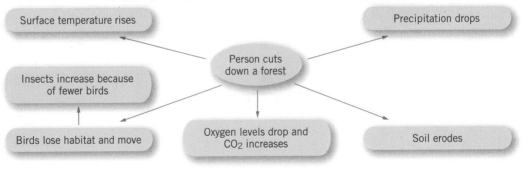

THE IMPACT OF PEOPLE ON FORESTS

Surface temperature rises

Precipitation drops

Person cuts down a forest

Insects increase because of fewer birds

Birds lose habitat and move

Oxygen levels drop and CO_2 increases

Soil erodes

Solar Energy Takes Other Forms

Winds and ocean currents are natural processes created by differences in the heating and cooling of the earth's surface. When air or water is heated, it rises, and cooler air or water rushes in to replace it. Precipitation is another manifestation of solar energy since thermal energy from the sun is required to evaporate water. The energy used up through evaporation results in less energy for heating, so the temperature drops. Flooding flat apartment roofs can reduce urban temperatures. As the water evaporates, the temperature over the roof drops because of the energy used to dry up the roof. The opposite happens when water vapour condenses: heat is given off.

Whenever we use **fossil fuels** to heat our homes and run our machines, we are releasing into the atmosphere solar energy that was created long before humans ever existed. Natural gas, for example, was created millions of years ago from decomposing swamp vegetation. While these plants were alive, they stored solar energy in the form of carbohydrates, a substance made through the chemical process of photosynthesis. After the plants broke it down, the energy was stored until we burned it as fuel. Oil and coal are other fossil fuels that were created in a similar way and which also release greenhouse gases when they are burned.

Even the food we eat contains energy from the sun. Plants are called **producers** because they use sunlight to actually *produce* living material from inorganic substances. Animals cannot produce organic matter directly from sunlight, but they obtain solar energy by eating, or *consuming*, plant matter or animal matter that came from eating plants. So instead of producers, they are called **consumers**. Through digestion, the energy received from these plants and other animals is sent to all the animal's body parts that need it.

Energy from Other Sources

Minimal amounts of energy come from sources other than the sun. The earth, for example, creates some energy of its own. Its hot interior, with temperatures up to 2600°C, originated billions of years ago when the earth and sun were first created. However, little of this **geothermal energy** reaches the earth's surface, although massive amounts are released locally when volcanoes erupt. Compared with solar energy, geothermal energy is negligible, amounting to less than 0.0001 per cent of the earth's total energy supply.

Another source of energy is the tides, which produce kinetic energy caused by the pull of gravity from the moon and the sun. Light from the moon and the stars provides other sources of energy but the amounts are minuscule.

Although these sources seem substantial, their combined energy production is so insignificant compared to the amount generated by the sun, that if the sun were to suddenly stop shining, Earth would cease to be a living planet.

Seeing Energy Flows in Nature

Whenever there is something moving in nature, energy—originating either directly or indirectly from the sun—is being used. Clouds skim overhead, birds dart through the sky, and streams gurgle and splash. Other energy movements are more gradual or subtle and therefore less obvious, such as water evaporating from puddles, soil creeping down the side of a hill, or light being reflected off a pond.

Landscape systems show how energy flows through each of the spheres in a particular place. When you study a landscape system, you are not just studying what is there; you are studying *why* it is there. The study of systems is the same no matter what the subject. In computer science, for example, systems analysts study how information flows through computer hardware. It is not important what the equipment looks like.

What is important is how the equipment processes information. Similarly, geographers are more interested in processes—why things are the way they are.

geo.web resources

<http://parkscanada.pch.gc.ca/parks/main_e.htm>

The Parks Canada web site provides access to all national parks in Canada. Once at this site, choose Banff National Park from the list of selections and take a virtual tour of the Rocky Mountains to see and study more examples of landscape systems.

Have you ever visited the Canadian Rockies? The region is famous for its incredible beauty, great skiing, and fantastic wildlife. Fig. 3.4 on page 33 shows the Bow Valley, a particularly beautiful part of Canada. Look carefully at the photograph and try to visualize the energy that is flowing through this landscape system. If you study the photograph, you can imagine energy flows in each of the four spheres.

DEVELOPING SKILLS

Interpreting Landscape Photographs

In order to understand the processes that shape a landscape, geographers rely on different techniques. The landscape system shown in Figs. 3.4-3.6 illustrates three of these methods: a photograph, a diagram (or tracing) from a photograph, and a flow chart. (Other techniques could include field studies, quantitative analysis, and maps—all of which will be studied in other skills features throughout this book.) Follow these steps to study the energy flowing through a particular landscape system.

Part I: Analysing a Photograph

1. Obtain a good oblique air photo. Mountain scenes are very good because there is usually a lot happening in the scene. You can choose one of the pictures in this book or find your own (calendars often have good scenes and many are available on the web).

2. Take a piece of tracing paper (rice paper is best) and trace the main features with a sharp pencil. If you have a light-table or an overhead, the image is easier to see. Use masking tape to prevent the paper from slipping. Once the tracing is complete, go over it with fine-tipped black marker.

3. Try to identify at least ten natural objects shown in the photo and label each of them with block printing. You may notice clouds, ice-capped mountains, rivers, grass, and so on.

4. Categorize each object by the sphere it represents, using a colour code so that, for example, grass could be coloured green since it is in the biosphere; ice may be blue for hydrosphere; and sunlight yellow for atmosphere. The diagram does not have to be realistic since it is an analytical tool. Once the diagram is complete, you can use the information in it to prepare a flow chart.

Figure 3.4
Photo of a Landscape

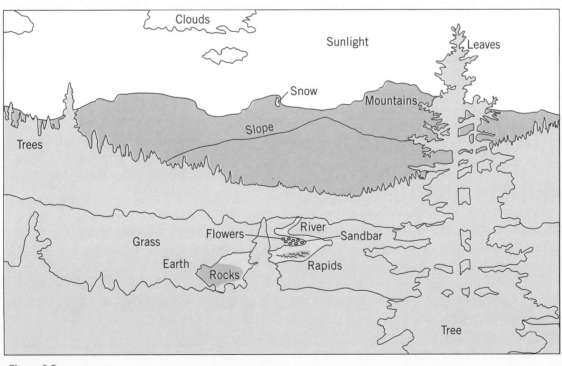

Figure 3.5
A Fully Labelled Tracing

Part II: Producing a Flow Chart

1. List the different labels from the tracing on a blank piece of paper. Using the colour code, put a box around each word to represent the sphere to which it belongs.

2. To show energy transfers between the different elements of the landscape system, draw arrows between the boxes. Along each arrow, print an action to show how energy moved from one aspect of the environment to another. It is possible that every element in the system interacts with every other element, so your flow chart could be very confusing.

    Study these pairs of words and determine what energy transfers could occur between each: Clouds and River, River and Trees, Grass and Clouds, Mountainside and River, Ice cap and Rocks.

3. Redo the flow chart using a computer word-processing program, if available. Reposition labels so those elements that are closely associated are together, and colour-code the labels to show the different spheres.

Part III: Writing a Report

1. The procedure so far has been done solely to make you more aware of the processes that occur in a landscape system. The diagram and the flow chart are organizers that help you to see the system more clearly. To write a report, simply describe the processes that occur between the labels.

2. Start anywhere on the flow chart and follow the arrows through the system. Try to end up where you started.

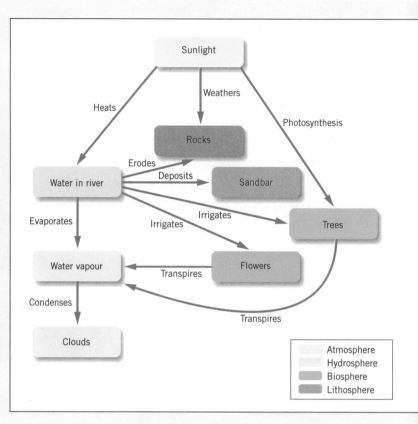

Figure 3.6
This is a partial flow chart describing the energy flows in the system. Copy and complete this diagram.

The whole point of this exercise is to understand that even a still picture evokes a changing scene. With a little imagination and a good understanding of energy flows in natural systems, anyone can begin to understand how incredibly complex, unique, and magnificent natural systems are.

PRACTISE IT!

1. Choose another landscape photo and follow the above steps to examine the energy flows in the scene.

ACTIVITIES

UNDERSTANDING CONCEPTS

1. a) Define the lithosphere, atmosphere, hydrosphere, and biosphere.
   b) What characteristics do all four spheres have in common?
   c) Explain how the sun is central to energy flows among the spheres.
2. Fig. 3.6 is a flow diagram similar to Fig. 3.3.
   a) Study the *Developing Skills: Interpreting Flow Diagrams* feature on page 30 and explain what steps would apply to Fig. 3.6.
   b) Go through the suggested questions that apply and write a paragraph explaining the diagram.
3. Explain what the term "albedo" means and give examples to show the difference between the albedos of different surfaces.
4. Air conditioning consumes vast amounts of energy in Canadian cities during the summer because many urban surfaces such as parking lots, roofs, and cement buildings absorb heat rather than reflect it. Imagine you are a city planner, and come up with as many suggestions as possible to help combat this problem.

DEVELOPING AND PRACTISING SKILLS

5. a) Trace a landscape photo using onionskin, rice paper, or a transparency (Fig. 3.5 illustrates a tracing).
   b) Label each element of the landscape system. Use a colour key for each different sphere. For example: hydrosphere—dark blue; lithosphere—brown; atmosphere—pale blue; biosphere—green. The more labels you have, the better. Try for 15 to 20. If you wish, lightly colour your scene, but do not cover up important details. It is a good idea if you go over your tracing with a fine-tipped black marker to improve presentation.
   c) Mount the tracing on a piece of stiff paper or cardboard.
6. Each of the elements you labeled in Question 5 b) is a feature of the landscape in your original photograph.
   a) Print these labels on a piece of paper and draw boxes around each one.
   b) Draw arrows between each of the boxes to indicate where a process is occurring, and write the process on the arrow. For example, between leaves and clouds you could draw an arrow labelled *transpiration*.
   c) When you have finished drawing the arrows, redo the flow chart, rearranging boxes that go together. Use a ruler and fine-tipped marker to draw your finished flow chart. (Refer to Fig. 3.6 for a sample a of flow chart.)
7. a) Draw a sketch map showing what the landscape in Question 5 (a) would look like from directly overhead.
   b) Use the flow chart to write an analysis of how energy flows operate in the scene.

LEARNING THROUGH APPLICATION

8. Study five or six surfaces with different colours and textures, which are exposed to direct sunlight. Consider using surfaces such as tarmac, cement, grass, bare ground, a car hood, a black shingled roof, or a white shingled roof. Using a thermometer, record the temperature of the air above each surface and rank these areas from highest to lowest albedo. Explain what you observed.

9. Construct a two-column chart to show how energy from the sun is used in your everyday life. In the first column, list 10 examples of your average everyday activities. In the second column, explain a connection between the activity and energy derived from the sun. For example,

Daily Activity	Energy Derived From The Sun
Drive to school	Fossil fuel used by the car (or bus) is stored solar energy

10. What implications does the fact that our environment is constantly changing have for people today? Consider changes in each of the lithosphere, the atmosphere, the hydrosphere, and the biosphere.

Culminating Activity: Making Connections Among Earth's Spheres

The eruption of Mount Usu, as illustrated in the article at the beginning of this unit, was ferocious, but the people in this particular incident were lucky since no deaths were reported. However, the impacts of the explosion on the people living in the vicinity of the volcano, as well as on the natural ecosystems surrounding it, were significant.

The story is an example of the tremendous powers at work in the lithosphere. But that is not all it is about. A careful reading of the story will also bring to light the human element, as well as information pertaining to the hydrosphere and the atmosphere. This is because the spheres of this planet, while differing in composition and characteristics, are tightly intertwined such that almost no occurrence in one sphere on planet Earth is independent of the others.

To get a better sense of Earth's spheres, this culminating activity asks you to gather articles about the physical world and analyze the interactions between the lithosphere, atmosphere, hydrosphere and biosphere taking place in each story.

Web Sites

You may find the following web sites helpful in your search for articles involving issues of physical geography.

- Planet Ark <http://www.planetark.org/> This site contains a database of environmental and natural disaster stories from several years ago to the present date.

- The Globe and Mail <http://www.globeandmail.com> One of Canada's national newspapers, this publication contains quality features related to Canada, as well as stories from around the world.

- Natural Resources Canada <http://www.NRCan-RNCan.gc.ca> Containing vast amounts of information on natural systems and the environment, this site is great for background research.

- Environmental News Network <http://www.enn.com/news/index.asp> Although this is an American site, it does contain stories from Canada and other countries around the world.

1. Monitor newspapers, magazines, the Internet, or any other available sources of recent information, for a period of one week. Clip or photocopy stories that relate to physical geography as well corresponding photographs and maps wherever possible. These stories could be about environmental issues, such as global warming, acid rain, and pollution; natural disasters such as volcanic activity, earthquakes, blizzards, floods, drought; wildlife and biodiversity; or issues involving sustainable development of the earth's resources.

   Amass at least three stories.

2. For each story, note the connections to or the implications for the four spheres by making and filling in a chart resembling the example on page 39. In the first column briefly describe what the story was about, as well as giving its date and location. Keep in mind that each story will probably have a very obvious connection to one sphere in particular, and you may have to do additional research to fill in the rest of the chart. The first one has been done for you, using the article in the Unit 1 opener as the example.

3. Within each story, there may be experts in the field of physical geography quoted or referred to. For example, in the article on Mount Usu, Japan, a volcano expert (volcanologist) and a professor from Hokkaido University were quoted on the status of the eruption and on the possibility of further dangers. Find the experts in your stories and do a career profile of his or her profession in terms of educational requirements, working conditions, and future prospects for others choosing to study in that particular field of expertise in Canada. If no expert is mentioned, surmise about the professionals who may have been consulted during the incident, and research that career.

4. After the charts and the career profiles are complete, present them and their corresponding articles, as well as photographs and maps, in a scrapbook.

Story	Lithosphere	Hydrosphere	Atmosphere	Biosphere
Date: April 2000 Location: Japan Description: Mount Usu erupted after a series of earthquakes, sending a vast column of smoke, gases and debris into the air. Fifteen thousand people were evacuated from the area, but no deaths were reported.	The earthquakes occurred because tectonic movement of crustal plates built up tremendous pressure which was released through the volcanic eruption.	Snow and rain fell on the volcano soon after the eruption. It was feared that the heat from the volcano would quickly melt the snow, turning it into a lubricant which could trigger additional mudslides down the sides of the volcano. Ash and debris falling in lakes and rivers would pollute the water.	The volcano sent massive plumes of thick smoke and toxic gases (sulfur) into the air. These emissions not only pollute the atmosphere, but also harm wildlife and people, who breathe it in. Lightning also resulted from the eruption, which could also be very dangerous to people and animals.	People were forced to evacuate the area around the volcano by the thousands. Searing volcanic ash, as well as rocks and debris raining down after the eruption, would likely have killed and/or harmed wildlife in the area.

UNIT 2

THE GROUND BENEATH OUR FEET: UNDERSTANDING THE LITHOSPHERE

Human Drama

TURKISH EARTHQUAKE!

Out of rubble from Turkey earthquake comes 'a miracle'

ISTANBUL, Turkey –Four-year-old Ismail Cimen couldn't sleep and was playing with his toy truck when his world went black.

For more than six days, alone in a tiny space below a collapsed balcony, the boy waited for someone to come. But for days, no one was looking. His relatives had given up the search and already prepared his grave.

"A miracle of God" occurred today, his uncle said. Sait Cimen was removing rubble to look for bodies when he shined his flashlight into a gap 18 inches high. Little Ismail squinted into the beam.

Bulgarian and Turkish rescuers helped pull the boy into the weak dawn light after 146 hours in darkness in Cinarcik, 30 miles south of Istanbul. At a time when many search teams are abandoning efforts to find survivors, the black-haired boy shows that the will to live can often defy the normal boundaries of human survival.

"I was playing with my truck. Then I fell," whispered the emaciated and severely dehydrated boy while he rested in an Istanbul hospital. His nails were filled with the brown dirt he clawed at just after the quake struck at 3 a.m. on Aug. 17.

When he realized he was trapped, the boy called for his parents. When they didn't answer, he simply waited. Through badly chapped lips, he summed up his ordeal in the unvarnished honesty of a child: "I was very scared."

"We thought he was dead, too," his uncle said. "I had even prepared a grave for him in his hometown."

But other graves will be filled: His father and three sisters, ages 8 to 13, were killed. The body of one sister was buried in rubble only a few yards from the boy. The boy's mother, Serife, survived the collapse of the building and is hospitalized in the city of Bursa.

"She is inquiring all the time about the whereabouts of her family," the boy's uncle said. She has not been informed of their fate. Dr. Murad Molla, an emergency-room physician, said the boy was in good condition and should fully recover.

The quake, which this boy and his mother survived, was centred in Izmit, a populous suburb of Istanbul, Turkey's largest city. It struck at 3:02 a.m., while

Continued on next page.

most of the city's citizens slept. In 45 seconds, nature's brute force levelled more than 40 000 buildings. Scientists labelled this quake a magnitude 7.4 on the Richter scale.

The earthquake that struck Turkey's North Anatolian fault, a deep fracture in the Earth's crust, now ranks as one of the five deadliest quakes of the 20th century. In its aftermath, Turkey has become a classroom for teams of seismologists, who are trying to glean lessons from the fury of a rumbling earth. The pressing question: Does this quake increase the likelihood that subsequent tremors could destroy nearby Istanbul, with its population of 12 million? And could the disaster in Turkey happen elsewhere in the world?

Neistat, Van, *Science World*, 11/01/99, vol. 56, issue 5, p.16

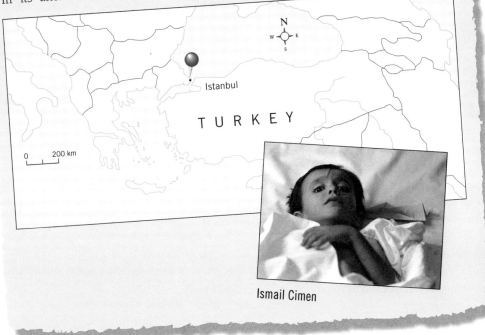

Ismail Cimen

Unit Focus Questions

1. What is the theory of plate tectonics and what evidence exists on land and at the bottom of the ocean to support this theory?

2. How do forces below and above the surface of the earth create and shape landforms and cause natural disasters in the lithosphere?

3. How do earthquakes, volcanoes, landslides, and other natural disasters occurring in the lithosphere affect the lives of the people living near them?

INTRODUCTION

The ground that feels so solid beneath our feet is not always so stable! In addition to earthquakes, our planet is plagued by other types of natural disasters, originating with processes that take place deep within the lithosphere and which shake the earth and disrupt our lives. Volcanic eruptions and landslides, for example, rank with earthquakes as major problems that have devastated the environment, killed and injured thousands of people, and even destroyed whole cities.

However, along with these problems, the lithosphere also provides us with many valuable resources that are an integral part of economies around the globe. We have come to depend on substances such as oil and natural gas, iron, gold, and diamonds, and their discovery and sale has a major impact on people and environments everywhere. It is for these reasons, among others, that studying the lithosphere has become such a crucial enterprise for geographers the world over.

The lithosphere was the first part of the planet to form and was responsible for the creation of the hydrosphere and the atmosphere (more or less at the same time), and eventually the biosphere. The lithosphere encompasses continental land masses and the floors of the oceans. It includes minerals and precious gems, fuels such as oil and natural gas, and the fossilized remains of creatures that roamed the planet millions of years ago. In this unit, we explore the forces of nature that have formed the lithosphere and that continue to change it today.

The scientific field of study that relates to studies of the lithosphere is geology, and much of what is presented in this section of the book is scientific in many ways. But we must not lose sight of the essence of geography. It is not enough to study the lithosphere without looking at the impact of geology on the plant and animal population and on other scientific disciplines. It is this holistic approach that sets geography apart from other sciences.

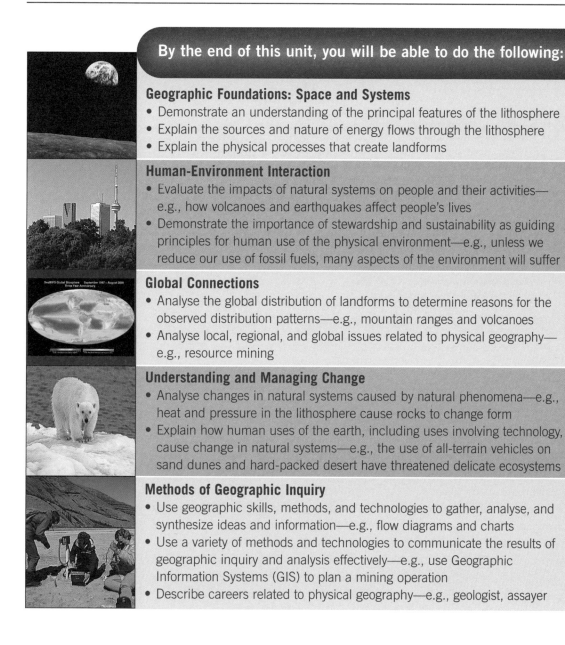

By the end of this unit, you will be able to do the following:

Geographic Foundations: Space and Systems
- Demonstrate an understanding of the principal features of the lithosphere
- Explain the sources and nature of energy flows through the lithosphere
- Explain the physical processes that create landforms

Human-Environment Interaction
- Evaluate the impacts of natural systems on people and their activities—e.g., how volcanoes and earthquakes affect people's lives
- Demonstrate the importance of stewardship and sustainability as guiding principles for human use of the physical environment—e.g., unless we reduce our use of fossil fuels, many aspects of the environment will suffer

Global Connections
- Analyse the global distribution of landforms to determine reasons for the observed distribution patterns—e.g., mountain ranges and volcanoes
- Analyse local, regional, and global issues related to physical geography—e.g., resource mining

Understanding and Managing Change
- Analyse changes in natural systems caused by natural phenomena—e.g., heat and pressure in the lithosphere cause rocks to change form
- Explain how human uses of the earth, including uses involving technology, cause change in natural systems—e.g., the use of all-terrain vehicles on sand dunes and hard-packed desert have threatened delicate ecosystems

Methods of Geographic Inquiry
- Use geographic skills, methods, and technologies to gather, analyse, and synthesize ideas and information—e.g., flow diagrams and charts
- Use a variety of methods and technologies to communicate the results of geographic inquiry and analysis effectively—e.g., use Geographic Information Systems (GIS) to plan a mining operation
- Describe careers related to physical geography—e.g., geologist, assayer

Contents

Chapter 4

CONTINENTS ADRIFT

FOCUS QUESTIONS

1. What is the difference between the geological and human time scales?
2. How does energy flow through the lithosphere?
3. What role do convection currents play in the movement of the earth's continents around the globe?

Key Terms

continental drift

geological time scale

human time scale

convection currents

plate tectonics

The lithosphere consists of the uppermost layers of the earth, namely the upper mantle, which lies above the asthenosphere, and the crust. Although the lithosphere came into being billions of years ago, it continues to change and evolve. Land that was once at the bottom of the ocean has been uplifted hundreds of metres. Continents have slid halfway around the world and crashed into other land masses. Ancient creatures have become extinct and their remains have become fossilized in rock. Coastlines have subsided and wetlands been created where the land was once dry.

Change is one of the most important concepts in the study of the lithosphere. It occurs when an object is transformed into something else over time. But what incredible sources of energy are powering these changes?

Energy Flows in the Lithosphere

As with the other spheres of our planet, the sun is the energy source that powers most of the changes that occur on the surface of the lithosphere. However, radioactive elements in the planet give off great amounts of energy as they **decay**, or change from one element to another. This process, along with currents in the asthenosphere, continues to power changes on the earth's surface.

The lithosphere produces its own heat as the radioactive elements, uranium and thorium, break down to form new elements. It is estimated that uranium accounts for about five parts per million of the earth's surface, and thorium comprises even less. Although this is a minute proportion of the planet, the radioactive decay of uranium has made Earth a living planet. Uranium changes into lead and helium over time. As the elements decay, vast amounts of heat energy are given off. Material in the crust and mantle absorb these energetic particles and convert nuclear energy into heat energy. As the amounts of uranium and thorium decrease through the process of decay, the amount of heat being released into the lithosphere decreases.

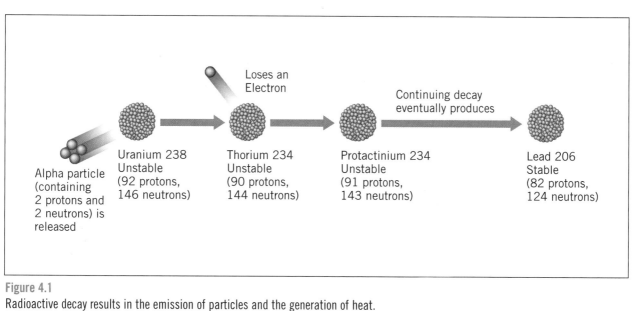

Figure 4.1
Radioactive decay results in the emission of particles and the generation of heat.

But don't worry, the planet will not stop producing its own energy for a long time. It is estimated that we will run out of uranium and thorium in 5 to 10 billion years.

Energy to Move Mountains

This geothermal energy beneath the lithosphere keeps the ground we stand on in constant motion and change. For example, the mountain where you and your friends go snowboarding and the island that you swim to in the summer have not always been there, and may not be there in the distant future.

Such incredible changes are almost unfathomable for most people, yet they continue to happen all round us. The reason we are unable to envision and experience them is that they happen so slowly. Geological changes, such as those mentioned, often take millions of years to occur and, as a result, often go completely unnoticed.

Not all geological changes happen slowly, however. Volcanic eruptions, earthquakes, and mudslides happen in such a short period of time that human lives are often threatened. In November 1998, Mount Soufriere sent a massive ash cloud 7000 metres over the Caribbean Island of Montserrat within minutes. Islanders were reminded of the 1995 eruption when three quarters of the island nation's residents were evacuated because of very sudden and dangerous eruptions.

Our perception of change is affected by how we think about time. Because people only live for 80 years or so, events taking many years to occur are perceived as taking a long time. If we lived a million years, then changes that last only a few hundred years might be perceived as happening relatively quickly. To most people, a recent event is just a matter of a day or two because we operate within a **human time scale**. Because the planet is billions of years old, geological change is perceived differently because it is framed within the context of the **geological time scale**. A recent event may be something that happened thousands of years ago!

Tectonic movement of the continents is slow, even on the geological time scale. These forces cause continents to glide snail-like over the surface of the earth, and mountains to form as continents crash into each other. It sounds dramatic, but these processes take millions and millions of years.

Figure 4.2
Toronto Island (created 100 ybp)

Each of these photos depicts changes in the lithosphere that took place tens, thousands and even millions of years ago. Which events could be experienced on the human time scale?

Figure 4.4
PEI Beach and Coastal Lagoons (created 20 000 ybp)

Figure 4.3
Ski Resort in B.C.
(created 20 years ago)
Rocky Mountains (created 60 x 10⁶ ybp)

Figure 4.5
Lava Flow Around Mauna Loa (created 20 years ago)

Continental Drift

Great thinkers as far back as Sir Francis Bacon (1620) have commented on the way the continents seem to fit together in one giant jigsaw puzzle. Examine a world map and judge for yourself. Look at the southwest coast of Africa, for example. It seems as though it would fit together fairly well with the east coast of South America, while the northwest coast of Africa looks as if it had been pulled apart from the northern coast of South America. The curve of the western coast of India matches the curve of the eastern coast of Africa, and Baffin Island looks as though it broke away from the northern coast of Quebec. These similarities in shape are not coincidental; they are the result of continental drift.

German meteorologist and physicist Alfred Wegener was not taken seriously when he proposed the theory of **continental drift** in 1912. He believed that the continents were once joined together in one single great land mass, which he called Pangaea. Wegener argued that about 200 million years ago, Pangaea split into two large continents, Laurasia and Gondwanaland. These broke up further to form even smaller continents as the land masses moved apart. Geologists did not accept the theory because Wegener could not explain how the continents moved. The rock structures underlying the continents seemed too rigid to allow for the continents to glide from place to place on beds of granite as he proposed. The continental drift theory was intriguing, but most geologists could not support it.

A better knowledge of the structure of the lithosphere, derived from seismic studies (described in Chapter 2), provided much of the background needed to understand how continents could, in fact, float on denser rock layers below. The discovery of the plastic asthenosphere made the idea seem plausible. Currents in this semi-fluid layer of the upper mantle could, theoretically, provide the force to move the continents.

In the 1960s, the idea of continental drift was revived by Tuzo Wilson. This Canadian geophysicist, working out of the University of Toronto, conducted a detailed analysis of glaciers, mountains, and especially sea beds. He expanded on Wegener's earlier ideas by establishing the concept that the continents moved on **plates**, or large

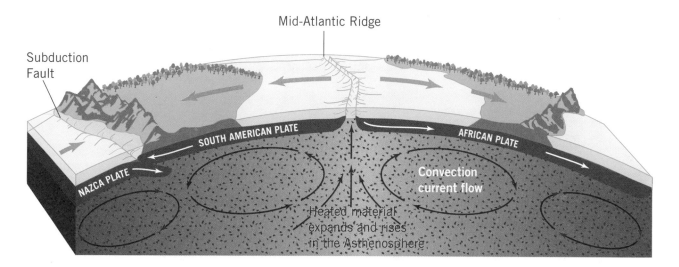

Figure 4.6
Plate Tectonics
Using your knowledge of the internal structure of the earth, explain what is happening in this illustration.

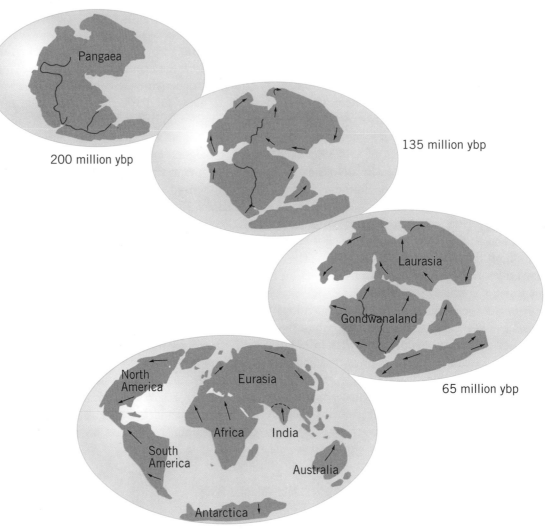

Figure 4.7
Location of Earth's Plates from 200 Million Years Ago to the Present

sections of crust, floating on a less dense upper mantle. He coined the term "**plate tectonics**" and provided the theoretical basis for many of the processes that occur in the lithosphere. Major scientific journals of the day were reluctant to publish his early work because it was so radical. In the 1970s, detailed sea-bed analyses confirmed that his ideas were indeed plausible. Wilson's hypothesis is one of the twentieth century's most significant advances in science.

It was a new technology that eventually helped to provide support for Wilson's theory of plate tectonics. After World War II, a military invention called sonar was used to map the floor of the Atlantic Ocean. Originally used as a form of underwater radar to detect submarines, sonar derives its name from **so**und + **n**avigation + **a**nd + **r**anging (meaning "finding the distance"). It works by sending high-frequency sound signals through the water, which reflect off the sea floor

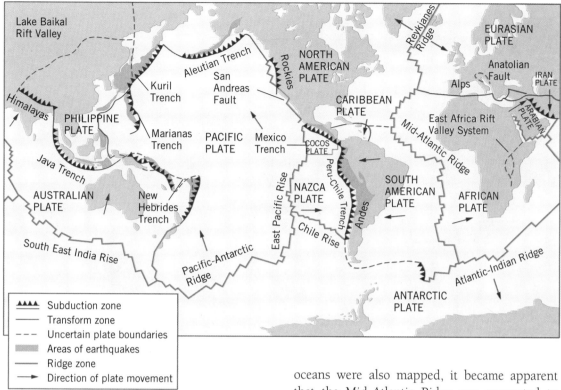

Figure 4.8
The Earth's Major Plates

and return to the sender. The depth of the ocean is determined by measuring the time it takes these signals to travel to the bottom and back. By 1953, ships equipped with sonar had finished mapping the floor of the Atlantic.

By the 1960s, all the oceans' floors had been mapped, and for the first time, geographers could see the surface of the earth unobscured by the oceans. Maps of continental shelves beneath coastal oceans show that the edges of continental shelves fit together even more closely than shorelines. There is less erosion under water, so shapes are closer to what they were like when the continents split apart.

The underwater maps also showed an astonishing feature that was previously unknown. At first, a Mid-Atlantic Ridge was discovered, running more or less equidistant from the Americas and Europe and Africa. When the other

oceans were also mapped, it became apparent that the Mid-Atlantic Ridge was connected to ridges in all the other oceans. A 64 000 km-long midoceanic ridge runs around the world through each ocean. It is by far the most significant geological feature on the planet! In places, the ridge is quite close to land, but in other oceans, such as the Atlantic, it runs down the middle of the body of water. On closer examination, it was found that the ridge was not like mountain ranges on earth, but was composed of basalt—a type of rock associated with the lava that oozes out of volcanic fissures in the sea floor.

geo.web resources

<http://www.ucmp.berkeley.edu/geology/tectonics.html>

This site is dedicated to exploring the history of the study of plate tectonics, and the science that supports the theory.

Go to the Plate Tectonics Animation section at the bottom of the home page and click on any of the globes to see the plates in motion throughout the ages.

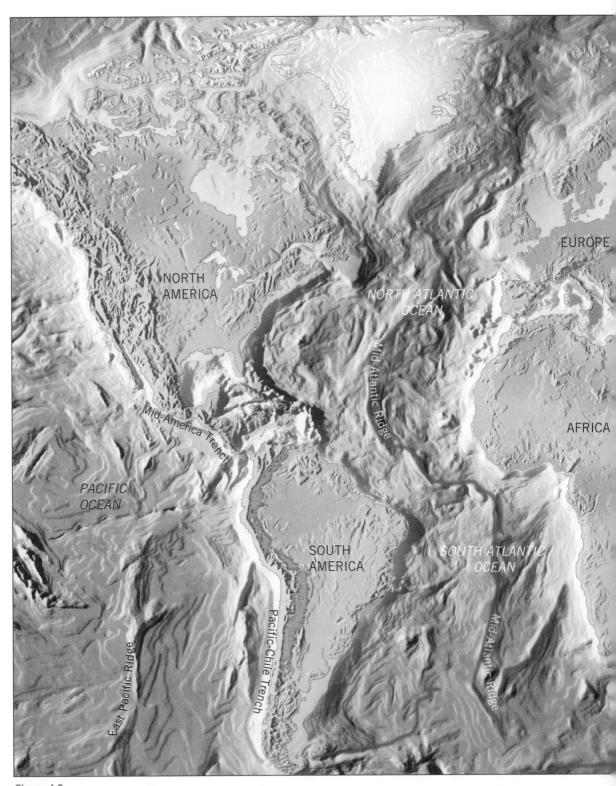

Figure 4.9
This map clearly shows the midoceanic ridges and trenches of the ocean floor.

As if the discovery of the midoceanic ridge was not enough, another feature adjacent to the ridge was also discovered. An enormous canyon splits the ridge in two. At first it seemed as if the rift was a continuous crack in the earth's surface. However, it was later determined that there were fairly short individual gorges set apart with fault lines on each side.

By now, you're probably wondering what exactly the midoceanic ridge has to do with plate tectonics. Evidence that the plates actually move lies hidden in this seafloor feature. Theorists believe that the midoceanic ridge is where the continental plates split apart. The rift occurs because the sea floor is continuously spreading apart and magma comes to the surface to fill in the gap created in the crust. The basalt ridge is formed from a build-up of the new material from within the lithosphere.

What needed to be proven was that rocks were younger close to the ridge and that they aged in a regular pattern as they progressed away from the ridge. In other words, the rock formations on either side of the ridge had to mirror each other. Sea core samples taken from sites equidistant from the east and west sides of the ridge proved this. Radiogeological dating (discussed in Chapter 1, page 12) supported the view that geological structures formed in pairs, with one feature moving west to the Americas and one moving east to Africa and Europe.

Magnetic evidence also supported the idea that the earth's crust was born out of the midoceanic ridge. As volcanic rock cools, magnetic elements align themselves with the earth's magnetic field. However, the magnetic field of the earth reverses from time to time: the north and south poles change places. Rocks formed at times of the reversal show opposite magnetic orientations in regular patterns on either side of the midoceanic ridge (see Fig. 4.10). Thus the sea floor must be moving away from midoceanic ridges. New crust is being created where the sea floor is spreading apart.

Fossilized Support for Plate Tectonics

Other evidence supporting plate tectonics was added by studying fossils. In 1968, a fossilized bone of an extinct amphibian was found in Antarctica. It was reasoned that the creature could not have evolved in so frigid a land, and that Antarctica must have moved to its present location from a region further north with a more salubrious climate. In addition, the same 300 million-year-old worm fossils have been found on all of the continents. This example of fossil correlation indicates that the continents must have been joined in order to share this common species.

Later sediments indicate that a reptile order called mesosaurus lived in present-day southern Africa and Brazil, but nowhere else. This suggests that the continents of Africa and South America were still joined 200 million years ago, but that the others had broken away. By 100 million years ago, according to the fossil record, each continent had its own distinct animals, except Australia and Antarctica.

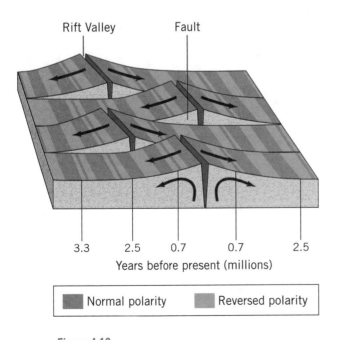

Figure 4.10
Rift Valley, Faults, and Patterns of Paleomagnetism

These two continents must have been joined for some time after the others had separated. Continental drift explains why the animals found on each continent today are unique to that continent—because they were separated from their ancestors and so evolved differently.

Even geological structures matched corresponding ones on opposite coastlines. For example, the same ancient rock is found on the west coast of Africa as is found in Brazil on the east coast of South America. Such evidence strongly suggests that the continents must have been joined and have since separated and drifted apart.

The Nature and Movement of Oceanic and Continental Plates

So, what causes the crust to split apart along the midoceanic ridge and the continental plates to drift around the planet? Seismologists have determined that the upper mantle (asthenosphere) is 10 to 15 per cent liquid. This **plasticity** allows rock layers deep beneath the surface to flow like any other fluid. It is difficult to conceive of a flowing solid, but consider this example: Suppose your little sister left some Plasticine on the window ledge on a cold winter day. It is a solid, so it stays where it is supposed to stay. The sun comes out and heats the windowsill to 30°C. What happens to the playdough? It becomes soft and starts to flatten out. The edges flow out under the weight in the centre.

In the asthenosphere, heat from friction, pressure, and radioactive decay make the granite upper mantle act just like the Plasticine. **Convection currents** cause this pliable semi-liquid rock to flow from regions with high temperatures to cooler regions. You can readily observe convection currents if you study a pot of soup boiling. We know that a fluid expands as it is heated (see fig. 4.11). Therefore, it becomes less dense and tends to float to the surface as do bubbles in hot soup. Cooler, denser soup at the surface along the edge of the saucepan sinks back to the bottom of the pot where it is heated and rises again in the middle of the saucepan (where the bubbles surface). Convection currents are very common in nature. They not only occur in the upper mantle, but are also important in the hydrosphere and the atmosphere.

The evidence collected from core samples showed that the oceanic crust was thinner than that of the continents, especially near the midoceanic ridges. It was also considerably younger, and it was made of volcanic rock that oozed out of midoceanic rifts.

Continental plates have very different characteristics. They are thicker, older, and have much more complex geomorphology. As the upper mantle flows from one place to another, these plates are dragged along with it. Canadian geophysicist Peter Hood described the plates as moving on giant conveyor belts. In regions where one plate collides with another, the continual pushing causes the plates to **subduct**, or sink back into the mantle. The pressure of the two plates grinding together is so great that the plates buckle, forming mountains.

By studying Fig. 4.6 (on page 47), you can see that the crust is not only pushing the continental plate away from the midoceanic ridge, but it is sliding under the continental plate where the oceanic plate and the continental plates meet. So,

Currents

Heat

Figure 4.11
Convection currents can be seen working in a pot of boiling soup.

plate tectonics accounts for the movement of the continents, but it also explains other tectonic processes and patterns, such as why mountains occur on the colliding edges of plates and why active volcanoes are located where they are. It also explains why oceanic trenches often occur alongside rugged-fold mountains. Even earthquakes and fault patterns are related to plate tectonics. Thus we can see that plate tectonics is an important basis for further studies in geological processes.

Shaking the Earth

Earthquakes are a direct result of plate tectonics. When plates come in contact, there are bound to be problems along the fault lines that separate them. As one plate moves one way and another resists, pressure builds up. If the plates are able to slide past one another gradually, then there will be many small **tremors** on an on-going basis. Tokyo, Japan, can have a dozen or more mini-quakes everyday, with little to no damage done. It is when the pressure keeps building up without any release that the really dangerous

geo.web resources

<www.pgc.nrcan.gc.ca/seismo/table.htm>

Natural Resources Canada and the Geological Survey of Canada have dedicated this site to earthquakes. Click on "Current Earthquake Activity" to find out where the most recent quakes occurred. Also click on "Earthquake Preparedness" in the "General Information" box to find out what you should do to ready yourself for such emergencies.

earthquakes occur.

Earthquakes are among the world's most costly natural disasters in terms of property damage, loss of life, and physical and psychological trauma experienced by survivors. It is not so much the actual shaking of the earth that causes the devastation, but rather the collapsing of the structures people build in their urban areas. Buildings crumble, trapping people inside; water mains burst, causing floods; gas lines burst; hydro poles come down; and hundreds of explosions add to the mayhem. Bridges buckle, roadways collapse, and subways cave in. All this happens in a matter of minutes!

Take, for example, the major earthquake that struck the state of Gujarat, India in January 2001. Measuring 7.9 on the Richter scale, the quake resulted in the deaths of approximately 30 000 people and destroyed whole cities leaving another 400 000 people homeless.

Some faults are more susceptible to earthquakes than others. Because plates are moving apart through **extension faults**, there is little tension, so earth movement is limited. Violent quakes are associated with **subduction** faults in which one plate slides under another. California is famous for its earthquakes, which are caused by another type of plate movement called a strike-slip fault (see page 73). The Californians have learned to live on the edge of disaster by adapting building codes, developing innovative civil engineering, and adopting emergency procedures appropriate to the problem.

Earthquakes are usually fairly shallow—less than 70 km below the surface. But earthquakes resulting from subduction can be as deep as 300 km. Earthquakes never occur deeper than this because the asthenosphere is plastic at these depths and rocks tend to bend rather than snap.

Using Logic to Support Theoretical Ideas

This section of the book focuses on the development of the theory of continental drift from the fanciful notion of a physicist to a widely accepted view that explains most tectonic processes. Scientists are by nature sceptical, and although very little in science is ever fully proven, supporting evidence is the key to allowing them to accept a concept as plausible. As the amount of supporting evidence increases, so too does scientists' confidence in the validity of a hypothesis.

The following strategy will help you to analyse theories and determine whether or not there is sufficient evidence to support them. This strategy will not only help you to study physical geography critically, but it can improve your analysis of theories in other fields such as medicine, engineering, and physics.

1. State the theory *in your own words* so that you fully understand it. Don't economize on your words, but explain the theory completely.

2. Decide whether you support or reject the theory before continuing, but keep an open mind.

3. Prepare a chart showing evidence and facts that seem to support the theory, as well as those that seem to contradict it. For Wegener's original theory, your chart might look like the one below.

4. For each positive and negative point in the chart, brainstorm what you would need to know in order to clarify and completely understand the statement. For example, you would need to know more about the rock layers beneath continents in order to know if movement could occur.

5. After you have fully explored each point, analyse the result by deciding whether or not you support the theory or if you cannot make a reasoned response either way because you do not have enough information.

6. Finally, support your decision with a logical explanation. If you could not make a reasoned choice because you still had unanswered questions and concerns, then suggest further research that would be needed to provide more data.

PRACTISE IT!

1. Follow the process you have learned, to analyse one of the following theories:
   - The big bang theory about the creation of the universe
   - The theory that life evolved from amino acids created by electric charges in the early atmosphere.
   - The theory that earthquakes are caused by plate movement.

Support for the Theory	Evidence against the Theory
The continents seem to fit together.	Many places like Scandinavia and North America don't seem to fit together.
The movement of continents would explain why they are not together.	Rock does not flow like Wegener suggested.
Landform features seem to match on opposite sides of continents.	

CASE STUDY

Tragedy in Turkey

On August 17, 1999, Turkey was hit with a series of devastating earthquakes. The primary tremor measured 7.4 on the logarithmic Richter Scale. About 20 earthquakes of this magnitude occur each year, so they are not considered infrequent. What made this a particularly tragic quake was the fact that it occurred in a populated region—a city called Izmit, located east of Turkey's main economic centre, Istanbul. The building standards were poor in this area and structures were not able to withstand the shock of the quake. Buildings collapsed on the victims, crushing them. The death toll was hard to determine because of the large number of missing people, but estimates range upwards of 15 000, while over 18 000 more were injured. Damage to power lines, roads and communications equipment made it impossible to reach people trapped in collapsed buildings.

This earthquake was the latest in a string of quakes that has plagued the region over the past 60 years. The quakes have been moving east to west along the North Anatolian Fault. In 1939, a magnitude 8.0 quake hit near the town of Erzincan, and from 1947 to 1967 five more quakes occurred, running in the same direction. The 1999 fault rupture comes right where the 1967 earthquake occurred. The tension seems to be moving along the fault line. Since Turkey is such a tectonically active area, the fault is one of the most studied, yet seismologists were not able to give any warning to the Turkish citizenry before the 1999 disaster. If the trend continues, the next big quake could be in the huge metropolis of Istanbul.

The North Anatolian Fault is known as a **strike-slip fault**. Rather than the earth moving up or down, the two plates are sliding past each other. Turkey is tectonically very active because it is located where several plates collide. The

Figure 4.12
The 1999 quake caused extreme devastation and killed thousands of people.

Anatolian Plate (which is where Turkey is located) is sliding west, while the Eurasian Plate is moving east. To the south, the Arabian Plate also slides east. It is as if Turkey is being squeezed out of Asia and into Europe by these two great tectonic plates. If the plates slide past each other smoothly, there is no problem. But when the two plates get stuck together, tension builds up in the rock to the point where the crust cannot take any more pressure and the plates snap past each other. The distance travelled does not have to be great; it is the suddenness of the movement that causes the damage. Fault slips in the 2.5 to 3 m range occurred about 110 km of the North Anatolian Fault. If you study Fig. 4.13, you will see that there is a definite pattern of earthquakes along the line.

Soon after the earthquake, experts rushed to the scene. They were interested in examining the extent of the damage. By studying the ruins left by an earthquake, scientists can assess which building structures are most durable. This invaluable information helps with the development of new engineering construction methods. Often, old structures like the mosque at Golcuk remain intact while newer apartments collapse. After the quake in Izmit, Turkish citizens were irate because of the apparently substandard buildings in the region.

QUESTIONS:

1. a) On a sketch map of the region, draw a vertical liine upward from each tremour to show its relative strength. Draw 1cm for every degree of magnitude.

b) Explain why Turkey is so tectonically active.

2. a) Study the map showing the history of Turkish earthquakes and decide whether the quake will occur west or east along the North Anatolian Fault.

b) Support your view with evidence from the map.

3. Why was the devastation following the 1999 quake greater than it would have been in Canada or the United States?

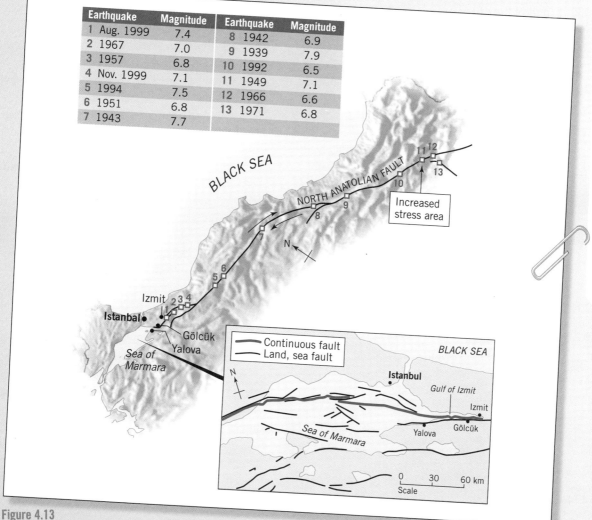

Earthquake	Magnitude	Earthquake	Magnitude
1 Aug. 1999	7.4	8 1942	6.9
2 1967	7.0	9 1939	7.9
3 1957	6.8	10 1992	6.5
4 Nov. 1999	7.1	11 1949	7.1
5 1994	7.5	12 1966	6.6
6 1951	6.8	13 1971	6.8
7 1943	7.7		

Figure 4.13
The North Anatolian fault runs through Turkey, and earthquakes follow the same path.

Measuring and Predicting Earthquakes

Seismometers measure the intensity of earthquakes. A rod anchored deep in the ground vibrates when a quake occurs. Joined to the rod is a pendulum with a pen attached to it. As the ground vibrates, the pen remains still due to its inertia. However, the rod, which is attached to the table with the drum of graph paper on it, vibrates. A motor rotates the drum at a steady rate and the pen draws a straight line. However, when there is an earthquake, the table moves, producing a squiggly line. The greater the vibration of the earth, the greater the amplitude of the waves drawn on the paper. The graph created is called a **seismograph**. Modern seismographs seldom use pens anymore. The graph is drawn by an optical scanner or a laser and is digitally transferred to a computerized plotter.

The seismograph records three types of vibrations. L waves travel along the earth's surface. Smaller P waves (primary waves) are followed by more violent S waves (secondary waves). By measuring the time between P and S waves, scientists can calculate how far away the quake was from the seismograph station. The exact location of an earthquake can be determined by drawing circles around three or more stations on a map. The radius of each circle is equal to the distance of that station from the quake. The place where the circles intersect is the epicentre. This method is called triangulation.

The **Richter scale** is the most popular scale used to measure earthquakes. It is based on intensity over a given distance. Scientists are often able to detect an earthquake thousands of kilometres away and to determine its intensity using a seismograph. However, seismographs do not predict earthquakes; they simply record them as they happen. Predictions are much more complex since three specific things must be known: when it will happen, where it will happen, and how intense it will be.

Computers and an understanding of chaos theory help scientists to find complex patterns in seismic readings. For example, Parkfield, California, has had an earthquake measuring between 5 and 6 on the Richter scale every 22 years on average (give or take two years) since 1857. The last one was in 1989. If the pattern holds, there should be another in 2011. Most earthquakes, however, follow much more chaotic patterns that are much harder to interpret.

More sophisticated prediction techniques rely on statistics gathered from subtle changes in the shape and movement of geological features. In California, the San Andreas Fault is closely monitored. Lasers on one side of the fault are aligned with sensors on the other side. The beam of intense light gradually moves along the sensor as one plate slides past the other. If the rate of movement slows or stops altogether, it is likely that an earthquake will occur as tension builds up along the fault plane. When the tension reaches the breaking point, a sudden jolt or earthquake occurs.

Size	Damage Expected	Number Each Year
10	felt worldwide	unrecorded
9	felt most places	unrecorded
8	most buildings collapse	less than 1
7	most buildings damaged	20
6	some buildings damaged	100
5	slight damage	500
4	felt by most	6000
3	felt by some	30 000
2	not felt but shown on a seismograph	more than 150 000

Figure 4.14
The Richter Scale

Note: Numbers are estimates.

CHANGING TECHNOLOGY: GPS and Earthquake Prediction

Global positioning systems, or GPS, have become almost commonplace in our modern technology-based world. These ingenious devices use satellites and radio transmitters to determine exact locations on the earth's surface. Not only are they being used for navigation and mapping, but GPS are also used to help forecast tectonic events such as earthquakes and volcanic eruptions.

Turkish scientists are working with the Massachusetts Institute of Technology to develop a new GPS-based monitoring system along the 1600 km-long Anatolian Fault. The Anatolian Plate moves about 2.5 cm each year while the Eurasian Plate remains still. When the movement slows, tension is built up in the crust and an earthquake is the result. At the present time, one GPS receiver has been installed, but the long-range plan is to install 15 receivers throughout the country. The movement of one plate relative to the others can be determined by measuring the exact position of each receiver over a period of weeks and months. From this data, locations where plate movement is unusually slow can be determined. These areas would theoretically be more susceptible to a quake than places where plate movement follows a regular pattern. Of course, the study will require time before patterns of plate movement and tremors can be documented.

This initiative is not the first of its kind. Networks of GPS receivers have been installed in other earthquake zones, most notably California and Japan. The Southern California Integrated GPS Network (SCIGN) was the first of these new technologies

installed. Movements as small as a millimetre can be measured from a distance of hundreds of kilometres in space.

Questions:
1. Think of four ways this earthquake monitoring system will help people in earthquake prone zones.
2. Make an illustration showing your understanding of how GPS is used to monitor earthquake activity.

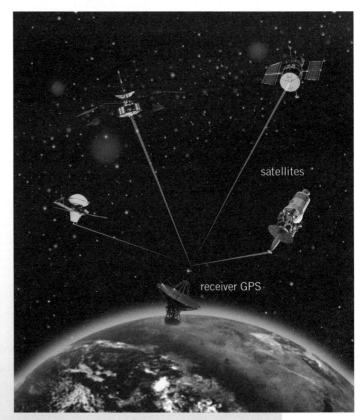

Figure 4.15
A GPS receiver must have readings from at least 3 satellites in order to pinpoint an exact location on the surface of the earth.

ACTIVITIES

UNDERSTANDING CONCEPTS

1. How do geological and human time scales differ?
2. Geological change can occur rapidly or slowly.
   a) Give an example of a cataclysmic geological event that has occurred recently.
   b) Give an example of a slow geological event that is occurring in your community.
   c) Give examples to show that the earth continues to change because of energy flows within the lithosphere.
3. a) Summarize the scientific advances that led to the widespread acceptance of plate tectonics as the main force responsible for tectonic processes.
   b) Identify the role technology has had in the acceptance of this theory.
4. a) Characterize the differences between continental and oceanic plates.
   b) Explain how the continents move from one place to another, using the example of a conveyor belt.
   c) In a paragraph, describe the process by which continents move, using the following terms: subduction, asthenosphere, convection currents, midoceanic ridge, seafloor spreading, plastic upper mantle.
5. Outline how the following geological evidence supports the theory of plate tectonics.
   a) Adjacent coastlines on opposite sides of oceans
   b) The midoceanic ridge
   c) The age of seafloor cores on either side of the midoceanic ridge
   d) The alignment of seafloor magnetic fields
   e) Fossils on adjacent continents
   f) Geological formations on adjacent continents.

DEVELOPING AND PRACTISING SKILLS

6. a) Using a pair of scissors and photocopied maps of the world, make cut-outs of each continent.
   b) Place the continents on a thick piece of paper so that they are all joined together to create Pangaea, which existed 300 million years ago. Trace each continent on the paper and colour them all one colour.
   c) Slide each cut-out continent into the position it would have had 200 million years ago. Trace each continent in its new position and colour it a new colour. Draw arrows to show how the continents moved.
   d) Continue the process described in part c) to show how each continent moved from 100 million years ago to the present. Add the midoceanic ridges and a symbol to show where collisions have occurred.
   e) Measure the arrows to find out which continent has moved the furthest and which has moved the least.

f) Complete your map display with a colour key and a title.

7. Many technical terms are associated with tectonic forces. Make a crossword puzzle for the new words in this section. (Use a computer if you have access to one to construct the puzzle).

8. a) Describe the devastation that occurred in the Turkish earthquake of 1999.
   b) Explain what caused the earthquake in Turkey. Include the following terms in your explanation: North Anatolian Fault, Anatolian Plate, Eurasian Plate, Arabian Plate, strike-slip fault.
   c) What particular pattern is shown by the map in Fig. 4.13?
   d) How can scientists predict where the next quake will be?

LEARNING THROUGH APPLICATION

9. a) Look through old geographic magazines and collect pictures that show energy in the lithosphere.
   b) Categorize your pictures by the type of energy they represent by displaying them in a series of three collages under the following headings: Geothermal Energy, Solar Energy, Kinetic Energy.
   c) Select one picture that represents many different forms of energy. Write an explanation of the energy flows that are shown.

10. Prepare an Internet search to find out more about one of the careers mentioned in the text. Include such subtopics as: nature of the work, educational requirements, aptitudes and special talents, remuneration, job satisfaction, and working conditions. Consider one of the following careers: seismologist, geophysicist, or geologist.

11. Read the following statements, then answer the accompanying questions:
    • Parkfield, California, will receive a tremor within the next two months.
    • Sichuan province in China will experience an earthquake measuring between 4 and 7 on the Richter scale within the next week.
    • South America will have a major earthquake in 2007.
    • Southern British Columbia will have an earthquake sometime in the next century.
    • Manila, the Philippines, will have a major earthquake within the next 24 hours.
    • Istanbul is near the Anatolian fault and will experience a serious earthquake.
    a) Which statements would help residents prepare for an earthquake?
    b) Which statements lack important information? What is missing in each of these?
    c) What three pieces of information are needed for an earthquake prediction to be useful?
    d) What precautions could people take if an earthquake was predicted for your area?
    e) What effect could inaccurate predictions ultimately have on a community?

12. What suggestions would you have for people living in Turkey to help them cope better with earthquakes?

13. Explain how planners could modify each of the following to make it less hazardous in earthquake-prone zones: shantytowns on mountain slopes, skyscrapers with elevators and no stairs, elevated highways.

Chapter 5

MOVERS AND SHAKERS: HOW LANDFORMS ARE CREATED

FOCUS QUESTIONS

1. How are mountains created?
2. What is the connection between the patterns that mountain ranges, volcanoes, and fault lines form around the globe?
3. What are some of the trade-offs that people who live in volcano-prone zones must face?

Key Terms

elevation

volcanism

faulting

folding

isostasy

It's no wonder the discovery of plate tectonics is considered one of the greatest scientific achievements of the twentieth century. This process explains how many of the features on the surface of the lithosphere came into being. The word "tectonic" derives its meaning from the ancient Greek word for carpenter. The term is appropriate since both tectonic forces and carpenters are builders of sorts—one of the main differences between them being the size of their creations. The extreme pressure caused by plates drifting across the earth's surface and crashing into one another is responsible for forcing many major landforms into shape.

Landform Types

There are essentially six different types of landforms on the earth's surface that are brought about by tectonic activity: mountains, highlands, plateaux, hills, plains, and valleys. Each of these can be defined by its **elevation** and surface **relief**. Elevation refers to a landform's height above sea level. For example, mountains have the highest elevation and valleys have the lowest. Relief refers to the surface of a landform. A feature is said to have a low relief if it is flat, and a high relief if it is rough, hilly, or jagged. The chart on page 63 summarizes the different landform types and provides a brief summary as to how each feature was formed.

Figure 5.1
Rocky Mountains
Find out how these magnificent mountains were created by reading this chapter.

	Landform Type	Description	Elevation	Relief	How Formed
	Mountains	Rugged peaks of varying heights and steep slopes	High	High	Tectonic folding, faulting and volcanism
	Highlands	Like mountains, but all the peaks at the same height	High	High	Isostatic uplift followed by millions of years of erosion
	Plateau	High, flat table land	High	Low	Isostatic uplift – often extrusive former lava flows
	Hills	Rounded mounds of no particular shape	Medium	Medium	Either old worn down mountains or depositional features
	Plains	Low flat land	Low	Low	Former sea floor uplifted, or deposited material from mountain erosion
	Valley	Low, flat land surrounded by hills or mountains	Low erosion	Low	Faulting, folding, or river

Figure 5.2
The Characteristics and Formation of Six Different Types of Landforms

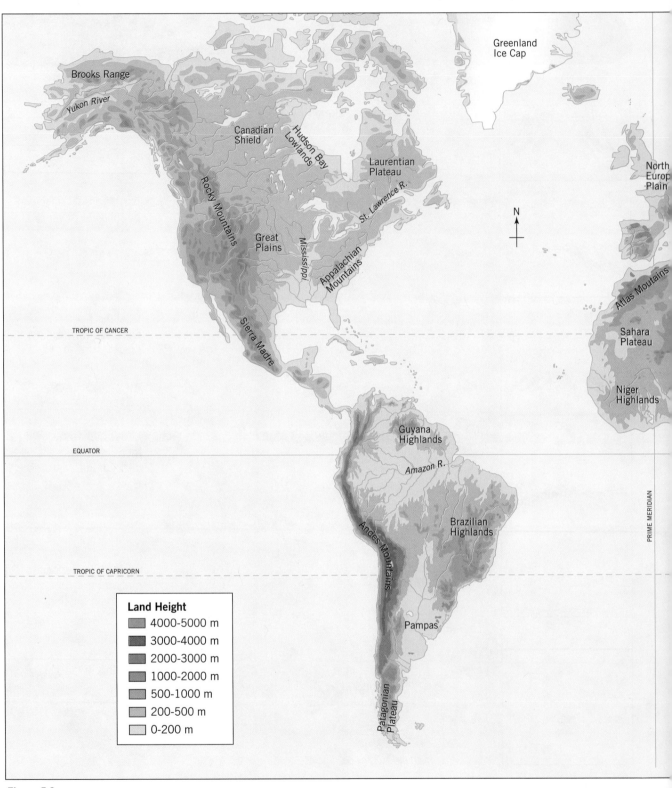

Figure 5.3
Landform Regions of the World

Scale at the Equator
0   2000   4000 km

Landforms Created through Isostatic Movement

Isostasy is one form of movement that is responsible for slowly elevating land in the lithosphere and creating new landforms. The crust of the earth can be thought of as floating on denser layers of rock below. If a weight sits on the earth's surface, the crust will sink. If the weight is removed, the crust will rebound. As you can imagine, it takes considerable time for the crust to rebound after a weight has been removed. Northern Ontario is still rebounding after the last glaciers left 12 000 years ago. Twelve thousand years is a long time within the human time scale, but when you consider that the planet is over 4 billion years old, it is a mere blink of a eye in geological time.

The concept of isostasy is easy to understand if you think of yourself lying on an air mattress floating in a pool. When you lie on it, it sinks down. When you get up off the mattress, it rebounds to its original height. The same thing happens to the lithosphere. When there is a large mass like an ocean pressing down, the rock layers are depressed. If the ocean dries up, the pressure is removed and the rock layers rebound. Seashells found in mountains may have ended up hundreds of metres above sea level because the layers that now form mountains were once under the sea.

Isostasy is often the reason why **fossil fuels** such as coal may be located near the earth's surface and far away from any oceans. After the drying up of the ancient oceans where they formed, the layers of fossil fuels left behind were thrust slowly toward the earth's surface by isostatic forces. Erosion wore away the overlying layers of accumulated rock, leaving these valuable fossil fuels close to the surface.

Mountain Building

Mountain building, also known as **orogeny**, is an involved process lasting hundreds of millions of years. The Himalayas seem to be a static pile of rocks, but this mountain range has been forming for about 200 million years and is still forming as the Australian Plate slowly grinds north into the Eurasian Plate. Even so, these mountains are considered to be young in comparison to the Appalachians, which started forming about 480 million years ago. Other landforms, such as plateaux, plains, and highlands, were also often created as a consequence of mountain building.

Mountains are formed in three ways: **folding**, **faulting**, and **volcanism**. Seldom are mountains formed by only one of these orogenic processes—usually all three are involved. Folding and faulting occur when pressures deep within the lithosphere cause the earth's surface to buckle, bend, and even split apart. Volcanism occurs when solid rock structures are created from molten rock. They may be created either below the surface or above ground, when a volcano spews lava, ashes, and other material to form a new mountain.

Figure 5.4
How do you think the Cape Breton Highlands in Nova Scotia were formed?

Landforms Created Through Folding

Folding occurs when the earth's crust is pushed up from either or both sides. You can see how this works with a simple piece of paper. Lay the paper on a flat surface, then gently slide both edges towards the middle. The paper "folds" up and flops down on itself. This is exactly what happens when the earth's crust is pushed from both sides. **Fold mountains** form as plates slide into each other and the crust is pushed up. Where the crust folds down, valleys are formed. Often, glaciers such as the Athabaska and rivers such as the Bow River in Alberta flow through fold-mountain valleys. They so modify the land-scape that it looks as if these **gradational** processes created the valley in the first place. In fact, orogenic forces were the prime factors involved in their creation.

Because they are associated with colliding plates, fold mountains are often found near the leading edges of these. Old mountains of this type may be difficult to recognize because they are often so worn down that they look more like large hills. For example, the mountains of Nova Scotia were once as mighty as the Alps or the Rockies, but over millions of years they have been eroded down to practically nothing. If a mountain chain seems far from plate boundaries, look again. It was likely on the edge of an ancient plate hundreds of millions of years ago. The Ural Mountains (the dividing line between northern Europe and northern Asia in Russia) show where an ancient plate boundary was.

You can tell where folding has occurred in eroded rock layers because the different layers run up and down in regular parallel bands. Identifying fold mountains is sometimes difficult for two reasons. First, erosion often wears away some of the folded layers. You have to imagine what the rock was like *before* the erosion occurred in order to see the parallel bands of rock strata. Second, folding often occurs along with faulting and even volcanism. This compli-cates the picture, making it difficult to determine how the mountains were formed.

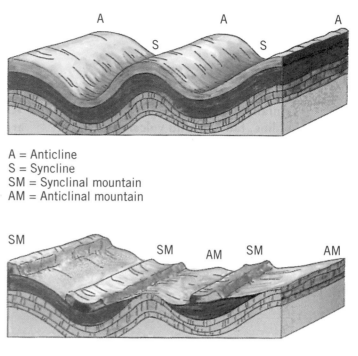

A = Anticline
S = Syncline
SM = Synclinal mountain
AM = Anticlinal mountain

Figure 5.5
A Simplified Model of a Fold Mountain

The structure of fold mountains can be complex. The simplest fold mountains are made up of layers of rock that rise and fall like waves of water. The peaks or hills are called **anticlines**; the troughs or valleys are called **synclines**. The layers of rock often vary in hardness. If the harder cap rock erodes away, a valley may be carved in an anticline (hill). Broad synclinal valleys, narrow ridges, and narrow anticlinal valleys are thus created. Symmetrical ridges of resistant rock and valleys of softer rock result (Fig. 5.5 shows this pattern).

Landforms Created Through Faulting

While folding occurs from plates crashing into each other and pushing upward, faulting occurs when blocks of rock either fracture or pull apart. The midoceanic ridge is an example of faulting where two plates have pulled away from each other. The crust splits in a gigantic crack hundreds of kilometres long. Faulting can be

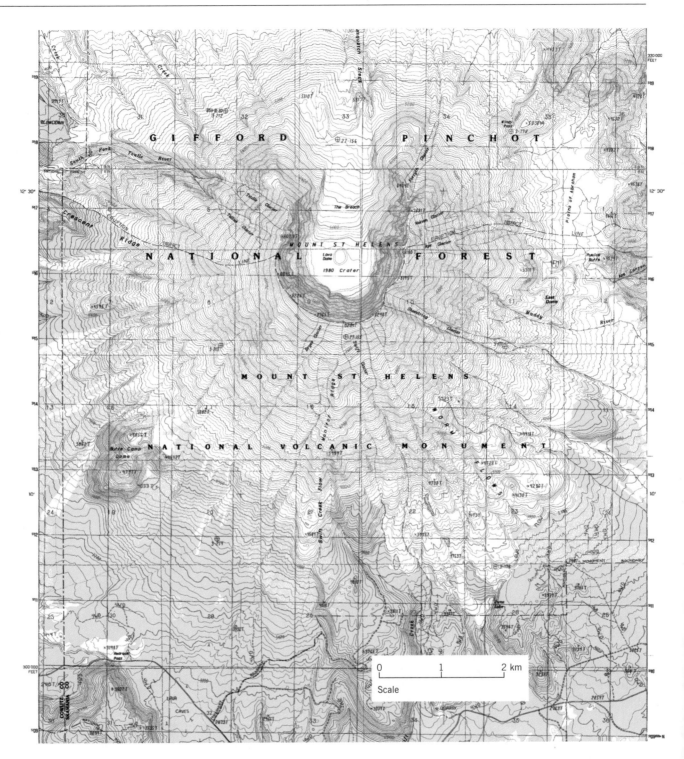

Figure 5.6
This contour map shows Mount St. Helens, Wash., USA.
What landform features can you identify?

cataclysmic, occurring in mere seconds or minutes, unlike folding, which occurs over thousands and millions of years.

Faults occur whenever a plate is subjected to tension or compression. Tension refers to the pulling apart of plates, but compression occurs when they are rammed up against each other. The many different landforms that faulting creates result from the different ways in which plates move in relation to each other. When an oceanic plate moves under a continental plate, a **subduction fault** occurs. These faults usually run along continental borders. Underwater canyons, thousands of metres deep, form ocean trenches where the fault occurs. Though the water is very deep offshore, the adjacent land is usually very mountainous, and the difference in

elevation between the two is often immense.

The Chile Trench is over 8 kilometres deep while the Andes Mountains, which run along the Pacific coast of the country, climb 7 kilometres or more into the South American sky. The pressure of the oceanic plate **subducting** (sliding) under the continental plate causes folding to occur. But in addition to folding, other forms of orogeny are created. Along the Andes, a string of volcanoes was built as the pressure of the two plates subducting melted parts of the crust and formed pockets of magma in the faults.

The volcanic mountains in the Andes form part of the **Ring of Fire**, a string of volcanoes that encircles the Pacific Ocean. These volcanoes occur just inland from the trenches and directly above subduction faults.

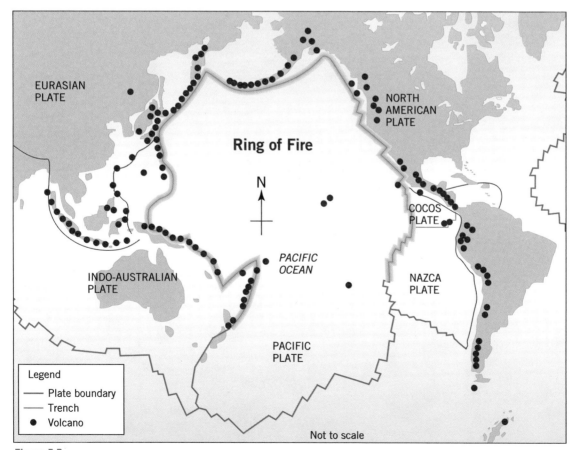

Figure 5.7
The Volcanoes and Fault Lines of the Ring of Fire

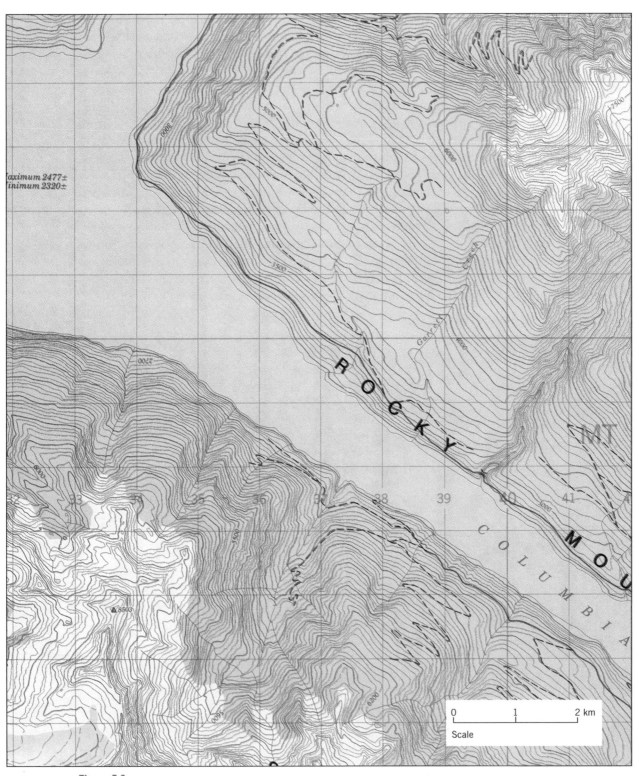

Figure 5.8
Contour Map of the Columbia River, B.C. What kind of fault is visible? How can you tell?

When two plates are pulling away from each other, **extension faults** occur. The midoceanic ridge (the line of ridges and canyons running through the centre the oceans) is the longest continuous landform feature on the planet. The rift valley in the centre of the ridge is being pulled apart. The crust is so thin under the midoceanic ridge that upwellings of molten rock ooze out of the cracks, slowly filling it with new basaltic lava.

Rift valleys, or **grābens**, form when there are two parallel faults. The land between the faults sinks as they pull apart from each other. The most notable grāben is the **Great Rift Valley** in Africa. It runs from Mozambique in the south to south-western Syria in the north. Many lakes and rivers developed in this broad central valley. Some geologists believe that the Great Rift Valley will one day become flooded as it sinks below sea level and water from the Red Sea flows south. If this happens, East Africa will split away from the rest of the continent and slide slowly toward the east into the Indian Ocean. Other notable rift valleys include the Danube River Basin and the Rocky Mountain Trench. In all cases, the valleys have become rich agricultural regions and excellent transportation routes through often rugged terrain.

The opposite formation to the grāben is the **horst**. This feature is formed when land rises between parallel faults. Also called block mountains, they are often hard to actually see as uplifted blocks because erosion and other tectonic processes have disguised them. The Grand Tetons in the northern United States are typical of these formations.

When two plates crash into each other, a **collision fault** occurs. One plate slides up relative to the other plate, creating a **fault plane**. The process is basically the same as that of the subduction fault, except that the two plates are continental. Because they are of equal thickness and relative strength, there is no subduction as there is when the relatively thinner oceanic plate meets a continental one. Instead, the two land masses plow into each other like two cars in a head-on collision. In the latter case, the length of the cars shortens as they are compacted together. To make room for the same amount of matter in a shortened length of space, the metal of the two hoods buckles and pops up into the air.

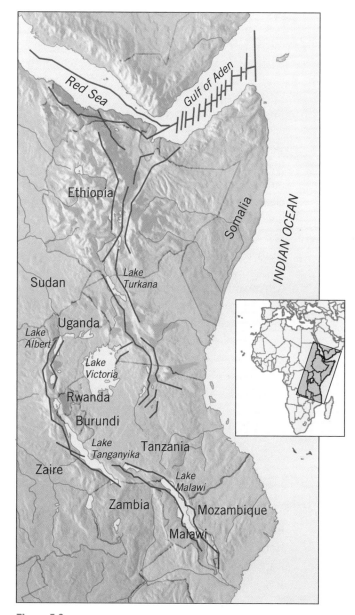

Figure 5.9
Contour Map of the Great Rift Valley in East Africa

DEVELOPING SKILLS

Interpreting Contour Maps

Geographers use many different mapping techniques to show physical features. The most difficult aspect to illustrate is **relief**, or the relative height and shape of landforms. Shading, cross-hatching, colouring, and symbols are all used with varying degrees of success. These methods provide an aerial view, but they are inaccurate because they do not represent relief in measurable terms. The method most commonly used today is **contour mapping**. This technique is relatively simple: it shows the exact height of the land in measurable terms and enables geographers to create cross-sectional diagrams, or **profiles**, as well as accurate models to scale.

Contour mapping is the standard means of showing elevation. Contour lines connect all places of the same height. Lines that are far apart indicate that the land is fairly flat. Lines that are close together indicate a slope; the closer the lines, the steeper the slope. With a little practice, you can visualize what landforms look like by studying contour maps.

Here are some basic rules to keep in mind when working with contours:

1. The **contour interval** is the number of units between each contour line—for example, the vertical distance between two contour lines could be 10 m.

2. Contour lines never cross because they show places with the same elevation.

3. Contour lines never end; they join together or run to the end of the map.

4. When a contour line crosses a river it creates a v-shape upstream. The valley is lower than the surrounding land so it is shown as contour lines pointing uphill.

A good way to interpret the contours on a map is to represent them in a landform profile. Made from contour measurements, profiles are two-dimensional, cross-sectional diagrams which resemble line graphs except that they are labelled to point out the names of the various landforms shown. When you are studying a map, they can help you to visualize what a landform looks like. To prepare a profile, follow these steps:

1. Place the straight edge of a small piece of paper across the map where you want to show the profile. (The edge of the paper should be perpendicular to the contour lines it intersects.) Carefully mark where each contour touches the piece of paper.

2. Label the contour lines and prominent features such as roads, rivers, and lakes on the paper.

3. Draw an x and y axis on a piece of graph paper. Select an appropriate scale for the x axis—for example, 1:10 000 (1 cm = 100 m). It is necessary to exaggerate the vertical scale to see the feature.

4. Lay the piece of paper on which you recorded the contour lines along the y axis on the graph paper. Plot the elevation using the scale on the x axis.

5. Join the dots together and label the features shown in the profile.

PRACTISE IT!

1. Prepare a profile of one of the topographic maps in this chapter to show one or more of the following tectonic features: a volcano, gräben, rift valley, or a fold mountain.

   a) For each profile, label significant features from the map and include a scale.

   b) Determine where the features are on the profile and label them also.

Of course, plates move infinitely slower than two speeding automobiles. The Himalayan Mountains are still being formed as the Indian plate slowly glides north into the Eurasian Plate. This has been going on for millions of years and will continue for millions more.

Strike slip faults occur when two plates slide laterally past each other. There is little to no up-and-down movement of the plates relative to each other. The San Andreas Fault, which has been responsible for so many earthquakes in California, is of this type. The Pacific Oceanic Plate slides in a northwest movement past the North American Continental Plate that is moving southeast. In time, the western part of California will slide away from the rest of the continent and move northwest into the ocean. Imagine—one day part of California will be an island off the coast of British Columbia! But don't start a ferry service yet—it won't happen for millions of years. The release of built-up energy from movement along this fault causes earthquakes and volcanoes such as Mount St. Helens, another part of the Ring of Fire further inland. Although the movement itself is slight, the sudden jerk of the plates past each other causes the destruction.

Landforms Created Through Volcanism

When molten rock reaches the surface of the earth, volcanoes are formed. These incredible features are among the most dangerous places on earth, yet people seem to love to live near them. All around the Ring of Fire and across the world people have populated the slopes of volcanoes. When Mount Vesuvius erupted in the year 79, the people of the city of Pompeii were instantly killed by the poisonous gases and coated with the ash that rained down on them. Their bodies rotted away and left cavities in the petrified ash. Plaster of Paris was injected into the ashen moulds to form life-like statues of the volcano's victims.

Volcanoes are examples of **extrusive volcanism**. They result from the friction between moving plates. Since the rock expands as the temperature increases, tremendous pressure is created beneath the earth's surface. The **magma** flows into cracks and crevasses in surrounding rock, creating **intrusive structures**. (*Intrusive* means within the rock, while *extrusive* means outside the rock.) When the magma reaches the

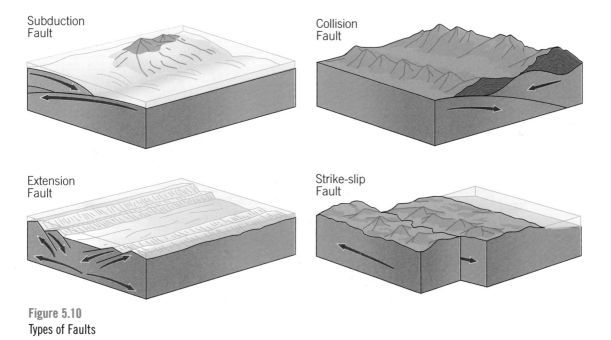

Subduction
Fault

Collision
Fault

Extension
Fault

Strike-slip
Fault

Figure 5.10
Types of Faults

surface, extrusive formations in the familiar form of volcanoes result. Plateaux are also created from lava flowing onto the earth's surface. Much of this

occurs out of sight under the world's oceans. The great basaltic plateaux that comprise much of the sea floor were formed by lava that flowed out of the midoceanic rift. Iceland, which has been formed entirely from lava flowing out from the Mid-Atlantic Ridge as the North American and Eurasian plates have pulled apart, is an example of this type of volcanism. Part of the Columbian Plateau in eastern Oregon and Washington state, as well as the Deccan Plateau in India, were formed when highly fluid lava erupted from fissures in the crust. The traditional cone mountain did not form because the lava did not solidify quickly enough; rather it flowed out, covering a vast expanse of land.

Many people think lava comes from the molten core of the earth, when in fact it originates much closer to the surface. Friction and pressure are so great along plate boundaries that part of the crust melts, and the expansion of the heated material as well as the action of plates colliding results in volcanism. Plate tectonics helps to explain how volcanoes are formed and

Figure 5.11
"Frozen" Pompeans, victims of Mount Vesuvius

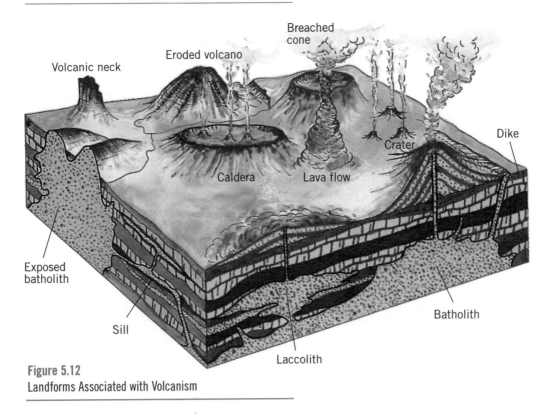

Figure 5.12
Landforms Associated with Volcanism

where they occur. When a plate rides up over another plate in a subduction zone, friction and pressure melt the rock where the two plates come together. The magma often accumulates underground in **magma chambers**. If the pressure is great enough and there are fault lines to facilitate movement, the magma flows to the surface through a **magma conduit**. Magma is often thin and flows quickly over a surface. It may ooze out of the ground and flow many metres before it solidifies. Sometimes the magma is thick, like maple syrup on a cold day. It does not flow as well as basaltic magma and solidifies quickly when it is cooled.

Sometimes the magma solidifies before it has a chance to flow out of the volcano, and a **volcanic plug** is formed. The plug prevents the volcano from erupting, but the pressure of rapidly expanding magma underground keeps building and building. Eventually, the pressure is so great

that a massive explosion occurs. In one of the most violent natural events that happens on earth, the volcano releases lava, ash, rocks, and other volcanic debris, which rain down on the earth's surface for hundreds of kilometres. Many of the volcanoes of the Ring of Fire are of this type, and are called **Vesuvian volcanoes**, after the famous Roman volcano. One of the most devastating eruptions in terms of loss of life happened on the Caribbean island of Martinique. In 1902, a **nuée ardente** (which means "glowing cloud" in French) killed 30 000 people when a 600° to 700°C cloud of ash, water vapour, and glowing gases instantly suffocated all life in the vicinity. What makes Vesuvian volcanoes so dangerous is their unpredictability. They lie dormant for hundreds or perhaps even thousands of years, like sleeping giants. Over time, people forget how dangerous they are—until they erupt again.

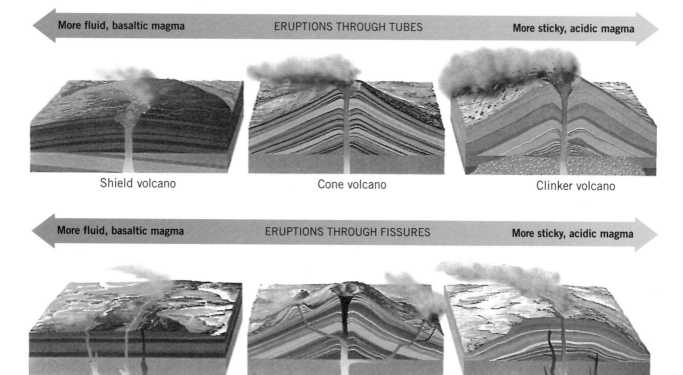

Figure 5.13
Different Types of Volcanoes

Mount Pinatubo, The Still-Active Giant

Not only must the people of Luzon Island in the Philippines live with the horrific memories of one of the largest volcanic eruptions in human memory, but they must also continue to deal with the economic damage it caused, not to mention the lahars and other physical threats posed by the still-active giant, Mount Pinatubo.

Pinatubo is a stratovolcano (also called a composite cone), which is the most common type of volcano, and is formed of alternating layers of ejected ash and lava. It was July 1990 when a magnitude 7.9 earthquake rocked the land 100 km to the northeast of Mount Pinatubo

Figure 5.15
Mount Pinatubo erupted, sending a massive plume of deadly gases 25 km into the sky over the vent.

on the island of Luzon, about 100 km northwest of Manila, shaking and squeezing the earth's crust beneath the volcano. This major quake caused a landslide, some local tremors and increased steam emissions, but little else—the 600-year-old giant continued its slumber undisturbed. At this time, 30 000 people lived in small villages on the sides of the volcano, while more than 500 000 others occupied towns and cities on the broad, gently sloping alluvial fan spreading out from around the base of the mountain. Most of the population made their living farming the extremely rich volcanic soil in the lowlands. Comprised of material brought down from the mountain's volcanic peaks, the deep, fertile soil was excellent for growing rice and sugar cane.

By April 1991, the giant was showing signs of awakening, and 100 000 people were evacuated from the area. Magma began rising to the surface of the volcano from more than 32 km underground, setting off thousands of small tremors and sending tons of noxious sulfur dioxide gas into the air. But this was only the beginning...

On June 7, the first magma reached the surface. Because it had lost most of its gas content along the way to the surface, it oozed up to form a lava dome rather than a major explosion. A few days later, on June 12, the first of many major

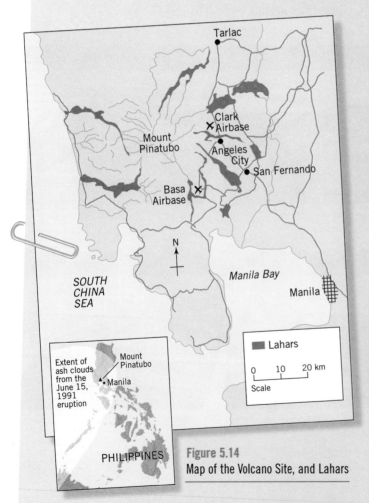

Figure 5.14
Map of the Volcano Site, and Lahars

eruptions blasted through the top of Pinatubo, sending millions of cubic metres of lava, ash, rocks and debris raining down on the surrounding landscape. The ejected material from a volcano is called **tephra**, and it produces a wide range of dangers. For example, when the debris is ejected into the atmosphere, it can become electrically charged and produce deadly lightning storms. Another hazard results from the material's accumulation on electrical wires, roads, bridges, buildings and homes, causing them to collapse and crush the people inside. This is how many of the 320 victims of the Pinatubo volcano died.

Another cataclysmic eruption on June 15 sent more than 5 km^3 of ash and gases 25 km into the atmosphere. The sulphur dioxide emissions from the eruptions were so immense that when they reached the stratosphere they caused world temperatures to drop by .5°C over a two year period. The aerosols produced glorious red sunsets and sunrises, which were seen around the world for up to a year after the eruptions. The ash was blown about by high winds before blanketing the countryside in a thick layer. On the same day, other explosions produced incandescent **pyroclastic flows**, which carried searing hot ash, gas, and pumice fragments down the mountain's slopes at 70-80 km/h. These flows travelled some 16 km from the source, devastating every living thing in their path.

By the end of the disaster, more than 19 major eruptions had been recorded, 320 people were dead, 20 000 people had been displaced, and 1.9 billion pesos worth of damage had been done (GNP per capita in the Philippines is 32 000 P). The destruction included the ruin of 99 200 ha of farmland and 18 000 ha of forest (which crippled the furniture industry), 700 schools, and most transportation systems. Airplanes flying over the area during the eruptions sustained approximately US $100 million worth of damage. And the devastation had not ended... .

In the months and years following the eruption, massive mudflows, called **lahars**, picked up where the volcano left off, destroying the homes of more than 100 000 people. Lahars form when heavy rain (or melting snow or ice) mix with loose volcanic deposits of rocks and ash at the mountain's peak. The resulting mudflows can travel at speeds of up to 65 km/h and reach a distance of 80 km from the source. The lahars that roared down the sides of Mount Pinatubo since 1991 carried the equivalent of 300 million dump-truck loads of debris to the surrounding lowlands, burying villages and sweeping away people, livestock, roads and crops. Even after dikes had been built in 1997 to contain the mudflows, experts warned that lahars would continue to pose a deadly threat until at least the year 2005. One geologist currently studying the problem has said that there is still a quantity of volcanic material on the slopes of Pinatubo: "Hence, potentially destructive lahars are likely to persist in the future, although their intensity and frequency will diminish."

These warnings have not stopped people from moving back onto the land at the base of Mount Pinatubo. There are currently thousands of Filipinos settled in the area, farming the mineral-rich volcanic soil. Meanwhile, the volcano continues to show menacing signs of life by sending an occasional column of billowing smoke into the sky over their heads.

QUESTIONS:

1. Look at the world lands forms map on page 64–5 and the map of the world's plates on page 49. Use them to explain what caused Mount Pinatubo to become active.

2. Why do you think the government of the Philippines allows people to live at the base of Mount Pinatubo? Is there anything the government and/or the people of the Philippines can do to make living around the volcano safer?

Different types of volcanoes are created by the nature of the magma and the conduit through which the magma flows. **Hawaiian volcanoes** are named after the Pacific island where the best examples of this type of volcano are found. Volcanologists believe these volcanoes form over "hot spots" in the asthenosphere. These hot spots occur because of convection currents resulting from radioactive minerals in the upper mantle. As the plates move across the earth's surface, the hot spot remains fixed beneath it. The result is a chain of volcanoes in a line perpendicular to the plate movement. Fig. 5.16 shows one such volcano that formed as the crust moved over the hot spot currently under Hawaii.

Hawaiian volcanoes are less violent than Vesuvian volcanoes. The lava has a lower viscosity, so it tends to flow freely and not form plugs. Instead of volcanic cones, massive dome-shaped mountains are created. Mauna Loa, the main volcano of the Hawaiian chain, is the largest mountain on earth, higher even than Mt. Everest. We do not realize how high it is because most of the mountain is under water.

Volcanism includes other structures as well as the familiar cone-shaped volcanic mountains. Intrusion occurs from the high-pressure injection of magma into existing rock structures. When magma hardens, igneous intrusions of various sizes and shapes are formed (see Fig. 5.12). Smaller ones are called **dikes**, **sills**, and **laccoliths**. Larger ones, called **batholiths**, may be hundreds of kilometres across. When the overlying rock erodes away, these harder igneous intrusions are left, often forming curious landforms that may seem out of place. For example, the Monteregian Hills, one of which is Ste. Hyacinthe, southeast of Montreal, are strangely rocky hills located in an otherwise flat river basin.

Scientists who study volcanoes are called volcanologists. If you like adventure and are willing to risk your life to help other people, this could be your calling. What the volcanologist does is often highly dangerous and requires many years of study. Often, training similar to that of a seismologist is required. A knowledge of how vibrations travel through rock layers allows the volcanologist to monitor the internal structure of the volcano. The way shock waves move through the different layers indicates how much of a mountain is molten rock, how much is gas, and how much is solid. If there is a change from solid to liquid or from liquid to gas, this indicates that pressures are building in a Vesuvian type volcano. As the frequency and strength of the vibrations increase, the likelihood of an eruption is increased.

Volcanologists may also specialize in atmospheric chemistry. Gases are collected over volcanic vents and analysed to determine their nature and volume, as well as their rate of change—which could also be a harbinger of tectonic disaster. Geologists who study the nature of the minerals within the lava are able to determine the viscosity of the flow and the type of eruption that will occur.

If you are interested in working in this exciting field, you will need a bachelor of science degree in either geography, geology, chemistry, or physics. Further studies in more specialized fields such as geomorphology, atmospheric chemistry, minerology, and seismology are also required. Most volcanologists are affiliated with universities and conduct research as part of their academic duties. Others are hired as consultants (as needed) by government agencies to monitor dangerous situations.

Figure 5.16
A volcano on the Hawaiian Islands

ACTIVITIES

UNDERSTANDING CONCEPTS

1. Explain how plate tectonics might account for each of the following:
   a) volcanic islands like Iceland in the Mid-Atlantic Ridge
   b) mountain ranges and volcanoes on the leading edges of moving continental plates
   c) unusual and unique animals evolving in Australia and Madagascar
   d) volcanic activity adjacent to subduction zones
2. a) Give examples to show kinetic energy (movement) in the lithosphere.
   b) What is isostasy and how has it helped people to obtain the resources necessary for modern industry?
   c) Describe the rate at which isostatic change occurs.
3. Describe the different geological structures associated with faulting.
4. a) Compare the main types of volcanoes in an organizer like the one below.

Type	Reason for its existence	Type of Eruption	Examples	Damage to the environment and/or civilization
Hawaiian Volcano				
Vesuvian Volcano				
Midoceanic Volcano				
Strato Volcano				

   b) Many technical terms are associated with volcanism. Make a crossword puzzle for the new words in this section. Use a computer if you have access to one.
   c) Explain why some people may live on Mount Pinatubo when they know the area is dangerous.
   d) What trade-offs must the people make when they live close to volcano-prone areas?

DEVELOPING AND PRACTISING SKILLS

5. a) Using an atlas, indicate the following mountain chains on a map of the world: Western Cordillera, Sierra Madre, Andes Mountains, Atlas Mountains, Alps, Zagros Mountains, Caucasus Mountains, Himalayas, Verkhoyansk Range.
   b) Complete an organizer like the one shown on page 80 for each of the mountain ranges in part a). The Western Cordillera has been completed as an example.

Mountain Range	Plate Boundary	Explanation
Western Cordillera	Western edge of North American Plate	Pacific Plate is subducting under the North American Plate

6. a) Prepare a map of the world on which you identify the major landform types. Use a colour key like the one below.

Landform	Colour	Landform	Colour
Mountains	dark brown	Hills	yellow
Highlands	light brown	Plains	light green
Plateaux	orange-brown	Valleys	dark green

   b) What patterns are evident?
   c) How do these patterns reflect plate tectonics?
7. Develop a theory to explain why old fold mountains like the Appalachians, the Juras Mountains, and the Ural Mountains do not occur on present plate boundaries.
8. Use heavy cardboard, plaster, or modelling clay to make working models to illustrate different types of geological structures associated with faults.
9. a) Use a copy of Fig. 5.3 to make a map showing the locations of major volcanic eruptions. Use a colour key to identify where each type of volcano occurs.
   b) Connect the volcanoes with a line to show the **Ring of Fire** around the Pacific.
   c) Compare your map to Fig. 5.7. How accurate were you?
10. Study Figs. 5.6 and 5.8.
    a) Draw several profiles using the method described on page 72.
    b) Identify the orogeny being shown in your map and explain your answer.
11. Research one tectonic disaster of your choice.
    a) Make a list of focus questions for your study. Narrow the list down to two or three questions.
    b) Use one of the following web sites to help you gather information:
       <http://ncweb-menlo.wr.usgs.gov>
       This web site has an enormous amount of information on all manner of natural disasters in the US and worldwide.
       <http://abcnews.go.com>
       This is an excellent news service that has an American slant.
       <www.cbc.ca>
       Canada's national news service is especially good for disasters of a local nature.
       <www.nasa.gov>
       This American website is excellent for satellite images and air photos.

   c) Make point-form notes of the information you find that is relevant to your focus questions. Be sure to include complete sources and works cited.

   d) Synthesize the information by adding new ideas and omitting material that is irrelevant.

   e) Evaluate your research material for accuracy and authenticity.

   f) Draw conclusions about this disaster.

   g) Apply what you have learned to predict what could happen in the future.

   h) Present your findings to your group or class. Decide on the method of presentation—a bulletin board display, a written paper, an oral presentation, or something else. What maps, diagrams, models, graphs, or charts will you include?

12. Obtain a topographic map of a field study area.

   a) Prepare a tracing that identifies the significant geological features of the area.

   b) Make several parallel profiles of the site.

   c) Prepare either a three-dimensional drawing or a model of your field study area. Label the significant features and colour your work appropriately.

13. Study the topographic map of Columbia River, B.C. (on page 70).

   a) Draw a sketch of this map, showing the major physical features. Include rivers, mountains, valleys, and so on.

   b) Describe the relief of the region.

   c) Make a profile to help you explain the geological history of the region.

   d) How have the different layers of folded strata affected drainage and land use patterns?

14. Study the illustrations that show different faults in Fig. 5.10.

   a) Find examples of faults from air photos on selected websites by using the key words "faults + images." (A particularly good site is, http://geoimages.berkeley.edu/GeoImages/Wells/geomorph/fault7.html)

   b) Describe how the geological structure of the area affects drainage and land use patterns in each example.

LEARNING THROUGH APPLICATION

15. What effect would the following fault structures have on geographic patterns such as drainage, transportation routes, and settlements?

   a) strike slip fault

   b) rift valley

   c) thrust fault

   d) horst

   e) collision fault.

16. Make a list of all the ways you can think of in which volcanoes are dangerous. Give an example of each.

17. Using selected topographic maps provided by your teacher, create a model by following these steps.

   a) Create a series of profiles arranged parallel to each other at 5 cm intervals. Draw each profile on a separate piece of cardboard so that they are rigid.

   b) Cut out each profile and stand each one up in a vertical position oriented the same way as they were on the map (5 cm apart). Attach them to a thin piece of plywood.

   c) Fill the spaces between each profile with crumpled newspaper.

   d) Soak gauze impregnated with plaster of Paris in water. (This type of plaster is available from craft stores and medical supply companies.)

   e) Lay each piece of gauze over the profiles, overlapping them so that each layer is at a right angle to the layer it covers. Press the gauze down to fit the hollows and shape the material to follow the form of the profiles.

   f) Once the model has dried, paint and label the exhibit. You now have an exact scale model of the map.

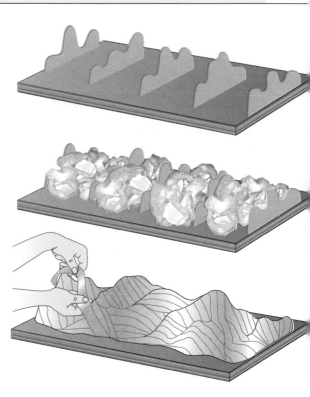

GIS Assignment on Volcanoes

18. The International Institute for Volcanic Awareness has announced funding to aid the countries most in need of volcanic prediction research. In this activity, your job is to prepare a map showing which country would most benefit from volcanic prediction research.

    You will need to download the instructions for the exercise from the ESRI Canada web site at http://www.esricanada.com/k-12/lesson/volcanoes/index.html and then click on the version of software that you are running. The document is in PDF format, so you will need to have Adobe Acrobat in order to read it. (Instructions for downloading are on the web site.)

    In this exercise you will do a number of things including creating a map showing the location of active and dormant volcanoes around the world. This exercise will also ask you to examine patterns in the location of volcanoes. Using this information, as well as other related data, you will then decide on the country that would most benefit from volcanic prediction research. Extension exercises are also included for those who wish to link to other sites dealing with the topic of volcanoes.

Supplemental Questions:

19. a) As per the downloaded instructions, determine the number of active and inactive volcanoes as well as their relationship to plate boundaries. Once you have determined where active volcanoes are located, zoom in on several countries that appear to have a significant number. Choose the country that, in your estimation, has the greatest number of active volcanoes.

b) Prepare a layout of your map and write a field report explaining the criteria behind your choice of country that would most benefit from volcanic prediction research.

20. Consider the relationship between the location of major world cities and their close proximity to active volcanoes. In order to complete this task create 100 KM buffers around all active volcanoes by doing the following:

- Make sure your "Volcanoes" theme is active. Go to Theme – Create Buffers.
- Choose "the features of a theme", which is your active volcanoes theme. Click on "Next."
- Choose "At a specified distance". Type in "100". Double check that "Distance units" are Kilometres. Click on "Next".
- Choose "No" for "Dissolve barriers within buffers?"
- Choose (at the bottom of the page) "in a new theme" and save the "100 KM Buffer" to your local directory.
- Click "Finish". Be sure to place the buffer layer underneath the "Volcano" theme.

a) Are there major cities that have more than one active volcano within the 100 km buffer range? Consider one of the largest cities in the world, Mexico City, for example.

b) Consider how cities continue to exist within the 100 km shadow of active volcanoes. How do people continue to justify living in an area of high risk of destruction due to volcanic activity?

21. The buffers that were created in question 12 depict danger zones. The danger to the citizens is increased as the distance from a volcano is decreased. Try experimenting with changing the buffer ranges.

a) Create a series of buffer themes in 10 KM increments starting from 10 KM up to a 50 KM range. These buffers would illustrate the increasing danger for those cities in closer proximity to active volcanoes.

b) Complete a field report that indicates a ranking of world cities that would make your Top 10 List of Cities Most Likely to Experience Destruction from Active Volcanoes.

Chapter 6

EARTH'S TREASURE TROVE: ELEMENTS, MINERALS, AND ROCKS

FOCUS QUESTIONS

1. What distinguishes one classification of rock from another?
2. How do resource mining operations affect areas of the Canadian environment?
3. What are the educational requirements, job descriptions, current opportunities, and future prospects for careers in mineral resource management?

Key Terms

igneous rock

sedimentary rock

metamorphic rock

magnetometers

assayer

The layers of the lithosphere are made up of elements, minerals, and rocks. **Elements** are substances that cannot be broken apart in any way by chemical or physical means. They include carbon, oxygen, and a host of other substances, each with specific chemical characteristics. Elements are the building blocks of **minerals**—inorganic compounds of one or more elements found naturally in the lithosphere. Minerals combine in infinite variety to make up rocks. Of the 92 elements found in nature, only eight form most of the earth's crust. Minerals such as gold, silver, and copper are rare, and are particularly valuable.

The combination of one or more elements creates a mineral. Yes, *one* is correct. An element can also be a mineral. Coal is an example. Made up of pure carbon, it is an element (carbon) and a mineral (coal). But there are usually at least two elements in a mineral. For example, silicon (Si) and oxygen (O) are both elements. When they join together chemically, they form the mineral silicon dioxide (SiO_2), more commonly known as

quartz. While minerals have common names, chemical formulas are better for identifying them. These formulas list all the elements contained in the mineral. Some may look complicated, but they are not too difficult to figure out. Take forsterite, for example. This common mineral has the formidable formula $(MgFe)_2SiO_4$. What this tells us is that forsterite is made of magnesium (Mg), iron (Fe), silicon (Si), and oxygen (O). Pure minerals are rarely found in nature. Usually, several minerals are cemented together as rocks. For example, granite is a common rock often made up of quartz, mica, and orthoclase or plagioclase feldspar. What is water? It is a **compound** since its formula H_2O means that hydrogen and oxygen are combined to create it. It is also inorganic and it is found in nature, which makes it a mineral. And what of glaciers? They can be considered rocks since they combine ice with other minerals.

Rocks and minerals seem indestructible, but believe it or not, they are constantly changing. Existing rocks are being worn down and crushed

Figure 6.1
Can you identify these rocks and minerals?

Element	Formula	% of the Earth's Crust	
		Mass	Volume
oxygen	O	46%	91%
silicon	Si	28%	1%
aluminum	Al	8%	1%
iron	Fe	5%	1%
calcium	Ca	4%	1%
sodium	Na	3%	2%
potassium	K	3%	2%
magnesium	Mg	2%	<1%
carbon	C	<1%	<1%
sulphur	S	<1%	<1%
lead	Pb	<1%	<1%
hydrogen	H	<1%	<1%

Figure 6.2
Major Elements of the Earth's Crust

by natural processes, and new rocks are constantly being formed as sediments are cemented together or as volcanoes spew lava into the air. Rocks are classified as either igneous, sedimentary, or metamorphic, according to how they were created.

Igneous Rocks

Igneous rocks are created from molten rock, or magma, deep within the crust and upper mantle. (On the surface of the lithosphere, molten rock is called "lava"; when it is underground, the term is "magma.") These rocks are often found on the earth's surface as well as deep within it. They reach the surface in one of two ways: via volcano eruptions or erosion.

Extrusive igneous rocks are formed when a volcano erupts and molten rock, or lava, flows over the earth's surface. When lava cools, new rock is formed. Depending on the minerals in the lava and the speed with which it cools, a vast variety of different igneous rocks can be created. Obsidian is one of the most beautiful. Resembling black glass, this rock is formed when lava is cooled so rapidly that crystals do not get a chance to form, as is usually the case when lava flows under water. However, more often than not the rock forms a dull, amorphous mass that can

accumulate to thousands of meters in thickness and cover vast areas of former lava flows. A material called "tuff" is the result of volcanic ash that is cemented together as mineral-rich water percolates through it.

Intrusive igneous rocks originate when molten rock solidifies deep within the lithosphere. These plutonic rocks eventually reach the surface as erosion gradually wears away the rock layers above it. Much of the igneous rock in Canada was formed deep in the earth millions and even billions of years ago.

geo.web resources

<www.cobweb.net/~bug2/rock1.htm>

This site, called the "Rock Doctor," is dedicated to rock classification. With a rock in hand, go to the site and choose the sedimentary, metamorphic, or igneous button, then follow the charts to identify your sample.

Figure 6.3
An Igneous Rock Formation

Igneous rocks are classified not only by the minerals they contain, but also by how quickly they came into being and by their resultant texture. The size of the crystallized minerals in rocks is determined by how fast the magma cooled. If it cooled slowly, the texture is coarse and individual crystals can be seen clearly. For example, basalt often has a crystalline structure. These coarse-grained igneous rocks are usually intrusive—that is, they were formed deep beneath the earth's surface where cooling is slow. Rocks with a fine texture result when the magma cooled so quickly that there was no time for individual crystals to form. These extrusive rocks are usually formed when volcanic lava comes into contact with relatively cold air or water. Sometimes an igneous rock contains both coarse and fine grains, which indicates that cooling occurred in two stages. Perhaps the outside cooled rapidly since it was in contact with the air, but the inside cooled slowly because of the internal heat of the lava. Granite is one of the most common forms of plutonic igneous rock. Made up of either pink feldspar or gray feldspar, plus quartz, hornblende, and mica, much of the rock in the Canadian Shield is of this type.

Sedimentary Rocks

Sedimentary rocks are different from igneous rocks because they are not formed from molten rock but are created from deposits of broken-up material that accumulate in oceans and lakes. There are three types of sedimentary rocks: clastic, chemical, and biogenic. **Clastic sedimentary rocks**, such as breccia, are formed when accumulations of stones and smaller pieces of weathered rock are cemented together naturally. **Chemical sedimentary rocks**, such as gypsum, are formed from chemical processes. In the case of gypsum, water evaporated, leaving the dissolved salts on the sea floor. In time, this useful building material was created. **Biogenic sedimentary rocks** are those that formed from living organisms, such as dolomite and limestone, which were both created from tiny sea creatures.

Sediment builds up when layers of material are deposited by rivers, glaciers, and other erosive agents. First, rock is weathered, or broken up into little pieces. Then it is transported to another place by wind, glaciers, or water before finally being deposited. Layers are created as more and more weathered material accumulates over time until thick deposits of sedimentary rock are formed.

For sediment to be transformed into rock, it must be compacted and cemented together. Compaction occurs when new layers of sediment

Figure 6.4
A Sedimentary Rock Formation

are deposited on top of older layers. The weight of upper layers squeezes out any spaces between particles that make up the layers beneath, and presses the weathered material tightly together. This flattens the individual particles and causes them to interlock with one another. Cementation occurs when minerals, dissolved in water, filter through the sediment. At a certain temperature and pressure, the minerals precipitate out of the water solution and remain in the spaces between the rock particles. They now act to cement the grains of source material together to form sedimentary rock. This is basically the same process used in making concrete, which, once it has been weathered, looks very much like sedimentary rock.

Sedimentary rocks are classified by their origin and texture. Clastic sedimentary rocks are made from other rocks that have been weathered over time and deposited in thick layers. Textures range from shale to sandstone to conglomerate. Made from clay, shale contains minute particles, usually deposited in a lake or other still body of water. Sandstone, of course, is made from sand that is laid down in moving water. Conglomerates are stones and particles as big as boulders, which have been deposited in rapidly moving water and cemented together. These three rocks—shale, sandstone, and conglomerate—are the main clastic sedimentary rocks.

Chemical sedimentary rocks are classified by texture and source material. Salt and gypsum are formed when the water in which these minerals were dissolved partially evaporates. Thick deposits of salt occur where inland seas once existed. Chert, or flint, is a hard chemical sedimentary rock that forms from quartz crystals that are cemented together by a fine silica gel.

Limestone and dolomite are the most common types of biogenic sedimentary rocks. The shell and skeletal remains of marine animals leave calcium deposits. Calcium carbonate cements these fragments together, creating limestone. Dolomite is formed when magnesium carbonate is the cement that binds the biogenic particles. Like other sedimentary rocks, biogenic rocks usually form where

Figure 6.5
Sample of a Sedimentary Rock

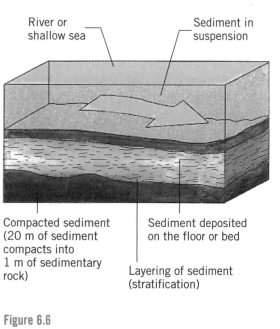

River or shallow sea

Sediment in suspension

Compacted sediment (20 m of sediment compacts into 1 m of sedimentary rock)

Sediment deposited on the floor or bed

Layering of sediment (stratification)

Figure 6.6
How Sedimentary Rocks Are Laid Down

inland seas once were. All three types of sedimentary rocks can be found mixed together. Limestone, for instance, may contain fragments of flint, and sandstone and dolomite may be found with beds of salt or gypsum.

Metamorphic Rocks

The third category of rock is **metamorphic**. "Meta" means *change* and "morph" means *shape*. Metamorphic rocks change more than just their shape, however. They change in mineral composition, structure, and texture as a result of the great pressure and heat that exist in the lithosphere. Unlike igneous rocks, in which change occurs during melting, changes in metamorphic rocks occur while the rock is solid. The degree of change depends on the amount of heat and pressure exerted on it.

There are more types of metamorphic rock than there are igneous or sedimentary rocks. In fact, each sedimentary and igneous rock has at least one metamorphic equivalent, while others have several. For example, the metamorphosed form of sandstone is quartzite, limestone changes to marble, granite becomes gneiss (pronounced "nice"), and shale changes to slate. But as the temperature and pressure increase even further, the slate changes again to schist. It has been estimated that 85 per cent of the upper crust is made up of metamorphic rock—most of which is

Figure 6.7
Schist, a Metamorphic Rock

buried under sedimentary rock, where it remains unexposed at the surface until erosion has removed the earth's upper layers.

Metamorphic rocks are formed in places where there is enormous pressure and temperatures reach over 300°C. Where these conditions exist, two types of metamorphic rocks are formed: **contact metamorphic rocks**—those that change as a result of the heat given off during the formation of intrusive igneous rocks; and **dynamic metamorphic rocks**, which are formed when compressed by the weight of rock layers above them or by tectonic forces.

Metamorphic rocks are sometimes hard to identify since they often look like igneous rocks. But there is one trait that sets them apart—a banded structure called **foliation**. When pressure is intense, minerals may align themselves in layers within the rock, such as in gneiss, for example. The minerals in the original granite from which gneiss is made—feldspar and quartz—are concentrated in alternating bands.

The Rock Cycle

The fact that rocks are constantly changing is indicated by the Rock Cycle flow chart shown in Fig. 6.8. Starting at the bottom of the chart and following the arrows, you can start to see how even the ancient rocks beneath our feet evolve and change constantly. New minerals from the asthenosphere travel by the force of convection up toward the surface, moving through cracks in the existing rock. As the temperature drops, the minerals form into veins within the rock or sometimes into vast domes of molten material, which cools to form intrusive features called batholiths. These intrusive features lay locked in stone, sometimes for billions of years, until they are eventually exposed at the surface by the forces of weathering and erosion. Some molten rock reaches the surface when it oozes out of cracks at midoceanic ridges or explodes from volcanoes.

As soon as the igneous rock reaches the surface, the physical action of wind, rain, ice, and waves starts breaking it down. Chemicals work to dissolve certain minerals faster than others, and over time the rock falls apart. Tiny fragments or huge chunks wash into the sea or form into soil under the vegetative cover of the land. Sediment left by the igneous rock is joined by broken pieces of other rock types and the remains of plants and animals. The combined accumulation of all this matter provides the building materials for sedimentary rock. As layer upon layer of sediment accumulates, minerals in the water that percolates through the soil cements them together, and sedimentary rock is created. As soon as the sedimentary rock reaches the surface, the elements of weather start breaking it down to form new sediments, so the cycle continues.

Sedimentary and igneous rocks that are forced under continental plates by tectonic forces are subjected to enormous pressure and heat. The minerals in them change and the rock is transformed into metamorphic rock. As with the other rock types, when it reaches the surface again, millions upon millions of years later, the forces of weathering are able to break it down into sediments so that the cycle continues over again. It is amazing that the rocks we stand on, the rocks that seem so solid, are as changeable as they are.

Building Resources

Rocks and minerals provide many of the raw materials used to manufacture a wide range of consumer items. If you look around your bedroom, you will see all kinds of examples. The graphite in the pencil on your desk, the metal filing cabinet under your desk, the plasterboard of the walls, and even the linoleum floor are all made from mineral resources. We take many of these minerals for granted because they are hidden from our view. We don't usually see the aluminum wiring and steel beams hidden in the walls, so we forget that we are dependent on these essential raw materials.

In southern Ontario, many of the building materials needed by modern society are readily accessible through the numerous deposits of sand and gravel that resulted from the last ice age. The Oak Ridges Moraine is one such source. This landform was created when the great continental ice sheet started to recede, and the load it was

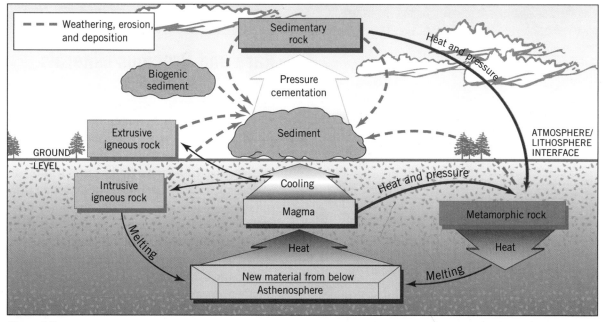

Figure 6.8
The Rock Cycle

Figure 6.9
Vast quantities of sand and gravel are needed to maintain transportation routes across Canada.

Mineral Resource Development

Even though resources such as sand and gravel are essential for continued urbanization in southern Ontario, many people who live in resource-rich areas are sensitive to the development of these resources because this process has a huge impact on local ecosystems. One of the foremost problems is not so much with the development of the resource, but with the condition the land is left in after the quarry is closed. Often the big hole which remains is used as a landfill site, such as the Keele Valley Dump—the largest waste management facility in Canada. The Keele Valley Dump is convenient to Toronto but is also in an ecologically sensitive area. Since the Oak Ridges Moraine is the source of all the water that flows into Lake Ontario in the GTA (Greater Toronto Area), it is essential that hazardous wastes do not leach into the soil. Governments have to be sensitive to the needs of the people and to the preservation of natural ecosystems, as well as allow resource development to occur.

Question:
How does the quarry impact on the natural systems of the Oak Ridges Moraine?

carrying was deposited as the glacier melted. Much of the material transported by the glacier (including tiny grains of clay and giant boulders alike) was carried away by meltwater running through the enormous spillways. Where there was a fast flow, large rocks were carried, but as the river slowed, ever-smaller particles of rock settled out. All along the top of the moraine, deposits of sand are found today where the post-glacial channels took away the meltwater. In some places, lakes formed and tiny particles of clay settled on the lake floor. The sand is an important building material used in the making of cement and mortar for construction. Without it, big cities like Toronto could not have been as easily built.

Another area in southern Ontario where building materials are found is the Niagara Escarpment. This dominant cliff, which runs all the way from Niagara Falls to the Bruce Peninsula and extends through to Manitoulin Island, is the remains of an ancient sea bed that was raised and tilted by tectonic forces. The rock is much more resistant than the surrounding rock and so did not wear down as much. When crushed, the limestone of the escarpment makes excellent aggregate (gravel), which is used in road construction and building.

Rare and Precious Minerals

Some of the minerals we use are very rare and therefore difficult to find. However, processes in the lithosphere tend to concentrate these minerals into deposits. It is the work of the geologist to find prospective mineral concentrations so they can be extracted from the earth's crust. Part of the geologist's job is to determine if the mineral is in sufficient quantity and concentration to mine profitably. If it costs more to extract a resource than a company would make selling it, then there is no point in mining the mineral. World prices and market demand will also often dictate whether or not a resource can be profitably extracted. Only when these factors combine to create an "economic deposit" will a company make an investment to open a mine.

Many economic deposits of igneous rocks are found in the Canadian Shield and the Western Cordillera. The three main types of minerals that are mined in these regions include precious metals, such as gold, silver, and platinum; ferrous metals, such as iron and nickel; and non-ferrous (meaning without iron) metals, such as copper, lead, and zinc. We usually think of precious metals as being used solely in the production of jewellery; however, they have a great many industrial uses as well. Gold and silver are used in medicine and dentistry because they are easy to work with and do not oxidize readily. Platinum is used industrially for many things, including catalytic converters in the emission controls of all cars. While these valuable miner-als are found in minute quantities often comprising only a tiny part of the ore, they are so valuable that they are often still worth mining. Gold, for example, can be economically mined even if it makes up a mere 5 per 100 000 parts of its ore. Of course, whenever the price of gold drops, so too does the feasibility of mining marginally profitable deposits.

Non-ferrous metals are used in many consumer products. Copper, lead, zinc, tin, and aluminum are used to make everything from auto parts to food containers to construction materials. Ferrous metals are those minerals that can be combined to make steel alloys. Iron, nickel, molybdenum, chromium, and manganese are the main minerals in this group.

Figure 6.10
Our use of minerals is extensive.

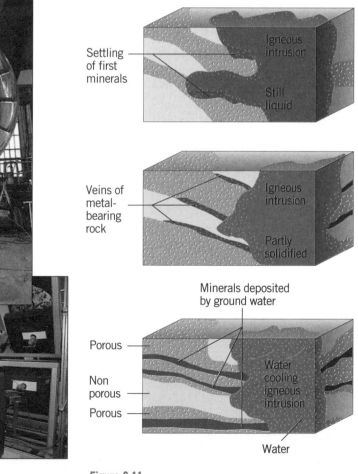

Figure 6.11
Veins of Minerals in Igneous Rock

CHANGING TECHNOLOGY: Magnetometers

Remote sensing is used to determine the location of potential mineral deposits. Airplanes fly over the study area recording the magnetic properties of the rock below. In the past, prospectors used maps and their knowledge of geological formations to scour the land and scout out potential deposits, but their methods were hit-and-miss and often relied on luck as much as anything else.

Today, remote sensing has revolutionized the process. Airplanes fly over the designated study area in a grid, while powerful magnetometers onboard measure the magnetic properties of the rock below. At each point, the reading is **georeferenced** using satellite-based GPS (global positioning systems) technology. Georeferencing is a digital mapping technique in which each point on a map is identified using its exact location on Earth. A digitizing tablet (like a computer mouse) is used to trace an image onto the computer screen. Each point is identified as a particular location using latitude and longitude coordinates. If three points are thus referenced, a computer software program can georeference every other point on the map.

Back in the lab, the readings are plotted on a map and an **iso map** is created. Igneous intrusions can be spotted by analysing these magnetic surveys. Where igneous intrusions reach the earth's surface, roughly circular "signatures" appear on the iso map. Those areas that look promising are investigated further by field crews.

Question:
What implications do you think this technology has for the extent and impact of mineral resource mining in Canada?

In Canada, mining these mineral deposits has become a way of life for thousands of workers and scores of northern communities. If it were not for the mines and the forest industry, most of northern Canada would be barely inhabited. Jobs in mining are far from glamorous, but they can be well-paid. Miners spend their days kilometres below the earth's surface in damp, cramped quarters, often working under dangerous conditions. In Cape Breton's coal mines, conditions were brutal until the late 40s. Workers endured unspeakable hardships for starvation wages. Over the past 50 years, labour unions have worked hard with mining companies to improve working conditions. Today, many people in the mining communities of Canada earn good wages and have the benefits of modern technology to help extract valuable ore.

While these less valuable minerals are found in minute quantities in many rock layers, it is only when nature concentrates the minerals in deposits that mining them makes economic sense. Many of the metals mined in Canada are concentrated in **igneous intrusions**. These geologic formations were created millions of years ago, when molten rock filled cracks in the earth's crust. As the **magma** flowed through the cracks, minerals formed at various temperatures along the veins in one of three ways. Sometimes heavier metals such as lead and nickel sank in molten rock and solidified at the bottom of the igneous intrusion; the nickel in Thompson Mine,

Manitoba, was concentrated in this way. The second method results from minerals precipitating or solidifying along the edges of the vein. For example, as the magma cools in the intrusion, it changes from a liquid to a solid. As with most substances, molecules within the material come closer together, and it shrinks in volume. Hot, mineral-rich water flows into the spaces that the shrinking magma leaves behind, and as the water cools, the minerals precipitate at different temperatures. So, it is common in the Canadian Shield to see veins in igneous rock with valuable metal deposits along the edges of these intrusions.

Sometimes water is driven through the spaces between the rock layers in front of igneous intrusions. This is the third way mineral deposits are concentrated in the Canadian Shield. Most often, mineral deposits form from complex variations and combinations of all three processes.

In the mining industry, many different professionals work to plan and develop mineral deposits. The economic mineralogist studies the site to determine if the minerals in the igneous pipe are present in sufficient volumes to make mining profitable. A huge sample—usually many tons—is taken, and the cost of extracting the mineral from the ore is carefully documented. The sample is sent to an assayer—a geologist with an expertise in the chemical properties of rocks—and the value of the ore is determined. If the ore is worth more than the cost of extracting it, then the deposit can be mined profitably. However, if other mines come on stream and the price of the metal on the global market drops, the value of the deposit may no longer be worth mining. The whole business is very risky, but it has provided thousands of Canadians with employment and made many of them very wealthy. Internationally, Canadian mining companies are held in great esteem, and our geologists can be found all over the world developing innumerable resources.

Digging deep into the earth to get at the deposits is not the only way valuable minerals are found. Sometimes veins of economic minerals are exposed on the surface of the earth through erosion and are extracted through open-pit mines—a method that is easier and cheaper than tunneling into the earth. Such mines are commonly seen operating on the glacial deposits of southern Ontario and on the Niagara Escarpment, where sand and limestone are often extracted this way. More often, however, tunnels follow the ore back horizontally into a mountain. In mountainous regions of Alberta, British Columbia, and Yukon Territory, these operations are predominant.

Sometimes running water removes minerals from one place and concentrates them somewhere else. These deposits are called **placer deposits** (pronounced *plasser*) and can be found where river currents are fast enough to wash away the sand, but slow enough to allow heavy minerals such as gold to be deposited. The famous Klondike Gold Rush of the late 1800s occurred because gold had washed out of gold veins high in the mountains and was eventually found in sandbars along the Klondike River. Finding these rich deposits requires a concrete understanding of geology—and a lot of good luck!

Both the assayer and the economic mineralogist are specialized professionals who require extensive training. Upon attaining a four-year geology or engineering degree at a university like Laurentian or Lake Head, most graduates work for several years in a mine. They oversee the extraction of ore by mine workers and mining operations. Often they go back to school and specialize by taking extra courses. The assayer takes courses in chemistry, geology, and mineralogy. The economic mineralogist studies economics as it pertains to mining, mineralogy, and cartography. After two years, they are qualified to go back to work in the mining industry.

In recent years, there have not been a lot of opportunities in the Canadian mining industry. Increased production in developing countries has resulted in reduced prices for many minerals on world commodities markets. Add to this the increased operating costs brought about by more stringent environmental controls in Canada, and many mines struggle to make a profit.

Ekati Diamond Mine

The Ekati Diamond Mine is a profitable Canadian company that was given permission to operate only after agreeing to meet and maintain certain environmental standards in the ecologically sensitive northern region.

The use of magnetic surveys led to the eventual development of the mine 300 kilometres northeast of Yellowknife in the Northwest Territories. Like other geological regions where diamonds are found, Ekati™ is located on ancient rocks more than a billion years old. Kimberlite, a diamond bearing ore, was deposited when magma flowed through the igneous intrusion. Since the region was swept clear of most soil and surface features 10 000 years ago in the last glacial period, the deposit was easy to discover using advanced magnetic surveys. The reason nobody found the deposit before now is that the region is so remote.

Five kimberlite pipes are being mined at the site including Panada Pit, which is 650 m in diameter and expected to reach down 320 m into the ground. The rock removed from the pit is being used to construct building pads on the permafrost, roads, and dams. The processing plant handles 9 000 tons of kimberlite each day. The ore is crushed, scrubbed with water to remove stones, and sorted by density. X-rays sort the diamonds from the other heavy minerals. The diamonds are then exported off-site for cleaning, sorting, and cutting.

In its first month of operation, the company sold 68 500 carats at $124 per carat for a total of $8.5 million. This did not include the sale of larger stones over 10 carats. Production in December of 1999 was 170 000 carats; full production capacity of 250 000 carats per month was reached in the Spring of 2000. Antwerp diamond merchants (where 80 per cent of all diamond sales are made) commented on the excellent quality, the abundant supply, and the stability of the country where the diamonds come from. By 2002, analysts predict Canadian diamonds will make up 10 per cent of the global market share.

But what are the environmental costs of such a project? Although mining is by nature an intrusive industry that disrupts natural systems, and given that diamond mining is one of the most disruptive of all forms of mining, the Ekati Diamond Mine™ was required to adhere to strict environmental controls in order to operate in the ecologically sensitive Northwest Territories. The land is predominantly Canadian Shield covered with tundra. No trees grow in the area except for willows in the sheltered river valleys and 3-metre-high spruce trees on south-facing slopes. Sedge wetlands provide important habitats for many animals. However, most of the region is polar desert with less than 400 mm of precipitation per year. Although precipitation is low, evaporation is also low because it is so

Figure 6.12
The Ekati Diamond Mine™

Figure 6.13
Water monitoring is only one of the environmental programs carried out by the Ekati Diamond Mine™.

cold. The ground is permanently frozen to a depth of 250 metres, so meltwater sits on the surface, making the ground so wet and boggy in summer that travel is limited and mosquitoes thrive.

Tremendous amounts of waste material are generated for every tiny carat of diamond produced. Ekati™ received permission to construct the mine after the parent company submitted an eight-volume Environmental Impact Statement. Obviously, the ground has to be disturbed where the mine is located; however, the company supervises more than 30 environmental monitoring programs to reduce the impact on the region that is the traditional territory of the Dene Dogrib Nation.

In addition to analysing the water, aquatic plants and animals are surveyed on an on-going basis. Lakes that lie on top of ore-bearing kimberlites will be drained. This loss of fish habitat is unavoidable, but the company has compensated the Department of Fisheries and Oceans for the loss, and is obligated to restore the lake once mining operations cease in about 30 years.

Unfortunately, the programs may not be running as well as was hoped. After an investigation by the Department of Fisheries and Oceans (DFO), eight charges under the Fisheries Act were brought against the mining company's owners, BHP Diamonds Inc. The maximum fine for each of these charges is $1 million. DFO alleged that BHP Diamonds Inc. disrupted and altered the habitat of the trout, whitefish, grayling, and slimy sculpin in three lakes near the mining operation by allowing silt and sediments to build up in the water. BHP Diamonds Inc. denies the charges. At the time of writing this book, this case was still before the courts.

Canada stands to benefit immensely from entry into this new mining industry. It joins South Africa, Russia, and a handful of west African nations in the diamond mining business. In Africa, the outbreak of civil war and extreme violence over the control of diamond mines has made many European diamond merchants anxious to find new sources of gems outside that troubled region. Ekati™ could not have come on stream at a better time with regard to diamond prices and increased demand from secure buyers.

QUESTIONS:

1. Explain why it seems to be a logical time for a mine like Ekati™ to be operating in Canada.

2. Why might it be difficult for a mining company to operate without disrupting the environment?

3. Explain how advanced technology helps in the mining of diamonds.

Flowing Resources

Oil and natural gas are two other valuable resources found in the earth's treasure trove. While these resources are fluids as opposed to solids, such as gold or iron, their extraction from the earth is also considered a form of mining.

Natural gas and oil are created in a complex process that takes millions of years. The deposits we mine today were formed when minute floating plants and animals called plankton accumulated in shallow seas during the Palaeozoic and Mesozoic eras. (The Palaeozoic was the era when marine life dominated the earth; the Mesozoic Era was the period of the dinosaurs.) Plankton stored immense quantities of carbon as CO_2 was converted into carbohydrates through the process of photosynthesis. Some of this organic material may have been converted to animal tissue as microscopic animals fed on the tiny plants. This "fossilized sunshine" was trapped for millions of years in the sedimentary rocks that formed above it.

This layer of organic ooze decomposed very slowly because there was limited oxygen.

Figure 6.14
The Hibernia Oil Well

However, bacteria transformed it into methane and a complex hydrocarbon called kerogen. If the temperature rose to 100°C, the kerogen changed into another chemical compound—oil. If the temperature continued to rise above 150°C, the oil was changed back into carbon dioxide. Oil is really a freak of nature that occurs when conditions are just right.

As with metallic minerals, natural gas and oil have to be concentrated before they can be extracted for a profit. Concentration occurs when the precious fossil fuels accumulate in the spaces of porous reservoir rocks, which are layered between non-porous rocks. The non-porous rock prevents the oil from seeping out of the deposit, while the **cap rock** prevents the natural gas and oil from floating up to the surface. Salt water under the reservoir rock usually prevents the oil from seeping down deeper into the crust. Because natural gas is lighter than oil, it usually rises above the oil deposit. When a hole is drilled in the cap rock, the natural gas explodes out of it, with the oil following soon after.

The Athabaska Oil Sands of northern Saskatchewan and Alberta are very interesting because the oil is not found in a neat reservoir underground; rather, it is mixed up with sand and shale. Because of this, extraction is very difficult and costly. A company called Sun Corp. has developed an environmentally sound process that extracts oil without causing surface pollution. Hot water is pumped into the deposit through one well and extracted through another. The oil becomes a liquid as it is heated and can be more easily removed.

The deposit is massive, rivalling the reserves found in the Middle East and the vast reserves found elsewhere in the world. Estimates of 160 billion cubic metres of oil cover an area about the size of New Brunswick. These deposits can fulfil all of Canada's oil needs for the next 300 years. Despite what you may believe, we are not running out of oil.

ENVIRONMENT WATCH

Side Effects of Oil Production

It has been estimated that the oil sands project produces more pollution than any other industrial development in the world. All the waste from the extraction process is left as surface pollution, which has had a devastating impact on the plants and animals of this sub-polar taiga forest region. Because the climate is so cold, it takes longer for plants to recover from ecological damage. Those in Canada's southern cities would argue that we need the oil for industry and to maintain our urban lifestyle. Even the residents of the oil sands area, desperate for work in an economically depressed region, support the project. But some environmentalists and Aboriginal people worry that the cost of extraction may be too much for what was once a pristine wilderness.

Many farmers in Alberta have been concerned with another ecological problem caused by the oil industry. Along with the oil that is extracted comes a significant quantity of natural gas. This gas is treated as a waste product and is burned off as it is encountered, rather than collected. The problem is that the gas contains sulphur, which is released into the atmosphere when it is burned and affects the health of animals. Cattle ranchers in the area complain that their cattle are dying, and the incidence of stillborn calves is higher than anywhere else in Canada.

Are the economic benefits of oil production more important than the preservation of the environment? This is a difficult question and there is no easy answer. However, there is a way that all of us can help reduce pollution in the "oil patch." By carpooling, using public transit, cycling, and buying fuel efficient cars, we can make a big difference in the amount of oil that needs to be extracted from the Tar Sands and other mega-projects, and thus we can help reduce the harmful side effects that this activity has on the environment.

Question:
Make a chart that compares the pros and cons of oil production. In your opinion, do the positive aspects of this industry outweigh the negative impacts? If not, do you think limiting our reliance on oil will remedy the situation?

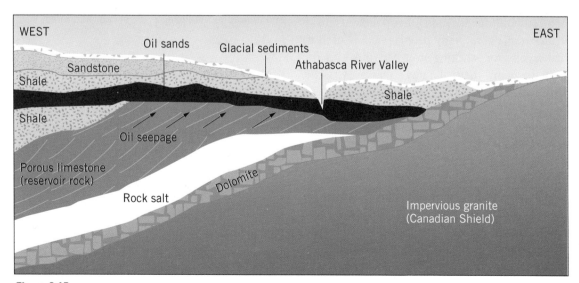

Figure 6.15
The Athabaska oil reserves are squeezed into layers of porous rock beneath the surface.

Coal: Fueling Industries

Coal is another valuable fossil fuel found in sedimentary layers. Like natural gas and oil, it formed from living things. In the Carboniferous Period, giant forests grew in the shallow tropical swamps. When the trees fell into the water, they decomposed slowly (see Fig. 6.16). Eventually, methane and peat—a flammable organic substance that can be used as fuel—were formed.

If the layers of peat were buried under sediment and heated, water vapour was squeezed out of the deposit. Eventually, the carbon concentration in these deposits rose and bituminous coal was formed. This concentrated fossilized vegetation burns hot and makes an excellent fuel. If further heat and pressure drive off more impurities and further concentrate the carbon, anthracite is formed. This metamorphic form of coal burns hotter and with less pollution than bituminous coal.

Unlike oil, coal forms in thick seams within sedimentary structures. It does not need to be held in place by non-porous layers of rock. It can be mined easily if the layers of ore are exposed through erosion. Often, shafts and tunnels follow the seams deep under the earth's surface.

Today, coal's popularity has declined because it does not burn as cleanly as natural gas or oil. Soot, sulphur dioxide, and other pollutants make it unacceptable to many people. Coal is used to make coke for smelting iron and provides the heat for many thermal power plants. A useful resource, coal fuelled the Industrial Revolution in Europe and North America, and may be just as important a resource for emerging industrial nations like India and China.

In addition to the precious and semi-precious minerals mentioned, many others are used by people for a wide variety of purposes. Clays are used to make everything from bricks to fine china. Gypsum is used to make wallboard for use in construction, and cement is made from a mixture of ground limestone and clay. In addition, many fertilizers are made from mineral deposits. All of these minerals are derived from rock formations found in abundance in Canada.

a. Swampy forest by the sea

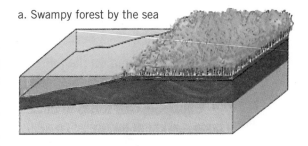

b. Sea level rises about 20 m

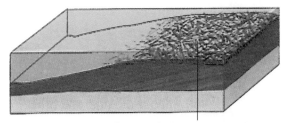

Trees and plants drowned by sea

c. Sea level remains high

Buried trees are compressed and altered to form coal   Mud deposited on top of drowned forest

d. Sea level falls again   Forest grows again on swampy land when sea level falls

Layers of mud and sand hardened into rocks   Coal seam

Figure 6.16
Coal Sedimentary Structures

ACTIVITIES

UNDERSTANDING CONCEPTS

1. a) Outline the differences between intrusive and extrusive igneous features.
   b) How can you account for the difference in appearance of such rocks as obsidian, basalt and tuff?
   c) How do intrusive features eventually end up on the surface?
2. a) Explain what sediment is and how it contributes to the formation of sedimentary rocks.
   b) Outline how compaction and cementation contribute to the creation of sedimentary rock.
3. Classify each of the following rocks as clastic, chemical, or biogenic and explain your choice.
   a) conglomerate: a coarse-grained rock made up of many tiny pebbles.
   b) rock salt: the residue left by evaporated sea water
   c) sandstone: sand glued together to form a rough, brittle rock
   d) coal: the remains of plant matter that has decomposed anaerobically.
4. a) Explain how metamorphic rocks are formed.
   b) Explain why there are more metamorphic rocks than any other rock type.
5. Using the flow chart that shows the rock cycle (on page 89), explain how
     • an igneous rock can become a sedimentary rock
     • a sedimentary rock can become a metamorphic rock
     • a metamorphic rock can become a sedimentary rock
     • a sedimentary rock can become an igneous rock.
6. Give examples to show how mineral deposits are concentrated in geological structures.
7. In what geological structures would you expect to find each of the following economic minerals:
   a) coal
   b) silver and gold
   c) oil and natural gas
   d) nickel, lead, and zinc
   e) diamonds
8. Describe the process whereby a mine is brought into production.
9. a) Describe some of the positive and negative effects of the oil industry.
   b) Describe what can be done to reduce the problems associated with the oil industry.
10. a) Explain how people have derived mineral resources from glacial deposits such as the Oak Ridges Moraine.
    b) What concerns do people have about the development of the moraine?

DEVELOPING AND PRACTISING SKILLS

11. Study Figure 6.2 and determine what elements make up the following minerals:

    - quartz: SiO_2
    - pyrite: FeS_2
    - galena: PbS
    - gypsum: $CaSo_4 \bullet 2H_2O$
    - orthoclase: $KAlSi_3O_8$

    - calcite: $CaCO_3$
    - magnetite: Fe_2O_3
    - corundum: Al_2O_3
    - dolomite: $CaMg(CO_3)_2$

12. Obtain a collection of 10 to 20 different minerals from your teacher.

    a) Prepare an organizer comparing the different samples. Criteria could include colour, hardness, density, and other qualities.

    b) Use a field guide to identify the minerals.

    c) What criteria were used in the field guide to identify minerals?

13. a) Write a short report on one of the following topics:
    - The economic feasibility of mining in Canada
    - The environmental damage caused by mineral development
    - The positive and negative aspects of the mining industry and whether or not the Canadian government should continue to support the industry
    - Whether the expansion of the oil industry in Canada should continue

    b) Self-evaluate your paragraph. Give one mark for each point you believe has been fully explained.

    c) Exchange your work with another student and evaluate each other's work.

    d) Discuss any discrepancies between your mark and the mark that your peer gave you.

14. a) Explain where aggregates are found in southern Ontario.

    b) Assess the importance of quarries to each of the following: builders, homeowners on the Moraine or Escarpment, conservationists, politicians, waste management companies, hydrogeologists.

    c) Explain why there may be differing attitudes and conflicts among these people.

15. Refer to the following web sites to find out more about the impact of mining on the Canadian environment. Write a summary of the information in a report. Make improvements on your report-writing skills by considering the suggestions from Question 13.

    Environment Canada: The Impact of Mining on the Environment
    <www.ns/ec/gc/epb/progs/mining.html>

    J. N. Desmarais Library, Laurentian University: Mining Environment Database
    <www.laurentian.ca.www/library/medlib.htm>

    Natural Resources Canada: Mining and the Environment
    <www.nr.gc.ca.mms/school/env/mining.htm>

    Labour Net Canada Mining Watch: Organized labour's concerns about the industry
    <www.labournet.ca.mine.html>

    Environmental Mining Council of BC: a primer on mining and the environment
    <www.miningwatch.org/emcbc/default.htm>

LEARNING THROUGH APPLICATION

16. a) Obtain a piece of rock. Take it home and change it in some way.
    b) Show the rock to your group. Have them guess how you altered it. Explain how what you did to the rock could have occurred naturally.
17. Collect a representative sample of rocks and minerals.
    a) Display your samples on a piece of plywood, in an egg carton, or in some other way.
    b) If there is a lot of variety in your rock samples, identify each one and classify it as igneous, sedimentary, or metamorphic. Write a brief explanation to support your classification.
    c) If all of your samples are of the same rock type, write an explanation of how you think the rock was formed. What generalizations can you make about the geology of your study site?
18. Visit a local quarry or mine. Interview a worker and determine:
    • the nature of the mineral being mined   • how the mineral was formed
    • how the ore is mined   • how the minerals are removed from the ore
19. a) What examples of human interaction with nature were mentioned in the chapter?
    b) Assess whether each interaction was positive or negative.
    c) Provide suggestions to improve human interaction with the lithosphere.
20. a) Describe how each of the following professions relate to mining, and explain why they are important to the industry: miner, geologist, economic mineralogist, assayer, ecologist.
    b) Explain what training each profession requires.
    c) Outline the prospects for the future growth of these industries.

GIS Assignment on Mining

21. You are a consultant for mining companies throughout Ontario. Your job is to propose ideal sites to mine for specific minerals. There are three main types of mineral deposits: metallic, fuel, and industrial. Use ArcView GIS to create a map that will show the location of the ideal mine sites in Ontario.

    You will need to download the instructions for the exercise from the ESRI Canada web site at http://www.esricanada.com/k-12/lesson/mining/index.html and then click on the version of software that you are running. The document is in PDF format so you will need to have Adobe Acrobat in order to read it. Instructions for downloading are on the web site.

    In this exercise you will do a number of things including creating a map showing the generalized geology for Canada and examining patterns in the location of geologic features therein (e.g., the relationship between the location of fault lines and rock types). Using this information, as well as other related data, you will then decide on the optimal locations for four new mining sites in Ontario. Extension exercises are also included for those who wish to examine the topic of mining more closely.

    Supplemental Questions:
22. a) Is there a relationship between geologic patterns and any other thematic maps of Canada?
    b) Indicate the primary rock type found in each of Canada's provinces and territories.
    c) Which provinces have the greatest variety of rock types within their borders?
    d) Examine the minerals data in the ArcCanada\Disk2\world\minerals.shp file. Describe the relationship between geologic rock types and minerals found there. List the location of the specific minerals that have been found within geologic rock types.

Chapter 7

WEARING DOWN THE LAND FROM ABOVE

FOCUS QUESTIONS

1. How is the surface of the lithosphere constantly being worn down and reshaped?
2. What processes were responsible for shaping the landforms in your community?
3. How do gradational forces affect the way people live?

Key Terms

weathering

transport

deposition

base level

mass wasting

While tectonic processes operating within the earth formed the lithosphere, forces operating outside the lithosphere also impact on the earth's surface. These **processes of gradation** originate in the atmosphere and the hydrosphere, and include mass wasting, running water, wave action, glaciation, and wind action.

Gradation includes three different and complimentary processes that are often confused. These are **weathering**, **transport**, and **deposition**. Weathering is the wearing away and breaking down of the surface of the lithosphere. Many different processes, both chemical and mechanical, serve to weather surfaces. Transport refers to the movement of weathered material from one place to another. **Erosion** occurs when both weathering and transport take place in an area. When the agent transporting the weathered material eventually loses the energy needed to carry its load, the material is dropped and this is called deposition. Gradation is the term used to collectively represent all those activities of the earth's surface that build up some areas of land and wear down others.

Gradational forces are at work everywhere. Rivers cut deep valleys through mountain passes and create deltas far downstream. Waves and currents carve arches and deposit sand on beaches. Glaciers ebb and flow over vast continental regions and in remote mountain uplands, sometimes sculpting landforms while at other times erecting massive **moraines**. Desert winds create beautiful rock formations and build up giant sand dunes. All of these forces shape the planet on which we live.

Base Level

If you watch a mechanical grader operating on a construction site, you will notice that much of the action is similar to natural processes in the lithosphere. The machine scrapes away the hills and fills in the hollows. When water runs over a rough surface, it tends to do exactly the same thing. In a riverbed, the high points are worn

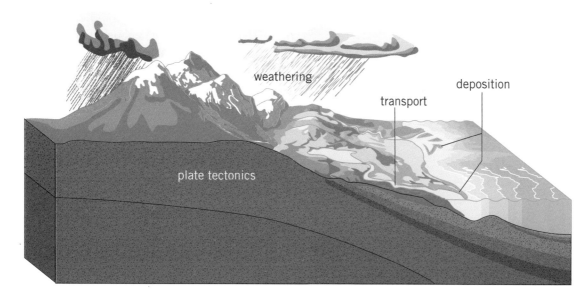

Figure 7.1
Forces that Shape the Earth's Surface

down and the depressions are filled with the sediment the water is carrying. When wind blows sand over a desert landscape, it works in a similar way—rocks and protuberances are sand-blasted and the worn material is used to fill in recesses in the desert floor. This constant wearing away and filling in is why so many landscapes are naturally flat and smooth.

Places such as rough mountain chains may be anything but flat, but it is not for want of trying. Gradational forces are working to reach base level, even though they are sometimes overpowered by tectonic forces that build the land up faster than it can be worn down. For this reason, many landscapes seem untouched by the forces of gradation.

John Powell, a nineteenth-century geologist, first came up with the idea of **base level**. He hypothesized that base level is the point where a river does not deepen a valley any more but diverts its energy to widening it. Base level is described as a smooth curve running under land masses gently rising from sea level. Gradational processes try to reach base level by filling depressions and smoothing down high points.

If gradational processes were at work without tectonic processes constantly changing surface elevation and relief, the planet would be as smooth as a ping pong ball! This can never happen because forces within the lithosphere are constantly causing mountains to rise, valleys to form, oceans to sink, and millions of other changes to happen over and over again. The interaction of tectonic and gradational forces creates the many interesting and varied landscapes that form the surface of our planet. Each gradational process is different and shapes the land in its own distinct way, but they all operate under the same basic principles of weathering, transport, and deposition.

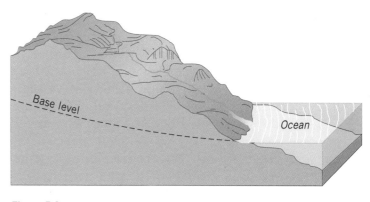

Figure 7.2
Base Level

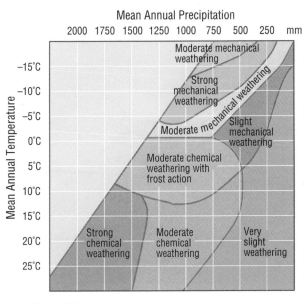

Figure 7.3
The Relative Importance of Different Types of Weathering Under Different Temperature and Precipitation Conditions

Weathering

As the name implies, soil and loose matter is stripped away through the process of weathering. Forces at work on the surface of the earth break down rock into weathered material. Running water, snow and ice, rapid temperature change, crashing waves, and blowing wind all work to wear down the rough surface of the earth either through mechanical processes or by chemically changing the nature of the rock. As you would expect, the weathering process is influenced by aspects of the weather, such as the temperature and the amount and type of precipitation.

When rock is worn down by the friction of running water, flowing ice, or wind energy, we use the term **mechanical weathering**. In addition, plant growth and rapid temperature changes also break down even the most resistant rock. Mechanical weathering is common in deserts and arctic environments where the lack of vegetation exposes the surface to the elements. **Chemical weathering** is more or less absent in these cold, dry regions, but prevalent in warm, wet environments. This is because chemicals

work best when there is moisture to carry them through the rocks and high enough temperatures to facilitate chemical reactions.

Forms of Mechanical Weathering

Frost shattering is a form of mechanical weathering that occurs when ice expands within cracks in rocks and forces them to break apart. During the day, warmer temperatures melt the snow and ice on rock surfaces, a process which allows the moisture to seep into tiny cracks in the rock. At night, or when the sun goes behind a cloud, the temperature drops and the water freezes. Since ice has a lower density than water, it expands when it freezes. The strength of the ice is so great that it splits the rock into pieces. Frost shattering is more common in temperate regions where the temperature rises above freezing during the day and drops below freezing at night. Therefore, this process may not be as significant in the arctic because the temperature remains below freezing for months on end.

In northern Canada, an interesting sorting of surface material occurs as frost action works on the rocky surface of the ground. Moisture seeps into the ground during the daytime and moistens the particles and larger rocks in the soil. At night,

Figure 7.4
A Frost-Shattered Rock

Figure 7.5
Patterned Ground Due to Frost Action

Figure 7.6
Differential Weathering

the water freezes and the particles are thrust to the earth's surface ever so slowly. Frost action moves particles of roughly the same size the same distance, so large rocks all move approximately the same amount each night. Similarly, smaller pebbles all move in more or less the same way. When they reach the surface, the tiny pebbles are all in one spot. Around them is a circle of larger cobbles, and further out lies an even larger circle of small boulders. From close up there may not appear to be much of a pattern, but from a distance one can see that definite polygons of coarser material, with finer fragments in the middle, cover the ground.

Another northern phenomenon that results from frost action is a curious hill called a **pingo**. Although arctic lakes freeze in winter, the water generally keeps the sediments below the lake warmer than the surrounding permafrost. If the lake gradually fills in through the **process of sedimentation**, the water will no longer act as an insulating agent. The saturated sediments begin to freeze and as they do so they expand. Held in by surrounding ground, they have nowhere to go but up. When they emerge from the surface they crack into sections like the top of a muffin as it

cools. These unusual features, which dot arctic landscapes, are particularly prevalent around Tuktoyaktuk just east of the Mackenzie Delta on the Arctic coastal plain.

Differential weathering is another form of mechanical weathering. Not all rocks have the same properties—some are harder and more resistant to the elements, while layers of softer rock wear away more quickly. When this happens in a cliff, the more resistant layers above often overhang the softer rock until gravity causes the resistant rock to collapse. If the less resistant material is spread throughout the rock, the resistant particles come unglued when the weaker rock is weathered away. The result is a pile of resistant particles that may become re-cemented to form a new sedimentary rock as mineral-rich water percolates through it.

When there are sudden extreme changes in temperature, another form of mechanical weathering called **thermal expansion** takes place. If you have ever put an ice cube into a glass of warm pop, you probably know what happens—the ice cube shatters with a loud crack. Thermal expansion causes this to happen. The molecules in the ice expand so quickly when it is placed in

Figure 7.7
Even massive rocks can crumble under the power of tree roots.

the warm drink that the structural integrity of the object is lost. The same thing happens to rocks in desert regions where daytime temperatures rise into the high thirties after a cold night when it may drop below freezing. When the hot desert sun rises, rocks heat up so rapidly that they shatter with a bang.

Mechanical weathering also occurs as a result of plant growth. Hardy plants often grow on the scraps of weathered material that form in frost-shattered cracks. Even mighty pine trees in the Canadian Shield extend their roots between rocks when seeking nutrients from the thin soil. As they do, the roots force the rocks apart with a passive strength that would amaze many people.

Exfoliation, or **sheeting**, is another form of mechanical weathering common in Canada. Intrusive volcanism was the process that formed most of the rock in the Canadian Shield. Magma solidified deep beneath the surface under incredible pressure. After millions of years of weathering, these rocks end up on the earth's surface. The pressure that held the rock together is gone, so it literally falls apart. Layers of rock "peel" off, just like the layers of an onion.

Forms of Chemical Weathering

Chemical weathering is more common in the tropics, where high temperatures and abundant moisture are available. Weathering by solution occurs when natural chemicals, such as carbonic acid (formed when carbon dioxide is dissolved in water), eat away rock. Carbonic acid, for example, reacts with calcite to form calcium bicarbonate. Since calcium bicarbonate dissolves readily in water, this mineral is washed out of the rocks that contain it. What is left are rock fragments containing the residual minerals.

Chemical weathering also occurs when carbonic acid acts on rocks that contain silicon (such as sandstone). This process, called **hydrolysis**, replaces ions of silicate with ions of water, and in doing so causes the rock to fall apart. In the tropics, the process of hydrolysis creates soils of incredible depth as rock layers further and further from the surface are dissolved. Undisturbed by glaciation or tectonic processes, the soils of the Amazon rain forest may be 30 metres deep because of this form of chemical weathering. Though the soils are deep, the lack of silicates and other water-soluble minerals, as well as the fact that clay particles tend to stick together when they are wet, result in very infertile soils.

When metals are exposed to air, they **oxidize**. The example of oxidation we see most often is the change from iron to rust. Oxygen dissolved in water combines with the iron molecules to make iron oxide. Like the calcium bicarbonate, it is carried away when dissolved in water. Since many rocks contain iron and other metals, **oxidation** is a common form of chemical weathering. You can tell when this process has occurred because the rocks are stained rust-red in the case of iron, blue-green for copper, and a variety of other colours for different metals. The different forms of chemical weathering usually all work at the same time, so it is often difficult to tell which one has caused the rocky surface to break down.

Transport and Deposition

Transport occurs when weathered material is carried away as gradational processes move across the earth's surface. The more energy there is, the more material can be carried. For example, when there are gentle breezes on a beach, barely any sand moves about and sunbathers can relax in comfort. But if the wind picks up, sand is hurled with greater force across the beach and stings when it hits people's bare skin. Taking shelter behind a beach umbrella or a windbreak is often all that is needed. The wind speed is low in these spots and the sand stays on the beach. Wherever the wind slows and its ability to carry sand is diminished, sand accumulates. This is why sand often accumulates in the grasses that line beaches above the high-tide line.

The same principles exist in other gradational processes. If a storm at sea whips the waves into a frenzy, the transport of weathered material is much greater than if the sea is relatively calm. Similarly, fast flowing rivers transport more

Figure 7.8
Sand Deposits in Marram Grass

material than sluggish streams with the same discharge rate.

When the **load** (the material being carried) comes to rest, we say it has been **deposited**. So the laying down of weathered material is called **deposition**. When the speed of an agent of

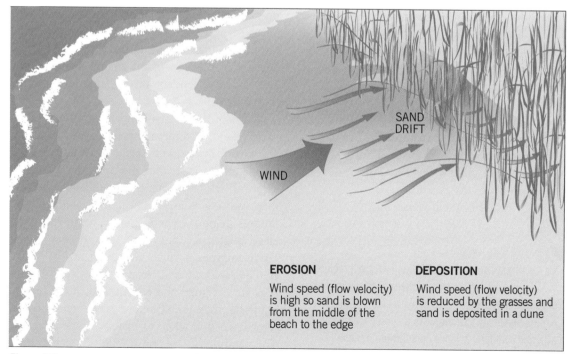

WIND

SAND DRIFT

EROSION

Wind speed (flow velocity) is high so sand is blown from the middle of the beach to the edge

DEPOSITION

Wind speed (flow velocity) is reduced by the grasses and sand is deposited in a dune

Figure 7.9
Why are vacationers encouraged to stay off the grass along beaches in Canada's National Parks?

deposition decreases, its ability to carry the load is reduced and deposition occurs. You can see deposition in operation when winds deposit sand in sheltered areas of a beach. When the flow velocity of a river decreases, similar deposits of sand are made, forming a **delta** or sandbar along the stream. Along seashores, wave action is slowed by shallow water, so sandbars, hooks, and beaches form. **Scree slopes** are masses of coarse rock fragments that accumulate where landslides come to rest when they reach a flat surface. Glaciers form rocky hills called **moraines** when they no longer have enough energy to keep transporting the load forward. These examples of depositional features were basically all formed under the same principles of flow dynamics. When energy increases, the load increases and transport occurs. When energy decreases, the load is reduced and deposition occurs.

Mass Wasting

Gravity is one gradational force that operates on all objects no matter how big or small. Landslides, rockfalls, avalanches, and soil creep are all examples of gravity moving weathered material down a slope. Called **mass wasting**, the energy that is exerted by gravity on a load is determined by the following factors:

- steepness of a slope
- shape and size of particles
- nature of the material that forms a slope
- depth of the weathered material
- nature of the ground cover
  - stability of the ground
    - water content of the soil.

If you like mathematics, enjoy tricky problems, and appreciate the creativity that comes with building things, you may consider becoming a civil engineer. Engineers require university training, with a course load heavy in physics, math, and computer science. In addition to these subjects, civil engineers should have a capacity for creative problem solving, and have a knack for figuring out how things work.

Figure 7.10
This avalanche in Quebec killed 9 people in 1999.

The type of mass wasting that occurs is caused by the way these factors relate to each other in a specific situation. For example, a slope that has large, jagged rocks is more stable than a slope made up of small, round pebbles because the pebbles are more likely to roll downhill than the sharp rocks. However, if there is a heavy rainfall on the slope with the jagged rocks, a slide may occur because the slope is more lubricated than the pebbly one. **Slope failure** therefore occurs because of the interaction among many factors and is not dependent on any one factor more than others.

Because of this dynamic relationship, engineers take careful measurements of all factors on a slope and apply mathematical models based on simulations done either on computer or using slopes in lab experiments. An understanding of mass wasting is especially important in mountainous regions where slopes form relatively steep angles to the valleys that dissect them. **Civil engineers** take measurements of slope stability before roads, dams, railways and buildings are designed and constructed. If the region is unsafe, then the structure can be relocated or remedial action taken to increase slope integrity. The planting of trees on the hillside helps since roots hold the surface soil and reduce the lubricating properties of rainfall. Other solutions include constructing retaining walls or rock barriers, or simply levelling the slope itself.

The chance of mass wasting occurring increases with the steepness of the slope. A change in the steepness of a slope is usually the result of another gradational process in operation. For example, a river may undercut its bank or wave action may erode part of a shoreline, the resulting change in slope may cause the soil to collapse and move.

The shapes and sizes of rocks in the weathered material affect mass wasting since smooth particles roll more easily than rocks with jagged edges. Therefore, slopes with large, jagged rocks have a greater **angle of repose** than those with smaller, rounder material. This means that the maximum angle at which the slope remains stable is greater for jagged material. Similarly, smaller particles are likely to have a steeper angle of repose than larger rocks, which gravity can start moving more easily.

Still another factor affecting the stability of a slope is the nature of the material. For example, snow is one of the least stable materials.

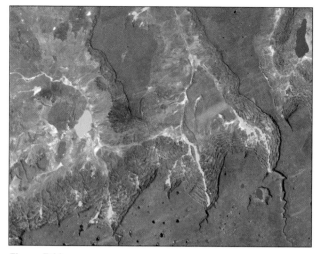

Figure 7.11
Landslides are clearly a major agent of erosion in this area of Patagonia: the "stairs" were likely formed by large slivers of basalt rock breaking off from, then sliding down slope and away from the caprock.

Composed of air as well as water in both solid and liquid form, it can transform rapidly from a stable slope to an extremely dangerous situation

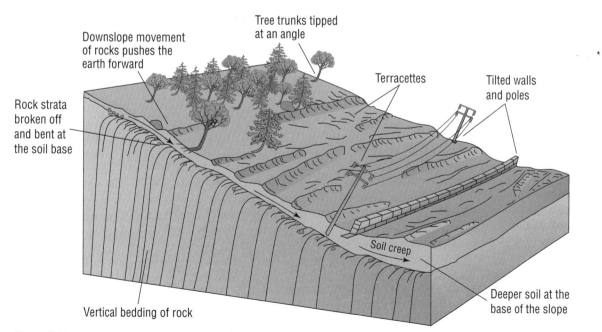

Tree trunks tipped at an angle

Downslope movement of rocks pushes the earth forward

Terracettes

Tilted walls and poles

Rock strata broken off and bent at the soil base

Soil creep

Vertical bedding of rock

Deeper soil at the base of the slope

Figure 7.12
Soil creep is the gradual movement of soil down an incline, even though vegetation would seem to hold the earth in place.

A Deadly Avalanche

Although we often hear of terrible avalanches killing people in alpine regions, more adventurous types have been known to risk their lives in skiing challenging slopes off the beaten path.

Such was the case when Michel Trudeau (son of former prime minister, Pierre Trudeau) went skiing with some friends in a remote valley in Kokanee Glacier Park, British Columbia, early in the season before the snow had set. The young men were skiing on a Friday afternoon in November when two avalanches roared down the mountain. The avalanche swept all the skiers into Kokanee Lake. Two members of the group managed to pull themselves out of the freezing water, but the young Trudeau, age 23, could not. His body was never recovered. Heavy snowfall in the area during the days prior to the accident was blamed for triggering the avalanche.

The location of the slide was known to be a hazard. Just the January before, six skiers were killed in an avalanche only a few kilometres away.

With a view to increasing awareness, especially for skiers, the Experimental Centre for Avalanche and Hydrogeological Defence created the following Avalanche Hazard Scale. By following it, skiers can enjoy their pastime reasonably safely. Check out their web site to learn more about avalanches <www.avalanche.org>.

QUESTIONS:

1. Explain all the aspects of mass wasting that could contribute to an avalanche.

2. How could a skier determine if a mountain slope was safe from any risk of an avalanche?

3. Do some research to determine the methods used by experts to prevent deadly incidents of mass wasting such as the avalanche discussed in this case study.

Degree of Hazard	Snowpack	Avalanche Probability
1 LOW	Well-bonded and stable	• only small avalanches (sluffs) • triggering only possible with high additional loads*
2 MODERATE	Moderately well-bonded	• large avalanches unlikely • triggering possible on steep slopes with high additional loads *
3 CONSIDERABLE	Weakly bonded on steep slopes	• medium and large avalanches may occur • triggering possible on steep slopes with low additional loads *
4 HIGH	Weakly bonded on most slopes	• frequent medium and large avalanches are likely • triggering probable on most slopes with low additional loads *
5 VERY HIGH	Weakly bonded and largely unstable on most slopes	• numerous large avalanches are likely • triggering probable on most slopes with no additional loads *

Figure 7.13
Avalanche Hazard Scale

* Low additional loads would be a single skier or hiker. High additional loads would include a snowmobile or a group of skiers.

by the mere increase of a few degrees in temperature. Clay-based soils are also very changeable. The whole chemistry of the clay changes as water is added or removed. When clay is wet, the particles stick together like paste, but they increase in mass, sometimes so much that slope failure may result.

The depth of the weathered material is also a major consideration affecting slope integrity. The deeper the soil is, the more likely it is to slide down-slope. In such cases, it may take very little to start a devastating rockslide. The island of Hawaii is overlaid with a massive amount of volcanic material that has accumulated to a great depth along the shoreline. There are fears that a gigantic landslide will eventually occur as a major chunk of the island slides into the Pacific Ocean. All that is needed is a trigger to start it off. Being in a tectonically active volcano zone, the chances that a small earthquake will be that trigger make the possibility of slope failure a likely event. The resultant **tsunami** could be devastating to people all around the Pacific Rim. (For more on tsunamis see pp. 174–5.)

Ground cover affects mass wasting as well. The roots of trees and grasses on mountain slopes hold unconsolidated material in place. This means that transport is less likely in areas where there are a lot of plants. Grass is often planted on the sloping ground adjacent to highways to reduce the risk of mudslides. These are especially likely to occur in the Canadian spring when heavy rains, coupled with melting snow and warming ground temperatures, reduce slope stability. When clear-cutting occurs on mountain slopes, the soil is much more susceptible to mass wasting. The clear-cutting of forests in coastal British Columbia resulted in so much erosion of mountain slopes that rivers became silted-up and native salmon spawning was jeopardized. Removal of forest cover has been even more devastating in the Developing World, where whole mountains are washed into the sea.

Even where vegetation covers slopes, mass wasting can occur. In some situations, the soil slides away beneath the vegetation when other

Figure 7.14
A Californian Home Sliding Down a Cliff

forces undermine the holding power of the plant roots. **Soil creep** is the slow and gradual movement of soil down-slope, usually under intense pressure (see Figure 7.12). This is particularly noticeable in pastures where the grass is kept short by grazing animals. Root systems are less extensive, and the soil under the turf subsides. The sod on the surface sinks along with it. This can be remedied by planting bushes and trees that the animals will not eat. The roots go deeper and hold the soil better.

The lack of **tectonic stability** frequently provides the impetus to start soil movement. While earthquakes and volcanoes are the main culprits, natural vibrations, explosions, loud noises, and even heavy traffic can trigger mass wasting. In some alpine ski areas, explosions are purposely set off to start avalanches in order to remove dangerous accumulations of snow above ski slopes. When the amount of tectonic activity is limited, mass wasting is less likely to occur.

By filling in the spaces between particles, water lubricates weathered material, allowing it to slide better. As each piece of rock or pebble is coated with water and separated from other particles, the angle of repose is reduced and therefore the chance of a landslide is increased. When there are heavy storms, mass wasting becomes commonplace in areas with high relief. California, for example, has a Mediterranean climate, which means it gets heavy winter rains and dry summers. Natural vegetation tends to be somewhat scrubby because plants are starved for water during the summer growing season. The combination of rain, sparse natural vegetation, steep mountain slopes, and frequent earthquake tremors provides all the ingredients for the devastating mudslides that plague the region.

Solifluction is a form of mass wasting that is common in Canada and other northern regions where permafrost occurs. The upper part of the earth thaws each summer, but the temperature of the soil 1 to 2 m below the surface never rises much above freezing. The soil becomes saturated as this upper layer thaws and the water is unable to seep lower into the soil. Weathered material is often able to slide as much as 5 cm per year down slopes as gentle as one or two degrees.

People living in areas prone to mudslides and avalanches are often aware of the risks, but for financial reasons are sometimes unable, or unwilling, to move elsewhere. Such was the case for many of the thousands of people who were killed when a massive mudslide roared down the Avila Mountains of Venezuela in 1999.

CASE STUDY

Mudslides in Venezuela

Venezuela received the heaviest precipitation its citizens had seen in a century when over 300 mm of rain fell during a two-week period in December of 1999. The rain itself caused massive flooding, but it was the raging mudslides that caused most of the deaths and devastation during one of the country's worst natural disasters.

It has been estimated that over 50 000 lives were lost, 500 000 people were left homeless, and billions of dollars worth of damage was done when a wall of mud, boulders, trees, and debris crashed down the slopes of the Avila Mountain, burying entire villages.

One eyewitness, a woman from the capital city of Caracas, where severe damage occurred, recounted her tale of survival. She and her family had stayed awake for three nights, afraid that their house would be next to be buried by the

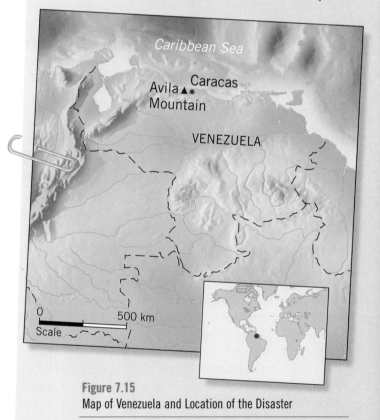

Figure 7.15
Map of Venezuela and Location of the Disaster

Figure 7.16
Aftermath of the 1999 Mudslide in Venezuela

mud. Finally, the family heard the thunderous rush of cascading mud and debris approach their house from behind. They ran outside and down the hill to safety, but when they looked back, they were horrified by the scene. "The mountain came down and the walls of our house broke. We lost everything. The house split into two parts," she said.

In the wake of the disaster, officials surveying the damage claimed that it was largely human disregard for nature that led to the destruction. For example, large chunks of land on the steep slopes of the Avila Mountain had been destroyed by periodic fires, leaving the area at risk for mudslides. The trees and plants would have held the soil together with their roots and lessened the possibility of such a massive mudslide. The deforestation also meant that there was very little blockage to slow the progress of the mud once it began its course down the mountain slope. Yet, despite the risks, the area continued to be populated.

The Venezuelan government also came under attack for the extremely high number of dead, most of whom were villagers who had been living on the slopes and at the foot of the mountain. Poor Venezuelans lived in dwellings made of corrugated iron and cinderblocks, perched precariously on the hillsides. Their housing went largely unchecked by government established standards. Critics said the government shouldn't have allowed the villagers to live there in the first place since it was aware that the slopes were dangerous and had given way in the past.

Forty years of government corruption and incompetence resulted in billions of wasted dollars and thousands, if not millions, of impoverished Venezuelans fleeing the agricultural regions of the country for industrial jobs in the cities. These people worked for meagre daily wages and began settling on the mountain because the government-owned property was seen as free land. "Sure I knew it was dangerous, but it's the land I live on," said one of the mountain villagers, summing up the situation of many poor Venezuelans. "Only the rich get to choose."

QUESTIONS:

1. What could have been done to prevent or reduce the damage done by the mudslides discussed in this case study?

2. Explain the trade-offs made by the villagers for building their homes and eking out a living on the slopes and at the base of the Avila Mountain.

3. Explain all the factors that contributed to this incident of mass wasting.

ACTIVITIES

UNDERSTANDING CONCEPTS

1. a) Explain the term "base level."
    b) Outline how it manifests itself in each of the following:
        • coastal features
        • glacial features
        • river features
    c) Explain flow velocity and how it relates to the processes of transportation and deposition.
2. Give definitions for each of the following, along with an example of each: weathering, transport, deposition, slope stability, slope failure, and angle of repose.
3. a) Describe each of the following features of weathering: frost shattering, thermal expansion, differential weathering, patterned ground, pingos, exfoliation, solution weathering, hydrolysis, and oxidation.
    b) Outline how climate affects each of the processes in a).
    c) For each of the processes in a), describe the effects of the nature of the material involved.
4. a) Explain the differences between chemical and mechanical weathering and outline how they contribute to the creation of soil.
    b) Identify the factors that influence mass wasting and write an explanation for each.

DEVELOPING AND PRACTISING SKILLS

5. a) Use an organizer to differentiate between rockslides, mudslides, soil creep, solifluction, and avalanches. Copy the following organizer and complete it. Some parts have been completed to get you started.

Type/ Factor	Degree of Slope	Nature of Weathered Material	Size and Shape of Weathered Material	Nature of Ground Cover	Tectonic Stability	Moisture Content
Rockslides			Jagged rocks of indeterminate size			
Mudslides						Saturated with water
Soil creep				Soil creeps under grass		
Solifluction	Very slight					
Avalanches		Snow, ice, and rock				

b) Determine which of the types seems to be the most unstable, and explain your choice.

c) How do engineers overcome the problems associated with slope instability?

6. a) Using an atlas or a GIS program, decide which maps or layers would help you to determine regions where mass wasting would be a problem.

b) List regions of the world where mass wasting could be a serious problem.

c) Choose one area for investigation. (If you are using a GIS application, prepare a series of maps or layers to show the region under study.)

d) Conduct some research to find out if there have been problems in the region.

e) If there have been problems, find out why. If there have not been problems, determine how they were avoided.

f) Write a report on your findings and present it along with your map in an attractive display.

7. Identify careers that relate to mass wasting. Determine the educational requirements and assess if any of these careers is a possibility for you.

LEARNING THROUGH APPLICATION

8. a) What precautions should skiers take when skiing in regions where avalanches occur?

b) Using the Avalanche Hazard Scale (on page 110) explain what precautions skiers should take at each of the different levels.

c) Assume that the snow is currently at Level 2. Which of the following events could result in a progression to Level 3 or even Level 4? Explain your answer fully.
   • Weather change from heavy snow to light drizzle
   • Weather change from heavy snow to overcast with no precipitation
   • Increasing northerly winds lowering temperatures
   • Weather change from light snow to blizzard conditions
   • Weather change to bright and sunny on slopes, valleys remain below freezing
   • Slight earthquake activity felt in neighbouring city
   • Clear-cutting the summer before on the mountain slope.

9. a) Describe the gradational processes that caused the tragic mudslide in Venezuela.

b) How did human factors make the situation worse?

c) What solutions could help improve conditions?

10. a) Find an area in your community that is prone to mass wasting. Determine what steps could be taken to reduce the possible damage. (Be sure to take appropriate safety precautions when dealing with potentially dangerous situations.)

b) Give examples of the trade-offs people must make when they live and play on mountains and cliffs.

c) Use the Internet to find other examples of people living in places where mass wasting is a problem.

Chapter 8

THE WORK OF WIND AND WATER

FOCUS QUESTIONS

1. What roles do wind and running water play in shaping physical features?
2. What are the trade-offs for people living in Bangladesh—a coastal zone subject to flooding?
3. How do human uses of the earth, including uses involving technology, cause changes in natural systems?

Key Terms

aeolian landscapes

flow velocity

pedestal rock

alluvial fan

karst topography

Both wind and water create unique and varied landscapes around the world. For example, wherever significant amounts of precipitation fall on the earth's surface, the work of running water shapes and reshapes the land, wearing down rough spots and filling in hollows. While running water often reaches base level in river valleys close to its month, base level is harder to achieve further inland because of tectonic forces. However, there are ancient river systems where base level has been reached for much of the river's length. Rivers such as the Amazon, the Congo, and the Mississippi no longer wear down the land in their lower reaches; they merely extend the flood plain outwards in all directions.

With low rates of precipitation, **aeolian landscapes** are formed mainly by wind action. The lack of significant ground cover in these landscapes exposes the surface to the erosive powers of wind. Where the wind is strong, sand is torn away from the desert pavement and hurled at rock faces. The sandblasting forms beautiful, streamlined features, as rough surfaces are worn smooth. Where the wind slows down, the sand is deposited in massive sand dunes that march across the desert floor. Just as rivers attempt to reach base level, winds smooth out the rough areas and fill in the hollows.

River Landscapes

Like all gradational processes, running surface water is constantly working to reach base level. In the case of rivers, this base level is a curved line extending from sea level inland in a graceful sweeping arch. Sometimes mountains and other landforms block the river's passage to the ocean. When this happens, a **temporary base level** is formed as water creates lakes and inland seas. The water stays in this temporary basin until it is able to continue its passage downstream. Water in the Great Lakes eventually arrives at the Atlantic Ocean, although it may linger in each of the lakes for many years before it actually gets to sea level. Other times the water is held in land-locked seas, such as Great Salt Lake in Utah, the Caspian Sea in Eurasia, and the Dead Sea in the Middle East. This water can never get to the ocean via rivers, and eventually rejoins the atmosphere as water vapour.

The dynamics of lakes are very different from rivers. Because the water doesn't usually flow downstream, lakes are relatively still. Unlike the oceans, tides and currents in lakes are much less significant except in really large lakes such as Lake Superior and Lake Baykal in Siberia. Waves do occur as a result of winds acting on the surface of the water, but they are usually smaller and less powerful than ocean waves because the area of exposed water is smaller than for oceans. Nevertheless, shoreline erosion is a significant problem in the Great Lakes, especially on the windward shore.

In rivers, erosion occurs when water flows over land above base level. The water carried is deposited in hollows that are below base level as the water slows down and even stops altogether, as is common in lakes. Because the water is not flowing very fast, it has very little energy, so even the smallest particles of dust settle out and sink to the bottom. This is why former lake beds are often very flat and made up of fine deposits of clay. These **lacustrine** plains are among the most fertile agricultural areas in the world. In the St. Lawrence-Great Lakes Basin, erosion occurs where water flows rapidly—in places like Niagara Falls and La Chine Rapids. Sediment deposits occur in the Great Lakes because this is where the water's **flow velocity** slows down. It takes thousands of years for large lakes to be completely filled with sediment. Lake Winnipeg—the remnant of the much larger Lake Agassiz—lies in the middle of such a lacustrine plain.

In addition to flow velocity, a river's erosive power is also determined by its **discharge rate**, or the amount of water flowing through it. A tiny stream flowing rapidly down a steep hill has a high flow velocity but it does not have the erosive power of a huge river with an enormous volume of water, even though the larger river may have a much slower flow velocity. The great St. Lawrence River flows very slowly at its mouth, but is still a massively powerful force because of the volume of water it carries.

The third factor that affects how efficiently a river erodes a landscape has nothing to do with the running water, but rather involves the nature of the riverbed. If a riverbed is composed of hard, resistant material, the river will have a difficult time wearing it down to base level. Softer, less resistant rock erodes more easily, so these riverbeds are often deeply cut into the surface. To summarize, flow velocity, discharge rate, and the nature of the stream bed are the factors that determine the ability of the river to wear down the earth's surface.

There are three ways that rivers transport material: **solution**, **suspension**, and **saltation**. River water dissolves water-soluble minerals as it flows through its channel. For example, some rivers of the Canadian Shield are tea-coloured

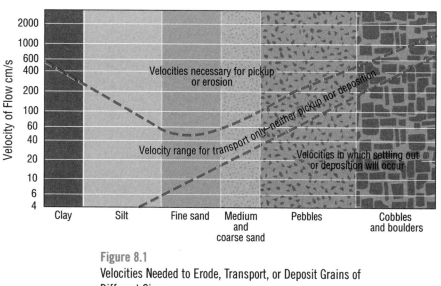

Figure 8.1
Velocities Needed to Erode, Transport, or Deposit Grains of Different Sizes

because the water dissolved certain reddish minerals. When the water evaporates and the dissolved minerals become more concentrated, the solution becomes saturated and the mineral **precipitates** out of the water.

Larger particles are also carried by water. These particles are *suspended* in the water; they do not bounce along the bottom or become dissolved. The flow velocity determines the size of the particles the river is able to carry in suspension. Rapidly flowing rivers are able to sweep everything from tiny silt and grains of sand to pebbles along in their path, while the slowest rivers may only be able to carry fine particles of dust. This material settles out when the water's flow velocity decreases or stops.

Even larger particles are swept along the river by *saltation*. They do not remain suspended in the water, but bounce along, sometimes high in the channel and other times, as the speed of the water decreases, roll along the riverbed. In the last glacial period, channels carrying meltwaters had so much energy that they were able to carry boulders the size of small cars.

There is a positive correlation between how fast a river is flowing and the size of particles it can carry: as stream velocity increases, so too does the particle size. Conversely, as the stream velocity decreases, so does the size of the particles it can carry. When running water flows steadily into another body of water, an interesting pattern forms as a result of this correlation. The largest particles are deposited first as the stream slows down a little. Further into the lake or ocean, successively smaller materials are dropped until the river stops flowing into the water body altogether. The result is a river **delta**. These features are found at the mouths of most streams, whether they are tiny rivulets flowing into a mud puddle or the mighty River Nile flowing into the Mediterranean Sea. Known as **sorted sediment**, some deltas, such as those found in the Oak Ridges Moraine, are thousands of years old. Today, this particular delta is mined for the various grades of gravel and sand used in the construction industry.

The same process occurs when rivers flow out of the mountains into an arid landscape. Instead of forming a delta, an **alluvial fan** of sorted material sweeps out from the canyon floor as the gradient of the river decreases and it loses momentum. The result is exactly the same as the delta that occurs in oceans and lakes. The positive correlation between flow velocity and particle size is one of the features that distinguishes river deposits from materials laid down by other gradational processes.

Underground River Landscapes

Some places have no surface rivers. If the region is a desert, this is understandable because there is no surface water; however there are humid regions where there are absolutely no rivers. Where did they go? In regions where the underlying bedrock is porous, the surface water seeps into the rock and flows underground. These underground rivers exhibit all the dynamics of surface running water; weathering occurs as the water dissolves soluble minerals in the rock, and valleys become caverns running underground. Deposition occurs as dissolved minerals precipitate out in columns, **stalactites**, and petrified waterfalls.

Underground caves are mysterious places, which can be fascinating to explore if you know what you are doing. Otherwise they can be very dangerous. **Spelunking** is the term used to describe cave exploration. Seldom a vocation but often a hobby, this pastime requires explorers to have many unusual qualities, including the agility of the rock climber, the courage of a miner, and the strength of an ox. In addition, they must not be afraid to squeeze through tiny spaces, come face to face with a bat, or walk submerged up to their neck in freezing cold water. Obviously, this is not everybody's idea of fun, but if you ever do decide to go spelunking, do it with a trained guide, go properly equipped, and never enter an underground cavern alone!

The first geologic study of caves occurred in the Karst Mountain region in Slovenia. Since this

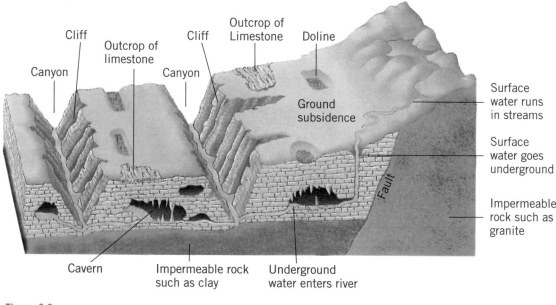

Figure 8.2
Karst Formations

was the first region studied, other regions with similar topography are called **karst** regions. Some of the features of karst topography include caverns, sinkholes or **dolines**, **stalactites**, and **stalagmites**. You may find it hard to believe, but about 15 per cent of the earth's land surface has karst topography. In order for caves to form, the area has to be tectonically stable and unaffected by glaciation for thousands of years. Regions in southern Europe, the United States, and southern China are well known for their caves, whereas Canada has few karst features because of its recent ice age.

If you look at a topographic map of a karst region, one odd thing you may notice is the absence of rivers. If there does happen to be a river, it may travel along the map for a distance, and then seem to disappear into thin air, only to re-emerge some distance away. Some valleys look just like river valleys, but there are no rivers in them. All over the map, you'll see strange little craters and sink holes pocking the surface. There is a logical explanation for all of these features.

Limestone with a calcium carbonate ($CaCO_2$) content of at least 80 per cent makes up the

underlying rock in karst regions. The rock is **impermeable**, so when it rains, water does not percolate through it. Instead, it seeps through cracks and joints in the limestone. Over time, more and more of the $CaCO_2$ in the limestone around the cracks and joints is dissolved, making the holes ever larger until caverns and caves are created beneath the surface. The water, which is constantly trying to find its base level, settles in underground lakes or pools. When one of these caves becomes too big, the ceiling collapses, creating the odd sinkholes and craters for which karst regions are famous. Running water underground creates dry valleys as the land subsides into caverns created underground.

Karst topography also has interesting depositional features. As water constantly trickles through cracks in the rock, it picks up calcium carbonate. When it drips from the roof of a cave, it leaves behind tiny traces of limestone. **Stalactites** are created from deposits of calcium carbonate that gradually build layer upon layer until massive icicle-like objects hang from the ceiling. On the floor of the cave, upside-down rock icicles called **stalagmites** form where the calcium-rich water drips onto the floor. When these two features join together, a **column** is

Figure 8.3
An Aeolian Landscape: The Sahara Desert in Libya

created. Other unusual formations, such as rock curtains and waterfalls frozen in stone, are also formed by this process. Karst topography provides a unique example of how water shapes the land in interesting and bizarre ways because of the underlying surface rock.

Landscapes Shaped by Wind

Landscapes shaped by winds are commonly called **aeolian landscapes**, so named after the Greek god of wind, Aeolus. Aeolian processes are most often found in desert and steppe regions where two characteristics allow wind action to form unique landscapes differently than in more humid regions. The first characteristic is the reduced moisture content of the earth. Dry soil does not stick together, so particles are smaller and more susceptible to wind action. The second, more important characteristic has to do with groundcover. The lack of surface vegetation means the soil is not protected by root systems, so wind erosion is greater.

Surprisingly, the main gradational process in arid lands is water. The lack of vegetation means that rainfall, while it may be infrequent, does have a profound effect on the surface when it finally does happen.

Another factor that accounts for the unusually strong erosive power of infrequent rainstorms is the fact that desert soils often have a very hard coating on the surface. Moisture deep beneath the ground is drawn to the surface by the desiccating rays of the sun. When the moisture quickly evaporates, the mineral deposits are left as salt pans and alkali flats. In addition, the strong wind—unhampered by trees and other vegetation that could act as a windbreak—removes any loose material and leaves a hard-baked desert pavement. When it rains, the water does not seep into the ground because of the hard shell. Ironically, many desert-dwelling plants and animals die by drowning in the seldom-experienced, but usually violent, flash floods. The water flowing along the surface searches for the lowest point and concentrates its energy there.

Figure 8.4
This satellite image shows Saudi Arabia. What evidence of wind action can you see?

Figure 8.5
Pedestal Rocks

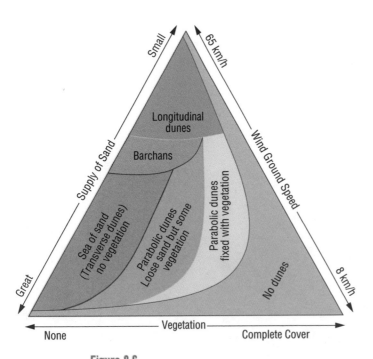

Figure 8.6
The Three Variables Responsible for Dune Creation: Sand
Supply, Wind Velocity, and Vegetation

In time, the tiny cracks through which the water flows are widened, deepened and carved until deep gullies cut through the surface crust. **Wadis**, or intermittent streams, flow across the desert with a sudden violence but quickly dry up shortly after the storm is past. These temporary desert streams have the same features as other rivers. Meanders, undercut banks, and alluvial fans develop as mere memories of water that once flowed over the parched surface.

People often contribute to the erosion of desert sands. For example, all-terrain vehicles have been banned from the deserts of Southern California because the tracks of the vehicles break through the hard-packed layer and destroy what fragile plant cover there is. By eliminating these destructive machines, hikers can enjoy the desert scenery while having a limited impact on the soils.

Once the hard-packed layer is removed by running water, the softer material underneath is exposed to the steady, strong desert winds. As air flows over the surface of the desert, it picks up tiny grains of sand. The sand is hurled with great force against anything that gets in its way. Just as a piece of wood becomes smoother as sand-paper is rubbed across its surface, rocks are polished to form weird looking **pedestals**, **balancing rocks**, and **arches**. Looking like some cartoon landscape, these aeolian regions are formed because the sand wears away the softer layers of rock and those layers closer to the ground where the sand is more concentrated. Taller features, or those features made from more resistant rock, protrude over the sections that have been worn away.

Pedestals form because gravity keeps the most powerful sandblasting action closer to the ground. This process results in the lower layers of a rock column being worn away faster than the upper layers. As the column supporting the top part of the feature erodes, it sometimes creates a weird "pedestal" of thin rock with a boulder balanced on top. In time, of course, the boulder will fall to the ground and the pillar will disappear. Arches form when local landform features concentrate the wind to a certain place in a cliff face. The concentration of wind on one place wears the rock face away so that in time a hole forms through the feature. Eventually, an arch is created. As with running water, strong winds are able to carry larger particles than weaker breezes until the flow velocity decreases to the point when the wind deposits its load. However, unlike running water, the wind does not sort the deposits.

Not all deserts are covered with sand. Usually, the sand has been blown away, leaving only stones and rocks. The larger particles that are left form a desert pavement referred to as **erg**. So, what does the wind do with all the sand? Huge **erg deserts** do have very large concentrations of sand, but these account for only 20 per cent of all deserts. The Grand Erg Oriental of the central Sahara is so large that it would bury an area as big as the Canadian Maritime provinces under a layer of sand up to 1200 m thick. Some of the fine particles are deposited in oceans or even on other continents. Much of the prime agricultural land of the southern Ukraine was formed from layers of fine desert silt that were blown there from deserts far away.

Sand dunes are aeolian depositional features. **Barchans** are crescent-shaped dunes formed in areas where there is not much sand and the winds always blow from the same direction. The sand first accumulates around a small bush or stone when the speed at which the wind is blowing is reduced. As more and more sand builds up, the dune starts to travel forward across the desert. When winds are irregular and there is a lot of sand, **transverse dunes** form giant ripples across the landscape. **Parabolic dunes** are created when vegetation prevents erosion at each end of the dune. **Longitudinal dunes** form parallel to the prevailing winds, and **star dunes** form when the winds blow from many different directions over a long period of time.

Coastal Landscapes

Wind and water come together in the coastal landscapes that border continental land masses. Devoid of vegetation, many shorelines exhibit the same features as aeolian landscapes. Sand dunes

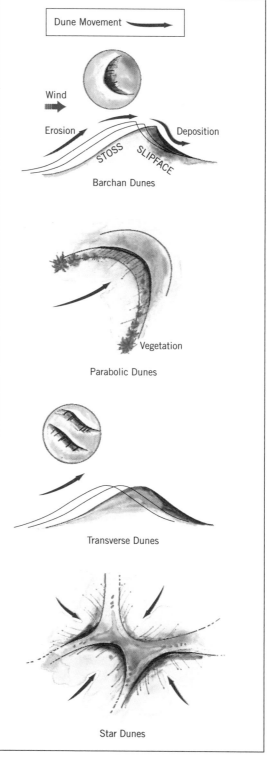

Figure 8.7
Different Types of Sand Dunes

Figure 8.8
Wave Damage: Sea Caves in Newfoundland

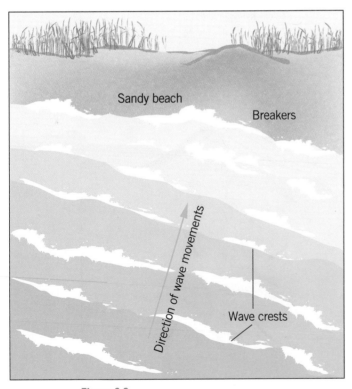

Figure 8.9
Notice that the waves flow up the beach on an angle to the shoreline, creating longshore drift.

form, while other features are sandblasted into graceful shapes. Wave action in the tidal zone wears away headlands that project into the sea. It also fills in the bays and inlets with beaches and other depositional features. As with other gradational forces, wave action seeks to smooth out coastlines. If you study the coastlines of many regions, you will see that, with the exception of inlets cut by glaciers, it has largely succeeded.

Shore erosion occurs because of the action of waves that constantly roll onto the shore. Waves are just like big ripples transporting wind energy through the water body. When a wave washes up a beach, the lower portion of the wave is slowed as it drags along the submerged beach. However, the top portion of the wave continues to travel forward, pushed on by the forward momentum and the pressure of more waves coming from behind, until it breaks on the shore. The line along the beach where the waves break is where the most erosive damage occurs. The pounding hydraulic action, abrasion from particles carried by the water, and corrosion from the salt in the water all work to form sea caves and arches, smooth out headlands, and create sand.

Not every part of the coastline erodes at the same rate. **Headlands**—shorelines that project into the ocean—are subject to greater erosion than sheltered bays. This is the result of **wave refraction** (that is, waves bending around the headland), which concentrates wave action on these landforms. Notches are formed when rock is eroded at the point at which waves meet the cliff face. Overhanging rock above the wave action is not affected, so a rock shelf juts out into the sea. Eventually, the mass of the projecting rock becomes too great for the underlying rock to support and it collapses into the sea. Arches, caves, and sea stacks are formed in similar ways.

Beaches are formed as waves—carrying particles of sand along the shore—deposit their load when the flow velocity of the water decreases. Often, sand dunes created by wind form inland from the beach. Grasses hold the dunes in place. If the grasses are removed, the sand blows away and wave action may penetrate inland. This is

Map of the areas

Cross-sections of main erosional features

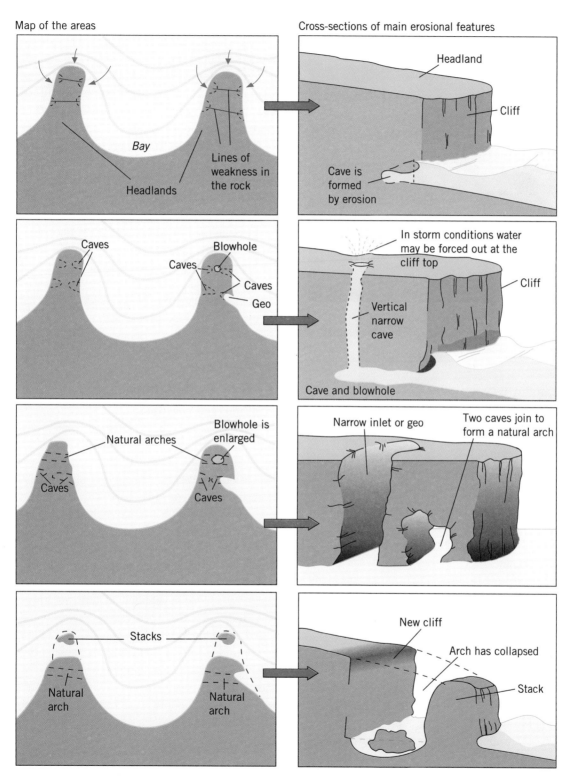

Figure 8.10
Landforms Produced by Wave Erosion

Figure 8.11
A lagoon is visible in the distance behind this emergent coastline in Nova Scotia.

why authorities in many tourist areas warn people to protect the grasses and stay off the dunes. Sandbars and spits are formed wherever waves move sand along the beach. **Longshore drift** is responsible for many of the intricate coastal features found along the Atlantic coastline. If you study waves crashing on beaches, you will probably notice that they are never exactly parallel to the shore, but instead approach the beach on an angle. (This phenomenon can be seen in Figure 8.9.) As they do this, the waves move sand along the beach, depriving some areas of sand while building up sand in other areas. Features associated with longshore drift include sandbars, spits, and hooks.

Emergent Coastlines

Emergent coastlines are coastlines that are gradually coming out of the sea. Long, thin barrier islands form just off the coast of these types of beaches. Through longshore drift, waves move

diagonally across the beach, stealing sand from one location and dumping it on another. Between the mainland and the islands, freshwater sounds are formed by rivers flowing into the area. Sediment carried by the rivers eventually fills in these sounds, creating swamps, saltwater marshes, bogs, and lagoons. In time, the area between the barrier islands and the mainland becomes dry land as the sediment builds up. Often, a new series of barrier islands starts to form further out into the ocean.

Emergent coastlines also form when the land rises through isostasy, after a period of glaciation. Raised **terraces** show where ancient beaches once were. The raised beaches all along the Gulf of St. Lawrence are good examples of this type of coastline. The lowering of sea level during ice ages also creates emergent coastlines, but since we are not currently experiencing an ice age, this is not a factor in today's world.

Submerged Coastlines

The **submerged coastline** is the opposite of an emergent coastline. It is formed when river valleys and low-lying areas are flooded as the sea level rises, or when the shoreline sinks as a result of tectonic processes. Ice-age alpine glaciers carved river valleys into U-shape features. When the sea level rose after the ice melted, these U-shaped valleys became flooded with sea water and formed fjords. Along the west coast of Newfoundland, the situation is more complicated, however. As the ice left, the coast rebounded so that it re-emerged from its lower levels. Today, the U-shaped valleys have become flooded, forming fjords, but because the shore has rebounded, they are cut off from the sea. The result is a coastline of land-locked fjords or ponds lying in a kilometre or so from the shoreline. Check the atlas and see if you can find other examples of submerged coastlines in Canada.

ENVIRONMENT WATCH

Coastal Erosion in PEI

The north shore of Prince Edward Island is a favourite vacation spot for many Canadians whether they come from Charlottetown or Chilliwack. The Prince Edward Island National Park along this coast is made up of five landscapes: beaches, lagoons and salt marshes, sea cliffs, coastal meadows, and river estuaries, which form rich ecosystems where blue heron and innumerable aquatic animals live. Between the lagoons and the beaches, the land rises a hundred metres or so above the ocean as a result of isostatic uplift. The rich red clay of the island province is no match for the swirling waters of the Gulf of St. Lawrence, however.

The erosion along these PEI cliffs is so dramatic it can be scary! Each year, the sea moves inland as much as a metre. Hiking trails that run along cliffs one year disappear the next. There is no threat to buildings and other structures because it is a national park. The park road is about a hundred metres from the cliffs, so it is not in danger of being washed away. Still, this island is not very big: the islanders need all the land they have!

Erosion is also a problem along the beach. In the past, people crossed over the sand dunes, through the protective layer of marram grass to the seashore. The continued action of all those feet crossing the dunes killed the grass and exposed the sand to wind action. In winter, as strong north winds buffet the coast, sand blows away in the unprotected areas. With the sand gone, the ocean can destroy the ecosystems and invade meadows inland.

The National Park Service, seeing that there was a problem, has worked to prevent the destruction of marram grass and the sand dunes of the beach areas. Boardwalks have been built to provide an elevated walkway over the dunes. To discourage people from parking anywhere along the park road and hiking to the beach, parking lots have been built. Furthermore, signs posted along the walkway educate the public about the importance of the grass in preventing beach erosion.

Question:

Although the measures taken may save the sand dunes of P.E.I, what—if anything—can be done to save the cliffs?

Figure 8.12
PEI's North Shore is a combination of beaches, cliffs, meadows and lagoons.

Flooding in Bangladesh

The people of Bangladesh have been living with disaster for generations. Theirs is a poor country economically, but the land is incredibly rich agriculturally, and the sea is excellent for fishing. This nation of about 135 million people is one of the most densely populated countries in the world. Most people live on a low-lying alluvial plain less than 1 m above sea level. The Brahmaputra, the Ganges, and the Meghna rivers come together to form a massive river delta that occupies 80 per cent of the country's area. With their sources in the Himalayan Mountains, these three rivers provide abundant water and rich nutrients in the form of silt to the low-lying agricultural country. From mid-March to October, the rains come, while in the spring, the snow in the Himalayas melts. The rivers carry the meltwater and the heavy rains through India to Bangladesh.

In recent years, the forests have been cut on the slopes of the Himalayas. As a result, the land upstream does not absorb as much of the water as it once did and the rivers are even more overburdened. In addition, landslides upstream from deforestation have added tons of sediment to the streams. When the flow velocity decreases, the rivers deposit their load, blocking channels and causing them to overflow. You can imagine how this inundation of flood water affects the people. They have no high ground in the fertile plain, so they have to try to cope as best as they can with the annual deluge.

Unfortunately, water from the rivers is not the only problem in Bangladesh. In the fall, just when discharge rates are starting to subside, tropical cyclones (hurricanes) hit the coast. The coastline is so devastated by the storm surges that whole villages are regularly destroyed and thousands die almost annually. In 1970, the largest sea flood disaster of all time occurred. Over a quarter of a million people were swept away and drowned. More recently, in July 1999, heavy rains once again caused havoc when 2 million people were displaced. Officials say the floods affect as many as 17 million people throughout Bangladesh and surrounding countries.

Why do the Bengalis stay? For one thing, most are very poor and cannot afford to leave. Others stay because the land of this beautiful country is their home. More likely they stay because the soil is rich and farmers can produce enough food for their families, with extra leftover, on relatively tiny plots of land. Rice yields are among the highest in the world.

One particularly difficult legal matter in this country is land ownership. Each year, the rivers redefine the land. Islands that were farmed one year are gone, and new ones appear as river

Figure 8.13
River Systems of Bangladesh

channels change after every rainy season. The people are adaptable and move to new islands in the delta as the landscape changes. You can't help but admire their tenacity and incredible resilience.

Solving the problem is almost impossible. With too little land and too much water, there is not much that can be done. Bengalis have built up the **levees** on the river banks to try to contain the water. This has not worked. When a storm surge from a cyclone flows over the levees, it is next to impossible to get rid of the sea water since it is dammed behind the embankments. As one Bengali commentator observed, "we should live with the rivers and benefit from them rather than fight them and go against nature." To this end, new remedial plans of action include the following:

- Riverbeds need to be dredged of the deposits that block them, thus facilitating water flow.
- Funding needs to be given for adequate *elevated* housing, using the material dredged from river channels.
- The use of water transportation rather than roads should be encouraged because then the Bengalis won't have to rebuild their transportation network every year when it is destroyed.
- Permanent food shelters should be established for use in times when relief is needed.
- Communications technology should be used to alert residents to dangerous storms so they can take to higher ground.

While most people agree that these strategies will help solve Bangladesh's problems, work is hampered by the lack of money available. Dredging, elevated housing, and improved communication are being implemented. This holistic approach will not solve all of Bangladesh's problems, but it could do much to

Figure 8.14
Bangladesh Flood Victims Catch Fish in the Street

alleviate the suffering the people endure on an on-going basis. But there is still a need for seawalls to keep storm surges from washing far up the river estuary, eroding the valuable land, and washing people out to sea.

QUESTIONS:

1. Explain the factors that contribute to flooding in Bangladesh.

2. Analyse the damage and casualties resulting from flooding in Bangladesh. What could be done to minimize these?

3. Explain why embankments on the natural levees have not worked.

4. Do some research to find out how other countries have used seawalls to stop the ocean from flooding and eroding the coast. Could this solution be implemented easily in Bangladesh?

ACTIVITIES

UNDERSTANDING CONCEPTS

1. a) Explain the relationship of base level to erosion and deposition in flowing water.
    b) List and explain the factors that determine the erosive power of flowing water.
    c) Why are most lakes temporary landforms?
2. a) What geographic characteristics are necessary for karst topography to develop?
    b) Classify the following karst features as being caused by erosion or deposition: doline, stalactite, rock curtain, dry valley, cave, column, underground lake.
    c) Draw a sketch of each feature and explain how it was formed.
    d) What challenges does karst topography pose for people?
3. a) List all the gradational features highlighted in bold in the section on aeolian landscapes. Classify each as erosional, depositional, or other, and explain how it is formed.
    b) Describe the role of running water in aeolian landscapes.
    c) Why are desert landscapes more susceptible to erosion than humid regions?
    d) Explain how the flow dynamics of running water and winds are similar to and different from one another.
4. a) Identify the factors that cause erosion and deposition in coastal features.
    b) How is wave action similar to and different from other gradational processes?

DEVELOPING AND PRACTISING SKILLS

5. Experiment with a stream table.
    a) Set the table perfectly flat. Smooth the sand so that it is flat and add water at one end. What do you observe? What does this simulate?
    b) Increase the slope by raising one end. Add a steady flow of water at the high end, and observe what happens to the material on the table. Where does transportation occur? Where does deposition occur? Make a sketch to show your simulation.
    c) Gradually reduce the slope. Note changes in flow velocity, transportation, and depositional features.
6. a) Study Figure 8.1. What do each of the two lines on the graph represent?
    b) What velocity is needed for water to erode
        • fine sand?
        • pebbles?
        • cobbles and boulders?
        • clay and silt?
    c) Create a graph to show the correlation—either positive or negative—between flow velocity and the erosion of particles larger than fine sand. Explain why this is so.
    d) Why do you think fine particles require a greater flow velocity than larger particles?
    e) Prepare a chart to show the velocities at which deposition occurs for different sized particles. When would clay and fine silts settle out? Why?

f) Is it possible for a river to be neither eroding nor depositing material? When would this occur?

7. Produce diagrams to illustrate and explain the processes that lead to the formation of the following physical features: blow hole, sea cave, arch, stack, emergent coastline, submerged coastline.

8. Study Figure 8.12 on page 127 and a topographical map of Prince Edward Island from an atlas.

   a) Give examples to show that both submerged and emergent coastlines exist around Charlottetown.

   b) Explain why most of the tourist industry in Prince Edward Island would be concentrated on the north shore.

   c) Explain how both the north shore and the south shore of the island were formed.

LEARNING THROUGH APPLICATION

9. a) How might global warming affect the people of Bangladesh?

   b) How might they deal with this new problem?

   c) What trade-offs do people have to make when living on coastlines that potentially flood?

10. a) Explain how wind erosion could affect coastal dwellers' lives.

    b) Explain how wind deposition could affect coastal dwellers' lives.

    c) What has been done to reduce coastal wind erosion in Prince Edward Island?

    d) Why is nothing being done about cliff erosion?

Chapter 9

ICE SCULPTING THE LANDSCAPE

FOCUS QUESTIONS

1. What is the role of ice in changing and shaping physical features?
2. How often and where do glaciers form?
3. How have the people of Ontario derived benefits from the glaciers that occupied the province in the past?

Key Terms

continental glaciers

alpine glaciers

fjords

drumlins

kettles

During the ice ages, giant sheets of ice carved and reworked much of the land mass that constitutes Canada. It was only 12 000 years ago that the large continental ice sheets left Canada. In northern regions and on some arctic islands, ice sheets still remain to this day as frigid reminders of what Canada used to be like. Enormous sheets of ice, some up to 2 km thick, flowed out of the north and out of the western mountains. The impact these glaciers had on the land was unbelievable. Even though most of the glaciers are gone today, examples of glacial weathering and erosion are still with us.

During the many ice ages that the earth has experienced, there have been essentially two types of glaciers, **continental** and **alpine**. The term "ice age" refers to a period when the climate cools and glaciers cover large parts of the earth's surface. The last period of continental glaciation took place in Canada, most of Europe, and northern Asia. In a way, you could say we are currently in an ice age since continental glaciers do still occur, specifically on Antarctica,

Greenland, and some islands in the Canadian High Arctic. Generally, people consider this period to be an **interglacial period** since large ice sheets do not cover most continents. The Antarctic ice sheet alone accounts for over 90 per cent of all glacial ice on the planet. Interestingly, the human species has never lived in a period when the earth was without glaciers. Compared with other periods, the earth is now experiencing a cold snap 1.5 million years long! It was once thought that there had been four ice ages, but recent analysis of deep-sea sediments indicate that there could have been as many as 18 ice ages over the past 900 000 years.

Alpine glaciation is of a much smaller scale and is still occurring in many parts of the world. At high elevations, the temperature is so cold that snow does not melt during the summer. The accumulated snow gradually turns to ice and a glacier is formed. Alpine glaciers are found predominantly in the Alps (from which the name was derived), the Himalayas, the Western Cordillera, and the Andes Mountains. Many

Figure 9.1
Bow Glacier, Alberta

alpine features are similar to continental features, but the ice sculpts interesting features out of the mountains that are not found when glaciers move over flatter ground.

The point at which year-round snow occurs is called the **snow line**. In southern Greenland, the snow line is about 500 m **above mean sea level** (amsl). In the middle latitudes, it is about 2700 m amsl because of the more temperate climate. Near the equator, it is even higher. In the Andes Mountains, year-round snow does not occur until 5000 m amsl. During ice ages, these snow lines moved lower until they joined with the continental glaciers to create a single blanket of ice.

Of course, it is not enough just to have cold temperatures. There must be significant accumulations of snow each year to create a glacier. In the last ice age, parts of northern Alaska, Siberia, and the western edge of the Yukon were not glaciated. These regions were arctic deserts that did not receive enough precipitation to be glaciated. Many west coast glaciers are presently active because they receive enormous amounts of orographic precipitation in the form of snow.

Continental Glaciation

Continental glaciation was introduced as a theory in the early 1800s. Some people followed the creationist view that the earth's surface features were created by running water and flooding as described in the Book of Genesis in the Judeo-Christian Bible. Glacial deposits were thought to have been laid down by icebergs that had drifted over the area—hence the term **drift**. Scientists acknowledged that glaciation occurred in mountains because they could see them at work. They did not make the connection between alpine and continental features, however. How could there be glaciers that covered whole continents?

In 1836, Louis Agassiz, a Swiss scientist, compared glacial deposits in Swiss valleys with other deposits in Scandinavia. He discovered that huge boulders in Switzerland were of the same igneous rock as the bedrock in Scandinavia hundreds of kilometres away. Using the theory of uniformitarianism (see page 17), Agassiz theorized that glacial movement was the only way these huge rocks could have been carried such great distances. Like most visionaries, Agassiz was scorned in his day. His theories were

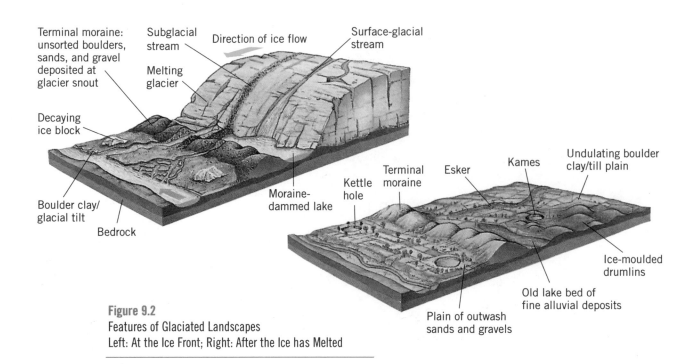

Figure 9.2
Features of Glaciated Landscapes
Left: At the Ice Front; Right: After the Ice has Melted

considered credible only much later. Today continental glaciation is widely accepted as a major gradational process.

The erosive power of glaciers is incredible! There is practically nothing a glacier cannot pick up. In the last ice age, boulders as large as houses were moved hundreds of kilometres. Loose material on the surface was swallowed up as part of the glacier's load. Frozen into the ice, these particles scraped, sanded, and polished whatever bedrock the glacier could not move. This action is called **abrasion**. The material the glaciers collected was not limited to loose particles. When a weak section of the bedrock was encountered, a large chunk of rock was sometimes plucked right out of the ground! This was possible because friction created by the glacier's advance would cause some of the ice to melt and seep into cracks in the rock where it would refreeze. When the glacier began to advance again, the frozen chunk of bedrock was wrenched along with it.

Some people describe glaciers as being like giant bulldozers. This is not entirely correct, however. A bulldozer moves material with its

front only, whereas a glacier picks up material along the entire length of its base. In this way glaciers are similar to rivers. Glacial erosion throughout the Canadian Shield is evident in the fact that the region was cleared of most of its soil during the last ice age. The soil it has today was either deposited by the glacier or has formed since the ice age ended. Bedrock is exposed over most of the Shield, and rock surfaces are smooth and often polished. Stripped of most of its soil, the Shield has little agricultural value. However, the region is rich in mineral resources, which are easy to find because of the absence of overburden. These deposits include precious minerals such as gold and silver, metallic minerals such as nickel and iron, and non-ferrous metals such as copper, lead, and zinc.

There are millions of depressions in the Canadian Shield, formed mainly as the result of abrasion. When the glacier left, many hollows were filled with water, forming long, thin **finger lakes**. The most famous of these glacial lakes are the Great Lakes. There are several theories about the formation of these lakes. Some believe they existed before the Pleistocene Epoch and so were not formed by glaciers. Ancient fault lines have been found in Lake Ontario, making it therefore conceivable that the Great Lakes are the remnants of ancient coastlines of undiscovered continents pushed into place by plate tectonics untold hundreds of millions of years ago. Other people contend that the Great Lakes Basin was originally a river valley, and that the deep, sedimentary basin was excavated over several ice ages until the lakes, as we know them, were created. There is no question, however, that the Great Lakes were enlarged and shaped, at least in part, by glaciers.

Another way in which glaciers affect the earth's surface is through **isostasy**. The surface of the continental crust is depressed by the mass of glacial ice. (It is similar to denudation because the surface is lowered, although it cannot be considered denudation because no material is actually removed.) When the glaciers are gone, the crust rebounds because the enormous weight has been removed. Isostatic rebound is found in many parts of Canada. The "ponds" found in Gros Morne National Park (see pp. 140–5), were once **fjords** that became cut off from the ocean as the shoreline rose after glacial retreat.

The mechanics of glacial processes are complex. Much of the enormous load carried by the glacier is frozen into the ice and is only deposited when the ice melts. Some of the material is deposited directly by the ice and some is carried away and eventually deposited by streams of meltwater. Many depositional features in the last ice age formed at the southern edge of the glacier, where there were many periods of advance and retreat. Each time the glacier moved, the drift was moved around and reshaped, so across much of southern Canada and the northern United States there are many different glacial deposits.

Where the glaciers melted, glacial deposits often formed into hills. These **moraines**, as they are called, contain a variety of unsorted drift material. Tiny particles may lie alongside huge **erratics**. Sometimes blocks of ice were buried inside a moraine. After the glaciers retreated, these ice chunks melted, creating hollows in the moraine. The hills in these formations are called **kames**, and the hollows are called **kettles**. Often, water fills the kettles, creating round kettle lakes. This hummocky landscape is common in many areas where glacial material was deposited.

One of the most famous moraines is the Oak Ridges Moraine in southern Ontario. Formed between two lobes of the glacier, this **interlobate moraine** forms the divide between Lake Ontario and Lake Simcoe. Since runoff flowing into Lake Ontario originates in the moraine, it is important that the area be preserved in its natural state to ensure that the watershed will remain healthy. Unfortunately, this environmentally sensitive area already houses numerous landfills and development sites.

Drumlins are curious hills that frequently appear in groups. What is curious about them is their strange symmetry. They are all more or less the same shape, with one end wide and rounded and the other end thin and tapered. The thin end, or tail, of the hill points in the direction in which the glacier moved. These formations are created when a glacier encounters an obstacle or bedrock it cannot move. The moving ice reworks the till, creating the streamlined shape. The area around Peterborough, Ontario, is a classic drumlin field.

Stratified glacial deposits can be found in amazing variety. When a glacier melts, it leaves behind an incredible amount of water and till. Rapidly flowing glacial streams exhibit the same characteristics as any other river. Outwash plains of stratified and sorted sediment form at the glacier's front end, or snout. After the last ice age, pre-existing drainage systems expanded into enormous U-shaped river valleys known as **spillways**. The tiny streams in these spillways today are indicators of these massive post-glacial water flows. Sometimes the sediment carried by spillways is deposited in a temporary lake that may have been dammed by melting glaciers or moraines. Fine particles slowly sink to the

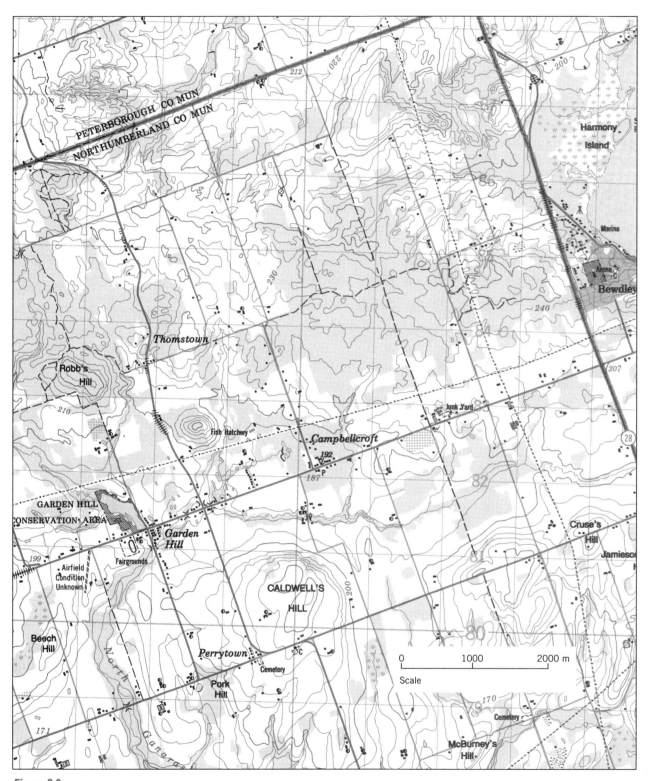

Figure 9.3
Identify the drumlins in this topographic map of Rice Lake near Peterborough, Ontario.

bottom, leaving a rich lacustrine deposit. One such **ponding** occurred around present-day Schomberg, Ontario, where the rich clay soils that were left behind make the area prime agricultural land.

Eskers look like upside-down river beds. These thin, meandering hills of layered material, which cross glaciated landscapes, are formed when water flows through a stagnant glacier. This may occur on the surface of the ice, but it is more likely that the water flows at ground level or within the ice itself. Like other running water, this stream eventually drops its load. When the ice melts, the unusual esker landform is left. Eskers and **outwash fans**—deltas that form on land—provide important deposits of sand and gravel used in the construction industry.

Canada is not the only country to experience continental glaciation. Parts of the northern United States as well as Scandinavia and much of northern Russia share many of the same gradational features that are found in Canada.

Glaciation in Southern Ontario

Continental glaciation has had a great influence in shaping the landscape of Ontario. The features described in this section are readily found all over that province. Ontario is more or less divided into two major landform regions: the Canadian Shield in the north and the Great Lakes-St. Lawrence Lowlands in the south. The shield is very rocky and has thousands of lakes, rivers and wetlands, and is heavily forested. The lowlands, by contrast, have better soil, are flat to gently rolling, and are predominantly used for farming or other intensive forms of human development.

The striking differences between the two regions are mainly due to continental glaciation. As it moved relentlessly south, the glacier acted like a conveyer belt and removed much of the soil, rock, and other debris from the Shield. When it got far enough south so that the temperature was warmer, the ice melted and its load was dropped.

So, over the course of several thousand years, the glacier picked up soil from northern Ontario and laid it down in a variety of depositional features in the lowlands of southern Ontario. Of course, there are pockets of the Shield where soil was laid down too. For example, depressions were often filled up with muddy water from the melting glacier. These pondings could have lasted for thousands of years as the glacier melted away (15 000 to 10 000 ybp). The silty material that settled to the bottom of the ponding gradually formed layers. When the glacier left and the ponding dried up, a flat **lacustrine plain** was left. These clay plains are good for farming and are found in isolated pockets, not only in the Shield but also in the lowlands.

The Lowlands also have their share of rugged landscape, such as the Oak Ridges Moraine and the Peterborough Drumlin Field. The difference is that the rugged features of the Shield are erosional, while the features of the Lowlands are depositional. There are some erosional features in the Lowlands, however, which were formed by water running from glaciers. The volume of water flowing out of these enormous ice sheets is mind-boggling. Imagine ice a kilometre or two thick, covering most of Ontario and melting for 3000–5000 years. Have you ever noticed the enormous valleys of the rather puny rivers of southern Ontario? Those rivers weren't so small when the glacier melted. That is why the Don Valley, the Rouge Valley, and the Humber Valley in the GTA (Greater Toronto Area) are so deep and so broad. Toronto's many ravines, carved by water from melting ice sheets, makes it a beautiful city.

All across Ontario, evidence of the once-present giant ice sheets is found. The next time you travel in an undeveloped part of Ontario, look for some of its interesting glacial features. You may be hiking on a ridge of land snaking through the forest, when you realize you are walking on an esker. Or you may be driving along with regular cigar-shaped drumlins all around. And if you go canoeing up north, you can't help but notice the scratches on the bedrock caused by sliding ice sheets.

Alpine Glaciation

Although mountain glaciers occur on a much smaller scale than continental glaciers, most middle and upper latitude mountain ranges have been shaped by them. The source area for these glaciers is high in the mountains, where snowfall is heavy and temperatures are low enough for snow to last all year.

Freeze-thaw action at the base of the glacier allows water to enter cracks in the rock. When the water freezes and the glacier moves away, surface rock is carried away with it. Over many years, horseshoe-shaped depressions called **cirques** are formed by this action. These eroded hollows are not visible until the glacier retreats. When two or more cirques develop close to one another, picturesque alpine features are formed. Two cirques against each other make a chiseled ridge known as an **arête**. If the two cirques break through the arête, a **col**, or pass, is formed. Three or more cirques around a mountain peak result in a **horn**—that sharp-toothed feature so loved by mountain climbers. The Matterhorn of the Swiss Alps is the most famous example. The rugged beauty of alpine mountains is caused to a large extend by these cirque formations.

From the source region in the mountains, glaciers flow into mountain valleys. The force of gravity allows the ice floe to move steadily down and out of the mountains. Everywhere it goes, its erosive power modifies the shape of the land. Young V-shaped river valleys are carved into wide U-shaped valleys. **Hanging valleys** are carved where tributary glaciers flow into main glaciers. When glaciers eventually reach the ocean, they continue to flow out to sea until they are broken up by ocean currents and waves. **Fjords** are U-shaped valleys that are flooded by sea water when the glaciers melt. Unlike continental glaciation, the erosive power of alpine glaciers is concentrated by the relief of the land.

If you ever travel to Gros Morne or any of Canada's National Parks, you will find them staffed with intelligent, sociable people. Most have a scientific background and conduct research on the environment, as well as provide tours and educate the public. Many are university students working for the summer, but a large number are full-time employees. Some of the experts available at these parks include geologists, wildlife managers, ecologists, and glaciologists.

Even though the fields are all quite different, the basic training they require is similar. Because Canada has two official languages, job applicants who are bilingual have a definite advantage. A bachelor of science degree in biology, geography, geology, or ecology is usually required. In order to conduct more field research, post-graduate degrees are also needed.

Figure 9.4
What glacial features can you identify in this photograph?

The depositional features of alpine glaciation are more or less the same as those of continental glaciation. Moraines are common, but instead of interlobate moraines, there are **lateral moraines** and **medial moraines**. Lateral moraines form along the sides of a glacier as it flows through a mountain valley. When two glaciers come together, they remain separate, flowing along side by side. The ridge of till formed between them is a medial moraine. This moraine is made up of the two lateral moraines, one from each glacier. It can be a significant landform feature because there is twice as much till accumulating in the same place. Lateral and medial moraines are recognizable as dark streaks of sediment in the glacial ice.

Terminal moraines that form in fjords are called **skerries**. Most often, these hills are submerged under water, but sometimes they emerge to form islands at the mouths of the fjords. In northern climates, skerries have proven to be beneficial landforms as they provide protection against violent winter storms for some harbours.

Living with Alpine Glaciation

Alpine glaciers have so altered mountain landscapes that they significantly affect human land-use patterns. The huge U-shaped valleys of glaciated mountains allow for much greater development on the broad valley floor than would normally occur in the narrow, non-glaciated valleys. Roads, railways, settlements, and farms all crowd into these inviting flat regions in an otherwise impossibly rugged landscape. Cirques form convenient upland pastures for Swiss herders during the summer. These flat hollows high up a mountain also serve as good staging areas for mountain-climbers, skiers, and hikers preparing to make it to the summit. Often the col, or pass as it is also known, is the most convenient way from one U-shaped valley to another over a range of mountains. In the Swiss Alps, several passes allow traffic to flow between Switzerland, France, and Italy. Canadians who have taken the train or driven the road between Calgary and Vancouver may never forget the route through Crowsnest Pass or Kicking Horse Pass—the two main ways through the Rocky Mountains. The scenery is magnificent and the road an engineering marvel.

Figure 9.5
What type of valley is visible in this photograph?

Gros Morne

Gros Morne National Park provides many opportunities to review the concepts covered in this chapter. Its wild landscape of alpine meadows, seacoast, and mountains make it an amazing place to visit, but the park is more than just pretty scenery. Gros Morne was declared a World Heritage Site by the United Nations Educational, Scientific, and Cultural Organization because the underlying geology records over a billion years of the earth's history and provides evidence to validate the theory of plate tectonics.

Figure 9.7
This magnificent landscape, in Gros Morne Park, was created by glaciers.

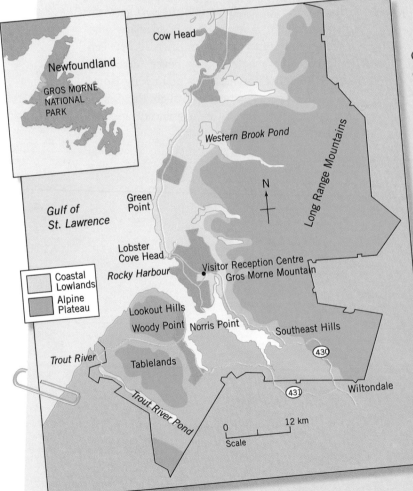

Figure 9.6
The Location of Gros Morne in Newfoundland

Geological features that usually lie dozens of kilometres beneath the earth's surface are exposed at the surface.

The park includes three landscape regions: an alpine tableland, a coastal lowland, and the Long Range Mountains. The old fold mountains that make up the Long Range are remnants of the ancient Canadian Shield. The old fold mountains have been sculpted by recent glacial activity and exhibit many classic alpine glacial features such as fjords, cirques, and hanging valleys. The coastal lowlands show evidence of terraces formed when the shoreline isostatically rebounded after the glacial ice melted. More recent examples of shoreline gradational processes are also evident, but the most fascinating aspect of Gros Morne is the tableland region.

The rock in the tableland is seldom found on the earth's surface. It is **peridotite**, a rock found only in the earth's mantle. The rock is so alien to the earth's surface that few things will grow in the soil formed from it. How did this exotic rock get to the earth's surface? The following organizer summarizes how Gros Morne evolved.

Age (ybp)	Explanation	Diagram
1000 – 650 million	The rocks of the Canadian Shield were metamorphosed into gneiss and schist through heat and pressure deep beneath fold mountains. Granite formed and magma entered the cracks within the older rock. Gross Morne was part of a super continent.	
650 – 600 million	The super continent started to split apart. Magma started to ooze up through the fault and hardened into basaltic dikes. Deposits of sediment from the eroding mountains partially filled in the valley.	
600 – 500 million	The rift valley widened and filled with sea water. Lapetus Ocean was formed. (This ocean is named after the Greek god who fathered Atlantis.) Sediments continued to form over the sea floor. A 1000 metre-thick deposit of sedimentary rock was formed along the shoreline.	
500 – 450 million	Plate movement reversed, with the continents on either side of Lapetus moving back together again. The western plate subducted beneath the eastern plate. Volcanic islands rose above the subduction zone.	

Age (ybp)	Explanation	Diagram
450 – 400 million	As the process continued, layers that once lay deep under the earth were thrust up and ended up on the surface. Basaltic deposits formed under the ocean as lava seeped out from the midoceanic rift. Peridotite rocks from the upper mantle were exposed on the surface. Seamounts formed from lava flows from the volcanic islands. Breccia resulted from broken up limestone that was cemented together along the shoreline.	
400 – 350 million	A new super continent called Pangaea was formed as the Lapetus Sea disappeared and dry land was formed.	
350 – 2 million	The continents started to split apart again. This time, the split occurred 500 km east of the old fault lines, so Gros Morne was no longer on the edge of the North American Plate.	
2 million – present	During the ice age, the landscape was eroded into many glacial features. The crust rebounded as the rock and ice were removed from the surface. Sea level dropped, but the rebound was greater, so terraces delineating former beaches are now found along the coastal plain. Wave action, ice, mass wasting, and flowing water further modify the landscape.	

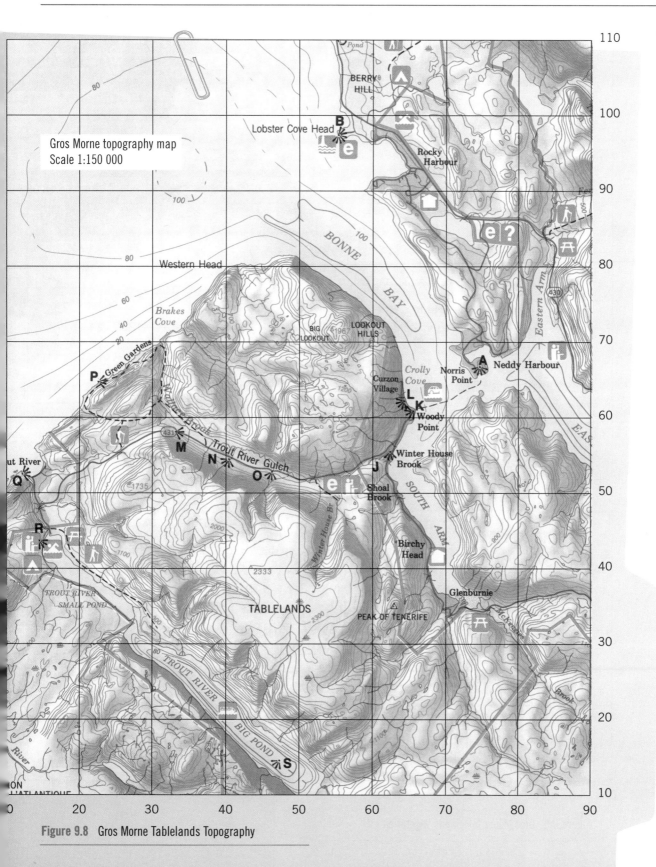

Figure 9.8 Gros Morne Tablelands Topography

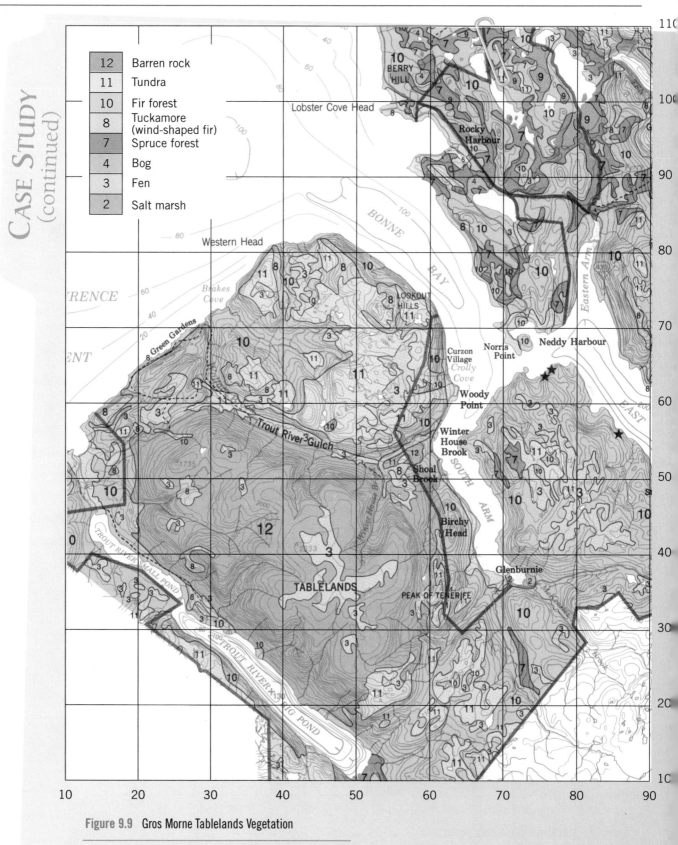

Figure 9.9 Gros Morne Tablelands Vegetation

QUESTIONS:

1. Study the two maps showing the southern portion of Gros Morne on page 143 and 144.

   a) Sketch or trace the map showing the shoreline and significant features.

   b) Identify on your base map the following features: steep slopes, tablelands, lakes, rivers, fjords, and other glacial features.

   c) For each natural vegetation type describe the topography using the map and the geological history in the case study. Also state the grid reference for the region using an organizer like the one at top, right (the first is done as an example).

   d) Explain how such factors as topography, elevation, geology, exposure, drainage, and climate affect each vegetation type. For example, Tuckamore is a forest made up of wind-shaped fir trees. By looking at the location (along exposed shore lines) it is apparent that strong winds off the ocean have prevented the trees from attaining their full height. Trees grow here instead of on the tundra because the forest is relatively warm compared to the colder temperatures on top of the rocky knoll north of the tablelands (4070). The surface geology must have some soil to allow for root systems, but the area seems to be well drained because there are no bogs or water-loving black spruce.

Vegetation	Topography	Grid Reference
Barren Rock	Tablelands – flat topped mantle rock	2050 to 5030
Tundra		
Fir Forest		
Tukamore		
Spruce Forest		
Bog		
Fen		
Salt Marsh		

   e) Explain how the locations in the chart below were formed using the information in the case study and the maps.

   f) Find examples of the following features and use military grid references to locate them on your sketch map. Explain how each was formed.
   - cirque in the Tablelands
   - evidence of isostatic rebound at the mouths of fjords
   - U-shaped valley by Trout River Gulch

   g) Describe the recreational activities that would be suited to this national park.

   h) Design a hiking trip through the section of the park in the maps and show the route on your sketch map. What aspects of the landscape would you direct people through?

Feature	Military Grid Reference	Feature	Military Grid Reference
Table lands	4040	South Arm	6060 to 7040
Trout River Big Pond	3030 to 5010	Norris Pont	7070
Trout River Gulch	3060 to 5050	Kettle Lakes	7090, 70100, 80100

ACTIVITIES

UNDERSTANDING CONCEPTS

1. Why do alpine glaciers still exist in most of the world's continents, while continental glaciation is restricted to Antarctica and Greenland?
2. Describe the role played by glaciers in shaping the landscape of Ontario.
3. How do glaciers modify the earth's surface through erosion? Through deposition?
4. Make a list of all the highlighted words in the section on glaciation. Classify each feature as erosional or depositional, and explain how each was created.
5. Prepare an organizer comparing alpine and continental glaciation. Use the following criteria: formation, existing locations, movement, land features created through deposition, features resulting from erosion.

DEVELOPING AND PRACTISING SKILLS

6. Study the topographic map of part of the Canadian Shield in Figure 9.3.
   a) Which gradational process, erosion or deposition, is more noticeable?
   b) Describe the drainage pattern. How has it been affected by glaciers?
   c) What glacial features are obvious from the map?
   d) Draw profiles of two different glacial features.
   e) How could this map be used by people in the area?
7. Use a variety of reference materials, including atlases, satellite images, and air photos, to find global patterns for each of the following: fjords, continental ice caps, alpine glaciers, U-shaped valleys, glacial drift, and finger lakes.
   a) Using a legend, show the location of each of these features on a world map.
   b) Give a generalized statement about where each feature is found in terms of **absolute location** and **relative location**. Absolute location includes latitude, altitude, relief, etc. Relative location includes the relationship between each feature and the other features. For example, fjords have a lower elevation than alpine glaciers, they are extensions of U-shaped valleys, and they have glacial till at their mouths.

LEARNING THROUGH APPLICATION

8. Assume that you are an entrepreneur about to develop the Gros Morne area shown in Fig. 9.8. Choose one of the following development projects:
   • a ski resort, including chalet, lifts, and runs
   • a quarry mining gravel for road construction
   • a mountaineering and hang-gliding school
   • an east-west highway showing bridges, tunnels, and gas stations
   • a whitewater rafting enterprise

a) Show the location of your project.

b) Produce a map to a scale of 1:5000.

c) Draw three profiles of the site. Explain why the terrain here is more suitable for your project than other sites on the map.

d) What other information would you need to know about the site before you proceeded further with your development?

9. a) How has glaciation affected the Canadian people?

b) How does alpine glaciation allow for human activity globally?

GIS Assignment on Glaciation

10. This is an ArcView Extension from ESRI Canada. Much of Canada was heavily glaciated during the last ice age. The ice left this area about 10,000 years ago and the pattern of ice movement is still very much in evidence. Your task is to learn more about glacial features left behind with the retreat of the glaciers. This particular activity deals with the province of Saskatchewan. Use ArcView GIS to create a detailed map of the glacial deposits and analyze the patterns of these glacial features.

You will need to download the instructions for the exercise from the ESRI Canada web site at http://www.esricanada.com/k-12/lesson/glaciation/index.html and then click on the version of software that you are running. The document is in PDF format so you will need to have Adobe Acrobat in order to read it. (Instructions for downloading are on the web site.)

In this exercise you will be asked to do a number of things including creating a map showing the eskers, moraines, and drumlin features of North Saskatchewan to examine patterns in the location of these features. Using this information, as well as other related data, you will determine the direction of the glacial advance and retreat. Extension exercises are also included for those who wish to examine the topic of glaciation more closely.

Supplemental Questions:

11. a) What does the pattern tell you about the direction of ice movement in the area during the last ice age?

b) Follow the same procedure using data for the province of Ontario:
Locate the drumlin fields and eskers of Southern Ontario. Describe the relationship between drumlins and eskers and their formation. Compare these features to those found in North Saskatchewan.

c) Briefly, describe the more complex pattern of moraines in Southern Ontario compared to North Saskatchewan.

d) Account for this more complex pattern and the glacial advances that affected the area of Southern Ontario.

UNIT 2

Culminating Activity: Holding a Natural Disasters Conference

We saw the human tragedy of the Turkish earthquake at the beginning of this unit. Unfortunately, disasters from forces in the lithosphere are very common, hitting with devastating frequency all over the world. Some disasters occur because of forces within the earth (**diastrophism**), others result from forces acting on the surface (gradational processes), and some happen because of unsustainable human practices. These different disasters are summarized in the table below.

Nature of the Disaster	Topics	Examples of Locations Where Tragedy May Strike
Diastrophism	Volcanoes	Pacific Rim
	Earthquakes	Plate boundaries
	Tsunamis	Coastal locations
Gradational Processes	Mass Wasting	Unstable slopes in California, Hong Kong, Colombia
	Avalanches	Mountainous regions like the Alps, Rockies, Andes
	River Flooding	Mississippi, Red River, Saguenay, Huang He
	Wind Erosion	Saharan oases, coastal beaches in PEI, North Carolina
	Coastal Flooding	Bangladesh, Netherlands, New Orleans
Unsustainable Practices	Pollution from Mining	Canadian Shield, former Soviet republics, mines in developing countries
	Oil Spills	Coastal Alaska, South Africa, St. of Hormuz

Choose one disaster or geographic process from the topic column in the chart. Do some initial research (use the Internet, library, CD ROMs, etc.) to find an example of a specific disaster. Using your chosen example, prepare a research paper on how damage from a similar disaster could be minimized in the future, or if possible, prevented altogether. Follow the format explained below when writing your paper.

1. Once you have chosen a disaster, brainstorm two (or more) questions you would need to research, under the following headings. The first one has been done for you.
   - Nature of the disaster (What happened? When did it happen? Who was affected?)
   - Location of the disaster
   - Reasons for the disaster
   - Factors related to predicting the disaster
   - Solutions
   - Remedial action taken
   - Future steps
   - Further research

2. Using your list of questions as a guide, begin your research by gathering together relevant information from magazine articles, books, CD ROMs, Internet web sites, pamphlets from organizations, etc.

   Use a number of references to corroborate the facts and assumptions you uncover—especially those found through the Internet—to make sure they are correct.

Gather and use information from no less than five different sources, and make sure you keep an accurate bibliographical list of everything you use.

3. Once you have gathered all the necessary information, write your paper by answering your own questions. You may find that you need to do more research before you are able to finish covering all the important points for your paper. Proofread your final draft and carefully check spelling and grammar.

4. Communicate your findings in a "Disasters Conference."
   - Make a display board including your research paper, maps, diagrams, graphs, and charts.
   - As other students examine your work, explain your findings.
   - Take notes on others' presentations and evaluate their projects.

5. Summarize your findings for at least three projects on a similar theme—e.g., "Unsustainable Human Practices"—and make generalizations as to how the problem could be made less traumatic for all people.

6. Have a general discussion to debrief the activity and decide on a class project to help people affected by disaster. For example, have a bake sale to raise money for earthquake victims.

Earthquake damage in California

UNIT 3

THE WATER ALL AROUND: UNDERSTANDING THE HYDROSPHERE

Human Drama

WELL WATER TRAGEDY
Searching for Answers: Residents of Walkerton ask who is to blame and how the disaster could have been averted

Contaminated water led to the death of seven Walkerton residents.

Walkerton, Ontario—Even in the seclusion of her church office, Pastor Beth Conroy could not escape Walkerton's toll of tragedy... Now the minister was trying to steal a few moments to contemplate how the town of 5000 could heal itself. The phone rang. As she listened Conroy's face became sad, her voice even more sombre—as the caller informed her that deaths from the lethal strain of E. coli in the town's water had reached seven... Seconds after Conroy hung up, the whirr of helicopter blades could be heard as yet another chronically ill patient was transferred from the local hospital to a larger facility in London Ontario. But Conroy tried to put a brave face on things. People in poorer parts of the world, she noted, "live with this kind of water on a daily basis, and they don't get generous gifts or so many people volunteering to help..."

For many residents nestled along this part of the Saugeen River valley in southwestern Ontario, in the richest province in one of the richest countries of the world, understanding was in short supply. Last week Walkerton seemed to have become part movie set, part ghost town. As the media invasion – including reports from BBC and CNN—broadcast the community's misfortune to the world, hundreds of

Continued on next page.

residents escaped to bunk with friends and relatives elsewhere. Some who had been affected with the Eschericha coli bacteria were recovering from symptoms which included severe bouts of bloody diarrhea, but others were not so fortunate. Everybody felt at least some connection to the deceased—Lenore Al was the former part-time librarian, Betty Trushinski was the town-hall janitor's wife, Mary Rose Raymond was the two-year old daughter of a doctor from nearby Hanover. Familiar faces from the Walkerton area – gone.

Questions, meanwhile, piled up faster than answers trickled out. At a town council meeting, Linda Dietrich, a grandmother of two Walkerton children stricken by the bug, epitomized the frustration. "When are we going to get a straight answer on what is happening to our children in this town?" she screamed. Later, Dietrich told reporters her questions were basic. "Why did this happen?" she asked. "How are we going to stop it? When will it be safe for our kids to go out and play? ... who is to blame? ..."

Investigators focused on the town's three main wells and underground water basins that feed them as possible sources of contamination. "A preliminary hydrogeological investigation established that all three wells have possible pathways that would allow contamination to enter," said engineer Steve Burns.

It was eventually concluded that the E. coli contamination originated in animal wastes, which washed into a well near a cattle ranch during the torrential downpour that struck on May 12.

(Adapted from MacLeans, 06/19/2000)

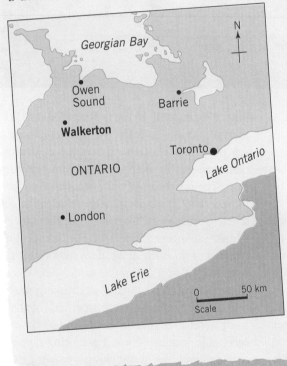

Georgian Bay

N

Owen Sound

Barrie

Walkerton

Toronto

Lake Ontario

ONTARIO

London

Lake Erie

0   50 km

Scale

Unit Focus Questions

1. What are the principal features of the hydrosphere?

2. What are the sources and nature of energy flows through the hydrosphere?

3. What can we do to ensure that there is safe and abundant drinking water for ourselves as well as for future generations?

INTRODUCTION

Many of us take water for granted, but it is essential to life. While this remarkable compound is relatively abundant on Earth, it is exceedingly rare in the solar system. Even though there is plenty of water in Canada, fresh, **potable** water is often lacking in many parts of the world. Plant and animal species either adapt to the limited availability of water or die out in arid regions. People often overcome water deficits using ingenuity. Whether they use ancient dug wells as in the Sahel, or modern desalination plants in Kuwait, people have the technology to deal with problems of water supply. All that is required is adequate funding and the desire to have clean water. These simple requirements are available in Canada, but as Beth Conroy states in the opening article, many parts of the world are not so lucky.

How much fresh water is there? Russian UN researcher Igor Shiklomanov of the State Hydrologic Institute was selected to do a world inventory of water. He estimated that there is about 1.4 billion km^3 of water in all its forms. The figure is not 100 per cent accurate since no one knows how much water is hidden in underground ice in the Arctic region or in the wetlands of northern Canada. Very little of this vast amount of water can be used for drinking. More than 97 per cent is too salty since it is in the world's oceans. Fresh water makes up only 2.5 per cent of total water resources, and more than two-thirds of that is locked up inside ice caps. The other .5 per cent, or 11 million km^3, is locked away in **aquifers** deep beneath the earth's surface. Freshwater lakes and rivers contain about 91 000 km^3, or less than 1/100 of 1 per cent of the total water on earth. If all the water on this planet were stored in a 5-litre container, less than one teaspoon would be suitable as drinking water.

People already use more than half of the total fresh water available on Earth, and all the readily accessible sources of water are being tapped. Yet our demand for water keeps growing. Global water consumption tripled from 1960 to 1999, and it is expected to double again before the middle of the next century. It is therefore essential that Canadians, along with the rest of the world's populations, start conserving water and ensuring that governments use sustainable methods to extract the water needed by growing urban populations. It has been widely stated that the major wars of the twenty-first century will be over water, not oil, national identity, or even religion.

Of course, water has significant effects on all of the planet's spheres, and as a result, it is important to the processes of physical geography as well as to people. Known as the hydrosphere, water is contained within the lithosphere in the form of groundwater and aquifer deposits located within the earth's crust. It is found on the earth's surface in streams, rivers, lakes, and oceans in its liquid form, and in glaciers in its solid form. It comprises much of the atmosphere, mainly in gaseous form, but also as a liquid and a solid when it forms rain, snow, and all kinds of precipitation in between. As part of the biosphere, water is an ingredient that is essential for life to exist. The Walkerton disaster is a prime example of our need for pure water and the deadly consequences that can result from not maintaining our supply.

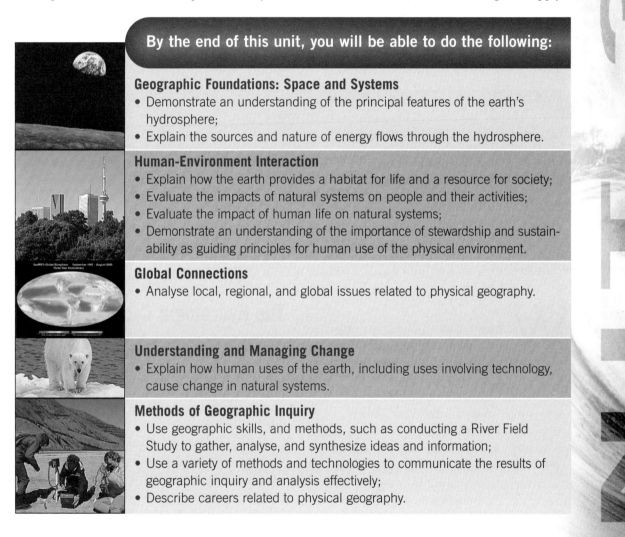

By the end of this unit, you will be able to do the following:

Geographic Foundations: Space and Systems
- Demonstrate an understanding of the principal features of the earth's hydrosphere;
- Explain the sources and nature of energy flows through the hydrosphere.

Human-Environment Interaction
- Explain how the earth provides a habitat for life and a resource for society;
- Evaluate the impacts of natural systems on people and their activities;
- Evaluate the impact of human life on natural systems;
- Demonstrate an understanding of the importance of stewardship and sustainability as guiding principles for human use of the physical environment.

Global Connections
- Analyse local, regional, and global issues related to physical geography.

Understanding and Managing Change
- Explain how human uses of the earth, including uses involving technology, cause change in natural systems.

Methods of Geographic Inquiry
- Use geographic skills, and methods, such as conducting a River Field Study to gather, analyse, and synthesize ideas and information;
- Use a variety of methods and technologies to communicate the results of geographic inquiry and analysis effectively;
- Describe careers related to physical geography.

Contents

Chapter 10

WATER: THE ULTIMATE SHAPE-SHIFTER

FOCUS QUESTIONS

1. How does water change state in the hydrologic cycle?
2. Why does precipitation occur?
3. What impact do cities and industries have on our water supply?

Key Terms

hydrologic cycle

dew point

relative humidity

adiabatic lapse rate

evapo-transpiration

When we think of water we tend to imagine oceans, lakes, and rivers—water in its liquid form. However, water exists in other states all around us whether we are in a Prairie wheat field or in the frozen Arctic. Water is unique because it can exist as a liquid, a solid, and a gas simultaneously. No other substance has this capability at the standard temperature and pressure that are commonly found on planet Earth. This amazing compound is continuously flowing through the lithosphere, atmosphere, and biosphere in a system called the hydrologic cycle. It is energy from the sun that sets this cycle in motion and keeps water flowing from one place to another through the processes of evaporation, transpiration, condensation, precipitation, and infiltration.

The Hydrologic Cycle

The hydrologic cycle may be represented in a flow chart that shows where water is found in natural systems and how it travels through those systems. Figure 10.2 shows the hydrologic cycle as a simple circular pattern; in reality, water movements are much more complex.

The hydrologic cycle takes place in the following way. After a rainstorm, water flows over the surface of the earth, and is held for a time in puddles, ponds, rivers, and lakes. The forces of gravity make it flow constantly downhill like all other liquids, and eventually it makes its way to the ocean. Some surface water seeps into the ground where it is held between the particles of soil as groundwater or deep beneath the surface in porous layers called **aquifers**. Some surface water

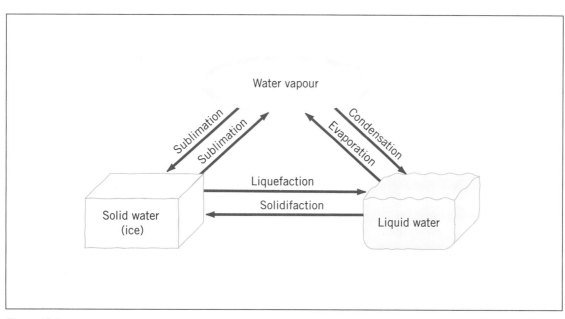

Figure 10.1
The States of Water

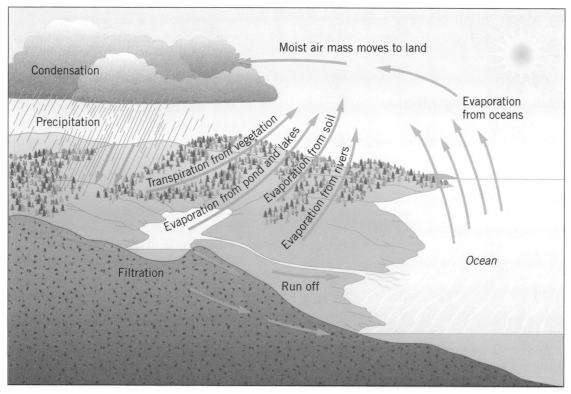

Figure 10.2
The Hydrologic Cycle

is absorbed by plants in the biosphere; they use water to transfer nutrients from the soil to their different parts. Plants also need water to produce carbohydrates through the process of photosynthesis. Animals, including people, need water too, and drink it in large quantities. Glaciers and ice caps, such as those found in Antarctica and Greenland, store enormous amounts of water. However, glaciers are not as significant a reserve of water today as they were in the ice ages, when much of the continental land mass was covered with glaciers.

Although the storage of water in aquifers, glaciers, and the biosphere temporarily removes it from the cycle, it is eventually returned to continue the process. While water is flowing over the surface of the land, it is evaporating. It rises into the sky and eventually condenses on cold surfaces such as ice crystals or dust in the atmosphere; clouds form as a result. If the water droplets in the clouds become too heavy for the air to hold up, they fall as precipitation, and the cycle continues. We will examine each of the processes in the hydrologic cycle, beginning with evaporation and transpiration.

Evaporation/Transpiration

Water is constantly evaporating. This is true whether it is salt water in the ocean, fresh water in a mountain stream, or meltwater on a glacier. In all cases, however, only surface water exposed to the air evaporates. The rate of evaporation depends on a variety of factors, one of which is air temperature. Evaporation rates are much higher in warmer climates than in frigid climates like the High Arctic where water is locked in ice for much of the year. This is the case because cold temperatures reduce the movement of water molecules, thus restricting their escape into the atmosphere.

Another factor that affects evaporation is the amount of water vapour that is already in the air. Evaporation rates in humid climates are lower than those in desert regions because humid air has little room to hold additional water vapour.

Dry winds in arid regions also affect evaporation because they have more room to hold water vapour than humid tropical winds. In Africa, for example, dry desert winds called **harmattans** often blow from the interior into coastal regions south of the Sahara Desert. Along the Guinea coast, where high humidity and hot temperatures result in an uncomfortable, energy-sapping climate, these dry winds bring welcome relief.

Water is purified when it evaporates because pollution, dust, and other substances are left behind in the original water source. For example, in desert regions, high rates of evaporation draw water to the surface from deep within the soil through capillary action. This water carries with it many of the soil's minerals. When the water evaporates, the minerals remain on the ground, forming the **salt pans** and **alkaline flats** that are common in arid regions.

Water also enters the air through transpiration. Transpiration is the term given to the process by which plants give off excess moisture. Many people underestimate the amount of water that plants pump into the atmosphere. As a rule of thumb, each actively growing plant transpires five to ten times as much moisture as the plant holds in its tissue. When you consider that soft plants like meadow grasses in spring are primarily made up of water, the amount of this precious resource being recycled into the atmosphere is enormous. A single mature tree pumps hundreds of litres of water into the atmosphere each day. Imagine the amount of water a whole forest recycles. Forests are often called the lungs of the planet because they produce oxygen. Maybe they should also be called the "kidneys of the planet."

Often the terms "evaporation" and "transpiration" are combined. The term, **evapo-transpiration** is used to encompass both processes. It is used because there is often so close a tie between the two that it is difficult to determine the impact of one separately from the other. Also, the two processes are affected by the same variables and both result in the increased humidity of atmosphere above highly vegetated or water-covered ground.

Sublimation

Sublimation is the process whereby a solid changes directly into a gas, or a gas changes into a solid, without the intermediate "liquid" stage. It usually occurs in areas where there are great differences in the temperatures of the atmosphere and the ground, such as in northern regions. But on an annual basis, it is less significant than evapo-transpiration as a process that adds moisture to the atmosphere. When dry, cold winds blow over snow surfaces or icefields, water changes directly from ice to vapour. Northern regions that have limited snowfall lose significant snow cover in the winter, as arctic winds literally suck the snow back up into the atmosphere.

Hoarfrost is common in the fall in many areas of Canada when fairly warm days give over to cold nights with temperatures below freezing. Moisture in the air condenses and sublimates when the relatively warm, moist air comes in contact with the relatively cold ground. The frost covers plants, bare ground, car windshields, and all other surfaces. This meeting of warm air and cold surface explains why you often have to scrape windshields in the late fall after a cold night. Delicate garden plants and crops are often killed by these periods of spring and fall frost.

Figure 10.3
Frost Forming on Leaves

A region's agricultural capability is often determined by the growing season—the period that is frost-free between the last frost of spring and the first frost of autumn.

Condensation and Moisture in the Air

The amount of moisture the air can hold varies. Warm air is able to hold more water vapour than cold air because there is more energy in the warmer water molecules, so they do not condense on surfaces as readily as the cooler molecules do. When a warm air mass containing a lot of moisture is cooled, the amount of water vapour it can hold is reduced, and the excess water vapour changes back to a liquid through the process of condensation. The temperature at which **condensation** occurs is called the **dew point**—dew being the moisture you often see on a cool summer night following a warm, humid day. If the condensation freezes, it is called frost.

When the air pressure increases, the molecules are forced together. The temperature goes up because the energy is concentrated into a smaller space. The opposite happens when air pressure is lowered—the air is spread out, so the temperature decreases. In either case, the amount of potential energy remains the same. It is just distributed differently. The rate at which the temperature changes, called the **dry adiabatic lapse rate**, is about 10°C for every 1000 m.

When air rises, it cools and its ability to hold water vapour decreases. Once moist air has reached the **dew point elevation**, clouds form. The dry adiabatic lapse rate has reduced the temperature of the air so much that it can no longer hold as much water vapour. When this happens, condensation takes place. But the water vapour has to have a surface on which to condense. Just like the "fog" of water droplets created when the steam from your shower condenses on your bathroom mirror, the water vapour in the air condenses on dust particles to form clouds. Now the pure water vapour may become polluted again, depending on the nature of the dust particles.

Temperature °C	Water Vapour (g/m³)
−15	1.4
−10	1.9
−5	3.0
10	4.9
5	6.9
10	9.4
15	12.6
20	17.3
25	23.0
30	30.4
35	39.8

Figure 10.4

Maximum Capacity for Holding Water Vapour at Given Temperatures

In these clouds, the air may continue to rise, and although it continues to cool, the rate of cooling decreases. This decrease occurs because energy is given off when the water vapour turns back into a gas. The energy that was used to evaporate the water in the first place returns to the air as the water vapour becomes liquid once again. So the air does not cool down as quickly above the dew point elevation. This rate of cooling is called the **wet adiabatic rate**. It varies between 3°C and 6°C for every 1000 m the moist air rises in the clouds.

The many different types of clouds that are created when water vapour condenses are classified according to their form, altitude, and the process by which they are created. Three main types are cumulus, stratus, and cirrus. Cumulus clouds are those fluffy mounds of white that are common on sunny summer days just before a cold front moves in. As the new weather system enters the region, the dew point elevation drops and heavy cumulonimbus clouds develop. A thunderstorm may soon follow. Convection currents within the clouds often result in these towering clouds having significant vertical development.

Stratus clouds, associated with warm fronts, are often low to the ground and tend to cover the sun with a solid overcast of leaden cloud cover. Wispy cirrus clouds, which are so high up that they are made of ice crystals, are usually associated with fair weather. There are many different combinations of clouds that form distinct shapes in the sky (see Figure 10.7). Weather forecasters study the clouds to help them understand how water is changing its state in the atmosphere.

Precipitation

Precipitation occurs when moist air in the atmosphere rises above the dew point. This happens in one of three ways: **through convectional precipitation**, **orographic precipitation**, or **frontal precipitation**. Although these are three distinct processes, the dynamics in each are the same.

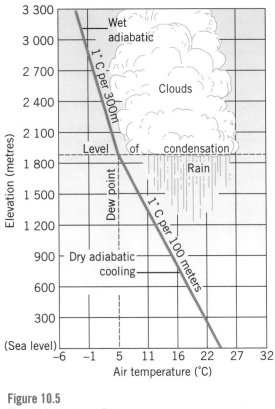

Figure 10.5
The Adiabatic Lapse Rate

CHANGING TECHNOLOGY: CERES

Scientists at NASA use sophisticated satellite imagery to study cloud cover. The Clouds and the Radiant Energy System (CERES) experiment measures light reflected from the tops of clouds and the earth's surface. The information derived will help researchers understand the role of clouds and the energy cycle in climate change.

As the earth heats up because of global warming, increased energy is released into the atmosphere. The result is often greater cloud cover. Depending on the cloud type, the increase in clouds could have one of two effects: Thermal energy reflected from the earth could be trapped under a blanket cover; or the clouds could block solar radiation from hitting the earth's surface, thereby resulting in an overall cooling of the atmosphere.

The image below shows that the sky during the 1997-98 El Nino anomaly had a pronounced radiation pattern over the southern Pacific Ocean and clearer skies to the west. The patterns in the image relate to cloud type, amount, and thickness.

Question:
Why is it important that we understand what the effects of global warming will be on cloud cover, and what effects cloud cover will have on climate?

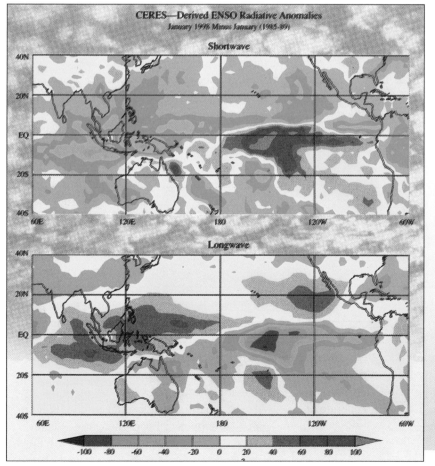

Figure 10.6
Satellite Image from the CERES Project

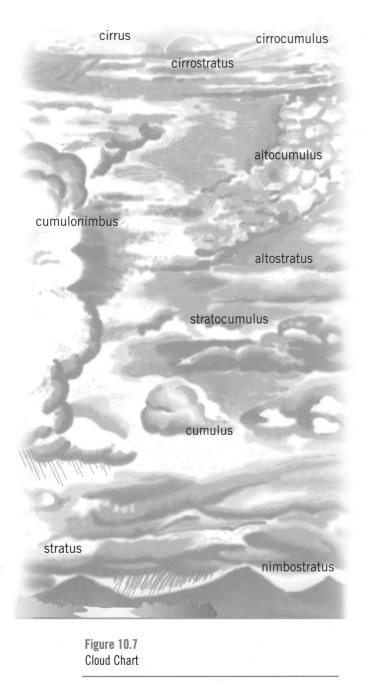

cirrus

cirrocumulus

cirrostratus

altocumulus

cumulonimbus

altostratus

stratocumulus

cumulus

stratus

nimbostratus

Figure 10.7
Cloud Chart

As air rises, its ability to hold water decreases. Once the dew point is reached, condensation forms on dust particles and precipitation starts to fall. Let's consider how these dynamics operate in each of the three precipitation types.

Convectional Precipitation

Convection currents in the atmosphere carry water vapour ever higher in a steady vertical flow of air. Because these currents occur only when there is hot air, convectional precipitation often happens in Canada during the summer. The sun heats the ground all day until, by late afternoon, the air pressure has dropped, warm air rises, and convection currents begin. Strong gusts often accompany the storm as the cooler air rushes in to replace the air that has risen. Friction between air rising in the current often creates static electricity, which manifests itself as lightning and thunder. Thunderstorms can be violent. They are one way in which nature discharges huge concentrations of thermal energy.

An interesting weather phenomenon that often accompanies thunderstorms is hail. Have you ever wondered why these balls of ice fall from the sky even though the temperature may be quite warm? Here's what happens. Water vapour condenses on dust particles, but the raindrops do not fall. Convection currents keep pushing them higher and higher in the atmosphere until they reach heights where the temperature is below freezing. The raindrops freeze and become more buoyant. Because ice is less dense than water, these icy drops are able to stay aloft longer. As they float up and down in the rising wind currents, they may pass the dew point elevation several times. As this happens, the ice balls get steadily larger and larger as more and more water vapour condenses on them and freezes. This up-and-down movement gradually increases the size of these frozen raindrops until eventually they are too heavy to be supported by the rising column of air. At this point, the hailstones fall to the ground. Smaller stones often melt on the way down, creating huge drops of rain. Others are so big that they remain frozen. You may have heard the expression "hail the size of golf balls." These giant hailstones can cause considerable damage.

Convectional rain does not occur only in Canada—it happens all over the world, wherever

Figure 10.8
Hail can be incredibly destructive to crops, houses, and cars.

heat causes convection currents to form. In equatorial regions, thunderstorms are common most afternoons as the rain reduces the energy built up during the hot daylight hours.

Orographic Precipitation

Orographic, or relief, precipitation is similar to convectional precipitation in that air is forced to rise above the dew point. In this case, however, it is not hot air that causes this movement, but rather a change in surface elevation. Orographic precipitation is often found in mountainous regions, such as the west coast of North America. Here the westerlies carry warm, humid air formed over the Pacific Ocean inland over the coastal mountains. Once this air reaches the mountain barrier, it has nowhere to go but up and over the mountains. Eventually, the moist air moves so high that it reaches the dew point, and rain or snow starts to fall.

As the air continues up the mountains, more and more moisture is released. By the time the air reaches the highest point, it has lost most of its water vapour. The air now descends the eastern slopes of the mountain range and the air molecules begin to spread apart. Because of the dry adiabatic lapse rate, the relative humidity drops even further as the air grows warmer. Between mountain ranges, near-desert conditions can prevail because of these dry winds. Called a **rain shadow**, this type of area is found between the mountain ranges of the Western Cordillera as well as on the leeward slope of most other mountains.

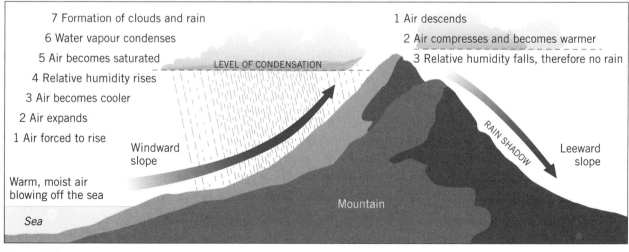

7 Formation of clouds and rain
6 Water vapour condenses
5 Air becomes saturated
4 Relative humidity rises
3 Air becomes cooler
2 Air expands
1 Air forced to rise

LEVEL OF CONDENSATION

Windward slope

Warm, moist air blowing off the sea

Sea

1 Air descends
2 Air compresses and becomes warmer
3 Relative humidity falls, therefore no rain

RAIN SHADOW

Leeward slope

Mountain

Figure 10.9
Orographic Precipitation

Frontal Precipitation

Frontal precipitation occurs when two air masses with different characteristics meet. Warm, moist air is forced to rise when it comes in contact with colder, denser air. Moisture in the lighter air mass condenses when the temperature drops below the dew point. This happens because the elevation of the lighter air mass has increased. Frontal precipitation is much like orographic precipitation except that instead of landforms forcing the air to rise, it is a denser air mass that pushes the air higher until the dew point is reached.

In the Canadian Prairies, cyclonic storms march across the region throughout most of the year. These storms occur when a cold, dry, arctic mass comes in contact with a warm, moist air mass from the Gulf of Mexico or the Atlantic Ocean. The cold air is heavier and forces the less stable warm air to rise. As it rises, the dry adiabatic lapse rate causes the air to cool until the dew point is reached and precipitation starts to fall. Frontal precipitation can drag on for days as a front moves slowly out of a region. Dull, wet weather or cold winter storms resulting from frontal systems are common in many mid-latitude locations, including much of southern Canada, Europe, and Russia.

Surface Runoff

Once the water hits the ground, it can go in many different directions. It may evaporate right back into the atmosphere again, end up in lakes, ponds, or the ocean, or it may even be absorbed by vegetation. If the water lands on ground that it is unable to penetrate, it becomes **surface runoff**, which is evident in rivers and streams carrying the water down toward the ocean.

As water flows over the land, into rivers, and back to the oceans, tremendous **kinetic energy** is generated. Gravity is constantly dragging water ever downward to the ocean. When the route to the ocean is cut off by high land, the water is detained temporarily in ponds, lakes, and inland seas. People often seek to convert this kinetic energy into electric energy to provide for human activities. In Canada, Ontario and Quebec have a lot of opportunities to harness this energy through hydroelectric plants. As the water is directed through turbines, great magnets are used to create electric current. This is a clean and

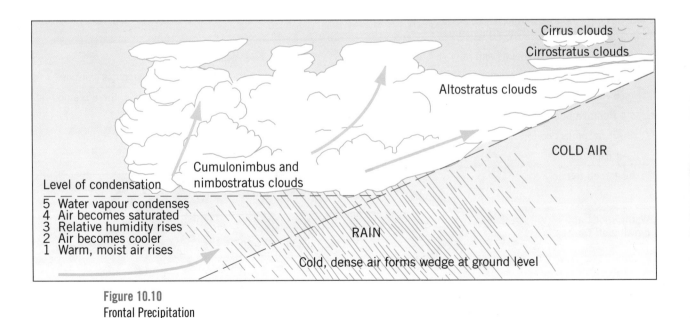

Figure 10.10
Frontal Precipitation

natural way to provide energy for the large urban population of the Windsor-Quebec City Corridor and the highly populated Eastern States.

While hydroelectricity has long been considered a sustainable energy alternative, people are increasingly worried that developing this resource harms natural systems. The Kemano II Power Project in B.C. and the Great Whale Project in Quebec were both cancelled by provincial governments because of their devastating effect on ecosystems. Dams that are built on rivers to contain the water (so it flows steadily all year) flood mountain valleys and disturb spawning fish and migrating wildlife. They also impact the lives of Aboriginal peoples who rely on the natural environment for hunting and fishing. In this complicated world, even sustainable alternatives may impact negatively on natural systems. (See Three Gorges Dam case study, p. 164)

Groundwater

If precipitation lands on a porous surface, it will seep into the earth rather than flow over the surface as runoff. Groundwater sinks ever lower, clinging to soil particles and remaining for a time in the pores of the earth. The degree to which the moisture flows down has to do with how porous the soil is. Sandy soils are very porous and water flows through them quickly. Clay soils, on the other hand, swell to a plastic, impervious mass when moisture is added. The layer where the moisture flows downward is called the **unsaturated zone**. Eventually, the water does not move downward any more. This **saturated zone** is where groundwater accumulates. The level between the saturated and the unsaturated zone is called the **water table**.

(continued on page 166)

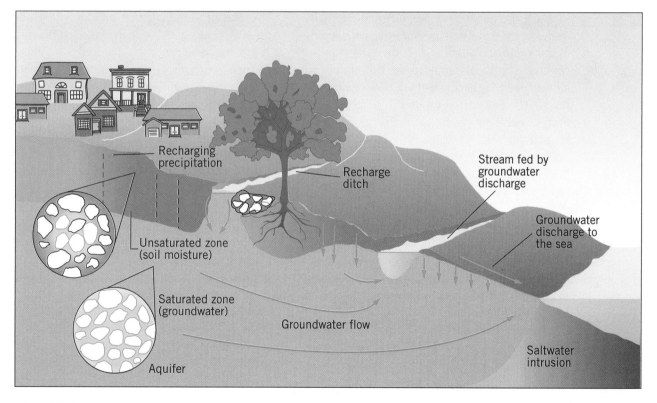

Figure 10.11
Groundwater Flow

CASE STUDY

The Three Gorges Dam

Not since the Great Wall have the Chinese undertaken such a massive project. At just under 2 km in length and 185 metres in height, with the ability to hold back 40 billion m³ of river water, the Three Gorges Hydroelectric Dam can be considered one of the greatest engineering feats in history. Currently under construction in a densely populated region of the Yangtze River valley, the dam is due to start operation by 2009. At $12 billion (US), this project will also have the distinction of costing more than any other single structure ever built.

Is it all worth it? Chinese officials say yes. The country has enormous energy needs. Not only does it have the world's largest population at over a billion people, but the population is also becoming more affluent, meaning that more Chinese people can afford an energy-rich lifestyle. Chinese industry also demands cheap, plentiful electricity to power the many new factories that are opening in the industrial central and southern parts of the country. The hydroelectric plant will supply an annual power generation of 84 billion kilowatt-hours. The power is clean, too. Unlike the coal-fired power plants of northern China, no fuel is burned and no emissions are produced. The amount of coal that would not need to be burned because of the building of this plant would amount to an estimated 40 to 50 million tons per year. Imagine the decrease in carbon dioxide emissions and improvements in respiratory health that the reduction in emissions would provide. At a time when the production of greenhouse gases and acid rain is under scrutiny, the development of a giant hydroelectric facility that will use no fossil fuels is appealing.

The dam will also relieve the threat of flooding downstream. A flood in 1954 killed an estimated 30 000 people and left a million people homeless. Because the dam will prevent the annual spring flood, tragedies like this will not happen again. Navigation capacities on the river will also improve, owing to the increased depth of the water.

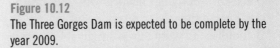

Figure 10.12
The Three Gorges Dam is expected to be complete by the year 2009.

Cargo ships will be able to travel an extra 600 km up the Yangtze River to the city of Chongqing, making it the largest ocean port in the world.

Despite all these potential benefits, the Three Gorges Dam in China is widely criticized because it is proving to be extremely disruptive to human settlement patterns. Chinese officials estimate that 1.2 million people will have to be relocated to make way for the reservoir. Two cities, 11 counties, 140 towns, 326 townships, and 1351 villages will be partially or completely flooded. Many critics believe resettlement will be a disaster, with displaced people unable to find work or the necessary food to sustain themselves since they are being forced to move from fertile farmland to much less desirable areas on steep mountain slopes.

Critics also oppose the project for environmental reasons. Even though carbon emissions will be greatly reduced, there will likely be an increased risk of earthquakes and landslides in this tectonically unstable region. The increased mass of the water and the erosive power on steep gorge slopes could prove locally devastating. There will also be a decline in many endangered species indigenous to the region. Rare and exotic animals as diverse as the Yangtze dolphin, the Chinese sturgeon, the Chinese tiger, the Chinese

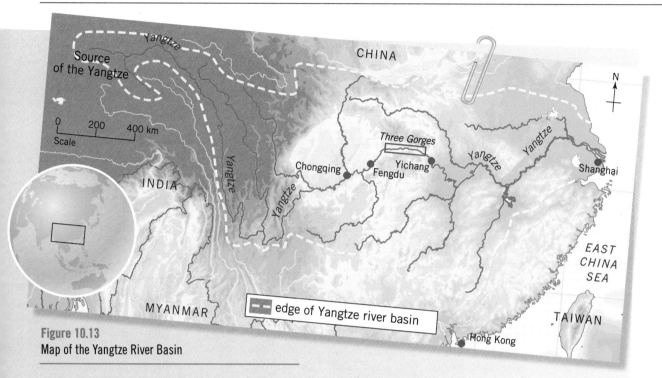

Figure 10.13
Map of the Yangtze River Basin

alligator, the Siberian crane, and the giant panda will all likely be rendered extinct.

Moreover, silt deposited in the reservoir will reduce the fertility of coastal plains since it will no longer be deposited on flood plains during the annual spring flood. It was the fertility of these flood plains that originally led to the development of the ancient Chinese culture millennia ago. Furthermore, the silt trapped behind the dam will reduce power-generating capability and eventually fill in the reservoir.

In addition to the cost of human resettlement and environmental damage, the country stands to lose enormously from a cultural and historical perspective. The dam and reservoir will destroy some of the most beautiful classical Chinese scenery in the country, including approximately 800 historic sites and cultural relics, which will be submerged under water. Authorities have agreed to remove some relics and rebuild others in locations not affected by the flooding, but they cannot save the famous beauty of the Three Gorges area, which has attracted artists, poets, and explorers throughout the ages.

Critics of the plan say that the government could have met most of its energy needs by developing many small-scale projects along the river. Small dams with modest generating stations providing limited power for the immediate area would have been less environmentally destructive and would not have resulted in tremendous upheaval. Because they would have been local projects to help small industries in the county where each would have been built, these dams might have empowered the people to be more productive because they would have had ownership of their own economic development.

QUESTIONS:

1. Why is greater power production needed in this area of China?

2. Assess the positive as well as the negative impacts of the project from economic, environmental, cultural, and ecological points of view.

3. What alternative to the government's strategy is presented?

4. Do you agree with the government's decision to go ahead with the Three Gorges Dam? Why or why not?

In spring, after the annual snowmelt, the water table can be quite close to the surface. If you are digging holes for fence posts in April, you will find that your hole may fill up with water when you have dug only 50 to 60 cm down. In summer, higher temperatures increase the evaporation rate on the surface. Moisture in the saturated zone moves to the surface through **capillary action**, and as a result the saturated zone is further down in the soil.

Capillary action is an interesting phenomenon. We know that water always flows downhill, but through capillary action it actually moves up. If you fill a glass to the very top, you will notice that there is a bulge on top of the glass. It is almost as if the water molecules are holding on to the ones on the top so they don't flow over the edge. This **surface tension** results in capillary action. Water molecules cling to the edges of the particles in the pores of the soil. They draw other molecules of water toward the surface of the earth as they keep moving up the tiny channels in the soil. Moisture in the upper layers of the soil evaporates back into the atmosphere.

Groundwater often filters deep down into the earth until it eventually reaches a point where it can go no lower because an impervious layer of bedrock blocks its downward passage. Here, it accumulates in a layer of gravel or sand deep beneath the surface called an **aquifer**. Water in these underground deposits can be ancient. Much of the aquifer water in southern Ontario was deposited thousands of years ago when the last ice age ended. Aquifers are constantly being **recharged** with water that filters down through the soil. Wetlands, lakes, and other surface water features **discharge** some of the aquifer water. The water flows into these features when the gravel or sandy material reaches the surface. Wetlands are especially important for preserving aquifers since swamps and bogs store surplus water when aquifer levels are high and recharge the aquifer when levels are low.

Water may be stored in aquifers for as little as a couple of weeks or as long as 10 000 years. By contrast, moisture seldom resides in soil longer than a year, and river water lasts only a couple of weeks. We have become increasingly conscious of the importance of groundwater as a resource in recent years. Just because we cannot see groundwater, this does not mean it is not important. For example, 7.9 million people, or 26 per cent of the Canadian population, rely on groundwater for domestic use. Therefore, it is very important that this supply be sustained and protected for our continued use.

Water Quality in the Soil

Water is added to the ground as precipitation seeps through layers of rock and soil. As it does this, most impurities are removed so that most well water is remarkably clean and safe to drink. However, don't assume that just because the water looks clean it is safe. Bacteria such as coliform and E. coli are dangerous micro-organisms that can have severely adverse effects on human health. Heavy metals like mercury can also be absorbed by aquifer water and pose a health risk. Most groundwater is contaminated by human intervention and not by natural occurrences, however. This **anthropogenic contamination** is almost impossible to clean up once it enters groundwater supplies. Sometimes the contamination is local and only affects water in shallow wells on one or two farms. Because limited natural filtering has occurred in this area, it is possible for dangerous bacteria to enter the well from the surface.

Often, however, pollution contaminates entire municipal water supplies. Dangerous chemicals may come from municipal landfills, industrial waste disposal sites, leaking gasoline storage tanks, inadequate septic tanks, accidental chemical spills, and agricultural runoff. Many landfill sites are located in old gravel pits where the resource has been completely mined out. The big hole in the ground provides a convenient location for a municipality's garbage. Unfortunately, the layers of sand and gravel are often connected underground to significant aquifers. **Leaching** from the garbage can easily enter aquifer water supplies. Waste management companies are required to line landfills with an impervious layer of clay to prevent leaching. However, it is conceivable that, over time, the initially impervious layer will become less effective at containing the waste. When rain falls on the garbage, this water slowly moves down as it would in any soil. Any water-soluble chemicals, bacteria, or heavy metals present in the mass of garbage are absorbed by the water as it moves downward. If it enters the aquifer, the bacteria can readily multiply and contaminate the entire water supply.

Industrial pollution can also create terrible problems in local water supplies. The disposal of industrial wastes in the lagoons of an old gravel pit can destroy the water for thousands of residents. If the contamination goes unnoticed, all kinds of diseases ranging from cancer to intestinal poisoning can occur. Leaking septic tanks

are examples of local small-scale pollution that can have serious consequences. Often, people living on lakes have problems because the bacteria from their septic tanks washes into the lake and contaminates groundwater supplies.

Sometimes the problem has to do with agricultural run-off. In the spring, farmers traditionally use chemical herbicides and fertilizer to control pests and help crops grow. Livestock farmers are keeping increasingly larger numbers of hogs, cows, chickens, and other animals in huge, intensive operations on relatively small plots of land. It is not inconceivable that a hog operation could produce 20 000 pigs in one year. Imagine the amount of bacteria that would be produced by that many animals. At present, government ministries in Canada have virtually no regulations regarding the treatment of manure from these agricultural businesses.

ACTIVITIES

UNDERSTANDING CONCEPTS

1. a) List the forms that water takes in the atmosphere.
   b) Describe how each affects the atmosphere.
2. a) Prepare a flow chart summarizing the hydrologic cycle.
   b) Explain the relationship of flows in the hydrosphere to landforms.
   c) Explain the relationship of flows in the hydrosphere to soils.
   d) Explain the relationship of flows in the hydrosphere to vegetation.
3. a) Describe the different ways precipitation can occur.
   b) Explain what is happening in the hydrosphere when
      i) water falls on the land
      ii) water evaporates into the air
      iii) water interacts with plants
      iv) water is forced to rise in the atmosphere
      v) water seeps into the ground
4. Explain the differences in the environmental lapse rate, the wet adiabatic lapse rate, and the dry adiabatic lapse rate. Include criteria such as the rate of cooling, why it happens, where it happens, and its effect on water vapour.

DEVELOPING AND PRACTISING SKILLS

5. The world's total water supply is 1.356×10^9 km³. Use this figure to calculate the value of each percentage in the following diagram. For example, water in oceans is 97% ($1.356 \times 10^9 \times 97\% = ?$).

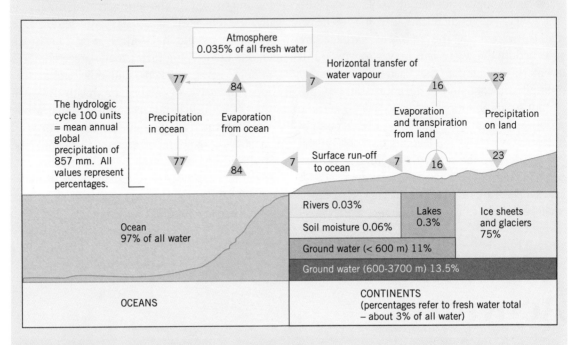

6. a) Prepare a scattergraph of the information in Fig. 10.4 (on page 158).
    b) What correlation do you notice? Why does this relationship exist?
7. Relative humidity measures the percentage of water vapour in the air compared to absolute humidity (the maximum capacity for holding water vapour at a given temperature).

	A	B	C	D	E	F	G	H
Temperature	35°C	25°C	10°C	5°C	2°C	0°C	-5°C	-10°C
Absolute humidity	25 g/m³	10 g/m³	7 g/m³	3 g/m³	4 g/m³	2 g/m³	4 g/m³	2 g/m³
Relative humidity	62.8%							
Dew point temperature	27°C							
Altitude to reach dew point	800 m							

a) Calculate the relative humidity for each temperature and absolute humidity using Figure 10.4 on page 158. For example, assume that the amount of moisture in the air was 25 g/m³ and the air temperature was 35°C. Fig. 10.4 shows that the water vapour holding capacity of air at 35°C is 39.8 g/m³. Therefore, the relative humidity would be $25/39.8 \times 100 = 62.8\%$.

b) Which of these would be experiencing precipitation? Explain.

c) Use the scattergraph from activity 6 to read the temperatures at which each dew point would be reached. For example, in A, 25 g/m³ is reached at about 27°C.

d) Use a dry adiabatic lapse rate of 1°C per 100 m to determine how much each body of air would have to rise before humidity reached 100 per cent (the dew point). For example, in A, the temperature has to drop 8°C (from 35°C to 27°C). Therefore, the air would have to rise 800 m before the humidity reached 100 per cent and the dew point was reached.

e) Take one example from the organizer in part a). How much would the humidity drop if the air flowed 2000 m down the side of a mountain?

LEARNING THROUGH APPLICATION

8. Explain how human disruption of the hydrologic cycle can affect natural systems.

9. a) Using the cloud chart on page 160, record the cloud types at the same time in the same place for a week.

   b) Determine what type of weather is associated with each different cloud type.

10. Access NASA through its web site, www.nasa.gov, and summarize an update on the CERES Project.

11. Reread the article on the Three Gorges Dam.

    a) Describe how each of the following people may feel about the project:
    - Chinese economic planner from Beijing
    - Canadian archaeologist studying Chinese antiquities in the area
    - hydrologist charged with protecting the flood plain
    - Chinese peasant being relocated
    - climatologist studying the effects of global warming
    - engineer working on the project
    - ecologist specializing in rare animals
    - Chinese industrialist planning to open a silk shirt-making factory
    - Chinese doctor specializing in respiratory diseases in the industrialized heartland of the country
    - Australian adventure-tour operator who sells travel packages in the area.

    b) Write a position paper from the point of view of one of the people in a) to convince others of the importance of your opinion.

    c) Suggest alternative strategies that would provide the "best of both worlds."

Chapter 11

WATER IN OCEANS AND SEAS

FOCUS QUESTIONS

1. What causes ocean currents?
2. What effect does the moon have on Earth's tides?
3. How do ocean currents, tides, and waves affect people's lives?

Key Terms

thermo-haline currents

oceanography

wave trains

tsunami

El Niño

Planet Earth is wrongly named! It should really be called "Planet Ocean." From space it is the water of the oceans—not the solid earth—that is most obvious. Not only do the oceans cover more than two-thirds of the planet, but they are three dimensional unlike the two-dimensional ground layer on which we live. Oceans provide an immense volume in which different habitats can evolve. Marine ecosystems can extend downward through many layers of ocean to great depths that have barely been explored by humans. In an interesting experi-

Figure 11.1
The Oceans hold approximately 70 per cent of Earth's water.

ment to understand more about the species of animals that live hundreds of metres below the surface of the ocean, marine biologists have attached camcorders to sea mammals that dive to great depths. Recorded images showed incredible luminescent creatures of immense size that seem to be primitive in their development yet are highly intelligent.

The many different layers that exist in the oceans have different characteristics based on temperature, salinity, oxygen content, nutrient levels, and the amount of light available for aquatic plants. Each living community is adapted to the water conditions at a particular layer. Because the oceans are interconnected, it is common for plants and animals to range freely over enormous distances and among the various layers, if the environmental conditions are favourable. So, you can find penguins—which you would expect to find in Antarctica—in cold waters off the tropical Galapagos Islands.

Water Density and Kinetic Energy

As water changes state among solid, liquid, and gas, its density changes, and it either sinks or floats relative to surrounding water. This motion results from the molecules moving closer together (becoming denser) or spreading apart (becoming less dense). In its gaseous state, water is very light and floats upward. This is how water from the oceans gets into the atmosphere. However, water is denser as a liquid than as a solid—a property few other substances have. The molecules of water are less tightly compacted in the solid state, so less matter is contained in a larger volume of material. Water is at its greatest density in its liquid state at 4°C. So at this temperature, it sinks relative to all other surrounding water, which explains why the temperature at the bottom of deep lakes is usually 4°C.

Because ice is less dense than water, it floats— a well known fact. But consider the implications

Oceanography is the study of oceans, and scientists who work in this field can specialize in a wide variety of branches. Those who study sediment cores are often concerned with paleoclimatology, which is the study of climates in the past. The information that scientists gain helps them determine what the earth's atmosphere was like in the past. Much of what we know today with regard to animals that have become extinct is a result of what these specialists have learned.

Several oceanographic studies relate to climate change. Many specialists—especially if they are geographers rather than scientists—have an understanding of both oceanography and climatology. Studying the oceans helps researchers to determine how global climates are changing.

Other oceanographers are interested in how ocean currents and waves occur in water. The information they gain can help engineers design breakwaters, seawalls, and other structures to protect people from inundation by rising seawater. Still others study salinity, nutrient levels, temperature, and other characteristics that marine biologists need to know about as they study the fascinating ecosystems under the ocean.

These scientists also study the ocean as a resource. Mineral deposits below the sea floor contain hydrocarbons such as oil and natural gas. These can be extracted using oil platforms that are among the largest, most complicated engineering structures on Earth. Oceanographers find the location of deposits, assess the ability of the sea floor to support engineering structures, and monitor the impact of potential mining projects on natural systems.

geo.web resources

<www.oceanlink.island.net>

Careers in Oceanography, Marine Science & Marine Biology is a web site that connects interested students to a variety of web pages on careers related to the fields of oceanography and marine biology. Identify Canadian institutions that offer programs of study in this field.

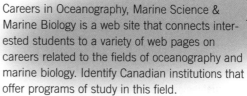

of this buoyant quality. If ice was like other substances and sank when it solidified, Arctic seawater would freeze on the surface as it does every winter and then sink to the bottom. Since it would continue to freeze at the surface, the Arctic Ocean would freeze solid from top to bottom. Can you imagine how this massive deep freeze would affect global temperatures? As the Arctic temperature dropped, seawater would continue to freeze into the middle latitudes and we would be thrust into a perpetual ice age. If water did not float when it freezes, it is unlikely life would have evolved as it did on this planet!

Convection Currents and Salinity Currents

Convection currents occur because of variations in the density of seawater. Warmer, less dense water flows to the surface while colder water sinks. So you would expect that the top layer would be warm and the lower layer would be cold. This in fact happens in lakes, but in seawater, where there is vertical movement, this is not the case. The reason for this is salt. Operating like convection currents, **thermo-haline currents** cause the overturning of seawater. You

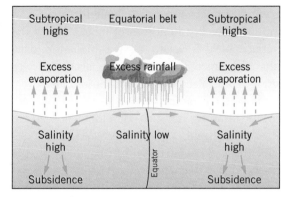

Figure 11.3
Ocean Salinity as it Relates to Latitude

may have noticed that you float better in salt water than in fresh water. This is because the greater the salinity of the water, the denser and heavier it is. Thus seawater that contains a lot of salt tends to sink, even if it is warmer than the less salty water beneath it. The amount of salinity varies with depth. Surface water is usually saltier than water at lower depths. This is because surface water is exposed to the air, and evaporation reduces the amount of water relative to the salt content. This creates warmer, saltier water at the surface. This overturning of seawater spreads energy from the surface—where it is heated and salinity increases—to the colder, less salty, lower layers.

Salinity levels are influenced by rates of evaporation and precipitation, which are not uniform across the earth's surface. Desert climates exist even over the oceans. Equatorial oceans receive heavy precipitation. Consequently, ocean water along the equator and middle latitudes, where rainfall is heavier, is less salty than water at the Tropics of Capricorn and Cancer. The salt water, diluted by the extra rainwater, flows toward the Tropics of Cancer and Capricorn, creating a thermo-haline flow (see Fig. 11.3).

Have you ever wondered why seas contain salt water and lakes are

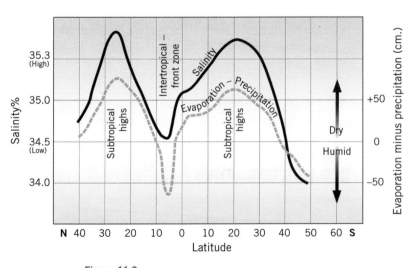

Figure 11.2
Because salinity is high in subtropical zones, but low in equatorial regions, salinity currents are produced.

comprised of fresh water? The reason has to do with the minerals that water carries. Since lakes are temporary storage areas for water, water is constantly moving through lakes en route to the ocean. Water-soluble salts, dissolved in water running over the land, are carried through the lakes. But when the water containing the salts finally ends up in the ocean, there is nowhere for the salts to go, and they accumulate. As the seawater evaporates, the salt remains.

Waves

Waves are caused by the movement of energy through water. Although you may think that waves move water forward, this is not actually the case. Waves move water in a circular motion as crests and troughs flow across the water's surface. Energy moves through the water without actually carrying the water anywhere. Conversely, ocean currents do actually cause the water to flow from one place to another, just like wind moves air.

Wind is the force that creates waves. If you gently blow across the top of a basin of water, little ripples will form on the water's surface. If you blow harder, the ripples will become bigger. If you blow over a longer surface, the waves will get even bigger. Wave size is dependent on three variables: **wind velocity**, **wind duration**, and **fetch**.

Wind velocity is the strength of the wind: the stronger the wind, the higher the waves. Duration is the length of time the wind blows from one direction—the longer the duration, the better able the waves are to organize themselves into regular **crests** and **troughs** called **wave trains**. If the wind shifts direction, wave trains are disorganized, and the water becomes choppy even though the wave size is small. For really big waves to form, the wind must blow steadily from one direction. The third variable, fetch, is the distance the wind blows over the ocean. The longer the distance, the greater the opportunity for wind to transfer some of its energy to the waves through friction. So, wherever strong winds blow steadily from the same direction over vast distances, the waves will contain enormous amounts of energy. Consider, for example, the steady northeast trade winds that blow across the vast Pacific Ocean to the beaches of Oahu in the Hawaiian Islands. Here, all of the factors that contribute to great wave energy are at work, and the results are huge waves that make the island a surfer's paradise!

The Cause and Charateristics of Tsunamis

Tsunamis are giant waves that can cause terrible devastation. They are not as common as other natural disasters, but they do cause considerable damage to communities and death to coastal residents. In the last decade, 4000 deaths have been attributed to tsunamis. This is a much higher death toll than for any other decade in the twentieth century. On average, 57 deaths a decade have been attributed to these killer waves. The reason for the increase has little to do with climate change or other changes in natural systems. The most likely reason is the increased coastal population, especially along the vulnerable Pacific Rim (where tsunamis are most common).

Tsunamis are different from other waves because they are produced by major tectonic events on the sea floor, not by wind blowing over the surface. Because of this, the wave reaches to the bottom of the sea; it is not just a surface wave. Changes in the sea floor due to volcanic eruptions, earthquakes, or underwater landslides are the most common causes of tsunamis. Tsunamis can travel up to 700 km per hour but are barely noticed because they are often only a metre or two high in open water. They have very long wavelengths. If a one-metre-high wave with a wavelength of 30 metres hit your boat at 700 km per hour, you would definitely notice the event. But if the wavelength were several hundred kilometres long, you would barely feel the wave. It is only once the wave slows at the front because of the shallow profile of the shore that the tsunami really becomes a noticeable phenomenon.

Tsunami in Southeast Asia

On July 17, 1998, disaster struck on the north coast of Papua New Guinea. At 6:49 p.m. a magnitude 7.1 earthquake struck small fishing villages along a sand bar between Sissano Lagoon and the Bismarck Sea triggering a devastating tsunami.

The earthquake occurred about 17 km offshore at a depth of less than 33 km under the surface. The relative closeness of the event resulted in warnings not being issued in time to alert residents. If the triggering mechanism had occurred farther away, then the alarm could have been sounded in enough time for people to evacuate the area. The effects of the resultant tsunami were localized in a small area of coastline because the giant wave had a small generating area of only 400 km². A more violent triggering event in the centre of the ocean, where the wave would not be so contained, could have sent the tsunami through coastal communities all along the Pacific Rim.

The offshore sea floor was deformed when the Caroline tectonic plate pushed under the Australian Plate. The ocean floor was estimated to have been thrust 2 m above its existing level, displacing an estimated 7–8 km³ of sea water. Three waves were observed, all within a relatively short 18-minute time span.

The event was one of the most destructive tsunamis to hit Papua New Guinea in recent years. The large waves destroyed three fishing villages along a 30-km stretch of beach west of Atape, in the West Sepik Province. Most of the deaths occurred at the villages on the shores of the Sissano lagoon area. Retired Colonel John Sanawe witnessed the disaster firsthand and lived to describe it. In the distance the sea rose about 30 meters above the horizon. Sounds like thunder and then a sound like a helicopter were heard in the distance. The sounds gradually faded as the sea slowly receded as if it was low tide, but much lower. After four or five minutes of silence, a low rumble was heard and a wave about 3–4 meters high was seen rolling up the shoreline. A second wave, 15-meters-high, flattened his village and

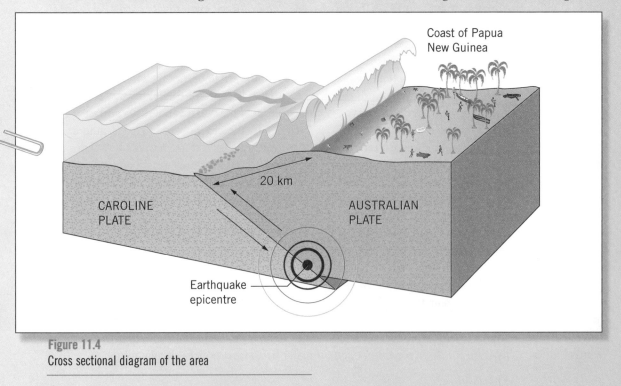

Figure 11.4
Cross sectional diagram of the area

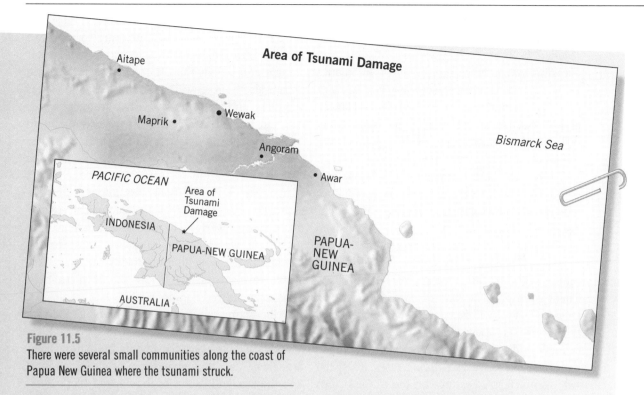

Figure 11.5
There were several small communities along the coast of
Papua New Guinea where the tsunami struck.

killed more than 2200 villagers along the coast. It
caused widespread injuries and devastated everything in its wake. More than 6000 people were
left homeless. Sanawe was lucky: He was swept a
kilometre inland and deposited in a mangrove
swamp along the coast. Fresh water crocodiles
ate many of the dead bodies of other victims
washed into the swamp.

While tsunamis cannot be avoided and forecasting is difficult especially for localized events
like this one, the building of refuge platforms for
vertical evacuation in low-lying regions would be
effective. Villagers working together could build
the structures from bamboo at safe distances
inland. Because Papua New Guinea is a developing country with many other problems to deal
with, it is unlikely that these preventative measures will be implemented by the authorities.
Public education may still be the best method. In
this tsunami—like most similar events—residents are drawn to the coast by the rapidly receding water along the shoreline. As the water flows
out to sea they become curious and are drawn
almost hypnotically onto the tidal flats. The water

is being sucked out to sea to feed the monster
wave building off shore. When the wave finally
hits, the people are too far out to reach safety and
drown as a result. The residents need to be taught
that when the ocean recedes in the characteristic
way it does before a monster wave hits they
should get inland to high ground as quickly as
possible. The people won't soon forget the 1998
killer wave, however, and future villagers will be
wary of similar situations.

QUESTIONS:

1. Why do you think people live near the
   coast of Papua New Guinea, knowing
   that they are in a tsunami-prone area?

2. Besides the loss of lives, what other
   damaging effects would a tsunami such
   as this have on coastal communities?

3. Do some research to determine if there
   are any new technologies available to
   predict tsunamis. Explain how the technology works.

The Papua New Guinea tsunami of 1998 resulted from an earthquake just offshore, but tsunamis often travel thousands of kilometres from their source before they cause any damage. Often communities as far apart as Chile, Hawaii, and Alaska are all affected by the same killer wave as the energy from the triggering event moves through the water in all directions.

There are four physical processes that tsunamis go through in their development: **generation**, **propagation**, **shoaling**, and **inundation**. Generation results when there is a seafloor disturbance such as movement along a fault line. The size of the tsunami is dependent on the degree to which the sea floor is distorted. There is virtually no way of predicting when a triggering event will generate a giant wave. Once the wave has been generated, propagation occurs. Studies have shown that as water depth increases, and as wavelength increases, the speed will also increase. Features on the sea floor can deflect the wave, sending it in different directions. When it hits a headland or peninsula jutting into the sea, the wave wraps around the feature, thereby intensifying the force with which it hits the land. Shoaling occurs when the water at the front of the wave reaches the shoreline. It slows down because the shallower water creates drag on the wave. The water coming from behind builds up ever higher and the wave has nowhere to go but up. The last stage, inundation, occurs when the wave breaks. While these waves can be many metres high, it takes only a 2–3 metre wave to be devastating. The wave often travels far inland and sucks people out to sea as the water recedes.

Prevention is not feasible, but early warning and education in prone areas can do much to minimize damage and loss of life. In Japan, a tsunami hazard-mitigation program has been developed over the years because of the susceptibility of this island state to the killer waves. People are educated as to what to do if a tsunami is imminent. Obviously, people should head inland to high ground as fast as possible. People who are ignorant of tsunamis often walk onto the freshly exposed sea floor, unaware that the sea will return more quickly and with much greater force and height than it receded. The Japanese have also built seawalls, planted coastal forests as buffers, and instituted an early warning system.

On July 12, 1993, the Japanese were able to evaluate the effectiveness of their programs. The small island of Okushiri was struck by a tsunami after a magnitude 7.8 earthquake in the Sea of Japan shook the sea floor. Five minutes after the shock wave, the Japan Meteorological Agency broadcast a warning to all coastal residents. The warning was too late for people close to the origin of the wave, but others further away were able to get to safety before the 10-metre-high waves destroyed fishing villages.

Predicting tsunamis is very difficult. Existing seismic stations could be used to detect underwater activity, but these only measure earthquakes. Also, they would give no information as to the size and extent of the impending disaster. What is needed is a way of determining when a wave occurs, how big it is, and where it is headed.

Ocean Currents

Currents are like rivers running through the ocean. Four dynamics are at work in creating ocean currents: prevailing winds, convection currents, the Coriolis effect, and the shape of the ocean basin. Winds blow over the water and transfer some of their energy to the sea, causing ripples. The ripples in the water then build up to form waves. Where the trade winds blow from the east, the equatorial current also flows from the east. Similarly, the North Atlantic Drift coincides with the westerlies. The constant drag of the prevailing winds on the surface of the ocean causes the currents to flow in a similar path. This shift in currents redistributes the energy generated by the heating and cooling of the atmosphere.

Currents that result from differences in water temperature and salinity accentuate the currents created by the prevailing winds. Frigid, less salty polar waters sink as the hot, saltier waters from the Tropics flow toward the poles to replace them.

CHANGING TECHNOLOGY: Monitoring Tsunamis

An international early warning system has been instituted under the direction of NOAA (the National Oceanic and Atmospheric Agency) in the US. Six deep-ocean reporting stations are able to track tsunamis and report when they are expected to hit Pacific Rim cities. The network, known as Deep Ocean Assessment and Reporting of Tsunamis (DART), is expected to start operation early in 2002.

This is how the network works. Assume that there is an earthquake along the Aleutian Trench in Alaska. Seismographs at stations around the Pacific Rim pinpoint the exact location of the tremor. Computer programs estimate the time of arrival at distant shorelines. There is no evidence of a wave yet, and a mass evacuation of a city like downtown Honolulu or Vancouver would be premature. Deep-ocean detectors would be expecting the wave to hit them at the time predicted by the computers. If it did, then measurements could be taken to determine the projected size of the wave as it came to shore. The DART system uses bottom pressure recorders to distinguish these waves from regular surface waves. As the wave crest passes over the sensor, the increased water pressure is recorded. Even 6 kilometres down, the sensor can register a tsunami only a centimetre high. The information is relayed to a buoy in the deep ocean, and from there satellites relay the warning to control centres. If a wave appears to be dangerous, then the warning may be relayed by satellite to the authorities, and evacuation may occur.

Question:

If this warning system had been instituted before the 1998 tsunami in Papua New Guinea, do you think the outcome—in terms of damage and loss of life—would have been significantly different? Why or why not?

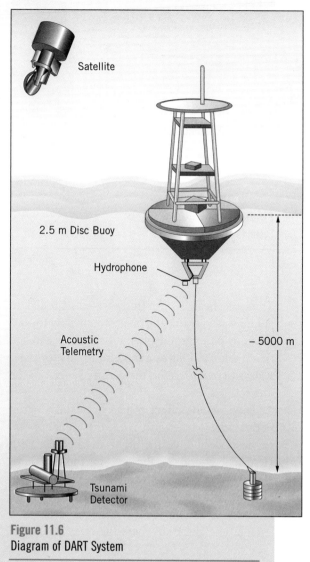

Figure 11.6
Diagram of DART System

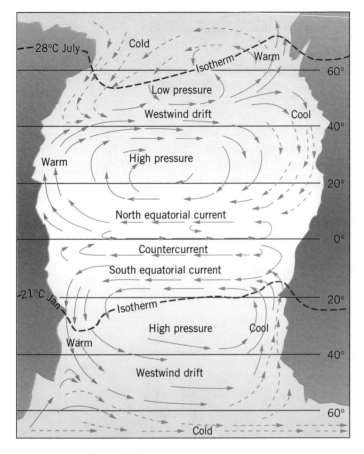

Figure 11.7
Systems of Ocean Currents

Thus the heat of the Tropics is distributed to colder waters, while the polar waters flow toward the equator at great depths. It has been estimated that it takes as long as a thousand years for polar waters to re-emerge on the ocean's surface in the Tropics.

The **Coriolis effect** results from the rotation of the earth. As the earth spins, the water appears to be deflected to the right in the Northern Hemisphere and to the left in the Southern Hemisphere. To understand the Coriolis effect, imagine you are playing catch with someone on a merry-go-round. You throw the ball in a straight line ahead of where the other person is,

knowing that this is where they will be when the ball arrives. From above, it appears that the ball is curving relative to the rotating platform. In a similar way, ocean currents that are actually going straight appear to be deflected because of the earth's rotation. This factor, combined with the shape of the ocean basins, results in ocean currents moving as they do.

Figure 11.7 shows a simplified model of ocean currents. Studying this model allows us to understand general patterns. In reality, however, the shape of coastlines, salinity levels, and other factors cause variations in this model. Circular movements, or **gyrals**, form on either side of the equator between 18° and 40° latitude. These are created by cold air masses descending directly above them. Between the two gyrals is the equatorial current. Powered mainly by the eastward flowing trade winds, this current forms the southern part of the gyral in the Northern Hemisphere and the northern part of the gyral in the Southern Hemisphere. Between the two equatorial currents is an eastward flowing counter-current in the area of calm over the equator known as the doldrums. The current returns some of the water sent west by the trade winds.

El Niño

Every three to seven years, an unusual event occurs in the Pacific Ocean off the west coast of Peru. Instead of a cold current flowing up the coast of South America and east across the Pacific Ocean, the flow reverses, and warm water from the eastern Pacific flows east toward Central and South America. Named for Jesus Christ by the Catholic peoples in South America, the event—"El Niño"—usually occurs around Christmastime. El Niño events have caused environmental changes worldwide in the past. Heavy flooding in California, mild winters in eastern Canada, droughts in South Africa, and even increased incidence of certain diseases have all been attributed to this chaotic event.

CHANGING TECHNOLOGY: Forecasting El Niño

The TOPEX/Poseidon satellite developed by NASA and the Centre National d'Études Spatiales provided the images in Figure 11.8. Scientists are able to use the data from this TOPEX/Poseidon satellite to forecast when an El Niño event will occur. This allows authorities to prepare for the anomalous weather conditions that result. Radar altimeters bounce radar signals off the surface of the ocean to determine the height of the seas. Global positioning systems (GPS) facilitate the process by determining exactly where each reading has been taken. Image maps of sea-surface height are the result. Along the equator, the elevated sea level indicates warmer than usual water (shown as white), while depressed, cooler surfaces are blue or purple. This detailed knowledge helps scientists calculate the speed and direction of ocean currents. At its peak in November 1997, the sea surface that was abnormally high and warm was larger than the area of Canada.

Question:

Why is it important that scientists be able to predict when an El Niño will occur? Do a web search to find out about La Niña (El Niño's evil sister).

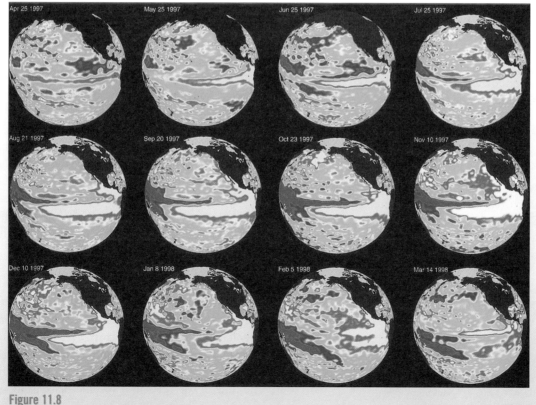

Figure 11.8
Images of El Niño from NASA

Figure 11.9
Stranded boats on Fundy Shore

El Niño events are likely triggered by changes in the atmosphere. Under normal conditions, the westerlies continually blow water across the ocean to Indonesia. If they weaken for some reason, this superheated water flows back toward the Americas. The unusually warm water off the coast of Peru increases evaporation and convection currents in the atmosphere. These changes are enough to affect world weather patterns.

geo.web resources

http://topex-www.jpl.nasa.gov/education/class-activities.html

This web page, run by NASA, contains lots of activities invloving aceans and ocean currents. Enter "El Niño Demonstration" and follow the instructions to see firsthand how El Niño works.

Tides

The Bay of Fundy, in the Maritimes, has the highest tides in the world. Evidence of extreme tides is seen in other areas of the East Coast as well, such as Digby, Nova Scotia, or Grand Manon Island, New Brunswick, where wharves are equipped with ladders as long as 10 metres. These unusual wharf ladders are needed so that people can access boats at low tide. When the tide is high, the boats float level with the dock.

Sailors developed a system long ago so that they could set out "on the tide," meaning they left as the tide was going out. The power of the water helped them get away from the dangerous shoreline. The tides occur because of the movement of the moon around the earth, and to a lesser extent the earth around the sun. Because the moon is very close (in astronomical terms), it exerts a significant gravitational pull on Earth. Most things on Earth are unaffected, but the waters in the oceans are drawn toward the moon. When the moon is directly overhead, the earth's oceans bulge out toward it. A corresponding bulge occurs on the opposite side of the earth to balance the low tides that occur at right angles to the moon's **azimuth**.

Tides move in 12 hour and 25 minute cycles, so if it is low tide at 7:00 a.m., you know it will be low tide again at 7:25 p.m. High tide occurs halfway between (at about 3:12 p.m.). The moon revolves around the earth every 27 days in the same direction that the earth rotates. Because the moon rotates more quickly than the earth, the time of the tides in a specific place is about 50 minutes later each day.

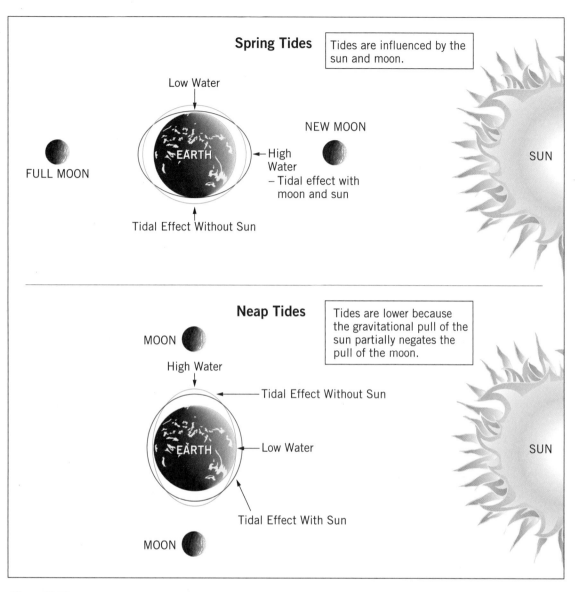

Figure 11.10
The Moon, Earth, Sun Relationships

While the sun is dramatically bigger than the moon, its gravitational pull is less obvious, having only five elevenths the power of the lunar tide. The pull of the sun is noticeable when the sun and moon are lined up together. When this happens (about twice a month), tides are abnormally high. You can easily tell when these **spring tides** occur, because the moon is either full (the sun is directly opposite it) or new (the moon shows no light because the sun is directly behind it). The **neap tide** is the opposite. A line drawn from the sun to the centre of the earth and another line drawn from the moon to the earth are perpendicular. So the gravitational pull of the sun is working against the pull of the moon, and the resulting tide is lower than usual. You can tell when there is a neap tide because the moon is half illuminated by the sun.

ENVIRONMENT WATCH

The Power of the Tides

Tidal energy is being harnessed as an alternative energy source at Annapolis Royale, in Nova Scotia. As the tide flows into the Bay of Fundy, **tidal bores** occur along all the rivers and estuaries. A tidal bore is the wave of water that flows up a river estuary when high tide moves up the shore. The power plant is built on an isthmus across the Annapolis River. When the tidal bore moves up the river, water gates open allowing the water to enter a lagoon north of the power plant. At low tides, the gates open again and the water flows through them and out to the ocean. As it does so, the water turns a turbine, generat-ing hydroelectricity. The scale of the plant is relatively small, but it is an ingenious way to use this sustainable energy source. This is a significant alternative power source because it requires no fuel, creates no greenhouse gases, and does not disturb ecosystems.

Questions:

1. The Annapolis Royale site is the only tidal power generating station in the Northern Hemisphere. Why do you think this type of power generation is so rare?
2. Look at maps of the Canadian coastline and of the river systems. Choose three sites which may be good candidates for tidal power generation.

Figure 11.11
Hydroelectric Power Plant at Annapolis Royale

ACTIVITIES

UNDERSTANDING CONCEPTS

1. Explain how each of the following properties of water affects Earth's climate:
   a) Water is densest at 4°C, not when it is frozen into ice.
   b) Water is translucent, so light can pass through it.
   c) Water is fluid and moves from place to place.
2. Why are the Dead Sea, Caspian Sea, and the Great Salt Lake salty?
3. Study Figure 11.7 (Ocean Currents). What generalizations can you make about
   a) equatorial currents, b) mid-latitude currents, c) polar currents, d) Southern Hemisphere currents, e) Northern Hemisphere currents, f) west-coast currents, and g) east-coast currents?
4. a) Explain what causes tsunamis.
   b) Describe the four physical processes that occur during the creation of a tsunami.
   c) Explain how the Deep Ocean Assessment and Reporting of Tsunamis initiative will help forecast when they will occur, where they will hit, and how strong they will be.
   d) What precautions should people take in tsunami-prone zones?
5. a) Explain what El Niño is, how it is caused, and why it is harmful.
   b) Explain how modern technology helps researchers to monitor El Niño.
6. a) Explain how the moon causes tides.
   b) What are neap tides and spring tides?
   c) How can tides be harnessed to produce energy?
7. a) Identify different careers that are discussed in the chapter.
   b) Use the Internet to find out more information about one of these careers.

DEVELOPING AND PRACTISING SKILLS

8. a) Prepare an organizer to compare thermo-haline currents, waves, tides, tsunamis, and ocean currents. Use the following criteria: characteristics, causes, influence on human geography, and energy distribution.
   b) Explain how salinity affects ocean currents.
9. For each of the following times, predict when the specified tide will occur.
   a) Monday 6:15 a.m. high tide—next low tide
   b) Sunday 7:30 p.m. low tide—next low tide
   c) Tuesday 12:30 a.m. high tide—next high tide
   d) Friday 1:43 p.m. low tide—high tide Saturday
   e) Wednesday 6:21 a.m. high tide—low tide Thursday
10. Evaluate the following web sites on tsunamis.
    Welcome to Tsunami! <www.geophys.washington.edu/tsunami>
    Tsunami Research Program <www.pmel.noaa.gov/tsunami/>
    Science of Tsunami Hazards <www.ccalmr.ogi.edu/STH/>
    a) In your evaluation, consider the following criteria: usefulness of the information, reading level, graphics, and visuals.

b)   Which web site was best, in your opinion? Explain.

c)   Report on any recent events in the implementation of the DART program, described on the NOAA web site <www.pmel.noaa.gov/tsunami/>.

11. a)   Prepare a world map showing the major oceans and seas of the world.

b)   Explain how oceans and seas facilitate the establishment of trade routes between continents.

c)   Indicate areas on the map where continents block possible trade routes.

d)   Identify key coastal cities located on trade routes such as Singapore, Hong Kong, Cape Town, Lisbon, Jakarta, St. John's and so on.

e)   Explain why cities develop in specific locations along trade routes.

f)   Identify cities that developed along coastal regions for recreational purposes. Examples include, Cancun, Miami, Nice and so on.

g)   Explain why cities developed along coastal regions for recreational purposes.

h)   Identify cities that developed along coastal regions to facilitate trade into the country or region. Examples include, New York, London, New Orleans, Vancouver, and so on

i)   Explain why cities developed along coastal regions to facilitate trade within countries.

j)   Think of other reasons why people live in cities along coastal regions.

LEARNING THROUGH APPLICATION

12. Explain how waves and ocean currents affect the way people live. Include such topics as leisure, fishing, shipping, agriculture, clothing, and lifestyle.

13. a)   Where are there tremendous amounts of stored potential energy in the oceans?

b)   How could this be harnessed to provide electricity?

14. Outline how tides affect the way people live in coastal areas. Consider such topics as swimming, fishing, travelling by boat, and camping on the beach.

15. a)   Summarize the various technological developments discussed in the chapter.

b)   Identify how each helps scientists to better understand natural systems.

c)   Describe the difficulties and limitations with different monitoring techniques.

16. a)   How are changes in the ocean water international in scope?

b)   Why is international co-operation essential if scientists are to be better able to monitor global patterns?

17. Describe each of the following leisure activities and identify how an understanding of water in oceans and seas affects each.

a) parasailing   b) surfing   c) sailing   d) windsurfing   e) ocean swimming

18. Devise a list of safety rules that should be observed when people are engaged in leisure activities on or near oceans and seas.

19. As fresh water supplies become increasingly scarce, people will no doubt turn to desalinated sea water as an alternative to water obtained from lakes, aquifers and rivers.

a)   Research sea water desalination and explain the process whereby fresh water is extracted from sea water.

b)   Determine the cost of desalination using appropriate web sites.

c)   The US navy among others uses desalination to provide drinking water. Provide instances where desalination would be feasible.

d)   Present an argument either supporting or refuting the feasibility of sea water desalination as a drinking water alternative.

Chapter 12

WATER IN RIVERS, LAKES, AND WETLANDS

FOCUS QUESTIONS

1. How is the protection of lakes and rivers a local, regional, and global issue?
2. What technological and geographical methods can we use to determine if a river is likely to flood?
3. What are the impacts of urbanization and industrialization on hydrology?

There is something about rivers that everybody loves. Maybe we love the languid tranquility of floating in an inner tube down a lazy river on a hot summer's day. Or perhaps there's a more exciting image we remember of playing hockey on a frozen river, running under a waterfall in a mountain stream, or whitewater rafting in the early spring. There is no doubt that rivers are marvellous natural features. They are not only great places for people to unwind and forget their troubles; rivers also provide valuable resources, excellent habitats for plants and animals, travel routes, and power sources. However, they can also be killers when they flood their banks. To understand how rivers work is to enjoy them, benefit from their gifts, and learn how to deal with them when they are out of control.

Figure 12.1
Travel, power generation, and recreation are but a few of the uses of rivers in Canada and around the world.

Key Terms

river capture

oxbow lake

ground truthing

tributaries

distributaries

There are many people who study rivers. Two important careers are those of the hydrologist and hydrogeologist. Hydrologists are people who study flowing water. They monitor water flows in rivers to determine when flooding may occur and evaluate water resources to determine if they are safe to drink. For civil engineers, knowledge of the forces that water places on bridges and dams, for example, is determined by studying how flowing water moves. Ecologists are scientists concerned with the preservation of ecosystems along rivers and in lakes and wetlands. As public concern increases over the environment, demand for professional ecologists seems to be on the rise.

Hydrogeologists study water wherever it exists: in rivers or aquifers, in lakes, glaciers, or in any other form. They are especially concerned with water as a resource and are frequently called on to estimate the amount of water available in a water body for municipal purposes. As clean, fresh water becomes an increasingly rare commodity, the demand for scientists knowledgeable in this field is increasing. To become either a hydrologist or a hydrogeologist, students need to be good in math, physics, and geography. A Bachelor of Science degree with a specialization in one of these three subjects is usually needed. Post-graduate work in hydrology, geology, and geography information systems, as well as physical geography and engineering, is common. Many universities allow students to do extensive fieldwork in such places as alpine glaciers in the Western Cordillera and other beautiful outdoor locations. If you like the outdoors, are good in science and math, and love rivers, this job could be just right for you!

River Patterns

While the overall form of rivers may seem unchanging, they are constantly subject to the swirling waters that shape and transform them from year to year. River systems evolve over many years. At first, **drainage patterns** are poorly organized, as rainwater washes over the new landscape in sheets. Where there are tiny cracks in the soil, the water follows the path of least resistance and runs along the depression.

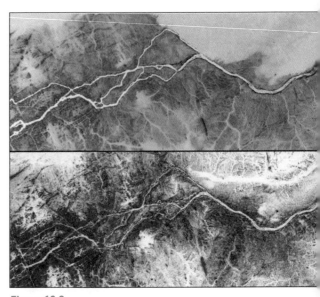

Figure 12.2
Two Views of the Nile River in Sudan

The water finds low areas through which to flow and hollows in which to settle. In time, channels form and the hollows are enlarged to become streams and wetlands. Eventually, a well-developed river system evolves and the land is efficiently drained of water.

Sometimes rivers actually steal water from other drainage basins. Two conditions promote **river capture**: there must be two river systems flowing close to each other and there must be a shallow divide between them. It is quite common for the larger, stronger river to undercut the bank of the smaller, weaker river. The **pirated river** dries up as its upstream flow is diverted into the stronger river. Called **wind gaps**, the dry valleys that are left seem oddly out of place in humid landscapes.

When we look at a map or satellite image, we see the patterns created by flowing water. From the air, river systems like the Amazon and its many tributaries often look much like trees. The main river is the trunk, the **tributaries** are the branches, and the **distributaries** in the delta are the roots. Where the tributaries join the main river, acute angles are formed. This **dendritic drainage pattern** occurs when the bedrock over

Figure 12.3
The Rio Negro and Rio Solimoes join to form the Amazon.

Figure 12.4
The Nile river and delta winds through Egypt. The Red Sea is on the right.

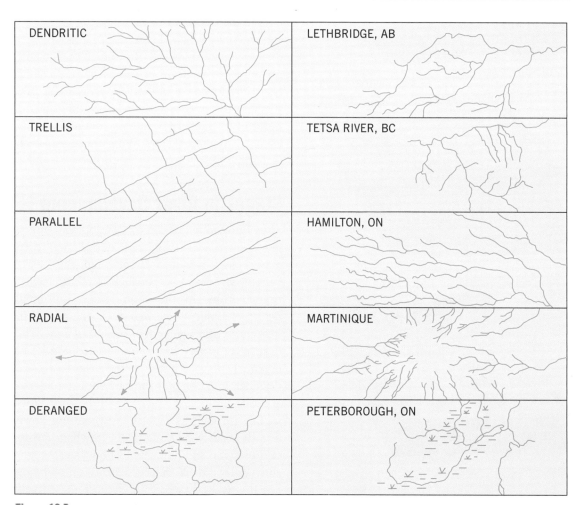

Figure 12.5
These diagrams compare theoretical and actual drainage patterns.

which the river flows is mainly uniform. When there are variations in the bedrock, water wears gullies in the less resistant rock, so the pattern tends to form differently. Drainage patterns can reveal a lot about the rock over which they flow. In many parts of Canada, where bare rock is exposed because of recent glaciation, surface water follows fracture lines in the rock that often run parallel to each other, creating **parallel drainage patterns**.

In areas where there are fold mountains, like the Himalayas and the Western Cordillera, rivers follow fault lines. A dendritic pattern is impossible because the mountains get in the way. Instead, **trellis drainage** is created. The tributaries join the main river at approximately right angles (90°), creating a formation resembling a garden trellis. Another drainage pattern influenced by landforms occurs where there are volcanoes or similar cone-shaped hills. This **radial drainage pattern** is found on many of the volcanic islands of the Pacific Ocean. As the name suggests, rivers flow out from a height of land in the centre.

Sometimes a river does not appear to have any drainage pattern at all. In much of Canada, drainage patterns are relatively recent, having been developed in the last 10 000 to 20 000 years, since the last ice age. This system, called a **deranged pattern**, often contains many wetlands, bogs, and lakes. What drainage pattern is found where you live?

Stages in River Development

Rivers go through periods of development, much like people do—they start out young, then mature, and eventually become old. But unlike people, rivers can experience a rebirth called **rejuvenation**. In the young stage, an initial period of uplift is followed by a long period in which the drainage system organizes itself. The **base level** is very low, so the water has a lot of potential energy as it tries to find a way to the sea. Channels and ponds are formed until an outlet to a lower elevation is found. Then the river flows rapidly through its new channel, cutting down into the bedrock. Young rivers are characteristically straight, and flow rapidly down steep gradients. Valleys are V-shaped, narrow, and straight like the rivers they contain. Because these rivers flow rapidly, they can transport huge amounts of unconsolidated material. The streambeds of

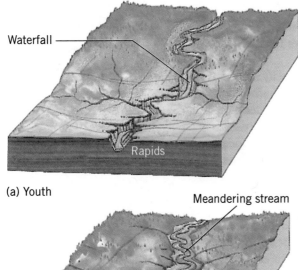

Waterfall

Rapids

(a) Youth

Meandering stream

Flood plain

(b) Maturity

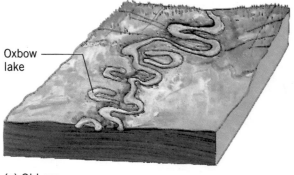

Oxbow lake

(c) Old age

Figure 12.6
The Cycle of a River from Youth to Old Age

young rivers are lined with rocks, cobbles, and boulders. Smaller particles are washed away. Between the river valleys are broad, poorly drained upland areas. Young rivers are found in many mountainous and highland regions of Canada.

Over time, the river changes. The main stream is close to reaching base level, but the river still has a lot of energy because of all the water flowing into it from tributaries upstream. Instead of cutting downwards, the river now begins to cut sideways into its banks, creating **meanders** or winding curves in the widening valley. The streambed now migrates across the land like a snake. The meandering river deposits sediment in old channels and cuts through its banks to build new ones. Characteristically, a mature river valley is a very wide U-shaped formation because of extensive side cutting. During periods of high water, the river may overflow its banks and flood the surrounding land. For this reason, mature valleys are often called **flood plains**. The **interfluve**, or land between rivers, is better drained here than in young rivers and covers a much smaller area. Mature rivers flow into coastal plains and other flat landforms all across Canada. The Saint John River between Edmundston and Fredericton, New Brunswick, is one such river.

A river's old age begins when it starts to deposit more sediment than it transports. Old rivers are slow-moving and capable of carrying only silt-sized particles and minerals contained in solution. Unlike more youthful rivers, the water is muddy and sluggish. Often the river actually rises above the flood plain. Sediments deposited in the stream channel build **levees** that contain the water (see Fig. 12.8). When heavy rains increase the discharge rate, the water breaks through the river's natural banks and fills the flood plain with silty brown water. It will remain there until it either evaporates or re-enters the river. The nutrients contained in the river water cover the flood plain with a rich natural fertilizer. Much of the world's best farmland has been the result of the flooding of old rivers. The Nile, the Indus, the Ganges, the Chang Jiang, and the

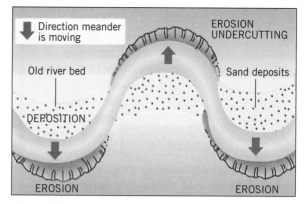

Figure 12.7
How Meanders Are Formed

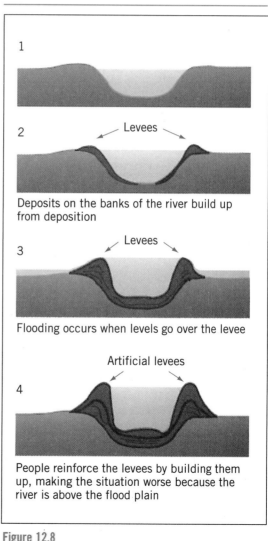

Figure 12.8
How Levees Are Made

Figure 12.9
This air photo shows the delta at the mouth of the Mackenzie River, NWT. At what stage in its development is this river?

Figure 12.10
Shown here is an oxbow lake beside the Kasanak River, AK. How was this feature created?

Mekong are just a few rivers whose rich sediments have provided the foundation for great agricultural societies.

The meanders that develop in old rivers are even more elaborate than in mature ones. To compensate for the increasingly shallow gradient, the river's meanders from side to side become ever wider. The length of the river actually increases, even though the straight-line distance from the source to the mouth remains the same. Several features are commonly found along old rivers, including **oxbow lakes**, which are formed when a river cuts through its levee and truncates a meander (see Fig. 12.6 c). When these curved wetlands dry up, they leave behind **meander scars**. Sometimes swampy areas called **bayous** develop where the river once flowed. When tributaries have difficulty cutting through the levees

to join the main stream, a **yazoo stream** may form. This will flow parallel to the main river for some distance until it can join it. The wetlands formed from oxbow lakes, meander scars, bayous, and yazoo streams make the flood plains of old rivers a haven for waterfowl and other wildlife. Unfortunately, the land is difficult for people to inhabit unless artificial levees are built to contain the river's waters.

A river valley that becomes flooded, either because of a rise in sea level or because of faulting, results in a river **estuary** such as the St. Lawrence River valley. Running from Montreal east to the tip of Gaspé, the St. Lawrence estuary forms a wide avenue into the heart of Quebec. The Quebecois have developed a rich culture along the banks of the St. Lawrence over the past 500 years. Fishing, lumbering, and farming (soil on the south side is fertile clay loam) all flourish on the estuary along the river's shores. Originally formed under the sea floor, the coastal plain has isostatically risen since the pressure of the ice was alleviated 12 000 years ago. Accumulations of rich sediments from the river washed over the land for thousands of years before the region was settled. Farmers have developed the land using the traditional French-Canadian land tenure system, known as the **seigneurial** system, in which farms are long and narrow. The small river frontage of each farm allows families to be close together in a linear village while the land stretches back from the river or the road. Since the soil is mainly clay, drainage ditches line the fields that are mounded up to further facilitate drainage. Flooding from the St. Lawrence is no longer a problem since the coastal plain is much higher than the river below.

When a river's water reaches the mouth of the river, the enormous amount of sediment it has carried finally comes to rest. Where the water enters the ocean, **deltas** are sometimes created through deposition.

Old rivers, such as the Mississippi, the Missouri, the Nile, the Amazon, the Zaire, and the lower Mackenzie, are found all over the world. If its base level remains constant, a river will pass through the three stages described here. In reality, however, this seldom happens. **Rejuvenation** occurs when a river gains new energy as a result of the land being uplifted by tectonic forces. So this could cause an old river to become youthful once again. Perhaps the best example of rejuvenation is the Colorado River as it flows through Arizona. As tectonic forces caused the land to continue to uplift, the river began to cut more deeply into the land. The incredible gorge known as the Grand Canyon was the result!

Rejuvenation can also occur as the result of a drop in the base level. The river now begins to cut down into the flood plain once again. When the base level rises, the flood plain becomes flooded with seawater, forming an estuary. Many North American rivers flow into the Atlantic through flooded estuaries. The Delaware, the Susquehanna, and the Saint John rivers were all flooded when the last ice age ended.

Flooding in Canada

Many communities in Canada are subject to flooding in the spring when the snow melts and rivers try to drain the excess water from flooded fields. In many large municipalities, conservation authorities have worked to reduce the risk of flooding by installing dams, planting trees, and creating artificial channels. The Metropolitan Toronto Conservation Authority instituted many of these features after Hurricane Hazel caused widespread flooding in the Greater Toronto Area in the early fifties. Winnipeg similarly installed a floodway to direct water around the city in times of flooding.

Figure 12.11
Image of the 1996 Flooding of the Saguenay River in Chicoutimi, Quebec. This flood was the most devasting in Canadian history, causing 10 deaths and $800 million in damage.

DEVELOPING SKILLS

Conducting a Field Study of a River

The field study is an essential part of geographic studies. Geographers, hydrologists, and engineers study rivers for vital information about the amount of water available for human consumption and the existence of possible flood conditions. By calculating flow velocity and discharge rate, it is possible to ascertain when and where rising water will reach the danger point. To obtain this information, we must begin by determining the width, depth, and area of a given river.

Before you begin your data collection, review the following safety tips:

- Do not work in a river where the water is over your head.
- Work under your teacher's supervision.
- Always work with at least one other person.
- Avoid rivers with strong currents.
- Take a cellphone for emergencies.
- Do not do fieldwork in the early spring just after a thaw or after heavy rains.

PART 1: Measuring Width

Measuring the width of a river is fairly easy as long as you don't mind getting wet. Two or three people are needed to take these measurements.

1. Have one person hold a tape measure at one end.

2. Another person then wades to the opposite shore, extending the tape measure across the width of the river.

3. The second person then reads the measurement from edge to edge. Taking three or four measurements and calculating the average leads to greater accuracy.

PART 2: Measuring Depth

1. Tie a weight to the end of a long piece of string. Holding one end of the string, drop it into the river until the weight hits the bottom.

2. Pull the string taut and mark where the surface of the water intersects with the string.

3. Haul the weight out of the water and measure the length of the string from your mark to the weight. The depth of the river varies from place to place, so it is necessary to get readings at regular intervals. (Try taking measurements one metre apart if the river is fairly narrow; increase the intervals if the river is wide.)

PART 3: Calculating Cross-sectional Area

This is important to do so that you can find the volume of water flowing past a given point in the river.

Multiply the average width you calculated in Part 1 by the average depth you calculated in Part 2. For example, if the stream was 12 m wide and the average depth was 1.8 m, the cross-sectional area would be 21.6 m^2 (12 x 1.8 = 21.6).

PART 4: Measuring Flow Velocity

The flow velocity, or speed at which the river is flowing, is measured using a float, a tape measure, and a stopwatch or a wristwatch with a second hand. Three people are needed to take this measurement: a timer/recorder, a starter, and someone at the finish line.

1. Measure a 10-m distance along the river. Mark a start line and a finish line at the beginning and end of the measured section.

2. Have the starter place a floating object, such as an orange, in the water, and signal to the timer to start the stopwatch. When the object passes the finish line, the person at this point signals the timer to stop the watch and record the time it took the object to move 10 metres.

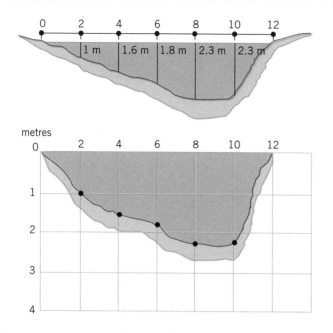

1. Measuring average depth:
$$\frac{\Sigma\,x}{n} = \frac{1 + 1.6 + 1.8 + 2.3 + 2.3}{5}$$
$$= 1.8 \text{ m}$$

2. Calculating cross-sectional area:
   A = depth x width
   A = 1.8 x 12 = 21.6 m²

3. Graphing the bank profile using depths:
   • plot each depth
   • join the dots

3. Flow velocities vary in rivers because of friction between the channel and the water. To ensure accuracy, repeat this procedure four or five times and calculate the average.

4. You can now calculate how far the float would travel in 1 second, using the formula d/t, where d is the distance and t is the time. For example, if the float moved 10 m downstream in an average time of 15.2 s, the speed would be 0.66 m/s (10/15.2). Multiply this by 60 to get the distance in 1 minute. In this case, the flow velocity would be 39.6 m/min (10/15.2 x 60). To get the speed in km/h, multiply by 60 once again to change minutes to hours, and divide by 1000 to convert m to km. The answer would be 2.38 km/h (10/15.2 x 60 x 60/1000). The only problem with this measurement is that it shows only the flow velocity on the surface. To get the speed at which the water is flowing at greater depths requires more sophisticated measuring devices.

PART 5: Calculating the Discharge Rate and Maximum Capacity

Now that you know the river's cross-sectional area and flow velocity, it is possible to determine the discharge rate in cubic metres per second (m³/s).

1. Multiply the flow velocity in metres per second by the cross-sectional area in metres squared (m²). In the example, the discharge rate would be 14.26 m³/s (21.6 x 0.66). This means that every second, 14.26 m³ (or ton) of water passes any given point.

2. Calculating the maximum discharge capacity is important in determining how much water the river channel can handle without the water overflowing its banks. First, follow the steps for determining the discharge rate; then calculate the cross-sectional area of the channel above the river's surface. To do this, measure the width of the channel from the top of the lower bank to the same height on the opposite bank. Estimate the average depth and then calculate the cross-sectional area. You now know how much higher the water can go before flooding could be a problem.

CHANGING TECHNOLOGY: Flood Predictions

Environmental engineers determine when rivers are about to flood by monitoring soil moisture along the banks of the river being studied. If the moisture content is high, then rainwater and snowmelt will likely run off the surface of the ground instead of being absorbed. In order to monitor the moisture content in the soil, geographers study images captured electronically by spectrometers on satellites and sent to earthbound stations. Sophisticated computers help geographers to analyse the information, which has been recorded from far out in space.

A spectrometer is a technology that measures the wavelength of reflected light in many different spectrums. We are able to see some of the **electromagnetic waves** reflected off surfaces, while other wavelengths are outside of our visual range. Each image is broken down into **pixels**, or tiny squares. A different value is assigned to each pixel, depending on the reflective nature of the surface. Field researchers study the same location on the ground and measure the surface characteristics of the feature they are studying—soil moisture, for example. Once they know the characteristics of that place and the spectral value of the same location, they are able to describe the surface for that specific value. In future, wherever that value is shown in a specific wavelength, researchers can determine what the surface is like. This process is known as **field verification** or **ground truthing**.

In addition to the spectrometer images, monitors along rivers automatically record surface levels. Using water level data, soil moisture analysis, and historical information about how the river usually acts, hydrologists are able to develop computer models to forecast when and where flooding will occur. These developments help authorities to prepare for flooding before it is too late.

Question:
Why is the process of ground truthing important in the analysis of satellite images?

Lakes

No matter what their shape or size, Canada's lakes are a tremendous resource—although one that is sometimes taken for granted. In the south, close to where most Canadians live, lakes provide many recreational opportunities. In the north, lakes are an integral part of the traditional lifestyle of many Aboriginal peoples. Moreover, the water stored in Canada's vast wilderness areas is becoming increasingly important in thirsty urban areas.

Water resources were included in the North American Free Trade Agreement. Many Canadians were concerned that our water resources could be depleted if they were diverted to meet the needs of American cities. In addition, the hydroelectric potential of the Canadian Shield's water resources has caused controversy. The James Bay Project has been widely criticized for the disruptions it caused in the lives of Aboriginal peoples and in the environment. Many Canadians don't want their wilderness

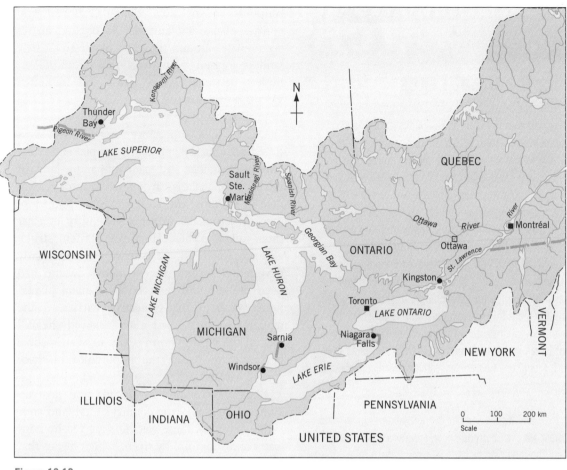

Figure 12.12
Map of the Great Lakes Basin

areas plundered to provide electricity to our neighbours south of the border.

Historically, Canada's lakes have served as our highways. In colonial times, the fur trade prospered because traders and trappers could travel great distances easily on the many lakes. Of course, the Great Lakes have always been and continue to be important transportation routes. Coal, iron, and other raw materials are loaded onto ocean-going vessels around the shores of the Great Lakes and transported to the many industrial cities in Canada, the United States, and around the world. There is no doubting the enormous contribution the Great Lakes have made to the prosperity of the region.

Wetlands

The term "wetlands" is a catchall phrase that includes bogs, swamps, marshes, and fens. Each of these wetland types has a precise meaning, but all wetlands have two things in common. First and most obviously, they are wet—water either covers the ground completely or the soil is so waterlogged that it is impossible for one to walk on it. Secondly, they provide habitats for many plants and animals. The categorization of the four types of wetlands is determined by the amount of water and the types of vegetation found in each.

Swamps have trees growing through the water. They are often found along the edges of

Protecting the Great Lakes

On March 15, 2000, the International Joint Commission on Protection of the Waters of the Great Lakes published its final report. The document supported the Canadian government's decision to prohibit the sale of water from Canadian drainage basins. Foreign Affairs Minister, Lloyd Axworthy stated that the protection of Canadian fresh water is "the most effective way of protecting ecosystems and is consistent with international trade obligations."

In addition to this new policy, which will ensure that corporations can no longer apply for a permit to sell water outside of Canada, new regulations will promote improved municipal water conservation using a new pricing structure. The International Joint Commission also called for governments to study Great Lakes water quality more fully, develop monitoring programs to detect threats to ecosystems, study the importance of groundwater in the Great Lakes Watershed, and research the impacts that water removal for local use has on ecosystems.

Question:
Research and then update the studies currently being undertaken by the Department for the Environment to monitor ecosystems in the Great Lakes. The following website is a good place to start http://www.epa.gov/glnpo/ecopage.html

lakes, in river ox-bows, or in poorly drained depressions. They are the only wetlands with trees growing in them. Of all the wetland types, swamps are the most rare in Canada. They are much more common in tropical environments such as the Amazon Basin and in subtropical regions like the Dismal Swamp in North Carolina. These ecozones are astonishing for the variety of life that inhabits them. Cypress trees, alligators, many varieties of snakes and birds, and innumerable types of insects thrive in the wetlands of the southern United States. Off the coast of Central America, and in many other tropical locales, mangrove swamps are found brimming with a huge variety of life forms. The mangrove is a tree that provides shelter for large numbers of specially adapted arboreal and aquatic plants and animals. As organic matter accumulates around the roots of the trees, new land is formed. Mangroves provide important buffers between coastal plains and the often violent hurricanes that rage off the coast of these tropical zones.

Despite their importance to wildlife, swamps have been much maligned by people, and many have been drained and made into arable land. In the tropics, malaria-carrying mosquitoes originate in swamps, and so it became a priority of most governments in the last century to clear them away. When Hurricane Mitch struck Nicaragua in 1998, the damage was particularly devastating because the mangrove swamp had been drained and replaced by banana plantations. Without the protective barrier of the mangroves, the coastal plain received the full fury of the violent storm. Only now are people beginning to realize the importance of these special wetlands.

Bogs are common in Canada and take up almost a quarter of the country's total land area. Unlike swamps, these wetlands are fed by rainwater and snow, not by rivers, which means that few nutrients are carried into them. They are common in **periglacial** environments where drainage patterns are not yet fully developed. Trees do not grow to full size in bogs because the soil is so infertile, although stunted tamaracks and spruce trees are common. If you count the tree rings on the cross-section of a stunted spruce tree, you may be surprised to learn that it is hundreds of years old even though it may be only less than a metre high. However, plants that have adapted to acidic, nutrient-poor, wet soil do thrive in these areas. One especially well-adapted plant is the **pitcher plant**. This carnivorous plant actually absorbs its nutrients from the remains of dead insects, which drown in the water reservoirs formed by its leaves. Other plants such as orchids and sedges find alternate ways to survive on few life-giving minerals.

Bogs contain very little oxygen, so organic matter accumulates in a thick mat of **peat** with-

Figure 12.13
How does the pitcher plant survive in nutrient-starved bogs?

out decomposing. The accumulated layer of sphagnum moss is the substance that gardeners use in their flowerbeds. Although it is able to absorb great amounts of water, this moss actually contains few nutrients. Bogs make up much of the Canadian Shield.

Fens are bogs that are drained by rivers. They form between lakes and rivers in the Canadian Shield and often lie adjacent to bogs. Nutrients enter from rivers and aquifers. While most fens do have a thick layer of peat underlying them, they have a greater diversity of life than bogs. Bulrushes, wildflowers, and varieties of sedge are common in this ecosystem. Animal life is varied and abundant in the fens of central Canada, where frogs, snakes, and a myriad of waterfowl thrive.

Figure 12.14
A Bog in NewFoundland

Groundwater in York Region

As is the case in many areas of the settled world, growing industrialization and urbanization in Canadian towns and cities are taking a heavy toll on groundwater supplies. For example, in parts of southern Ontario, many recharge areas are being built on and paved over. The Oak Ridges Moraine is a hilly region of forests, ponds and wetlands north of the Greater Toronto Area. In the spring, the snow stays longer in the forests than in the surrounding fields because of the microclimate produced by the trees. As it gradually melts, the water filters down through the forest mat of leaves and humus into wetlands and innumerable ponds. Eventually it enters the main aquifer about 90 metres below the surface. It provides much of the groundwater for municipal and rural wells in York Region and Durham Region. However, development is occurring at such a fast rate that the future of the groundwater in this area is being threatened.

As the trees are cut down, the bogs drained, and the rivers forced into underground storm sewers, the water that once entered the aquifer is being lost. In Richmond Hill, a suburb of Toronto, new subdivisions are being built at a furious rate on hilly moraine land that was once forested. Just west of Aurora, another golf course has been erected. While this land has not been paved over, golf courses make great demands on groundwater. For fairways irrigation, the average 18-hole course uses the equivalent of the water needs of a town of 20 000 people. In Newmarket,

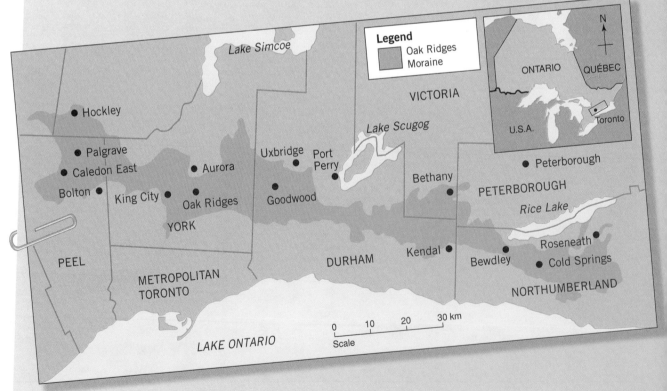

Figure 10.15
Map Showing the Oak Ridges Moraine and Towns of York Region

Figure 10.16
Environmentalists argue that the Oak Ridges forests should be left as they are, while developers want to erect thousands of new homes in this area.

approval has been granted for intensive development of town land located on the moraine. As of the summer of 2000, a group of developers was seeking approval to build another 8000 homes on 814 ha of farm land in the Oak Ridges region. Other groups of developers were waiting for this decision before deciding whether they, too, will seek approval for their housing plans. The developers argue that the growing Ontario population has to live somewhere, and this currently unused forested region is the answer.

Many concerned citizens have been lobbying municipalities to try to prevent further development on the moraine. The problem is that the towns' representatives are powerless in overseeing the development of town lands. Developers appeal to the Ontario Municipal Board, a provincial government agency, for zoning authorization.

In the end, this new subdivision, that highway or the other new plaza usually gets built. However, governments are starting to hear the cries of voters who not only want groundwater protected but want to preserve a greenbelt north of Canada's fastest growing urban area.

QUESTIONS:

1. **a)** Describe the water resources in the Oak Ridges Moraine.

    b) Analyse the impacts of urbanization and industrialization on water resources in the Oak Ridges Moraine.

2. What alternatives to the growth of housing developments do the municipalities have?

Figure 12.17
Why is Holland Marsh a prime agricultural area?

Marshes have the richest soil and the greatest diversity of life of the four wetland types. They are found in the glacial potholes of the south-central area of the Prairie provinces. Marshes also form along the shores of lakes and rivers when shorelines become flooded. In the Maritime provinces, salt marshes are common where offshore sandbars prevent drainage. Often, salt marshes are flooded and drained by the tides each day. Water has abundant oxygen in it since it flows through the region; therefore, decomposition occurs readily, and rich organic soil results. Many marshes have been drained to produce rich farmland. One such wetland called Holland Marsh provides many of the vegetables for the southern Ontario market.

Natural processes can dry up wetlands. As water drains into them and as organic matter accumulates, the amount of soil increases in proportion to the amount of water. In addition, if the source of the water dries up, the wetland could become a meadow or forest. While wetlands are naturally destroyed, they are also naturally created, since ponds and the borders of lakes are subject to **sedimentation**. As sediment is carried into a body of water, the water gradually becomes more and more shallow, until it no longer forms a lake but is a swamp or marsh. Of course, the greatest natural agent that creates wetlands is the beaver. These industrious rodents have done much to transform northern Canada into wetlands. In one season, a pair of beavers can dam a stream and flood the land for great distances in all directions.

Wetlands are created (in part) by beavers, enjoyed by ducks, and, until recently, destroyed by Canadians. Organizations such as Ducks Unlimited, the World Wildlife Fund, and local conservation groups are promoting wetlands because of the rich diversity of life they support. From the point of view of the physical geographer, they are also important because of the role they play in storing fresh water. However, urbanization has a huge impact on wetlands. As populations grow, so does our water consumption. New housing developments, especially in North America, can threaten groundwater supplies as wetlands are paved over and new wells are dug to sustain the increasing numbers of people.

geo.web resources

www.ducks.ca

Ducks Unlimited Canada is a private nonprofit organization dedicated to conserving wetlands. Go to the site and research the ways average Canadians can help save these ecosystems.

ACTIVITIES

UNDERSTANDING CONCEPTS

1. a) Identify and describe the stages that rivers go through from youth to old age.
    b) Explain the process whereby
        i) rivers become ponds and lakes.
        ii) ponds and lakes become wetlands.
        iii) wetlands become meadows and forests.
2. Copy down the highlighted words in this chapter and explain the meaning of each in your own words.
3. What local, regional, and global issues related to the management of water resources are discussed in the chapter?
4. Describe the differences between swamps, marshes, bogs and fens.
5. a) Identify the various careers that are discussed in the chapter.
    b) Use the Internet to find out more information about the career that interests you the most.

DEVELOPING AND PRACTISING SKILLS

6. a) Choose a river from a topographic map of a nearby area, and make a tracing of it. Include interesting features such as waterfalls, rapids, meanders, and oxbows for later investigation. Identify areas where flooding could be a problem.
    b) Determine the direction of flow, using contour lines, and indicate it with an arrow on your sketch map.
    c) Determine the gradient of the river for the section you are studying. To find the gradient of a river:
        i) Calculate the length of the river using the scale.
        ii) Calculate the altitude at both ends of the river section.
        iii) Subtract the lowest altitude from the highest.
        iv) Express the difference in iii) as a ratio to its length in i) to determine the m/km figure. For example, a river drops from 1000 m to 500 m amsl over a distance of 100 km: (1000 m – 500 m) / 100km = 500 m / 100 km = 5 m/km.
7. a) For the river chosen in Question 6, prepare two profiles of the valley showing prominent features. (See page 72 for how to make a profile.)
    b) Make several photocopies of your map for use in the field and back in the classroom.
    c) Prepare a field manual from folded paper stapled in the middle. This can be used to make notes in the field.
    d) What are the physical characteristics of the river and valley? Sketch or photograph interesting features and indicate their locations on a sketch map.
    e) Indicate on the map places where erosion, deposition, and flooding have occurred. What patterns of erosion and deposition do you notice? Explain why each occurs.

f)   What patterns of vegetation are evident? How does the river influence these patterns?

8.   a)   Measure the width, average depth, cross-sectional area, flow velocity, and discharge rate for three different sites along the river you chose in Question 6.

b)   Determine the **maximum discharge capacity** of the stream. Establish the height of water the river channel could manage, given the same flow velocity.

c)   Draw cross-sections of the river at the three study sites.

d)   Determine the river's stage in the geomorphic cycle and give evidence to support your decision.

e)   How do people make use of the river and the valley?

f)   What evidence of pollution is there?

g)   What improvements could be made to the river?

9.   Make a display for the river you chose in question 6 by completing the following activities:

a)   Using one of the copies of the river tracing you made in question 7 (b), add a scale, north arrow, and grid to it. Label prominent features, such as evidence of flooding, meanders, oxbows, sandbars, etc. Use a legend to indicate areas of erosion deposition, and flooding. Use another legend to indicate natural vegetation in the flood plain.

b)   Draw diagrams or use photographs to illustrate prominent features along the river. Mount these beside the map and use arrows to indicate their locations.

c)   Draw cross-sectional diagrams of the riverbed where you measured the depth, and reference these to the map.

d)   Provide written explanations of each of the features shown in the display.

e)   Prepare an environmental study to evaluate human impact on the river, using a **needs assessment** organizer similar to the one shown below.

Present Situation	Action Plan	Vision
Evidence of flooding	Build dams and Reduce flooding	Reservoirs upstream

10.   Use an atlas map or topographic sheet to make a tracing of a river system.

a)   Label the main river, significant tributaries, the mouths and sources of each tributary, and other significant drainage features such as lakes and wetlands.

b)   Establish where the divide exists between this drainage basin and adjacent ones by drawing a line along the highest contour line between the two basins.

c)   Estimate the area of the drainage basin, using the grid or scale on the map. If each square is a standard unit of measure (say 100 km^2), you can count up the squares to get the area. (If you also add up the partial squares and divide by two, this provides for a more accurate estimate than just tallying whole squares.)

d)   Determine the elevation of the source of each major tributary. Subtract the elevation at its mouth from the elevation at the source to determine the **rise** of the river.

e)   Measure the length of the main river and its major tributaries to find the **run** of each.

f)   Calculate the **gradient** of the main river and each tributary by dividing the rise by the run.

g)   Based on your findings in f), list the tributaries in order from fastest flowing to slowest flowing, using a numeric system (1 for fastest).

h) Determine the drainage pattern of your river system.

i) Based on your findings about this river, write a descriptive paragraph about the drainage basin. Evaluate the system's efficiency in draining the land.

j) Summarize the information you gathered through parts a–i of this question in a display.

11. a) Use a collection of topographic maps and satellite images to find examples of dendritic, trellis, parallel, radial, and deranged drainage systems like those shown in Fig. 12.5.

b) Make a tracing of each drainage system and mount it on a piece of cardboard.

c) For each drainage pattern, make assumptions about the rocks over which the water flows.

d) Study the maps to determine how drainage patterns have affected the way in which people use the land.

12. Prepare an organizer comparing the different stages of a river's development. Include the following criteria: flow velocity, valley shape, sediment size, gradient features, interfluve characteristics, and flood plain.

13. Explain the role of river estuaries in providing fertile soils for agriculture in the St. Lawrence estuary.

14. Explain how patterns of landforms, climate, soils, and vegetation have resulted in the different wetland types.

15. a) Describe changes in land use in your community over the past twenty years.

b) Assess the effects of these changes on water resources within your community.

LEARNING THROUGH APPLICATION

16. Which stage of river development do you think is best suited for human occupation? Explain your answer.

17. Experiment with a stream table to make simulations of rivers in the following stages of development: young, mature, old, rejuvenated.

18. a) Explain how to measure the maximum discharge capacity of a river.

b) Describe the technology used for measuring river levels and soil moisture on the surface of the earth.

c) Evaluate the ways in which technology is used to measure flooding.

d) Explain the importance of field verification (ground truthing) of data collected from remote sensing instruments, including satellites.

e) Describe the difficulties and limitations of these two ways of determining when flooding is imminent.

19. Analyse damage and casualty risks related to flooding in your community and identify factors that increase risk.

20. a) How have human activities affected wetlands?

b) What can be done to preserve these wetlands?

21. a) Describe how human activities have affected groundwater resources.

b) Why are area residents concerned about the development of the Oak Ridges Moraine?

c) How could the water resources of the moraine be sustainably managed?

22. Identify geopolitical issues that face nations with regard to water resources.

Chapter 13

THE CRYOSPHERE: STUDIES IN ICE AND SNOW

FOCUS QUESTIONS

1. How are the elements of the cryosphere being affected by global warming?
2. What is the relationship of the cycle of glacial advance and retreat to natural variations in global climate?
3. What are the geopolitical issues that face the nations that share the circumpolar regions?

Key Terms

cryosphere

permafrost

glacial surge

muskeg

zone of ablation

The term "cryosphere" is derived from the Greek word *kruos*, meaning frost. It is the part of the hydrosphere that is frozen, and includes snow cover, permanently frozen ground (**permafrost**), sea ice, and glaciers. The cryosphere is an essential part of studies in physical geography, and geographers, environmentalists, and scientists are beginning to realize the importance of this element of the hydrosphere to climate, oceanography, and life systems.

Because of developing awareness that global warming is perhaps the single most significant environmental issue in the world today, enormous effort and funding are going into cryosphere research. We tend to forget how much ice there is in the high latitudes because these areas are so remote from centres of population. Yet the cooling effect of these huge expanses of ice and snow has a profound effect on global climates and ocean circulation.

The average temperature of the earth has warmed up by 0.6° C over the past century. That does not seem like much of a temperature change, but the implications are very significant for ice, much of which hovers just below freezing. Ice and snow reflect as much as 80 per cent of the solar radiation hitting the earth's surface as light. Only 20 per cent is converted into heat energy. The ice is there because the temperature

Figure 13.1
Sea Ice in the Far North

is cold, but it is also cold because there is ice. By contrast, bare ground and open sea water only reflect 10–20 per cent and convert 80–90 per cent of the energy from the sun into heat. Therefore, these regions are warmer. It stands to reason that a reduction in snow and ice would result in significantly higher temperatures worldwide. It is a vicious cycle: as temperatures rise, snow and ice melt, and as they melt, temperatures rise.

Snow Cover

While snow lying on the ground does not seem as significant as the Antarctic ice sheet or the huge accumulations of sea ice in the Arctic, it is perhaps the single largest component of the cryosphere. In the Northern Hemisphere, winter snow cover at its maximum extent covers 47 million km². That is an area of land equivalent to almost five Canadas! Snow cover in the Southern Hemisphere is not significant because there are no land masses at latitudes high enough to warrant significant accumulations of snow (with the exception of Antarctica, which is covered with a glacier).

Since snow reflects about 80 per cent of the incoming solar radiation it receives, the region remains cold when the ground is covered with snow. But if the snow melts, the winter will be much warmer because of all the solar radiation that has been converted to thermal energy. Over the past 30 years, an American body called the National Oceanic Atmospheric Administration (NOAA), has monitored snow cover using satellite remote sensing in the Northern Hemisphere. The NOAA discovered a 20-year trend that indicates a decline of 0.4 per cent of snow cover per year there. This may not seem like much, but consider what the situation will be like in a hundred years if this decline continues. By simply multiplying 100 × 0.4%, you get a 40 per cent reduction in seasonal snow cover. It is likely that the rate at which snow cover is decreasing will speed up once large areas of open ground and sea are exposed. This will do more than just destroy snowboarding as a sport. It will have a profound impact on climate, ecozones, and human economies, and will completely change the dynamics of the hydrosphere.

Snow Cover in Canada

Snow cover is important for reasons other than just those related to climate change. It stores precipitation that falls in the winter until it melts in the spring. The spring thaw has an enormous impact on environmental systems in Canada and other countries around the world. Rivers that flow north are especially affected by the "spring break-up." Canada's longest river, the Mackenzie, flows north into the Beaufort Sea, near the border between the Yukon and the Northwest Territories. Since the ice melts faster upstream (in the south) than it does downstream, ice jams prevent the water from flowing north to the mouth. Flooding of the Mackenzie valley is an annual event that covers hundreds of square kilometres of tundra. When the pressure of all the built-up water becomes more than the ice jam in the river channel can bear, it breaks up with thunderous crashes and the water in this great northern river continues its journey to the sea. This same story is repeated hundreds of times for all the other rivers that flow north in Canada and in other countries such as Russia.

Figure 13.2
This map shows snow cover in the Northern Hemisphere.

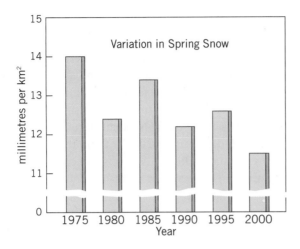

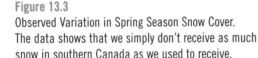

Figure 13.3

Observed Variation in Spring Season Snow Cover.
The data shows that we simply don't receive as much
snow in southern Canada as we used to receive.

In the agricultural regions of Canada, farmers
rely on the melting of snow to provide an infusion
of moisture for their crops. For example,
winter wheat, which is planted in the fall and lies
dormant all winter, needs this moisture to grow
to maturity. Even in the semi-arid lands of the
Prairies, winter wheat grows well because of the
snow cover. The snow acts as a blanket to insulate
tender seedlings from the bitterly cold, desiccating
winds that blast over these plains. In
recent years, the absence of snow cover has had
a dramatic effect on farms in many parts of
Canada. Winter frost-kill has reduced the
amount of alfalfa—a **perennial legume** used as a
hay crop in many parts of Canada—that survives
from one year to the next. Snow seldom stays on
the ground throughout the winter in some farming
regions that used to be blanketed from
December to March.

Of course, snow cover also affects animals. In
the winter of 1999, there were unusually high
accumulations in pockets of Northern Ontario.
The snow was so deep that moose and caribou
were starving to death because they could not
move through the drifts or dig down to the vegetation
below. A similar tragedy occurred that
same winter in northern Siberia. Instead of snowfall,
the ground became covered with a hard pack

of ice, resulting in the death of 20 000 reindeer.
However, smaller animals thrive when the snow
is deep. Rodents burrow under the snow and
gorge themselves on the grasses they find. In
spring, there are so many voles, mice, shrews,
and rabbits that carnivores have a rich diet just
when they need it after the long winter night.
Snow cover is clearly very important to the
ecosystem, and changes in its amount will have a
great effect on Canada's animal populations as
well as its agriculture.

Collecting data on snow accumulations is
extremely difficult. Regular daily observations are
made at several hundred weather stations across

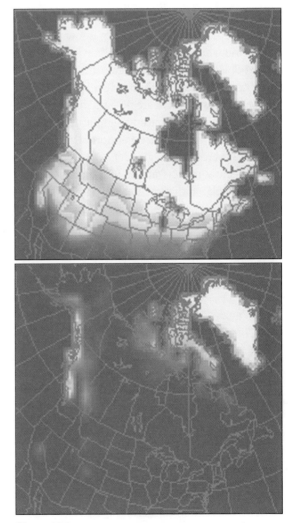

Figure 13.4

Satellite Image of Snow Cover in Canada in January and July

Canada. But this network is not uniformly spread across the country, and reports are inconsistent. Weather stations are located in populated areas, leaving many isolated wilderness areas with no direct monitoring at all. Passive microwave satellite data provides a much better picture. Satellites send back daily images showing the detailed and quantitative extent of snow cover for the entire country. The term "quantitative" means that the data is numerical, and as such it can be manipulated using statistical analysis methods. Variations in data indicate such factors about the snow as surface temperature, moisture content, and albedo. The results of the 20-year survey gave rise to the realization that snow cover has been becoming lower every year.

Permafrost

Permafrost is an element of the cryosphere that might be overlooked since it is hidden from view underground. Like groundwater, **permafrost** is water found in layers under the earth's surface; but unlike groundwater, it is frozen into ice. Permafrost is defined as rock or soil that remains below freezing for more than two years. Massive depths of permafrost underlie almost 23 million km² (nearly

Glaciologists from Wilfred Laurier University have done extensive work under the auspices of the Canadian International Development Agency and the United Nations in northern Pakistan. This developing country—with a population in excess of 120 million people—relies almost entirely on the Indus River for irrigation and municipal water. An arid land with high temperatures, Pakistan has huge water needs. Canadian glacial hydrologists are measuring the rate at which the glacier is melting in the Himalayan Mountains as well as determining how much of this resource is going to be available in the future. By studying the glaciers, these scientists are able to prepare water budgets and help Pakistanis plan how to best use their limited water resources. To work in the specialized field of glacial hydrology, you need university level courses in hydrology, geology, glaciology, mathematics, and remote sensing.

24 per cent) of the earth's land surface. There are places in the Far North where the permafrost is more than 500 metres thick.

The distribution, thickness, and temperature of permafrost are dependent on surface temperature, vegetative cover, snow cover, drainage, and soil type. Obviously, the temperature must be cold enough for the groundwater to freeze. While this happens every winter all across Canada, in permafrost zones the ice does not fully melt in summer. When temperatures rise, the top **active layer** of permafrost thaws, but the water does not seep to lower layers because it is blocked by the still solid ice layer below. The meltwater just sits in the upper layers of the soil. Poorly drained Arctic soils, where evaporation rates are insignificant due to low temperatures, become bogs in summer. This **muskeg** is home to caribou, innumerable waterfowl, and a myriad of insects. It is very difficult, if not impossible, for people to get around in the knee-deep mud, and some human activities must come to a standstill in summer. Only in winter are people able to travel, mine, and harvest trees.

An understanding of permafrost is important to engineers and architects, as well as to climatologists studying climate change. Any structure built

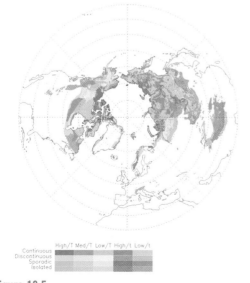

Continuous
Discontinuous
Sporadic
Isolated

High/T Med/T Low/T High/t Low/t

Figure 13.5
This map shows the extent of permafrost in the Northern Hemisphere.

on permafrost has to be specially designed to prevent it from thawing the ice beneath it. Oil travelling through pipelines in the Arctic must be insulated from the ground; this prevents the heat generated by the friction of the oil flowing through the pipe from melting the permafrost and causing a massive oil spill. Similarly, sewers are above ground in the Arctic. Buildings are often built on stilts so that the heat from the building will dissipate in the cold air between it and the ground.

Much of the permafrost in the Northern Hemisphere supports **boreal forest** and **taiga**. Boreal forest is made up of coniferous trees such as spruce, larch, and pine. Taiga also contains these species, but the growing season is so short that the trees are stunted. Larch trees of less than a metre in height may be 200 years old. The taiga is a transition zone between the boreal forest and the tundra where no trees grow. The trees in the boreal forest and taiga grow in the active layer where the permafrost melts each summer, and become dormant in the long dark winters. Interestingly, these forests are so extensive that they contain nearly one third of the earth's stored carbon. This is more than any other ecozone, including the tropical rainforests.

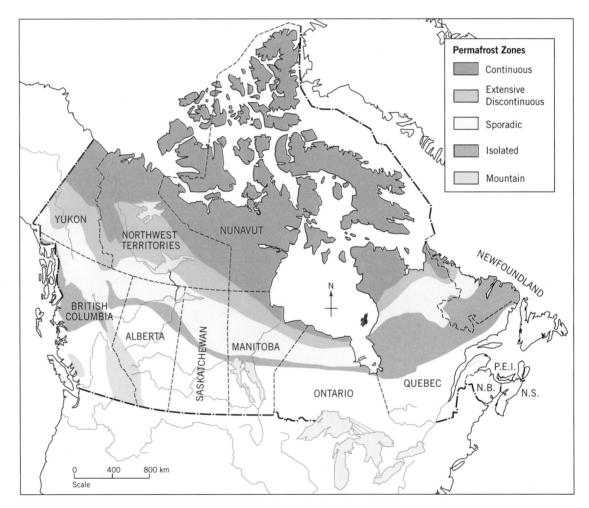

Figure 13.6
Permafrost Regions of Canada

Sea Ice

Sea ice typically covers 14 to 16 million km² in the Arctic and a further 17 to 20 million km² in the Southern Hemisphere. This is less than either snow cover or permafrost, but sea ice is very significant in terms of global climate change. Sea ice regulates the heat, moisture, and salinity in polar oceans. Sea water is relatively warm compared to the frigid air above because the ice acts as an insulator between the two. The formation of sea ice has important implications for people and animals alike, especially for those in the Arctic. For example, materials such as oil and nickel must be transported out of the Arctic in the summer, when the ice pack is thinnest. Ship captains manoeuvre their specially designed icebreakers through openings and away from treacherous ice. Polar bears, seals, and walruses, on the other hand, live almost entirely on sea ice and depend on its existence for their survival.

Hypertemporal satellite remote-sensed data indicates that a 2.9 per cent decline in the amount of sea ice in the Arctic is taking place each decade. The decline in the Southern Hemisphere is less dramatic at 1.3 per cent per decade. Not only is the area of sea ice declining but its thickness is also decreasing.

For humans, the increase of open water could have possible benefits such as easier transportation in the Arctic Ocean. Inuit and other traditional hunters and fishers will have greater access to the sea. Animals, however, will not be as fortunate. Polar bears in Hudson Bay were at the point of starvation in the winter of 2000. Sea ice was not staying as long in the giant bay and the bears were not able to hunt on ice floes as they always did. Polar bears hunt by waiting on an ice pack near an air hole. When seals and whales come to the hole to get air, the bears kill them. The absence of sea ice has deprived them of their main food source. Some biologists predict polar bears will be on the endangered list in 20 years if the amount of sea ice continues to decline.

Glaciers

When snow falls all winter and fails to melt in the summer, an ice age has begun. Considerable information about glaciers as gradational forces was presented in Chapter 9. In this section, the dynamics of glacial advance and retreat will be discussed.

Deposits of snow are the basis for glacial ice. In the summer, this snow changes to ice pellets called **firn** as periods of freezing and thawing

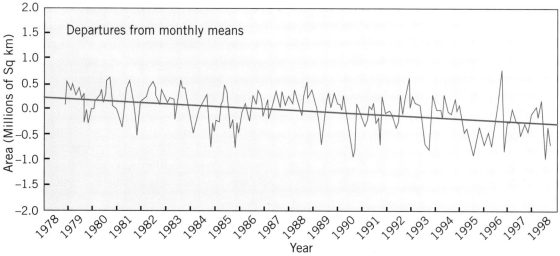

Figure13.7
This graph shows the decline in the extent of Northern Hemisphere sea ice from 1978 to 1999.

Permafrost: No Longer Permanent

The Geological Survey of Canada set up a series of monitoring stations several years ago along 1200 km of the Mackenzie Valley in the Northwest Territories; these stations continue to monitor permafrost today. Analysis of the active permafrost layer and its variability over time and through space are the objectives of the study. The Mackenzie Valley was chosen for the study for a number of reasons, not the least of which is the fact that the region has warmed more than anywhere else in Canada (1.7° C in the last century). The findings show an increase in thaw penetration.

If mean annual air temperature increases several degrees in the next century, the impact on permafrost will be catastrophic. Many people may not be concerned since the region is widely considered to be a wasteland, but if current trends continue, permafrost in Canada could virtually disappear by the year 2100. What would this mean? The land would be rendered useless for centuries as the surface gradually dried up. Thousands of years of accumulated organic matter in the soil would start to decompose, creating a massive infusion of methane into the atmosphere. The impact of all these new greenhouse gases could make global warming become even more of a problem in Canada and around the world.

Questions:
1. Explain how living with permafrost poses unique challenges for people living in northern communities.
2. What are the negative impacts that the melting of permafrost would have on each of the following.
   a) world climate change
   b) local habitats
   c) agriculture
   d) human habitation
   e) soil formation
   f) local drainage patterns
   g) human mobility
   h) animal migration
3. How could people use technology to help overcome some of the difficulties melting permafrost could pose?

alter its crystalline structure. If you are a skier, you may know firn as "corn snow" since it resembles the shape and size of corn kernels. Like sedimentary rock, glacial ice develops in layers as fresh accumulations of snow are added each winter. Deep beneath the surface, the layers of snow change under the pressure caused by the weight of the snow above. Air pockets between the ice crystals are squeezed out. Over a long period of time, the ice crystals grow and join together to form a solid sheet of ice. In Antarctica, where there is little precipitation and temperatures are extremely low, it may take 1000 years for surface snow to metamorphose into glacial ice.

The most significant property of glacial ice is that it flows like a thick liquid. The immense pressure of its own mass causes the ice to flow outward from its source. Most glaciers move so slowly—only a few metres a year—that change is unnoticeable from day to day. It is only when measurements are taken from year to year that movement is detected. Yet there are incidents of what is called **glacial surge**. The Bering Glacier, an Alaskan ice floe two-thirds the size of Prince Edward Island, has moved faster than any glacier in modern times—10 km during a nine-month period. A surge may occur in a glacier every 25–30 years. The reason for these surges is uncertain, but it could be the result of **basal slippage**: Heat and friction between the glacier and the ground cause some of the ice to melt. The meltwater then lubricates the surface, allowing the ice to slide more easily and rapidly.

The movement of alpine glaciers is directed by the shape of the landforms through which they flow. They move out of the mountains into the valleys, and sometimes end up flowing into the oceans. When either continental or alpine glaciers flow into regions where summer temperatures are high enough to melt the ice, the glacier starts to become thinner. This area is called the **zone of ablation**. The glacier is in equilibrium if the same amount of ice is being added at the source as is melting in the zone of ablation. This almost never happens, however. The glacier is

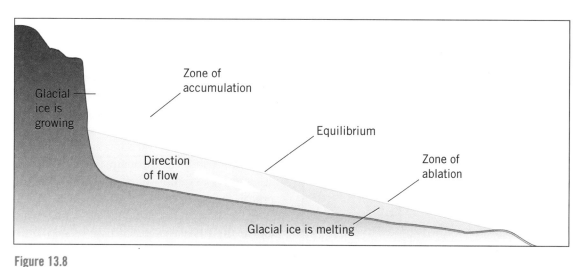

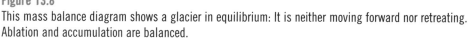

Figure 13.8
This mass balance diagram shows a glacier in equilibrium: It is neither moving forward nor retreating.
Ablation and accumulation are balanced.

usually either advancing or retreating. When it advances, it is building; when it retreats, it is melting. The term "retreat" is somewhat inaccurate because it suggests that the glacier is moving backward toward its source area, when in fact it is continuing to flow out of the source, but it is melting faster than it can build up.

Over the past billion years, there have been many glacial periods and many periods when glaciers retreated. Studies of sea cores indicate that recent ice ages started 36 million, 15 million, and 3 million years ago. In the most recent ice age, glaciers have advanced and retreated no less than 20 times. The last advance was at its height 20 000 years ago and ended about 11 000 years ago, although it will advance again.

It is possible to get some idea of what the climate was like thousands and even millions of years ago by studying aspects of the biosphere and the lithosphere, such as plant pollen, lake sediments, tree rings, and air bubbles in ice caps. We know, for example, that there has been a period of global cooling every 100 000 years during the most recent ice age. The pattern has repeated itself at least eight times over the past 800 000 years. Between each glacial period, there is a time when temperatures rise 4° to 6°C. We are currently in one of these **interglacial**

periods, but we are due for a new ice age to begin. Don't get your overcoat out yet, however. It could be 10 000 years before the effects are widely felt.

This seems to run counter to all the other evidence supporting the idea that the cryosphere is shrinking. Global temperatures may have been increasing over the past hundred years or so, but they also increased rapidly 125 000 years ago, just before the temperature dropped 10°C about 120 000 years ago. Could the same pattern repeat itself? We may experience massive global cooling in the next thousand years instead of the expected and dreaded global warming. Which would be worse?

There are many theories about why these glacial periods occur. One theory suggests that they are related to fluctuations in Earth's orbit and tilt on its axis. Just as a spinning top wobbles from time to time, the earth wobbles as it spins on its axis, causing a disruption to the solar energy entering the atmosphere and possibly resulting in an ice age. The orbit of the earth around the sun is elliptical. When the sun is closest to the earth (147 100 000 km), about 7 per cent more solar energy enters the atmosphere than when it is furthest away (152 000 000 km). At present, the sun is closest on January 3 and

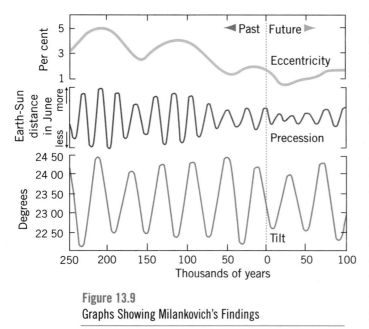

Figure 13.9
Graphs Showing Milankovich's Findings

furthest away on July 4. The time of the year when the earth is nearest to the sun changes over time, in a cycle that takes about 21 000 years. This shifting of the tilt is known as the **precession of the equinoxes**. If the time when the sun is furthest away from the earth coincides with winter in the Northern Hemisphere, snowfall could be greater and an ice age could be triggered. It is likely though that this effect would be too slight to cause an ice age. However, if combined with other cyclical fluctuations in orbit and tilt, the cooling could be significant enough that glaciation could increase.

Marked fluctuations in solar energy entering the atmosphere also occur because of changes in the shape of the orbit. At times it is nearly circular, while at others it is elliptical. This pattern is observed over a 90 000-year cycle and is known as the **eccentricity of orbit**. When the orbit is more or less circular, the difference between summer and winter is minimal. When it is elliptical, the earth is warmer when the planet is closer to the sun and colder when it is further away. If the orbit is such that the Northern Hemisphere is tilted away from the sun when the earth is at its maximum distance from the sun,

the summer temperatures may be so low that the snow that has fallen during the winter will not melt. When this happens over several years, an ice age has begun for the region where it occurs. However, scientists don't believe that this factor alone is enough to trigger an ice age, and their theory is supported by geological evidence.

A third source of variation in solar inputs results from shifts in the earth's axis. Although the earth is currently tilted at 23.5° from the vertical, it fluctuates by 2.4°, from about 22° to 24.4°. Following a 40 000-year cycle, this **variation in the tilt** affects seasonality. When the tilt is greater, seasonal variations are greater; when it is less, annual temperature ranges are smaller. Put simply, if the earth tilts more, winters become more severe. But still, the effect would probably not be enough to trigger an ice age.

On their own, none of these three variations in orbit and tilt were responsible for the commencing of each glacial period. But when cycles coincided—in other words, when the sun was furthest away from the Northern Hemisphere in winter, the orbit was at its maximum ellipticity, and the tilt was at its greatest angle—ice ages occurred. Yugoslav scientist Milutin Milankovich, by studying cores of sediments in the Indian Ocean, showed that there is a very strong correlation between glacial periods and the combined effect of these three cycles (see Fig. 13.9).

One interesting theory to explain glacial cycles has to do with the relationship between sea level changes and natural gas (methane) deposits in continental shelves. This is how the theory goes: When there is an interglacial period like the one we are experiencing now, ice caps melt and the sea level rises. Coastal plains become continental shelves as they are inundated by rising oceans. Methane deposits in these continental shelves become stable because of the pressure of all the water on top of them, and this natural greenhouse gas cannot bubble to the surface. The greenhouse effect decreases because of the reduction of methane in the atmosphere, world temperatures drop, and a new ice age is born as a result. Because so much water is now trapped in glacial ice, the methane deposits are uncovered. They are able to bubble to the surface and enter the atmosphere. The atmosphere consequently becomes warmer and the ice age ends.

Despite the possibility of another glacial advance, glaciers are generally shrinking worldwide. The National Snow and Ice Data Center indicates that 30 glaciers, for which there are records dating back 40 years, have been melting faster than they are growing, so we are unlikely to experience another glacial advance in our lifetimes.

Determining Central Tendency

Central tendency is a term used in statistical analysis to find the usual or most common number for a sample population. Geographers use central tendency to determine patterns. In analysing climate, for example, the mean monthly temperature is used as a measure of what the temperature is usually like. Median is also useful, especially if values are widely different. It is useful to know the middle number when there may be several very low values or very high numbers that could distort values. Median is also useful when studying chaotic patterns. Since median is the central value, it gives us an idea of what usually happens. If you were studying how glaciers were decreasing in mass on a global scale, the mean might not be significant because of extreme variations in some area. The median value could give glaciologists an idea of what one would normally find upon visiting any glacier randomly selected.

We all know what "average" means, and we know how to calculate it, but there are other ways to determine central tendency. These are summarized in the organizer below.

DEVELOPING SKILLS

Central Tendency	Description/Calculation	Example
Mean (average)	Divide the sum for all members by the number of members.	9 people had 35 showers, so 35/9 = 3.9 showers.
Mode	The most common number for the population	Herb had 4 showers, Jonathan had 2 showers, Tanya had 3 showers, Wendy had 4 showers, Luis had 6 showers, Sam had 6 showers, Sean had 4 showers, Ari had 5 showers, Jessica had 1 shower. The mode is 4 showers.
Median	If the number is listed sequentially, the value with the same number of examples above and the same number below is the median.	1, 2, 3, 4, 4, 4, 5, 6, 6 The median is 4.

TRY IT!

1. In Figure 13.7 on page 209, explain in detail what is being shown by the jagged and straight lines on the graph.

2. Study Figure 13.3 on page 206.
   a) Calculate the mean millimetres of snow cover per square kilometres for the years listed from 1975 to 2000.

   b) Can the median be shown for this graph?
   c) Can the mode be given for this graph?

ACTIVITIES

UNDERSTANDING CONCEPTS

1. a) Prepare an organizer summarizing the different elements of the cryosphere, using the model below. If all the information cannot be found in the text, do some research at the library or on the Internet to find it.

Factor	Snow Cover	Permafrost	Sea Ice	Glaciers
Extent				
Description				
Impact on the Atmosphere				
Impact on the Biosphere				
Impact on the Lithosphere				
Impact on People				
Trends				
Technology used for Monitoring				

b)   Which of the four areas in part a) do you think is the most significant in terms of its effect on the planet?

c)   What alarming similarity is evident in all the elements of the cryosphere?

2. a)   Identify the changes that are occurring in the cryosphere.

b)   Describe how these changes are occurring.

3. a)   Summarize the three theories provided to explain cyclical patterns of glaciation.

b)   Which theory do you believe to be the most plausible? Explain your answer.

DEVELOPING AND PRACTISING SKILLS

4.   Explain the relationships that link global patterns of ice and snow to climate, soils, and vegetation.

5.   Study the following two web sites.
State of the Cryosphere <www.ncidc.colorado.edu/NASA/SOTC>
State of the Canadian Cryosphere < www.msc-smc.ec.gc.ca/crysys/state/>

a)   Summarize the content of each web site.

b)   Report on any recent events or data contained in the site that show changes in the cryosphere.

LEARNING THROUGH APPLICATION

6.   Explain how human activities are affecting the cryosphere.

7. a)   Explain how technology is helping geographers and scientists to monitor the cryosphere.

b)   Describe the difficulties with and limitations of different monitoring techniques.

8. a)   How are changes in the cryosphere international in scope?

b)   Why is international co-operation essential if scientists are to be better able to monitor global patterns?

9.   Using the Internet, determine which Canadian universities offer programs suitable for a would-be glaciologist. Do further research to find out what employment prospects are available for such a professional.

UNIT 3

Culminating Activity: Analyzing Your Water Use

In this unit we have seen that water has a tremendous impact on the atmosphere, the lithosphere, and the biosphere. But most people are more concerned with the importance of water for people. North Americans use more water than any other group of people in the world. We shower in it, skate on it, swim in it, drink it, and use it for industrial processes. The Walkerton tragedy highlighted at the beginning of this section was a wake-up call for legislators, municipal politicians, and citizens alike to become more aware of our water resources.

1. Prepare a survey of water consumption in your home using an organizer similar to the one on the next page. The suggested Measurement Process allows you to estimate water consumption for your family. You will need a 2 L pop bottle or other measuring device and a bucket. The numbers that appear are just examples.

2. Summarize the data you collected and determine the total average water consumption per day for each family member. Compare it to the national average of 350 L per day. Compare it to the families of other members of your group or class.
   a) How did your family compare?
   b) Account for why your total may have been high or low.

3. Analyse water use by your family compared to other group members'. Determine the **mean**, **mode**, and **median** values.
   a) Graph your results compared to your classmates'.
   b) Which areas of consumption were high compared to other students?

c) Which areas of consumption were low compared to other students?
   d) Account for variations in b) and c).

4. Determine areas where water consumption can be reduced in your family. Consider some of the following conservation methods then come up with a list of your own.
   - Reducing shower time and using less bath water
   - Collecting rainwater from downspouts for garden irrigation
   - Reducing the volume of water used for flushing by putting a pop bottle full of water in the water storage tank at the back of the unit.

5. Present a plan to your family to reduce consumption. Encourage a commitment from each member to make your plan work. Make posters and reminders around taps, showers, and sinks to remind your family of your plan.

6. Record water usage for a week after implementing your conservation plan in your home. Use written, oral, or visual communication methods to present the results of your analyses to the class.

7. Determine the total savings for the whole class.

8. As a class project, encourage other students in the school to also reduce water consumption through skits at an assembly, posters, announcements, and so on.

9. Initiate a Water Festival in your school where you display the results of your study and encourage water conservation.

10. As a class, create a web site to encourage other schools to take up the challenge to reduce water consumption.

Water Use	Number of times used in one week	Measurement Process	Total Consumption in one week
Drinking	4 glasses x 4 people x 7 days = 196 glasses	Place a record sheet by the kitchen sink. (If bottled water is used, count the number of bottles discarded.)	196 glasses @ 500 ml each = 98 L
Showers	1 shower x 3 people x 7 days = 21 showers	Run the shower into a bucket for one minute. Place a record sheet by the shower.	Number of minutes of total showers x amount of water in one minute (127 x 9.0 L = 1143 L)
Baths	9 baths	After a bath empty it with a bucket to estimate the amount of water used. Post a record sheet by the bathtub.	Number of baths times bathtub capacity (9 x 40 L = 360 L
Lawn Irrigation	4 times	Determine how much water flows through the hose in one minute and multiply by the number of minutes used. Post a record sheet by the garden tap.	Number of minutes lawn is watered x amount of water in one minute (14 L x 85 minutes = 1190 L)
Toilet Flushes	4 people x 7 days	23 L is the average consumption for toilet flushing per day.	4 people x 7 days x 27 L = 756 L
Washing hands and face	4 people x 7 days	4 L is the average consumption for washing per day.	4 people x 7 days x 4 L = 112 L
Cooking	7 days	10 L is the average consumption for cooking for a family per day.	10 L x 7 = 70 L
Dishwasher	7 days	64 L is the average consumption for dishwashing for a family per load.	64 L x 7 = 448 L
Washing Clothes	7 days	230 L is the average consumption for clothes washing for a family per day.	230 L x 7 = 1610 L
Swimming Pool	Divide pool by 52 weeks to get the weekly consumption.	Estimate volume of water (length x width x average depth).	(4 x 8 x 1.5) / 52 = 923 L
Other *			

* Other could include washing the car, brushing teeth and so on.

UNIT 4

THE AIR ABOVE: UNDERSTANDING THE ATMOSPHERE

Human Drama

EFFECTS OF GLOBAL WARMING CLEAR IN CANADIAN ARCTIC

He may be only a hunter in Canada's remote Arctic, but Steven Kooneeliusie certainly knows as much about the practical effects of global warming as any environmental scientist.

He and the other Inuit whose job it is to brave snow and ice to find caribou, seal, and other animals say the signs of a gradual increase in temperature are everywhere.

"When I went hunting years ago I used to wear a full-length caribou skin coat, but now I just wear a light parka. It is so hot these days my snowmobile often overheats," Kooneeliusie said in the small town of Pangnirtung, some 1,500 miles (2,450 km) north of Ottawa nearly on the Arctic Circle.

"We're seeing animals here we've never seen before, and last year I spotted a swan. The sun is very hot, too hot. For the first time ever people are actually getting sunburned."

While arguments rage about whether global warming is primarily caused by pollution, the effects on the ground are all too real in the Arctic. One of the best places to observe them is the new territory of Nunavut, home to 27,000 people dotted across 750,000 square miles (2 million square km).

U.S. government researchers say average global temperatures over the last 25 years alone have been increasing at a rate equivalent to 2°C a century.

Studies show the Arctic sea ice has also thinned over the last 30 years or so to 2 metres from 3 metres and has shrunk by around 6 per cent since 1975.

This month, scientists from the United States and Europe said more than 60 per cent of the Arctic ozone layer some 18 km above the Earth had vanished over the winter due to record cold and continued pollution—one of the most substantial ozone losses at this altitude ever recorded.

As the Arctic gradually heats up, precipitation increases and helps push the tree line ever further to the north.

Some scientists say there is a flip side to global warming. You can anticipate warmer periods, increased opportunities for tourism, and even agricultural production. There would be an increase in marine

Continued on next page.

productivity as more plankton would be produced.

But Kilabuk is frustrated that once again Nunavut is paying the price for what he sees as polluting southern industries.

The solutions to these problems can only be determined once definite causes are found. But this will take time and money says Jamal Shirley, science and technology manager at the Nunavut Research Institute. "There is a vast amount of research to be done. These are long-term studies which need long-term funding."

*(Story by David Ljunggren,
REUTERS NEWS SERVICE)*

Some hunters in Canada's Far North say the climate change has been dramatic.

Unit Focus Questions

1. What are the sources and nature of energy flows through the atmosphere?

2. What are the causes and consequences of past and future climate change?

3. How do humans impact on natural systems and cause or exacerbate such problems as the depletion of the ozone layer, acid deposition, and global warming?

INTRODUCTION

In this section of the book you will begin to understand the incredible complexities that operate in the atmosphere. Whenever changes occur on the face of the planet, whether they relate to the hydrosphere, the lithosphere, or the biosphere, atmospheric conditions will also change. Sometimes the changes are minor; often they are significant.

Changeable weather is a daily occurrence brought on by differences in air pressure, but over the long term, climate conditions also change. The warming of global temperatures, for example, brings about dramatic changes in Canada's north. Many people are concerned that climate change is happening so fast that we will not be able to adequately adapt. Certainly the people of Nunavut have a great challenge ahead.

The thin outer shell of the earth is called the atmosphere. Because it is made up of gases and is often transparent, it is easy to forget that the air that surrounds Earth is really a part of our planet. The atmosphere is essential to life on Earth for several reasons, the most obvious of which is that it provides oxygen for animals to breathe. Less obvious is the fact that it provides the carbon dioxide that plants need for **photosynthesis** to occur. The atmosphere moves thermal energy from the equatorial regions to polar regions. If it did not do this, the temperatures would be too hot in the tropics and too cold at high latitudes for most life forms to survive. In fact, life would not exist on this planet at all if it were not for the warmth created by the greenhouse effect. You may think that the greenhouse effect is an environmental problem, but it is the greenhouse gases in the atmosphere that trap solar energy in the form of heat and prevent it from escaping into space. This makes Earth's environment warm enough for life to survive.

The final reason why the atmosphere is essential to life forms' survival is that it shields them from the sun's harmful ultraviolet rays. You can therefore see the importance of the atmosphere in creating and sustaining this remarkable planet.

By the end of this unit, you will be able to do the following:

Geographic Foundations: Space and Systems
- Demonstrate an understanding of the principal features of the earth's atmosphere;
- Explain the sources and nature of energy flows through the atmosphere.

Human-Environment Interaction
- Explain how the earth provides both a habitat for life and a resource for society;
- Evaluate the impacts of natural systems on people and their activities;
- Evaluate the impact of human life on natural systems;
- Demonstrate an understanding of the importance of stewardship and sustainability as guiding principles for human use of the earth.

Global Connections
- Analyse global climates to determine reasons for the observed patterns;
- Analyse local, regional, and global issues related to physical geography (i.e., ozone depletion, acid rain).

Understanding and Managing Change
- Analyse the causes and consequences of past and future climate change;
- Analyse changes in natural systems caused by natural phenomena;
- Explain how human uses of the earth, including uses involving technology, cause change in natural systems.

Methods of Geographic Inquiry
- Use geographic skills, methods, and technologies to gather, analyse, and synthesize ideas and information;
- Use a variety of methods and technologies to communicate the results of geographic inquiry and analysis effectively;
- Describe careers related to physical geography.

Contents

Chapter 14

THE ENERGY ABOVE: THE PROPERTIES OF THE ATMOSPHERE

FOCUS QUESTIONS

1. How does the earth's orbit and tilt relate to the seasons and annual variations in climate?
2. What are the mechanisms of change within the atmosphere?
3. How do human activities affect the ozone layer?

Key Terms

troposphere

air pressure

circle of illumination

isobars

magnetosphere

In order to understand the processes that occur in the atmosphere, we must first study its four main characteristics: the atmosphere is fluid, it is made up of various gases, it has mass, and it consists of layers. An understanding of these properties helps us to understand the complex processes that occur within this vital element of the planet.

The Atmosphere is Fluid

Fluids are substances that can flow from place to place. While solids can flow when they are exposed to enormous heat and pressure, most fluids are either liquid or gas. Because the atmosphere is made up mainly of gases, it flows from one place to another. When foreign substances enter the air at one place on the earth's surface, the atmosphere can spread it considerable distances from that point of origin.

These foreign substances can be natural or human-made, and include such things as smoke from forest fires, dust from volcanic eruptions, pesticides sprayed from airplanes, and chemical gases from factories. **Chlorofluorocarbons (CFCs)**, for example, are chemically stable gases manufactured in some developing countries for use in air conditioners and refrigerators. When they float up into the ozone layer, they eventually flow around the planet and destroy the ozone in the upper atmosphere. Ozone is essential because it filters out the ultra-violet rays that are harmful to most life on Earth. If the CFCs stayed in one place they could easily be dealt with.

The Atmosphere is Made up of Various Gases

While the main gases in the atmosphere include nitrogen and oxygen, other gases exist in smaller quantities. Carbon dioxide is one of these seemingly insignificant gases. While this form of oxidized carbon comprises only about 3/10 000 of the total atmosphere, it is the most essential of the greenhouse gases and is responsible for keeping heat energy from the sun close to the earth's surface. Water vapour, while also seemingly insignificant at 0–4 per cent (on average) is vital to both plants and animals to transport nutrients through cell membranes. These gases are not spread evenly throughout the atmosphere. Carbon dioxide concentrations are often higher over crowded cities where this gas is emitted by cars and factories through the burning of fossil fuels. The air over bodies of water and forests usually has a higher level of water vapour (humidity) than air over arid lands.

Of the main ingredients of the atmosphere, nitrogen makes up approximately 78 per cent and oxygen takes up most of the rest of the total at about 21 per cent. Nitrogen is an important nutrient used by both plants and animals. Oxygen is essential for life and combines with fuels when they are burned.

The Atmosphere Has Mass

Clean air is invisible, but this does not mean that nothing is there. Just like solids and liquids, gases occupy space and have mass. The weight of the air is referred to as **air pressure**. Fig. 14.1 shows how air pressure forces a column of mercury up a vacuum tube. This proves that the air pressing down on the surface of the mercury has mass.

Air pressure varies with elevation. As you go up a mountain, there is less air above you, so the air pressure is lower. Mountain climbers often experience altitude sickness because they cannot get enough oxygen into their bloodstreams due to the air's "thinness." Of course the air is not actually thin, but there is such a low mass of air per given volume that it takes a great effort to breathe in sufficient oxygen. Experienced climbers either use oxygen tanks or take their time, so as not to overtax their cardiovascular systems. Interestingly, Bolivians living in the high plateaux of their South American country have adapted to the lower air pressure. They have larger lungs and more red corpuscles in their bloodstream to compensate.

Air pressure does not stay constant at each elevation, however, because it is affected by the heating and cooling of the earth's surface. Hot air rises, so the air pressure at higher elevations is less than that of the cool air at lower elevations, which is usually heavier. The fact that air moves from areas of high pressure to areas of low pressure causes the weather systems in the atmosphere.

Air pressure is measured in millibars or kilopascals. A millibar is approximately one-thousandth of standard sea-level air pressure. At sea level, air pressure is standard at 1013.2 millibars or 101.32 kPa (kilopascals). Ten millibars equals one kilopascal—the measurement used by Atmospheric Environment Service in weather reports. In the daily weather map produced by the Atmospheric Environment Service, places across the country with the same air pressure are joined together with lines, forming **isobars**. Low-pressure cells and high-pressure cells are thus identified on the maps, which are used to

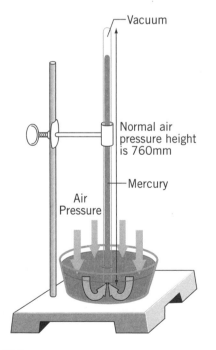

Figure 14.1
This barometer shows the column of mercury being raised in a glass tube by air pressure.

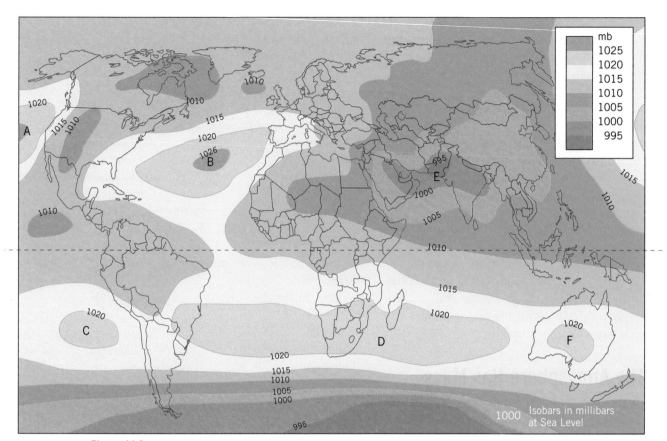

Figure 14.2
Isobar Map Showing Pressure Cells Around the World in July

make weather forecasts. Lows are relatively warm, moist air while highs are relatively cool and dry. Study the map in Fig. 14.2 to determine what the air is like in each of the places identified on the map.

The Atmosphere Consists of Layers

The atmosphere consists of five layers with transitional regions between most (as seen in Fig. 14.3). Not shown in the figure is the **magnetosphere**, the force field that extends far into space in a transition zone that blurs the lines between where the atmosphere ends and outer space begins. While each layer possesses individual characteristics, the most important differences are in air pressure and temperature.

If you were in a hot-air balloon, you would experience the characteristics of each layer as you floated into outer space. Starting directly above the earth's surface in the **troposphere**, you would likely experience great turbulence because this layer is where all the world's weather occurs. Most life on earth depends on the troposphere for survival. Even sea creatures need the atmosphere to provide them with essential gases such as oxygen, which is mixed into the water with each wave that breaks on the shore. Air currents and the friction caused by the earth's rotation make currents in the troposphere the roughest of all the layers. Since air is rising and falling as well as moving horizontally along the earth's surface, your balloon would be swept all over the place as it was buffeted by storms and prevailing winds.

Going up through the **troposphere**, the temperature gradually drops with the air pressure. Therefore, your balloon would become bigger as the air pressure in it increased relative to the air outside. By the time you reached the top of this layer, the temperature would be very cold and the air pressure very low since you would have passed through 90 per cent of the earth's atmosphere.

The tropopause is a transitional layer that separates the troposphere from the stratosphere. Its dimensions vary from about 16 km at the equator to only 9 km at the poles. In the tropopause, the temperature stops falling and stabilizes at about -55°C. The turbulence of the troposphere is left behind, and in this layer's cold, still environment, artificial breathing apparatus and warm clothing would be essential.

Once you passed through the tropopause, you would enter the **stratosphere**. This layer contains two features that greatly affect people far below: the **jet stream**, which affects the movement of storms in the troposphere; and the **ozone layer**, which filters out harmful solar rays. As in the tropopause, vertical air movement is minimal, but there are horizontal currents in this layer known as the jet stream, which guide storm systems. Studying jet streams helps forecasters determine daily temperatures and precipitation. If the currents loop down from the Yukon to the Great Lakes region, then the weather will likely be cold and dry; If the loop comes from the southwest, then it is often much warmer.

Molecules of **ozone**—a special form of oxygen that absorbs ultraviolet radiation—are spread throughout the stratosphere. Air temperature rises as energy is released from the interplay between the ozone and the ultraviolet rays. Heat from the ozone radiates up and down so that the lower layers of the stratosphere are colder than the upper layers where most of the ozone is located. At 40 km above the earth's surface, the temperature rises above freezing. In your balloon, you would need protection from ultraviolet radiation at this level since there would be little to no ozone layer to protect you.

In the **stratopause**, another transition zone, the temperature stops increasing as the stratospheric ozone thins out with altitude. This layer is

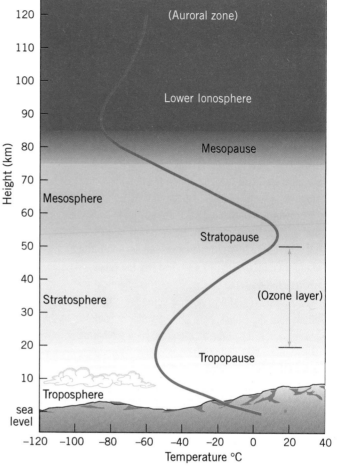

Figure 14.3
Layers of the Atmosphere. Explain why the temperature rises in the stratosphere.

the beginning of the outer atmosphere. For the next 30 km outside the stratopause, your balloon would pass through the **mesosphere**. The temperature drops steadily through this layer until it reaches about –100°C at the transition zone called the **mesopause**. Here, the temperature stabilizes, and then rises once again. The air is so thin here that it would seem as though you were already in outer space.

The next layer, the **ionosphere** (also called the **thermosphere**), is the widest one, ranging from 80 to 480 km. The lack of air pressing down from above results in very little air at this level.

ENVIRONMENT WATCH

Monitoring Ozone Depletion

The sun is the creator of most of the world's energy and is ultimately responsible for life on Earth. However, not all of the sun's rays are beneficial to living organisms. One type of ultraviolet radiation, UVB, causes mutations in the genetic structures of plant and animal cells. These changes can lead to skin cancer, disruptions in the immune system, and eye disease (cataracts) in people.

Chlorofluorocarbons (CFCs) are synthetic chemicals that destroy the ozone layer. Used mainly in air conditioning and refrigeration, these chemicals leak into the atmosphere where it dissipates and destroys the ozone.

Take the example CF_2Cl_2. When this chemical is released into the atmosphere, it spreads uniformly throughout the troposphere and very slowly floats up to the ozone layer. It may take as many as 10 years before it comes in contact with high-level ozone. When ultraviolet radiation hits the CFC in the upper atmosphere, atomic bonds holding the molecule together are destroyed. The CF_2Cl_2 is broken down into CF_2Cl and a free atom of chlorine. This chlorine atom grabs an atom of oxygen away from one of the highly unstable ozone molecules floating by. Two new molecules are created: a chlorine monoxide (ClO) molecule and an oxygen molecule. The ozone molecule was destroyed. But the chlorine is not out of circulation yet. The ClO molecule combines with a free-floating, highly unstable oxygen atom (O), forming a molecule of oxygen (O_2) and the original chlorine atom. The chlorine atom is then free to continue destroying more ozone. Nobody knows how long the chlorine lasts but estimates of 50 to 100 years have been made.

It is over the Antarctic that the hole in the ozone layer was first noticed because it is the polar regions where the ozone is being depleted more than anywhere else. Over the poles, the winter night lasts six months, meaning that for half of each year ozone production stops. However, CFCs continue to work regardless of the time of year. When the sun returns in the spring, ozone production starts up again, but by that time the layer has thinned so much that even more UV rays are able to pass through the atmosphere.

The Canadian government has shown leadership in developing policies to reduce CFC use. In 1987, 130 nations including Canada signed the Montreal Protocol, an agreement that set timelines for the elimination of CFCs. The agreement called for a 50 per cent reduction of CFC use by the year 2000.

In December 1999 an amendment was made to the earlier agreement calling for the end of the production of less hazardous CFCs by January 2001. This means the phasing out of these chemicals will be significantly earlier than the originally agreed upon deadline of 2030. The impetus for the amendment was international concern over the increased rate of ozone depletion. For example, by the summer of 2000, the amount of harmful UV rays entering the atmosphere in Canada rose by 6 per cent.

On March 8, 2000, the Canadian Space Agency announced the construction of a new satellite to be launched in 2002. The SCIATAT-1 will cost $13 million and will be used to monitor ozone depletion over the Canadian Arctic. This new technology will help Canadians keep track of this important global issue.

Question:

Why should all countries, not just those located close to polar regions, be concerned about ozone layer depletion?

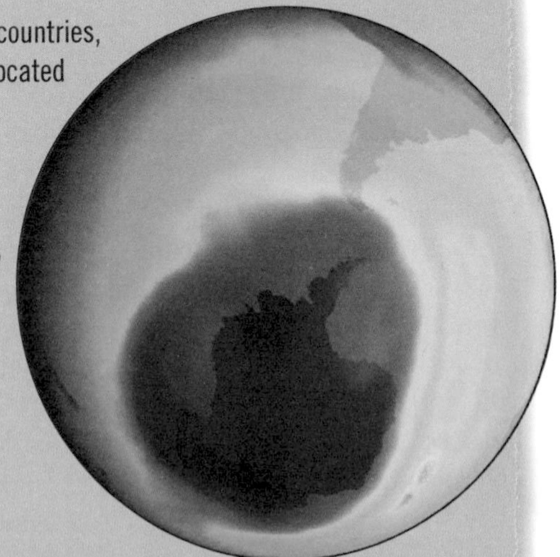

Figure 14.4
This image shows total ozone layer for December, 2000. The dark blue indicates thinnest areas.

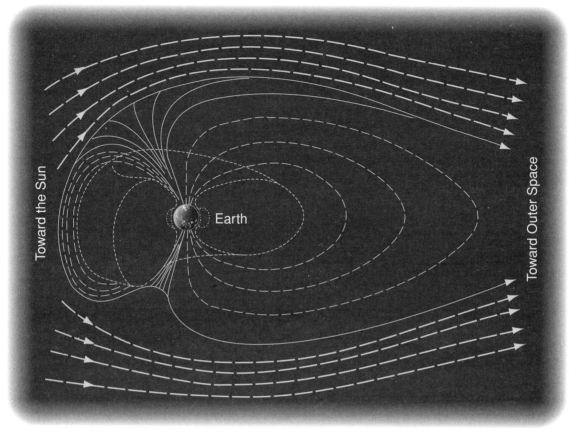

Figure 14.5
Diagram of the Magnetosphere

Air temperature increases as the sun's rays electrically break down the molecules of the atmosphere. As electrons and ions are created in the ionosphere, radiant energy is converted to thermal energy.

Outside these four layers of atmosphere is the **magnetosphere**, a layer that sometimes traps **solar wind**. Solar wind results when magnetic storms on the sun send streams of radioactive particles toward the earth. When these particles enter the magnetic field of the planet, they form into belts called Van Allen Belts, named after the man who discovered them. The rotation of the earth makes the planet behave like a magnet. The charged particles from the sun align themselves with the North and South poles, forming streaks of light in the sky. These Northern Lights, or **aurora borealis**, often light up the dark winter nights in northern Canada. Because the particles

are electrically charged, they affect radio and short-wave signals flowing through them. The crackling you hear on the radio is often caused by solar wind in the magnetosphere.

Bordering the magnetosphere is the final transition zone called the **magnetopause**. This layer forms a sharp dividing line between space and atmosphere, a location that accounts for its thickness. Unlike the other layers, it does not

geo.web resources

<www.ec.gc.ca/earthtones/index_e.html>

Environment Canada runs this site, which profiles numerous earth scientists. Explore their careers by clicking on the photo, then on a topic, then on the person's name.

form a symmetrical width around the earth but is shaped more like a teardrop. On the side facing the sun, the magnetopause is about 64 000 km from earth. The side facing away from the sun, towards space, may extend as far as 1.6 million kilometres—a distance so great that the magnetopause actually includes the moon.

Solar Energy in the Atmosphere

The sun sends most of its energy to Earth as light, or as super-charged radioactive particles as in the Van Allen Belts. This radiant energy passes through the atmosphere to reach the earth's surface. As it does, enormous amounts of energy are exchanged. Energy changes from radiant energy into thermal and kinetic energy. These complex energy transfers result in the common elements of daylight, heat, and wind in the troposphere.

Planet Earth is constantly in motion. It is spinning on its axis, tilted at 23.5° from the vertical, while at the same time revolving around the sun in an elliptical orbit. These two actions result in an unequal distribution of light at any one time.

Parts of the earth facing the sun get daylight while parts turned away are cloaked in darkness. The earth rotates in a counter clockwise direction every 24 hours (actually, the time period is slightly less), resulting in day and night.

The line that separates day and night is called the **circle of illumination**. A look at Fig. 14.7 shows that there is a transitional **twilight zone** that occurs at sunrise and sunset each day. During this time, the sun is so low on the horizon that only part of it is lighting the planet. Since the earth's position in Fig. 14.7 indicates that it is summer in the Northern Hemisphere, you will notice that there is no period of darkness in the High Arctic; it is either light or twilight. Imagine having six months when the sun never completely sets! During the sunset and sunrise, sunlight is reflected off dust particles and ice crystals in the atmosphere, often creating beautiful pink, gold, and orange colours in the sky. The sun sometimes seems much bigger as it sinks below the horizon. That is because the sunlight is travelling through more atmosphere than normal at this time and the air acts like a lens, bending the rays so that the sun looks as it would if viewed through a magnifying glass.

Because the earth is tilted, the lengths of day and night change with the seasons. When the earth is tilted toward the sun in summer, the sun's rays shine for a longer period of time each day. In winter, the earth is tilted away from the sun and the amount of sunlight received each day decreases. The only exception to this rule is at the equator (0° latitude) where day and night are both 12 hours long every day, all year.

Figure 14.6
Diagram showing the Circle of Illumination

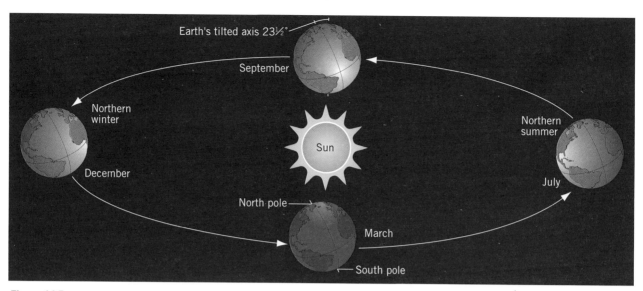

Figure 14.7
The Effect of Revolution and Tilt on Seasons

As you move away from the equator, the lengths of day and night become more extreme.

Around March 20 and September 20, the whole planet receives twelve hours of daylight and twelve hours of night. Called the **equinox**, this occurs when the sun is directly over the equator and the earth's axis is at right angles (90°) to the sun's rays. The regions poleward from the Arctic Circle and the Antarctic Circle experience at least one 24-hour day. The number of 24-hour days increases with latitude until you reach the poles, where half the year's days have 24 hours of light and half have 24 hours of night. By September 20 in the Northern Hemisphere, the trend reverses itself and darkness starts to take over. By December 20, the winter night may start just after lunch and last until after breakfast. Most Canadians, however, live further south where such extremes of day and night do not exist.

Thermal Energy – Intensity and Latitude

Every winter, thousands of Canadians travel south because Canada is a cold, northern country that lies in the mid to upper latitudes. Why do you think temperatures generally decrease as you move away from the equator? Some people might suggest that equatorial regions are warmer because the curvature of the earth results in the distance between the equator and the sun being less than the distance between the poles and the sun. But this difference is actually too small to have any significant impact on temperature. The reason it is colder at the poles than at the equator has to do with how the shape of the planet affects the **intensity** of sunlight. At the equinox, the sun is directly overhead at the equator, meaning that the angle of the noonday sun is perpendicular (90°) to the horizon. Moving away from the equator, the angle decreases steadily until it reaches 0° at the North and South poles where the sun sits right along the horizon.

As the sun's angle decreases, a greater area of the earth is exposed to the same amount of sunlight. It is as if the sunlight is diluted because it is spread over a larger area of the earth's surface. In other words, a larger area must be heated by the same amount of energy that heats a smaller area closer to the equator. Another, less significant factor has to do with the amount of atmosphere the sunlight passes through. At the equator, the sun enters the atmosphere at right angles and hits the earth at a 90° angle. This is the shortest distance through the atmosphere. There are fewer

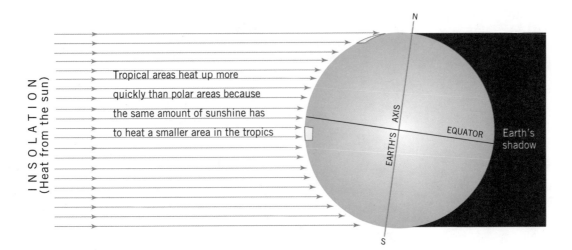

Figure 14.8
Solar Intensity and Latitude

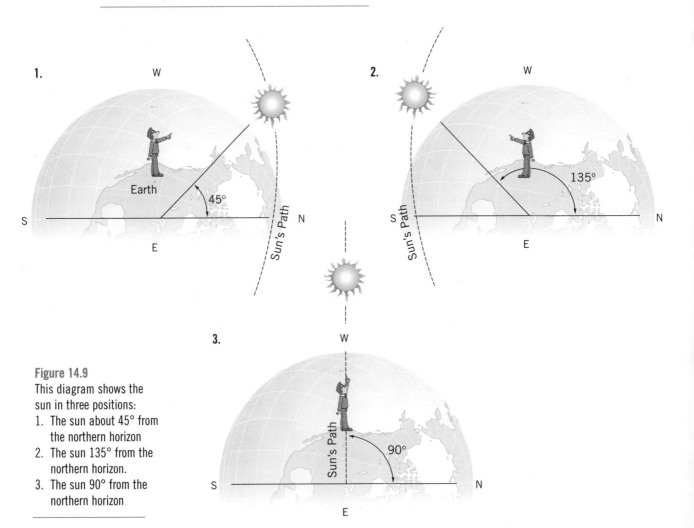

Figure 14.9
This diagram shows the
sun in three positions:
1. The sun about 45° from
   the northern horizon
2. The sun 135° from the
   northern horizon.
3. The sun 90° from the
   northern horizon

Date*	March 20	June 20	September 20	December 20
Sun is directly over:	Equator	Tropic of Cancer	Equator	Tropic of Capricorn
Season (N. Hem.):	Spring	Summer	Autumn	Winter
Season (S. Hem.):	Autumn	Winter	Spring	Summer
Name:	Equinox	Solstice	Equinox	Solstice

Figure 14.10
Seasons Organizer

*The date varies between the 20th and the 23rd of the month because of the leap year.

clouds, dust particles, and other objects to reflect sunlight back into space. As the angle steadily increases, the sun's rays have more atmosphere to pass through. Entering the atmosphere at an acute angle, rays lose increasingly more energy as they pass through layer after layer of atmosphere. This increased volume of air reduces the amount of radiant energy that reaches the earth's surface. Figure 14.8 shows this relationship.

Thermal Energy – Intensity and the Seasons

If you were to stand on the equator, look north, and measure the angle of the sun every day of the year, you would notice the following pattern: each day the sun rises in the east and sets in the west. In late December, the sun is rising behind your back because you are facing north. If you were to measure the sun's angle, you would find that it is closer to the southern horizon than the northern horizon. From December to March, the sun appears to move further north each day. Around March 20, the noonday sun is directly overhead at 90°. From March 20, this angle decreases until the sun appears to stop moving closer to the northern horizon on June 20. This day is called the **solstice** (solstice means "sun stand" in Latin). Now the sun appears to move back toward the southern horizon. By September

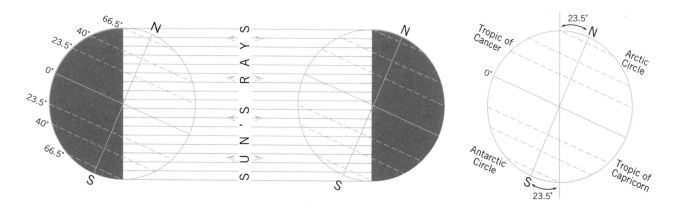

Figure 14.11
This diagram shows the relationship between the earth and the sun.

20, it is once again directly overhead at the equator. Finally, the sun sinks toward the southern horizon until the winter solstice around December 20. And so this pattern of the seasons continues year after year.

Of course, it only appears that the sun is moving. As our planet revolves around the sun, the Northern Hemisphere is tilted either toward the sun or away from it. When it is tilted toward the sun, the angle at which the sun's rays strike the surface is greater than when it is tilted away, so the amount of radiant energy is greater. The opposite process occurs in the Southern Hemisphere. Thus, when the Northern Hemisphere is tilted toward the sun, it is summer here in Canada and winter in Argentina.

The intensity of the sunlight at any given latitude changes as the seasons change. As the angle of the sun decreases, the amount of heat is reduced. Combined with fewer daylight hours, this makes for colder temperatures in winter. Generally, as latitude increases, the mean annual temperature of the winter months decreases. In summer, on the other hand, as the sun gets higher in the sky, the intensity of the sunlight and length of daylight increase. Summer returns as the temperatures rise.

Kinetic Energy – Wind

Kinetic energy refers to the energy of motion. Wind is the movement of air from one place to another across the surface of the earth, so it is a prime example of kinetic energy in the atmosphere. Air currents are actually the result of differences in surface heating. When a substance such as air is heated, it expands because the molecules move rapidly, causing the space between them to increase. This causes the molecules to spread out and become less dense, thereby causing the air to rise. Therefore, when one part of the earth is heated more than another, air rises over the warm surface and cooler air rushes in to fill the void. This action creates wind.

Maritime winds are local, caused by differences in surface temperature over the land and the sea. (Other winds are the result of mid-latitude storms, but these will be discussed in Chapter 15.) **Prevailing winds** are the most important of the winds because they occur on a global scale and spread the energy received at the equator to all parts of the globe.

Maritime Winds

Whenever two air masses have different temperatures, a **convectional flow** occurs. Consider maritime regions where air over the land interacts with air over the water. Water takes longer than land to heat up and cool down. In the summer, the air over water is often colder than the air over the land because the water has not yet warmed up since the winter freeze. This relatively cool maritime air is dense and therefore exerts a higher pressure on the earth's surface. Over land the air is warmer, so a low-pressure cell develops. This warmer air rises and the cooler maritime air is drawn in to take its place. For this reason, coastal cities often have cooler summer temperatures than cities further inland.

Another local wind factor has to do with **diurnal** differences in airflow. During the day, the air over land is often warmer than the air over the sea, so the winds blow inshore. At night, the maritime air is warmer than the land air, so the flow reverses.

Prevailing Winds

Prevailing winds are the winds that normally flow in any given place. Most Canadians are familiar with the westerlies. These are the winds that prevail in the middle latitudes. In polar regions and in the Tropics, winds tend to blow from the east. Prevailing winds blow as they do because of the dynamic forces of convection and the **Coriolis effect**.

British meteorologist George Hadley developed a theory in 1735 that explained the prevailing winds. He held that convection currents move hot air from the equator to the North Pole and South Pole. Air is heated over the equator and rises because the air pressure is reduced. Cooler air is drawn in to replace the rising column of warm air. With altitude, the warm air gradually cools and descends back to Earth.

CHANGING TECHNOLOGY:
The North Cape, PEI, Wind Turbine Test Site

Wind turbines are giant windmills that utilize modern engineering to produce electricity. While wind energy is still much more expensive to generate than conventional electricity, it is the fastest growing alternative fuel source worldwide.

Wind energy requires no fuel and produces no pollution. The drawbacks are that the windmills are expensive to erect, require frequent servicing, and can be dangerous if blown over in high winds.

North Cape in P.E.I. was chosen to test the many different types of wind turbines available since no matter when you visit the north shore, there is always a strong wind blowing from the frigid waters off the coast. In summer, the land is so much warmer that local convection currents draw the cool air over the cold water onto the north shore of the island. In winter, arctic gales blow south from Labrador. North Cape juts out into the Gulf of St. Lawrence, so it gets the full brunt of the wind.

Turbines work best when there are strong, steady winds. The violent gales that frequent the North Cape region give engineers the chance to experiment with override systems that shut the turbines down when winds are too high. The strong winds also bring freezing rain and sleet for much of the winter. Engineers want to test the various different turbines to see how experimental models will stand up in these severe weather conditions.

Worldwide, wind power is gaining considerable acceptance. Since ancient times, the coastal countries of the Netherlands, Belgium, and Denmark have

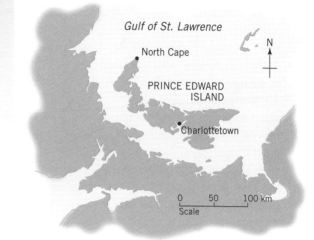

Figure 14.12
North Cape, P.E.I.

used windmills to pump water from low-lying fields. Today these countries are installing modern turbines along coastal areas to capture the wind energy. Since fossil fuels are much more expensive there than they are in North America, wind turbines are a cost-efficient source of energy in Europe.

Question:
Prepare a chart in which you compare the pro and cons of using wind turbines and fossil fuels to generate electricity.

Figure 14.13
Wind Turbines

But it does not come back down on the equator because there is more warm air constantly pushing it ever further from its origin. Finally, this cold air sinks back to Earth in polar regions, far from where it originated. As it drops, the air pressure increases and the air gains back some of the heat it lost when its molecules were so widely dispersed. In this way, equatorial heat is distributed around the planet.

Hadley lacked the technology to prove his theory, however. It was not until much later, in the middle of the twentieth century, that scientists studying prevailing winds found evidence to support it. They discovered that global circulation was considerably more complicated than Hadley had thought. Nevertheless, the model provided a good starting point for an understanding of global circulation patterns. Differences in surface elevation, the shape of continents and the presence of ice and snow, among other things, all complicated the pattern Hadley developed. Hadley's main premise that convection currents started the process was correct; however, a refinement in the model was needed. Instead of a single convection cell in each hemisphere, researchers found three separate cells in the Northern Hemisphere and three in the Southern Hemisphere. Fig. 14.14 illustrates this new model.

The Coriolis Effect

Prevailing winds are also influenced by the Coriolis effect. Northern Hemisphere winds are deflected to the right while Southern Hemisphere winds are swung to the left by the spinning of the earth on its axis. For a complete explanation of the Coriolis effect, turn to 178, where it is discussed as it affects ocean currents.

If you think back to Hadley's model, you'll remember that cooler air flows in to replace the warm air that has risen over the equator. Instead of flowing from the north in the Northern

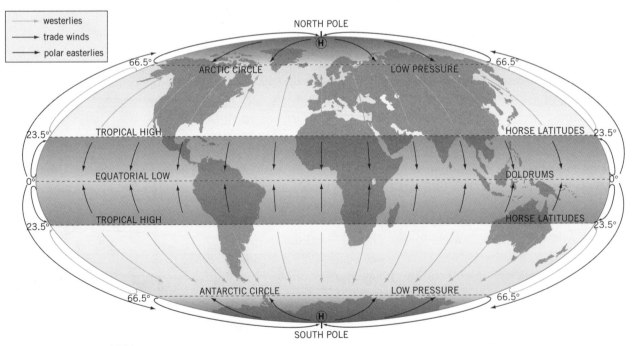

Figure 14.14
Cellular Model of Prevailing Winds. How is this model different from the one developed by meteorologist George Hadley?

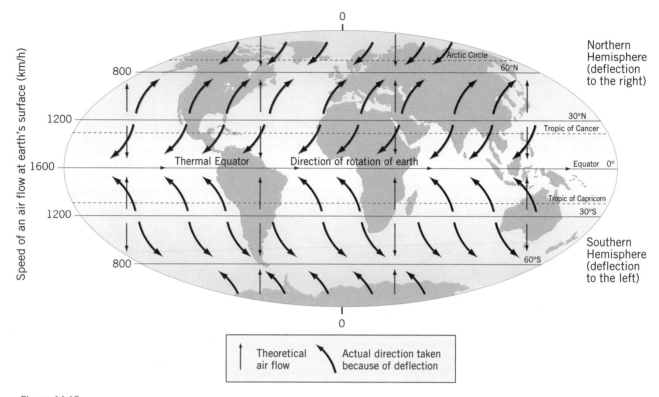

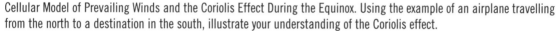

Figure 14.15
Cellular Model of Prevailing Winds and the Coriolis Effect During the Equinox. Using the example of an airplane travelling from the north to a destination in the south, illustrate your understanding of the Coriolis effect.

Hemisphere, these winds are deflected to the right. Therefore, they do not blow from the north but rather from the northeast. Similarly, in the Southern Hemisphere, winds originating over the Tropic of Capricorn blow from the southeast.

The trading ships of long ago used the force of the wind energy to get from one port to another—hence the name, the **trade winds**. In tropical climates where hot, muggy weather is common, refreshing winds off the ocean cool coastal regions. It is small wonder that most tropical cities are either coastal or in the cooler mountainous regions.

Directly over the equator, there is little to no wind because the air is rising in updrafts. These **doldrums** are characterized by violent storms in the late afternoon, as convection rainfall returns some of the moisture that evaporated from the sodden ground and the humid jungles.

In polar regions, frigid arctic air flows out over the polar ice sheets. The prevailing winds, called the **polar easterlies**, deflect once again to blow from the northeast in the Northern Hemisphere and the southeast in the Southern Hemisphere. As you can see, the earth's rotation and the Coriolis effect greatly modify the cellular model of prevailing winds.

As opposed to staying in one place, the prevailing winds change with the seasons. The sun is only directly over the equator in March and September. The rest of the time it is directly over a line of latitude somewhere between the equator and 23.5°. Geographers refer to the latitude directly under the noonday sun as the **thermal equator**. Its annual march back and forth between the Tropic of Cancer and the Tropic of Capricorn causes the belts of wind systems to also move north and south with the seasons.

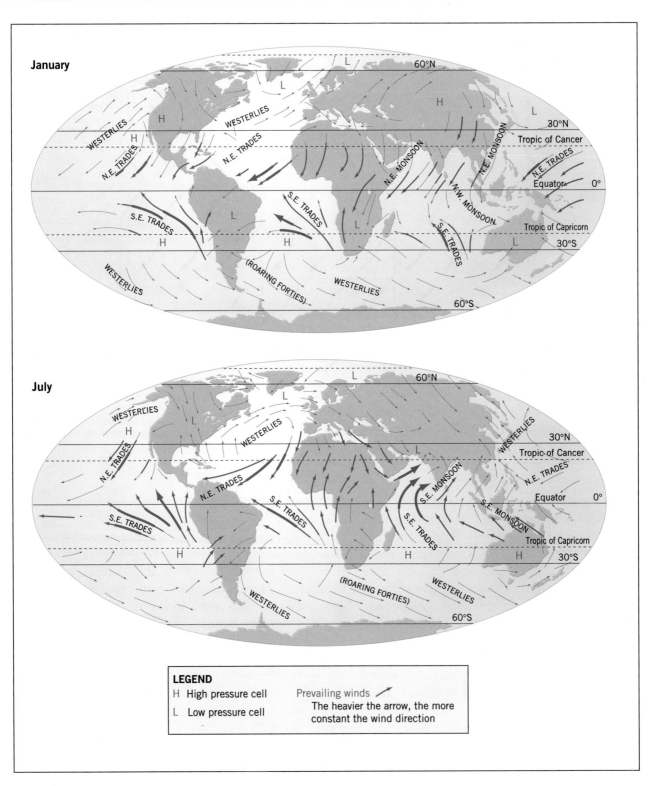

Figure 14.16
Prevailing Winds for January and July

ACTIVITIES

UNDERSTANDING CONCEPTS

1. Explain how each of the following properties of the atmosphere affects the biosphere.
   a) The atmosphere is a fluid.
   b) The atmosphere is made of various gases.
   c) The atmosphere has mass.
   d) The atmosphere is made up of layers.
2. a) Explain the chemical processes that result in ozone depletion.
   b) Analyse the effects that ozone production in developing countries could have on the ozone layer in Canada.
   c) Why is it necessary for all nations on the earth to cooperate with the monitoring of the ozone layer and the reduction of CFC production?
3. Copy and complete the organizer below, which compares the different layers of the atmosphere.

Layer	Width	Temperature	Air Movement	Distance from Earth	Special Features
Troposphere					
Tropopause					
Stratosphere					
Stratopause					
Mesosphere					
Mesopause					
Ionosphere					
Magnetosphere					
Magnetopause					

4. Using a small globe, an elastic band, a piece of string, and a ruler, complete the following exercise to show how the lengths of day and night change with latitude.
   a) Place the elastic band around the globe so that it crosses over the North and South poles. Align the band so that it crosses the equator at a 90° angle. One side of the globe represents day while the other side represents night. Use a stick-on label to remind yourself which side is which.

Latitude	Equator 0°	Tropic of Cancer 23.5°N	40°N	Arctic Circle 66.5°N	40°S	Antarctic Circle 66.5°S
Distance	_____cm	_____cm	_____cm	_____cm	_____cm	_____cm
• Day • Night	_____cm	_____cm	_____cm	_____cm	_____cm	_____cm
Ratio Day:Night						
Hours • Day • Night						

b) Measure the number of centimetres in daylight and the number of centimetres in dark-ness along the equator. The two distances should be the same. In other words, they should have a ratio of one to one (twelve hours of darkness and twelve hours of light). Continue measuring for other latitudes as indicated in the organizer above. Copy and complete the organizer in your notebook.

c) Move the position of the elastic band south (left), so that it lies between the North Pole and Arctic Circle. Adjust the elastic by sliding it to the east (right) in the Southern Hemisphere so that it is straight around the globe. Measure the distances of the dark and light halves of the globe along the equator. These should always add up to the same total. This simulation shows how the circle of illumination moves across the earth. Repeat the process in part b) in another organizer.

d) How did the lengths of day and night change in the Northern Hemisphere as you moved the elastic?

e) How did the lengths of day and night change in the Southern Hemisphere as you moved the elastic?

f) Follow the procedure in part c), but this time move the elastic to the east (right) in the Northern Hemisphere and to the west (left) in the Southern Hemisphere. Complete this simulation in an organizer.

g) How did the lengths of day and night change in the Northern Hemisphere as you moved the elastic?

h) How did the lengths of day and night change in the Southern Hemisphere as you moved the elastic?

i) What part of Fig. 14.11 does this simulation represent?

5. Use a copy of Fig. 14.11, a ruler, a calculator, and a pencil, to complete the following exercise to show how day and night vary with latitude.

a) Refer to Diagram A in Fig. 14.11. On your copy, draw a line separating the part of the earth in darkness from the part in light. The line should form a 90° angle with the sun's rays shown in the diagram. Label the line "circle of illumination." Shade the side of the earth facing away from the sun.

- At what degree of latitude does the circle of illumination intersect with the earth's surface in the Northern Hemisphere? In the Southern Hemisphere?
- What is this parallel of latitude called in each hemisphere?
- How much day and night does the Arctic receive in this time?
- How much day and night does the Antarctic receive at this time?
- Using a ruler, measure along the equator and express, as a ratio, the length of the line in daylight to the length of the line in darkness. How does this translate into day and night?
- Measure along each of the lines of latitude on the diagram. State the ratio of the length of the line that is in daylight to the length of the line that is in darkness. Translate this ratio into the length of day and night.

b) Follow the procedure in part a) to show the length of day and night in Diagram B of Figure 14.11.

6. a) Explain how tilt and rotation cause day and night.
   b) Explain how tilt and revolution result in variations in the lengths of day and night.
   c) In what way are the Arctic and Antarctic circles significant lines of latitude with respect to day and night?
   d) Explain the relationship between the earth's rotation and time.
   e) Explain how the earth's tilt and revolution cause the seasons.
7. Explain how convection currents cause local maritime winds.
8. Read the Changing Technology on Wind Turbines on page 233.
   a) Why is North Cape a good site for experiments with wind turbines?
   b) Why is acceptance of wind turbines higher in Europe than North America?
   c) What has to happen before wind turbines will become more widely accepted?
   d) How could wind turbine technology change how people impact on the environment?
9. In point form, explain prevailing winds. Include the following concepts: convection currents, Hadley Cell, the Coriolis effect, trade winds, westerlies, doldrums, polar easterlies, low pressure, high pressure, and thermal equator.

DEVELOPING AND PRACTISING SKILLS

10. Fig. 14.15 on page 235 shows the prevailing winds during the equinox. The sun is shining directly down on the equator. To get an idea of how wind belts move with the thermal equator, try this simulation.
    a) Trace the prevailing winds on a piece of tracing paper or acetate using Fig. 14.14 as a guide. Use the equator, the Tropics, and the polar circles as guidelines. Gradually slide the overlay north so that the thermal equator is over the Tropic of Cancer. Now slide the overlay south so that the thermal equator is over the Tropic of Capricorn.
    b) List latitudes where the winds reverse from season to season as you move the tracing paper. What effect could this have on the local climate?
    c) Place the overlay you made in activity a) over Fig. 14.16 at either January or July. Be careful to centre the thermal equator directly over the Tropic of Capricorn for January or the Tropic of Cancer for July.

d) Find at least three places where the prevailing winds differ between the overlay and Fig. 14.16. Mark the locations on the overlay.

e) The winds shown on the overlay are theoretical. No allowance has been made for differences in the earth's surface. The winds shown in Fig. 14.15 are what actually happen. Surface variations affect how the winds blow. Explain why the winds are blowing differently in the places you identified in b).

11. Compare Figure 14.10 and 14.11.

a) Use these figures to name the earth's position in A.

b) What is the name of the earth's position in B?

c) What is the name of the earth's position in C?

d) In Diagram C of Figure 14.11, assume that the sun is perpendicular to the paper.
  • At what latitude are the sun's rays perpendicular (90°) to the earth?
  • Why is there nothing to shade in as darkness in this diagram?
  • How many hours of sunlight are there at the equator?
  • How many hours of sunlight are there at the poles?
  • What position of the earth-sun relationship is Diagram C illustrating?

LEARNING THROUGH APPLICATION

12. Discuss how a change in the lengths of day and night would affect people's lifestyles in the Tropics, in the middle latitudes, and in the polar regions.

13. Explain how wind affects people's lives in positive and negative ways.

14. Locate each of the following latitudes on an atlas map. In a group, brainstorm how earth-sun relationships would affect the lifestyles of people living at one of the following locations (as directed by your teacher). Report your ideas to the class.

a) 45°S

b) 20°N

c) 0°

d) 80°N

e) 30°S.

Chapter 15

INTRODUCING WEATHER AND CLIMATE

FOCUS QUESTIONS

1. What are the differences between weather and climate?
2. How do climate controls act upon the elements of the atmosphere to produce the climatic zones on Earth?
3. What role do oceans and ocean currents play in moderating the climate of places having the same latitude around the world?

If you were to find yourself standing at a bus shelter with a group of total strangers, no matter how different they might all seem to you, you would have something in common with each and every one—the weather. No matter who we are, we all feel the cold blast of a winter wind, the warmth of the morning sun, the freezing cold of sleet hitting our faces, and the refreshing mist blowing into the shelter from a summer shower. Weather affects everyone and is therefore important to us all.

Everything we do is affected by the weather. It would be terrible if you planned to go skiing and a sudden thaw was forecast, or if you hoped to go to the beach for a picnic and rain spoiled your day. Weather forecasting has become a multibillion dollar industry. But there is more at stake than just a day's skiing or a day at the beach. Forecasters predict dangerous weather such as hurricanes and tornadoes. Countless thousands of lives have been saved because forecasters warned people of these dangerous storms.

Key Terms

insolation

elevation

isotherm

temperature inversion

environment lapse rate

Figure 15.1
Weather is one of the few things everyone has in common.

Farmers plan their harvesting and planting schedules, fishers decide when to go out to sea, and business people plan important meetings based at least in part on weather forecasts.

If you find the idea of predicting the weather fascinating, you may want to consider a career as either a **meteorologist** or a **climatologist**. Meteorologists are people who study the weather, while climatologists are more concerned with long-term atmospheric trends. There are essentially three ways to pursue a career in meteorology: as a technician, a forecaster, or a researcher. Technicians generally work as monitors of weather recording equipment or as weather and ice observers, data processors, and research assistants. A university degree is not necessary, but a high-school diploma and good marks in geography, sciences, and mathematics are important. Community college courses are available to prepare people who wish to enter this field.

Forecasters need a university degree with a major in physics, mathematics, or computers. Environment Canada provides specialized training to prepare the candidates they hire for the demanding field of weather forecasting. Research scientists studying the atmosphere usually have a post-graduate degree such as a Master of Environmental Studies, Master of Science, or a Doctorate of Philosophy. Areas of specialization are often related to fluid dynamics, computer programming, and communications technology. Researchers study a variety of topics including air pollution, the ozone layer, solar flares, global warming, changes in sea ice, and so on. Many research positions are joint studies conducted by the Ministry of the Environment and Canadian universities.

Climatologists also work for government agencies such as Environment Canada. They monitor how climate is changing locally, nationally, and globally. These professionals analyse statistical data collected from thousands of weather stations, satellites, and other sensors, and write reports for the many people and agencies that need advice from the government about climate. Unlike meteorologists who specialize in weather forecasting, climatologists are generalists who study the interaction and relationships between people and climate. In order to become a climatologist, you need a university degree in environmental studies, geography, or statistical analysis. Further studies in fluid dynamics, computer applications, or biology and geography at the graduate level are often necessary to secure a good position.

Defining Weather and Climate

Weather is defined as "all the atmospheric activities that occur at a given place at a given time." These atmospheric conditions include temperature, wind speed and direction, humidity, amount and type of precipitation, barometric pressure, and cloud cover. How these atmospheric conditions interact with each other ensures that every day is different from the one before.

The term "climate" also refers to the same atmospheric activities, but the difference between the two lies in the time scale. Unlike weather, which refers to day to day changes, climate refers to the usual atmospheric conditions a place has, averaged over a long period of time. For example, the *climate* during the spring in Ontario is usually warm and moist but not too wet. But in the spring of 2000, the *weather* was so cool and so wet that farmers could not grow their crops. Tractors were bogged down in fields, plant roots were drowned, and hay crops lay rotting in the fields. Weather is what occurs at a particular time, while climate is what is normally expected.

Weather and Climate Change

Even though climate refers to average weather conditions, the averages are constantly changing. If the weather for a particular place becomes consistently warmer year after year, the long-term average temperature will gradually increase. Because the earlier values are still factored into the equation, long-term averages often seem understated. A thousand years ago, Newfoundland's Northern Peninsula was three to four degrees warmer than it is today. The sea level was higher because there was less glacial ice globally and tall trees grew in the area. L'Anse aux Meadows looked to Viking sailors like the perfect spot for a settlement.

The Vikings also made settlements in Greenland, but those disappeared by about 1700, possibly because of climate change. The Little Ice Age is the term given to the period when summers were abnormally cold. All across the planet,

Figure 15.2
The Vikings built sod houses to protect them from the weather at L'Anse aux Meadows 1000 years ago.

winters were longer and summers cooler as bitter north winds replaced the usual westerly prevailing winds. In Greenland, farming supplemented fishing and hunting for the former Vikings who settled there. These settlements disappeared after hundreds of successful years, probably because the people were not able to grow enough food to survive. In addition, the numbers of sea mammals dwindled in the region because of the climate change. In Iceland, the climate was moderated by the North Atlantic Drift, so the effects of the Little Ice Age were less significant, and these hardy people continued living there.

How Weather and Climate Affect Us

Weather and climate have a huge impact on our daily lives. When you go to school, your choice of clothes is determined by the weather. If it's hot out, cool and comfortable is the only way to dress. If there is a blizzard brewing and you have to walk, then heavy clothes are in order. Your travel route and how you get to school may also

be determined by the weather. On a nice day, you could walk or even skateboard, but if it's snowing you will likely get a ride or take a bus.

Buildings are designed with climate in mind. Canadian schools are well insulated, heated in winter, and sometimes even air-conditioned. In the past, the expense of air conditioning was often considered too high for buildings that were not used in summer. However, the recent trend is toward year-round climate control in newer schools, since these modern structures are often used for summer classes. The other reason for the more expensive buildings is the increase in mean monthly temperatures in June and September. Because these months are often so hot nowadays, air conditioning is becoming as much a necessity as heating.

In tropical countries like Singapore and Brazil, heating in schools is unnecessary, but good ventilation and air conditioning are extremely important. In some countries where the cost of air conditioning is too high, classes may run during the cooler part of the day, from 7 a.m. to 1 p.m. This relief from the midday heat is the basis for the *siesta* that is common in many hot climates. In some Mediterranean countries, everything closes down during the hottest part of the day—the afternoon—but people keep active well into the small hours of the morning, when it is cooler.

Weather and climate also affect how people spend their leisure time. Different sports have become popular because of the climate that characterizes the places where they are played. For Canadians, one of the main sporting obsessions is hockey, which is not surprising considering that most of the country is covered in ice and snow for four months each year. Similarly, football is very popular in the United States in the autumn. Americans' fall season is longer and generally more temperate than ours in Canada, so their playing season starts later and lasts longer, extending well into winter. Of course, we do play football in Canada, but the season finale, the Grey Cup, is held in November, not in January like the American Super Bowl.

Figure 15.3
Our cold winter climate makes outdoor hockey a popular Canadian activity.

In southern Europe, soccer is all the rage. The temperate climate allows it to be played all year. The people of Scotland invented golf, a game well-suited to their climate of mild winters and cool, wet summers. This makes the growing of the grass needed for fairways and greens possible without irrigation. Scottish courses are natural unlike the artificially irrigated golf courses in parts of arid North America. Of course, in Scotland, you can play golf from March to December because the winters are so mild.

Weather and climate also influence economic growth, particularly in resource development industries. For example, in the summer of 2000, Ontario farmers could not get their crops to grow because of the wet spring. Mining and lumber activities often increase in winter because the freezing of northern wetlands allows heavy equipment to move across swamps that are impassable in summer. Extreme weather, such as flooding and high winds, results in higher insurance claims and more expensive premiums later on. The cost of lost work, hospital bills, and repairs to public structures due to storms can put a huge financial strain on a country's economy.

Weather is also very important in shaping history. In the French Revolution of the late eighteenth century, the people were rioting against the French monarchy. Queen Marie Antoinette, when told the people were rioting because they did not have bread, allegedly responded, "Let them eat cake." It was inconceivable to her that her subjects did not have any food when she lived in the lap of luxury. In fact, bad weather was the reason the people did not have enough to eat. The harvests had been poor because of the cold, wet weather, and the people resented the decadence of the monarchy. The result was the eventual birth of the French Revolution.

Another example of the role of weather in certain historical events is the day Thomas Jefferson wrote the text for the American Declaration of Independence from Britain. It was a stiflingly hot day in early July, and this weather helped him to get the support he needed. The delegates from the Thirteen Colonies, who were voting on the document, were so uncomfortable with the heat and humidity and all the flies buzzing about that they accepted Jefferson's recommendations and quickly declared war on Britain. Two days later, the Declaration was accepted by Congress, and the world's most powerful nation was born.

Climatic Controls

Different places on Earth occupying locations with similar characteristics invariably have climates that are very much alike. The climate of the southern United States, for instance, mirrors that of southern China. They are both located at about 30°N, are on the east coast of a major continent, and are at about the same elevation. Look at the west coast of north Africa and the west coast of southern Africa, at the Tropics of Cancer and Capricorn, and you will see that deserts occur at both locations. In the Far North of Canada, the climate is almost identical to the climate in northern Russia.

Four basic variables influence the climate a place has. It is possible to determine what the climate of a place is like by understanding how these four variables interact. They are as follows:

- **Insolation:** The amount of solar radiation a place receives is determined by the amount of daylight and the angle at which the sun's rays hit the surface.
- **Elevation:** The altitude (distance above sea level) of a place influences the surface temperature because of air pressure.
- **Proximity of water bodies:** The influence of water bodies moderates temperatures of coastal places.
- **Ocean currents:** The movement of heat energy from the equator toward the poles warms some shorelines, cools others, and influences precipitation patterns.

Insolation

Every March Break there is a mass exodus of thousands of Canadians travelling south to places such as Florida, Cuba, Mexico, or California to get a break from our cold winter weather. But why is Canada so cold, while countries to the south bask in warmth year-round?

The reason it is colder as one moves away from the equator is the result of two variables: the length of time a place is exposed to the sun, and the angle at which the sun's rays strike that place. In Chapter 14 (pp. 229-231), we saw why the duration of daylight a place receives varies with its latitude and the season it is experiencing. The less sunshine a place receives, the colder it becomes.

The second factor has to do with the angle at which the sun's rays hit the earth's surface. The earth's curvature affects the intensity of sunlight. At the equinox, the angle of the noonday sun is perpendicular (90°) to the horizon over the equator. Moving away from the equator, the angle decreases steadily toward the North and South poles. This means that at higher latitudes a larger area must be heated by the same amount of energy.

To summarize, there is a **negative correlation** between the latitude a place has and its mean annual temperature. A negative correlation occurs when one set of data increases, while the other decreases. For example, if the place has a latitude of 50°, then barring other factors, such as elevation or ocean currents, its mean annual temperature will likely be low (under 5°C, perhaps). As the latitude decreases, say to 25°, then temperature will increase to a mean annual temperature of over 20°C.

One could also say that the angle at which the sun's rays strike the earth has a **positive correlation** with energy received. This means that as one set of statistics rises, so does the other set. For example, the higher the angle (up to 90° at the equator), the higher the mean annual temperature of a place will be.

Elevation

Did you know that there are at least two places along the equator that are naturally covered in ice and snow? Mount Kilimanjaro in Africa and the Andes Mountains in South America stand out as frosty peaks from the tropical land surrounding them. The unusually cold temperatures occur because of the elevation, or **altitude**, above sea level. As the elevation increases, the temperature usually drops at a fixed rate. This is because heat energy is released when sunlight is absorbed by the earth's surfaces. So it is warmer at low elevations, which are closer to the heat-radiating surface.

Another reason why temperatures decrease as altitude increases is that higher altitudes have lower air pressure. At the base of a mountain, the mass of air pressing down from above compresses the air molecules. The air has a greater concentration of dust particles and higher humidity. These conditions allow the air in a valley to hold the heat radiating from the earth better than the air high in the mountains.

There is a negative correlation between altitude and air temperature. Temperatures drop about 6.4°C for every 1000 m of altitude. Called the **environmental lapse rate**, this relationship is not constant and varies with the amount of pollution and water vapour in the air. Regions where there

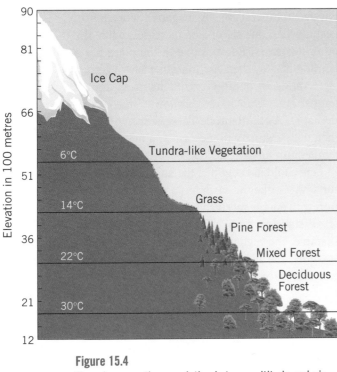

Figure 15.4
There is a negative correlation between altitude and air temperature. What is meant by this?

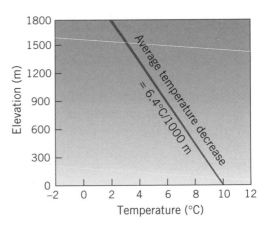

Figure 15.5
Environmental Lapse Rate. This graph shows the correlation between temperature and elevation.

is considerable dust or high humidity often do not cool down as rapidly with altitude as less polluted, drier zones. This is true in coastal British Columbia, where the high humidity of the maritime air results in warmer temperatures than one would expect at high altitudes.

The environmental lapse rate has a great influence on people living in mountainous areas. In Canada's Western Cordillera, for example, the colder temperatures mean that snow arrives early and leaves late. This makes it possible for ski resorts such as B.C.'s Whistler Mountain to thrive from November to April. Few people live at ski resorts year-round, however. In British Columbia, much of the population is found along the coastal plains or in the valleys, where the climate is warmer. In the Tropics, the opposite is often true. The cooler mountain air is more invigorating than the steamy heat of the lowlands. Compare a relief map of South America with a population map of the same region. Where do most of the people live?

There are **anomalies** regarding temperatures in high places, however. Since cold air is heavier than warm air and heated air rises, it is not uncommon for valleys surrounded by mountains to experience a **temperature inversion** when there is little wind. Instead of the air being warmer at ground level than at higher elevations, the temperature up a mountainside is higher than in the valley. The cold air near the mountaintops sinks into the valley, replacing the warmer air there. When an inversion occurs, the air in the valley can be relatively stagnant for days. If the valley contains a major city, as in the cases of Los Angeles and Mexico City, serious smog problems can develop. However, the anomaly is really a weather characteristic and not an aspect of climate control.

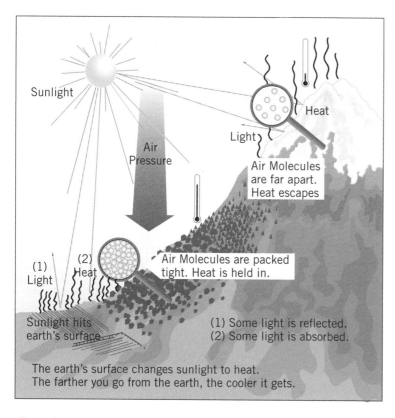

Figure 15.6
It is colder high up on a mountain than it is at the base because the earth's surface is the heat source.

The Moderating Influence of Large Bodies of Water

Have you ever wondered why Victoria, B.C., is so much warmer than Ottawa in the winter? While people in our nation's capital are still clearing snow from driveways and expecting another six weeks of winter, Victorians are planting gardens and playing golf, even though they live further north than people in Ottawa.

The reason Victoria is warmer is because the Pacific Ocean moderates its climate. Water takes longer to heat up and cool down than land because it has the highest heat capacity of any common substance—higher than rock or sand. Therefore, it takes a great deal of heat energy to raise the temperature of one kilometre of water.

In addition, water is **translucent**, so it absorbs sunlight to greater depths than land. In other words, a greater volume of material is being heated with the same amount of energy. Convection currents, waves, tides, and ocean currents mix the warmer surface water with the colder water below. This turbulence further slows down the heating process of water in comparison to land.

All summer long, the coastal waters of British Columbia absorb energy from the sun. When winter arrives, this heat is slowly released, warming coastal cities. Ottawa is situated far from the ocean and so does not get the benefit of the milder temperatures. However, summer temperatures on the coast are generally cooler than they are inland since the seawater is cooler than the land during this season. This is one reason why many people in the mid to low latitudes like to spend their summer vacations on the coast. The cooler temperatures and coastal breezes make the summertime heat a little more bearable. These coastal cities are said to have a **maritime climate**, while cities in the interior have what is known as a **continental climate**. Continental climates are marked by high annual temperature ranges, cold winters, hot summers, and meagre amounts of rainfall. Maritime climates are just the opposite.

Fog often blankets coastal regions during summer. The cool maritime air is blown in above the warmer air over the land. The water vapour in the warmer air condenses and fog or low cloud results. A similar situation occurs in late fall when the water is relatively warmer than the land. Homebuyers who want an ocean view on

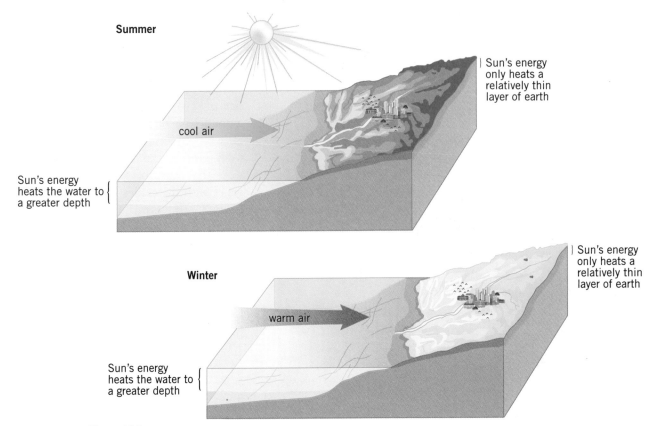

Summer

cool air

Sun's energy
only heats a
relatively thin
layer of earth

Sun's energy
heats the water to
a greater depth

Winter

warm air

Sun's energy
only heats a
relatively thin
layer of earth

Sun's energy
heats the water to
a greater depth

Figure 15.7
The Moderating Influence of Large Bodies of Water

Figure 15.8
Fog often rolls in to coastal Nova Scotia. Which other areas of Canada are likely to have regular fog? Why?

the south shore of Nova Scotia are advised to buy on high land overlooking the sea, not on the beach itself. The higher sites are often above the fog and are sunnier during the transitional months of spring and fall.

Ocean Currents

The processes that create ocean currents are explained in Chapter 11, on p. 176. This discussion explains how ocean currents influence the climates of regions adjacent to them.

Obviously, currents flowing out of polar waters are cold relative to surrounding waters. Similarly, currents flowing outward from equatorial regions into the mid-latitudes are relatively warm. Study the map in Figure 15.9 and the Developing Skills on page 250 to discover how ocean currents affect coastal temperatures.

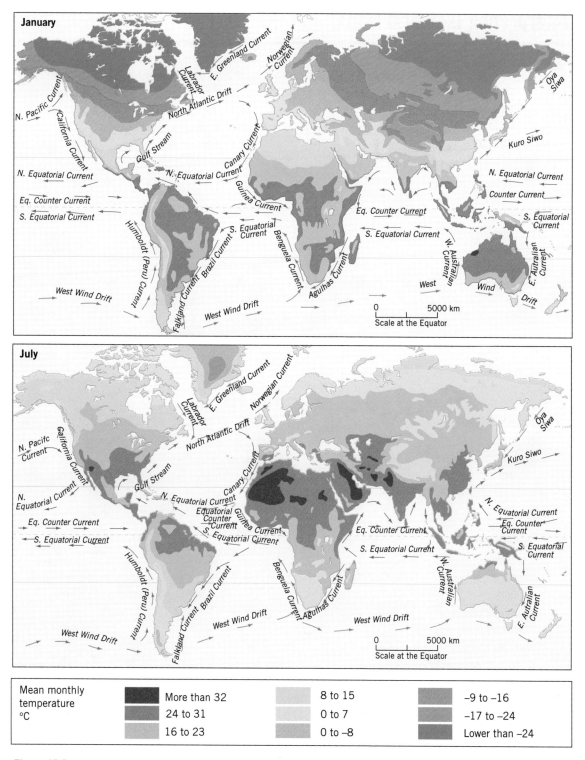

January

N. Pacific Current
California Current
N. Equatorial Current
Eq. Counter Current
S. Equatorial Current
Humboldt (Peru) Current
West Wind Drift
Gulf Stream
Labrador Current
E. Greenland Current
Norwegian Current
North Atlantic Drift
Canary Current
N. Equatorial Current
Guinea Current
S. Equatorial Current
Falkland Current
Brazil Current
Benguela Current
West Wind Drift
Agulhas Current
Eq. Counter Current
S. Equatorial Current
Oya Siwa
Kuro Siwo
N. Equatorial Current
Counter Current
S. Equatorial Current
W. Australian Current
E. Australian Current
West Wind Drift

0   5000 km
Scale at the Equator

July

N. Pacifc Current
California Current
N. Equatorial Current
Eq. Counter Current
S. Equatorial Current
Humboldt (Peru) Current
West Wind Drift
Gulf Stream
Labrador Current
E. Greenland Current
Norwegian Current
North Atlantic Drift
Canary Current
N. Equatorial Current
Equatorial Counter Current
Guinea Current
S. Equatorial Current
Falkland Current
Brazil Current
Benguela Current
West Wind Drift
Agulhas Current
Eq. Counter Current
S. Equatorial Current
Oya Siwa
Kuro Siwo
N. Equatorial Current
Eq. Counter Current
S. Equatorial Current
W. Australian Current
E. Australian Current
West Wind Drift

0   5000 km
Scale at the Equator

Mean monthly temperature °C			
More than 32	8 to 15	−9 to −16
24 to 31	0 to 7	−17 to −24
16 to 23	0 to −8	Lower than −24

Figure 15.9

These maps show isotherms and ocean currents for summer and winter. To analyse this figure, complete the exercises in the Developing Skills feature on page 250.

Interpreting Isotherm Maps

The term "isotherm" comes from the two Greek words *isos* meaning equal and *therm* meaning temperature. Isotherms are maps where places with equal temperatures are joined together. Studying these types of maps helps geographers see relationships between factors and answer questions such as, "Does the proximity of water affect the temperature?" "Are ocean currents important?" "Do high regions have different temperatures than low ones?" Of course, you often need other maps to compare to the isotherm map to garner this information.

Similar iso-maps can be used to explore other variables in physical geography. **Isohyet** maps show places with the same total amounts of precipitation and **Isobar** maps show places with similar air pressure (see p. 224 for an example).

1. Figure 15.9 shows isotherms for January and July, as well as ocean currents. So, it is possible to see how ocean currents, the moderating effect of water, and the size of continents affect average temperatures. Notice that the January isotherm map shows cold temperatures in the northern winter. In June, the middle and upper latitudes have higher temperatures.

2. By studying the location of ocean currents and adjacent coastlines, observations can be made about how the currents affect surface temperatures. For example, notice that the North Atlantic Drift flows out of the equatorial region toward northwestern Europe. In January, the temperature of this region, according to the colour-coded legend, is between 0° and 8°C. At the same latitude further west, the temperature drops to as low as −16°C. The assumption can be made that the warm ocean current warmed the climate of western Europe along the coast. As you move inland, the influence of the warm current diminishes. Of course, other variables, which the map does not show, could also be at work.

TRY IT!

1. Analyse the effect of ocean currents on adjacent land masses by copying the organizer below and filling it in, using the two isotherm maps in Fig. 15.9.

Location/Map	Ocean Current	Land Temperature	Explanation
Western Europe/ January	North Atlantic Drift	0° to 8°C	The warm current heats the coast, making it warmer than inland.
Eastern Canada (Labrador)/January			
Western Canada (British Columbia)/ January			
Eastern Russia/ January			
Eastern China/July			
Southwest Africa/July			
Coastal California/July			

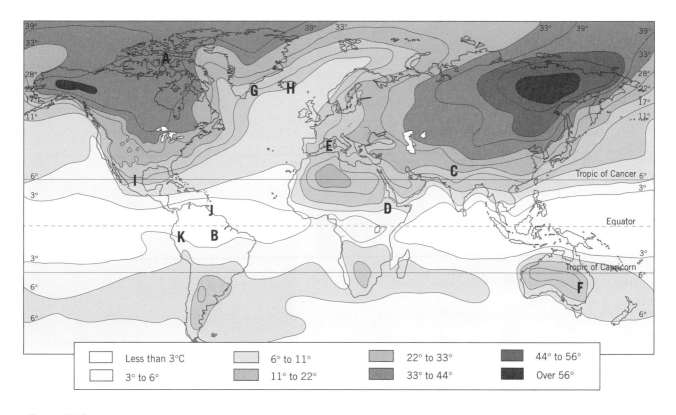

Figure 15.10
World Isotherm Map (Showing Normal Annual Range in Temperatures)

The North Atlantic Drift is one current that has a tremendous influence on the climate of Europe. An extension of the Gulf Stream, it carries warm tropical water from the Caribbean Sea across the North Atlantic to western Europe. England's southwest coast is remarkably warm considering that it lies at the same latitude as Northern Ontario—a place that is far from tropical in winter! Originating in warm tropical seas, the Gulf Stream is directed northeast by the North American coastline and the prevailing westerly winds. The frigid Labrador Current deflects the warm current further east until it reaches the northwest coast of Europe.

A look at the map in Figure 15.9 reveals interesting patterns in the ocean currents. The North Atlantic Ocean is a mirror image more or less of the South Atlantic. The Gulf Stream flows up the eastern seaboard of the United States. Just south of Boston, it veers away from the shore and becomes the North Atlantic Drift. South of the equator, the Brazil Current acts in the same way, sending warm water down the coast of Brazil and Uruguay. Rio de Janeiro has a tropical rainforest climate even though it is quite far from the equator at 18° S.

The frigid Labrador Current brings icebergs along the coast of Labrador as far south as southern Newfoundland. In the Southern Hemisphere, the Faulkland Current, while much closer to the equator than the Labrador Current, chills the southeastern coast of South America. Other cold currents in the Atlantic are the Canary and the Benguela Currents that mirror each other on the

Figure 15.11
Subtropical Plants in Western Europe

Figure 15.12
Icebergs off the Coast of Labrador

west coast of Africa, both of which contribute to the desert climates of northwest and southwest Africa.

Similar patterns also exist in the Pacific. The California Current and the Humboldt Current move toward the equator from the North and South poles respectively, along the west coast of the Americas. The Kuro Siwo Current and the East Australian Currents bring warm water from the Tropics north to moderate climates in East Asia and Australia. Along the equator the North Equatorial Current and the South Equatorial Current are mirrored with their respective counter currents. In the great Southern Ocean at the bottom of the world, the West Wind Drift whips around the globe unhindered by large land masses getting in its way. Clearly, ocean currents have a great influence on global climates.

The four climate controls discussed in this chapter help us to understand why different places have the climates they have. The examples given are textbook cases, where other variables are absent or minimal. In the real world, the situation is much more complicated. Insolation, elevation, seawater moderation, and ocean currents all work to create the unique climates of places around the world.

Microclimates

The climate controls described in the first half of this chapter all operate on a large scale; however, subtle variations in temperature, humidity, and precipitation occur on a small scale as well. If you walk around the outside of your school on a sunny March afternoon, you will notice surprisingly different climate conditions due to exposure and albedo. **Exposure** refers to the influence of wind on temperature and humidity. Albedo (as discussed in Chapter 3, p. 28) relates to how surfaces convert solar energy into heat. On a sunny side of the school, the temperature may be a balmy 16°C. The dark pavement, strong sun, and the fact that it is sheltered from the north winds make this spot very different from the other side of the school. Exposed to the wind and located in the shade, this spot may be close to freezing, and snow may still be lingering here long after it has melted on the other side of the building.

Figure 15.13
This school plan shows where the sun shines and where the wind blows, creating microclimates.

Exposure

Exposure to direct sunlight affects the climate of a place on a micro level. A slope that receives a lot of direct sunlight will be warmer than a slope that lies in the shade. In Switzerland, for example, southern slopes get more sunlight than northern slopes. As a result, trees grow at higher elevations on the southern slopes. In some Alpine valleys, grapes grow well on southern slopes but don't grow on northern slopes. Insolation has increased for this slope relative to the shaded slope. Because it receives more sun and the slope of the mountain compensates for the relatively shallow angle of the sun on a flat surface, the slope provides a grape-growing environment similar to those much further south.

Strong winds also reduce temperatures. A mountain slope that faces the prevailing winds is often much colder than one that is sheltered. We all know about **wind chill**, as it is commonly reported on cold winter days. Wind chill (see Fig. 15.14) refers to how cold the temperature feels to people because of the wind; it does not actually lower the temperature of inanimate objects. Under normal conditions, the sunlight a surface receives is converted to heat energy or reflected back as light. If there are winds, the heated air above the surface is blown away, so the area becomes colder. Surfaces exposed to high winds also tend to dry out faster than protected areas because the winds carry away water vapour from the surface. In mountain climates where temperature and precipitation rates can vary widely, exposure has a significant influence on microclimates.

Albedo

Generally, dark surfaces like pavement convert more of the available light to heat than light-coloured, shiny surfaces do. You have probably experienced this first-hand while walking barefoot on a sunny summer day: the grass is relatively cool as you walk across a lawn, but when your feet touch the black pavement, they feel like they are on fire. This happens because the grass reflects back the solar energy, while the pavement absorbs it. Albedo refers to the amount of light a surface reflects. Objects with low albedo (i.e., dark surfaces) are warmer than surfaces with high albedo (i.e., light surfaces).

Temperature (°C)	0	–5	–10	–15	–20	–25	–30	–35
Wind Speed (km/hr)				Wind Chill (°C)				
10	–2	–7	–12	–17	–22	–27	–32	–38
20	–7	–13	19	–25	–31	–37	–43	–50
30	–11	–17	–24	–31	–37	–44	–50	–57
40	–13	–20	–27	–34	–41	48	–55	–62
50	–15	–22	–29	–36	–44	–51	–58	–66
60	–16	–23	–31	–38	–45	–53	–60	–68

Figure 15.14
To calculate wind chill temperature, use the formula, 0.045 (5.270.5 + 10.45 – 0.28V) (T-33) + 33, where V is the wind speed in k/hr, and T is the temperature in degrees Celsius. So for -10°C with a wind speed of 30 km/hr, the number sentence would read: 0.045 (5.270.5 + 10.45 – 0.28 x 30) (10-33) + 33 = - 24°C

Urban Microclimates

Heat islands are common in most large cities. This term is used to describe the increased mean temperatures cities have, compared to the surrounding countryside. Figure 15.16 shows an infrared image of Atlanta. By studying the image, you can see how much hotter cities are than the surrounding areas.

Cities have become so large in recent years that they have a great influence on microclimates. If you compare the climates within cities to the atmospheric conditions in the surrounding countryside, you will notice the following differences: cities have higher mean annual temperatures, more thunderstorms and hail, lower ground-level wind speeds, lower humidity, more rain, more clouds, and less sunlight. Why is this the case?

Figure 15.15
Large cities are often warmer than surrounding countryside because more sunlight is converted into heat when it hits concrete. Also, technologies such as air conditioners and cars open heat into the air.

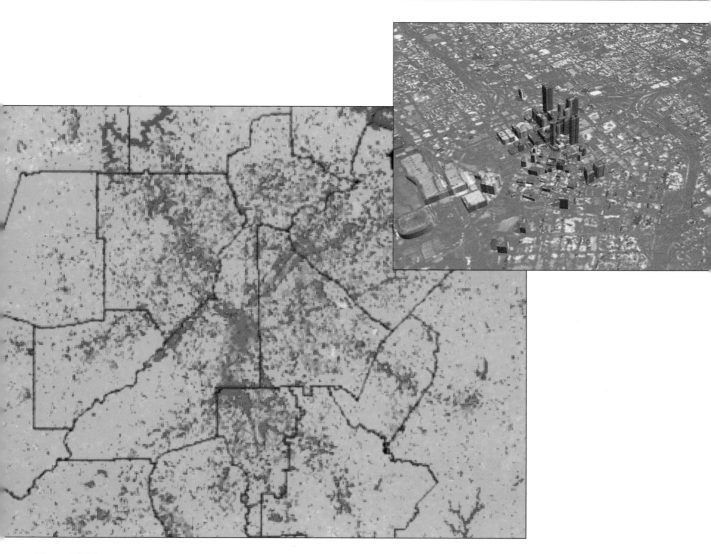

Figure 15.16
The inset photo shows the heat islands within the city of Atlanta, Georgia (the white areas are hottest, followed closely by the red areas). The main photo shows the heat generated by Atlanta in comparison to the surrounding countryside.

The decreased albedo from so much concrete is one factor. More sunlight is converted to thermal energy when it hits city structures. Tall buildings facing one another also increase the surface area that is heated. So, if you are standing between two tall buildings, you not only get the heat from the ground but you get it radiated off the buildings, too. In addition, there are many forms of technology spewing heat into the city, such as cars, air conditioners, and construction equipment. Have you ever walked over a ventilation grating over a subway? As the train roars by below, a gust of hot, smelly air explodes up from the grate. These fumes also act to increase the localized greenhouse effect in the city. Ground-level ozone produced by electrical engines, as well as carbon dioxide, carbon monoxide, nitrous oxide, and innumerable other gases pollute the air in cities. Add to these the **aerosols** such as soot from smokestacks, salty dust from snow clearing, and other substances, and it is no wonder temperatures are higher. The solar radiation is absorbed by greenhouse gases and particles in the air and re-radiated into the local atmosphere.

When water evaporates off the ground or from vegetation, a lot of energy is used up. In rural landscapes, where there is more vegetation and open water, more heat energy is used in evaporation than in cities with their concrete sidewalks and office towers. As a consequence, less energy is available for heating in rural areas because so much is used for evapo-transpiration. It has been estimated that a full-grown tree has the cooling capabilities of five small air conditioners.

In addition, the canyon effect of tall buildings affects wind currents, usually by blocking them. However, winds sometimes roar between buildings with chilling speed. In Toronto's financial district, near King and Bay streets, the strong winds between the buildings can be very unpleasant, especially in winter. And in summer, hot blasts sweep along Bay Street between these architectural cliffs.

Local convection currents in pockets of the city often cause strange weather conditions— for example, rising air flowing up past buildings can create thunderstorms and even hail that will not occur outside the city. It is possible for it to be snowing outside the 32nd floor, raining outside the 5th floor, and sunny on the other side of the building.

geo.web resources

<www.greenroofs.com>

This non-profit site is dedicated to educating people about the virtues of environmentally friendly urban building ideas. Write a paragraph discussing the feasibility of the "greenroof" idea for use in a city of your choice.

Despite the increased volatility of weather patterns in cities, tornadoes often skirt around urban areas because big buildings block winds and funnel these dangerous storms outside of urban centres.

Urban climatologists, engineers, and planners all work to improve the urban environment. One interesting architectural strategy is to plant gardens and grass on the roofs of urban structures. If more of these gardens were planted, not only would they provide a nice place for people to spend leisure time, but the albedo of the city would change, and less heat would be produced because solar energy would be used for evapo-transpiration.

Many planners have long acknowledged the benefits of keeping urban environments more natural. New York is the archetypal big city. It had the first skyscrapers and was the largest city in the world for decades. However, while it has many of the climate problems of other big cities, it also has Central Park. This enormous park in the middle of New York not only cools and moderates the climate of the city, but also provides a respite for urbanites from the hectic life in the Big Apple.

In Canada, we are fortunate to have many cities with ravines, parks, and forests within the metropolitan boundaries. Toronto's ravines and forested residential communities like Rosedale and Forest Hill act like islands of cool air within the city. Montreal has rivers and lakes that regulate air temperature; for Vancouver it is Stanley Park; and Winnipeg has The Forks. Ottawa has Gatineau Park on its border, the Ottawa River, and many gardens and parklands. All things considered, Canadian cities are relatively well planned with regard to climate.

ACTIVITIES

UNDERSTANDING CONCEPTS

1. a) Define the terms "weather" and "climate" and point out their similarities and differences.
   b) Provide examples to show how weather and climate have changed over time.
   c) Distinguish natural short-term variability from long-term trends in historical climate data.
2. a) List the four controls on climate and explain why each occurs.
   b) For each climate control, explain how it affects temperature and/or precipitation.
   c) Give examples, other than those in this book, to support each explanation.
   d) Why is an understanding of climate controls important in studying the geography of a place?
   e) What difficulties and limitations affect the quantifying of climate controls?
3. Compare the following Canadian cities.

City (Latitude)	January Mean Temperature	July Mean Temperature	Temperature Range	Mean Annual Temperature
Victoria (48° N)	4°C	16°C	20°C	10°C
Toronto (44° N)	-5°C	21°C	26°C	7°C
Ottawa (45° N)	-11°C	21°C	32°C	5°C

   a) Use the location of each city to determine the climate control illustrated.
   b) Explain why the differences occur.
4. Describe how each of the following factors affect microclimates.
   a) exposure
   b) albedo
   c) tall buildings
   d) greenhouse gases and aerosols
   e) ravines, waterways, and wetlands.

DEVELOPING AND PRACTISING SKILLS

5. For each of the following, state the correlation that exists between the pair of factors and sketch a simple line graph to illustrate this correlation.
   a) distance from a water body and mean temperature in January
   b) distance from a water body and total annual precipitation
   c) elevation above sea level and mean annual temperature
   d) coastal water temperatures and the incidence of fog.

6. Study the climate statistics for each pair of locations in the following chart. Each pair is at approximately the same parallel of latitude.

		Mean Temperature (°C)		Latitude
		January	July	
1.	Kabul, Afghanistan	-3	22	34°N
	Beirut, Lebanon	13	27	34°N
2.	Inverness, U.K.	3	14	58°N
	Moscow, Russia	-9	18	56°N
3.	Kraków, Poland	-3	19	50°N
	Southampton, England	5	17	51°N
4.	Nice, France	9	23	44°N
	Toronto, Canada	-5	19	44°N
5.	Reykjavik, Iceland	0	12	64°N
	Baker Lake, Canada	-32	10	64°N
6.	St. Louis, United States	0	26	39°N
	San Francisco, United States	10	15	39°N

a) Subtract the January and July temperatures to estimate the annual temperature range for each location.
b) Speculate which location is on the coast and which is inland. Check your answers in an atlas.
c) What generalization can you make about temperature range and coastal location?

7.

Place	Latitude	Mean Temp.	Place	Latitude	Mean Temp.
Aklavia, Northwest Territories	68°	-9°C	Alert, NWT	83°	-18°C
Atlanta, Georgia	33°	16°C	Baker Lake, NWT	64°	-12°C
Boston, Massachusetts	42°	10°C	Calgary, Alberta	51°	3°C
Chicago, Illinois	42°	10°C	Dallas, Texas	33°	18°C
Honolulu, Hawaii	21°	24°C	Key West, Florida	24°	26°C
Ottawa, Ontario	45°	5°C	Veracruz, Mexico	19°	25°C
Belém, Brazil	1°	27°C	Galapagos Islands	0°	25°C
Santa Cruz, Argentina	50°	9°C	Valparaiso, Chile	33°	14°C
Deception Island, UK	63°	-3°C	McMurdo Sound, Antarctica	77°	-18°C

a) Prepare a scattergraph to show the relationship between mean annual temperature and latitude using the statistics in the chart.
b) Is there a positive or negative correlation between temperature and latitude?
c) What conclusions can you draw from this scattergraph?
d) What could account for any anomalies?

8. Study the information in these charts.

Elevation and Population of the Ten Largest Tropical South American Cities		
	Population (000 000)	Elevation (Metres amsl)
Mexico City, Mexico	13.0	2239
São Paulo, Brazil	12.6	762
Rio de Janeiro, Brazil	5.6	10
Lima, Peru	5.0	152
Bogotá, Colombia	4.0	2610
Caracas, Venezuela	3.0	914
Belo Horizonte, Brazil	2.5	762
Recife, Brazil	2.3	10
Guayaquil, Ecuador	1.5	6
Medellin, Colombia	1.4	1470

Elevation and Population of the Ten Largest Canadian Cities		
	Population (000 000)	Elevation (Metres amsl)
Toronto, Ontario	3.0	116
Montreal, Quebec	2.8	57
Vancouver, British Columbia	1.3	14
Ottawa-Hull	0.7	103
Edmonton, Alberta	0.7	676
Calgary, Alberta	0.6	1078
Winnipeg, Manitoba	0.6	204
Quebec City, Quebec	0.6	90
Hamilton, Ontario	0.5	91
St. Catharines, Ontario	0.3	92

a) Calculate the mean elevation for cities in South American and for Canada cities (i.e., add up all the elevations and divide by the number of examples).
b) Which average is higher?
c) Develop a hypothesis to explain why the average elevation of major cities in these countries is so different.
d) See if there are other places where a pattern similar to the South American example exists.

9. Study Figure 15.4 (on page 246).
   a) Use the environmental lapse rate to determine the temperature at each altitude.
   b) Determine where the ice cap would likely occur.
   c) How could exposure affect the temperature at each level?
   d) How could a temperature inversion affect the result?
   e) What other variables may change the results of this example?
10. Use the map in Figure 15.10 and your knowledge from this chapter to determine which of the climate variables most likely resulted in the temperature range shown for each of a) to k).

LEARNING THROUGH APPLICATION

11. Study the section "How Weather and Climate Affect Us" on pages 243-44.
    a) Give your own examples to illustrate how weather and climate have influenced your life in positive and negative ways.
    b) Match each country in the chart to the sport it is associated with. Explain your choices and outline how climate affects each.

Country	Sport
1. Sweden	Alpine skiing
2. Australia	Baseball
3. Cuba	Nordic skiing
4. Switzerland	Surfing
5. The Netherlands	Bull fighting
6. Mexico	Speed skating

   c) Describe why suburban malls are particularly suitable as alternatives to downtown main streets in Canadian towns and small cities. Do you like the trend or abhor it?
12. a) Using clippings from newspapers and magazines, keep a scrapbook or prepare a bulletin board showing how weather and climate influence people's lives around the world.
    b) Prepare a map showing the locations of each of these new stories.
13. For a book or movie of your choice, explain how weather or climate affects the plot of the story. For example, the movie "The Perfect Storm" tells the story of a fishing crew who were lost at sea when a massive hurricane off the eastern coast of the United States sank their ship.
14. Interview a senior to find out how the climate has changed in your area over the years.

15. Locate each of the following latitudes on a world map. In a group, brainstorm how earth-sun relationships would affect the lifestyle of the people at one of the following locations (as directed by your teacher). Report your ideas to the class.
    a) 45°S
    b) 20°N
    c) 0°
    d) 80°N
    e) 30°S
16. Conduct a field study of an urban or a rural environment to monitor its microclimate.
    a) Prepare a site map of the location you are studying.
    b) Choose four or five locations in your study area.
    c) For each location, collect weather data on such things as temperature, wind movement, precipitation, sunlight, etc.
    d) After several days of collecting data (always at exactly the same time), average the results for each site.
    e) Take photos of each location and prepare data charts and graphs comparing the results.
    f) Develop reasons why variations in microclimates occurred.
    g) Outline how these results could affect plants, animals, and people.
    h) Display your findings in a folder or bristol board presentation.

Chapter 16

TORNADOES, HURRICANES, AND OTHER STORMS

FOCUS QUESTIONS

1. What are the origins, distribution, and frequency of the different kinds of storms that affect North America?

2. How do environmental hazards such as hurricanes and tornadoes affect human activities?

3. What are the difficulties and limitations inherent in quantifying processes and elements such as the severity of certain types of storms?

Key Terms

air mass

frontal depression

cumulonimbus cloud

fujita scale

jet stream

When fierce rain and thunder and lightning rumbled through the sky over ancient Greece, the people believed that Zeus, the celestial god of weather, was showing his anger with the mortals. While we are still fascinated by the awesome power of storms, we now understand that they are the product of the clash between masses of air, rather than the violent expression of an angry god.

Air masses sweep over the land bringing cold air from the north and warm air from the south. Some of these air masses are laden with moisture and some are dry. When these different air masses meet, a mid-latitude storm occurs. Sometimes violent storms cause terrible damage and kill thousands of people. This chapter helps us to understand why these storms occur.

Daily Weather Forecasts and Mid-Latitude Storms

While everybody loves warm, sunny weather, the work of the forecaster centres around determining when it is going to rain. Mid-latitude storms are the usual weather systems that bring rain to Canadian regions. The mid-latitudes, extending from about 25° to 50° latitude, form the area where cold, dry arctic air masses meet moist,

Figure 16.1
Thunderstorms are a result of a clash between air masses.

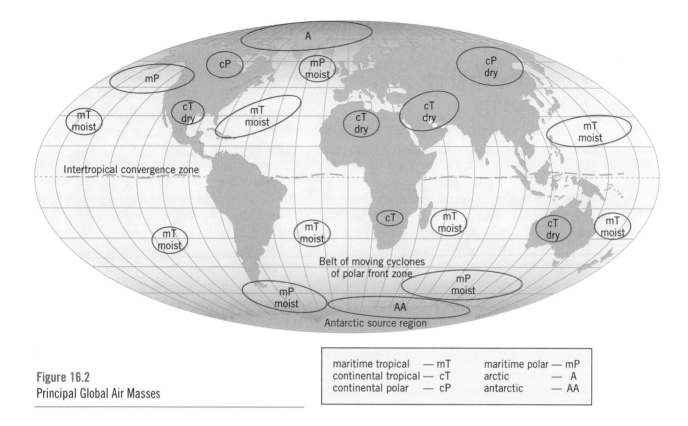

Figure 16.2
Principal Global Air Masses

maritime tropical — mT	maritime polar — mP
continental tropical — cT	arctic — A
continental polar — cP	antarctic — AA

warm maritime air masses. When the two air masses collide, storms are born.

Air masses are bodies of air that develop over large areas of the earth's surface. Two conditions are necessary for an air mass to form: first, the air must stay over the **source region** for a long period of time so that it can take on the characteristics of that region; second, the air must be stable. Air masses usually form where air is descending back to Earth. These high-pressure cells line up roughly over the polar circles and the Tropics. Because the air is descending, there are no convection currents to mix the air.

Air masses take on characteristics based on the nature of the surface over which they develop. When they form over water, they have greater moisture content than continental air masses. The temperature of these **maritime air masses** is usually warmer than land-based air masses in the winter, and cooler than they are in the summer. This is because oceans moderate the temperature of the air mass.

Variations in air-mass characteristics are also determined by how far north they are from the equator. Air masses that form in northern Canada are obviously much colder than those that form over Arizona, in the southwestern United States. As we learned in Chapters 14 and 15, this difference has to do with the fact that lower latitudes receive greater solar intensity than higher ones.

If air masses stayed where they were, there would be no mid-latitude storms. The air would just sit over the land without changing or interacting with other air masses. This is impossible because convection currents and the rotation of the earth move air masses from one place to another. When air masses with different characteristics meet, enormous amounts of energy are released. It is as if there were a battle in the sky. As in a battle, the line where the two air masses meet is called the **front**. Depending on the nature of the air masses, the temperature changes rapidly, winds pick up, and precipitation often occurs, especially if the "battle" is between a moist maritime air mass and a dry continental one.

Fronts: The Meeting of the Masses

Mid-latitude storms develop between polar and tropical source regions. Regular changes in weather occur as cold air masses meet warm ones and moist air masses meet dry ones. Energy moves through the environment in the form of precipitation, clouds, and strong winds when the two air masses clash. After the storm, one air mass dominates, but it is not long before it is modified by the land beneath it. Crisp, sunny days and clear, bitterly cold nights characterize polar continental air masses, but if one of these frigid, dry air masses ends up in Southern Canada, it is quickly modified because of relatively high insolation. Over two or three days, the earth converts solar energy from brilliant sunshine into thermal energy. Air temperatures rise, and air pressure begins to fall as the air becomes unstable.

Air masses also form over the poles. These Arctic and Antarctic air masses seldom venture into the middle latitudes. The lack of heating in the upper latitudes makes the air incredibly stable, so movement out of the region is rare. These air masses are responsible for severe blizzards in polar regions when Arctic air masses interact with polar air masses. (Keep in mind that Arctic air masses form over the poles, while polar air masses form between about 60° and 70° near the Arctic and Antarctic circles.) The same processes that create mid-latitude storms are common in these northern lands. There are no equatorial air masses because the air is too unstable. The **intertropical convergence zone** is a region where strong convection currents mix the air so much that it never develops into a high-pressure cell.

There are essentially two types of fronts. Warm fronts occur when a tropical air mass moves into a

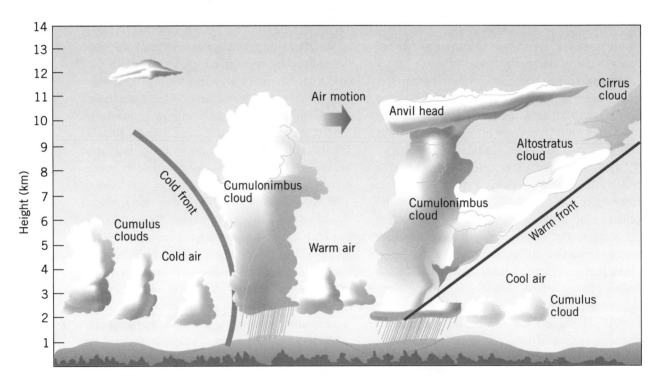

Figure 16.3
Cloud Development in Fronts

relatively cool region. This often happens in the spring as air from the Gulf of Mexico flows north into southern parts of Quebec. The cold, dry air over Quebec is much heavier than the warm, moist air of the southern states. This warm, moist air rises above the cold air, creating a winter storm. As the front moves north, the region it is travelling through becomes warmer. Precipitation, which often starts as snow, turns into freezing rain, and eventually warms up so that rain is the main form of precipitation. Cold fronts occur when a relatively cold polar air mass moves into a warmer region. The heavy, cold air bulldozes its way under the light, warm air. As the warm, moist air rises, the temperature drops because of the adiabatic lapse rate (see page 246). Water vapour in the air condenses on dust particles in the clouds and frontal precipitation occurs. The type of precipitation varies with the temperature. If the polar continental air from the north is strong enough, it dominates the area and snow is more likely. If the warmer air mass dominates, rain is the result. It is a tricky business trying to determine whether the precipitation will be snow, freezing rain, or rain. Only a degree or two determines which form of precipitation will occur. If freezing rain is forecast and school buses are cancelled because of the danger of slippery roads, school board officials and parents will be upset if all that falls is rain.

The types of clouds that form before a front arrives are used to forecast what will happen. Figure 16.3 shows how the front extends from the earth's surface into the troposphere. High above the earth's surface, the front forms well before it appears on the surface of the earth. By observing the types of clouds, forecasters can get an idea of the nature of the storm to come. When a warm front is approaching, a layer of wispy, high-altitude **cirrus clouds** develops. When increasingly more water vapour in the warmer air mass starts to condense, the clouds gradually thicken into **stratus clouds** and **nimbostratus clouds**. The increased cloud cover and loss of sunlight indicate that a storm is coming. Light rain or snow starts to fall, sometimes accompanied by fog. As the front moves closer, heavier

rain and thunderstorms often develop, depending on the intensity of the storm.

A similar pattern develops when a cold front passes into a region. Fair weather **cumulus clouds** indicate stable air, but as the cold front moves through, towering columns of **cumulonimbus clouds** form. Thunder, lightning, and hail may accompany heavy rain, again depending on how great the difference is between the two air masses. Temperatures drop, and the wind shifts in a clockwise direction. Cold fronts can occur at any time of the year, but are most common in the spring and fall. Extremely violent storms usually occur in late spring or early summer, when a cold front moves through an area dominated by a tropical air mass. The meeting of such fronts may trigger a tornado, the most violent of all storms. Meteorologists are particularly watchful when a cold front moves into an area of unstable maritime air during the spring. **Doppler radar** and satellites enable forecasters to track these dangerous conditions.

Cyclonic Storms

Cyclones are low-pressure cells that often form along fronts when a ripple or wave develops between the two air masses. Warm tropical air travels north along the front to the polar air mass. While this is happening, cold, dry air from the north moves south along a cold front. The result is a cyclonic storm, or low-pressure cell.

These cells have three components: a warm front, a cold front, and the air between them. As the warm front moves slowly north, its relatively warm, humid air slides over the cooler, drier air of the polar air mass. Because it has risen, air pressure drops, the dew point is reached, and heavy clouds form. On the ground, the temperature is still low compared with the warm and humid tropical air high above. Drizzle begins to fall, signalling the approach of the warm front. The precipitation gradually becomes heavier until the warm front finally passes. The rain can last for two or three days as these continent-sized storms travel across North America. When the warm front has left, the

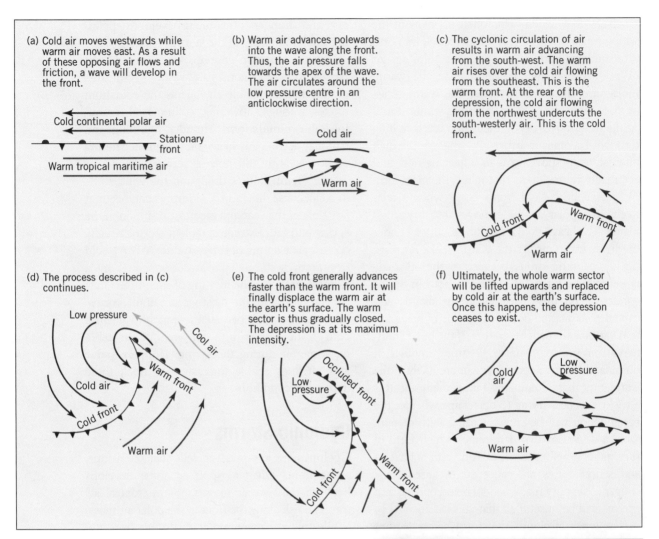

Figure 16.4
Stages in the Development of a Mid-Latitude Cyclonic Storm

sun comes out and the temperature rises. However, this welcomed break does not last long because the cold front is coming on fast behind.

The cold, dry air of the cP air mass slides under the warm, humid air high up in the troposphere. The adiabatic lapse rate results in the dew point being reached, and it starts to rain. The Coriolis effect causes the cyclone to spin in a counterclockwise direction in the Northern Hemisphere and in a clockwise direction in the Southern Hemisphere. This spinning increases the strength of the storm. Wind speed picks up,

Figure 16.5
Satellite Image of a Cyclone

the storm centre shrinks, and the storm begins to spin faster.

Satellite images (see Fig. 16.5) show cyclonic storms well. The clouds swirl into the low-pressure cell along the cold and warm fronts. Because the cold front moves faster than the warm front, it often catches up to it. When it does, the warm front disappears from the earth's surface but remains high in the atmosphere above the earth. This is called an **occluded front** or **trowel**.

When the temperature of the two air masses becomes similar and the humidity drops because of precipitation, the instability in the atmosphere gradually decreases until the storm dies. This period of stable air allows the air mass to become modified as it takes on the characteristics of the region it is above. These periods of pleasant weather are called **anticyclones**, or high-pressure cells.

The Jet Stream

Storms seem to follow set pathways. If you study weather maps over several weeks, you will notice that storms flow across North America in the same pattern, usually from northwest to southeast, often dipping far to the south. Upper atmosphere studies have determined that storms follow **jet streams** that exist at altitudes of between 9000 and 12 000 m. Jet-stream winds often reach speeds in excess of 300 km/h.

One such jet stream exists over Canada. The powerful winds in this stream meander from side to side. As these waves become more exaggerated, they extend further south, often invading tropical regions. Cyclones are dragged along by the jet stream, so when it loops south, cold arctic air moves south with it. Cyclonic storms soon result as tropical and polar air masses collide.

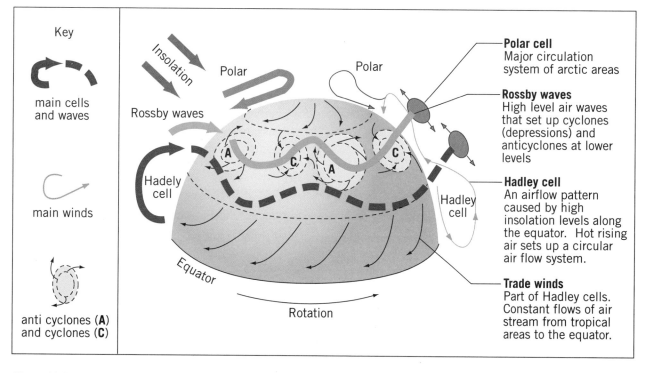

Figure 16.6
Storm Paths and Jet Streams. During a cold snap over the United States, the jet stream often dives south, sometimes as far as the Gulf of Mexico.

Meteorologists are able to monitor jet-stream activity using weather balloons and satellites. If they know where the jet stream is, they can easily predict where storms will move since they follow the same paths. Studying changes in jet streams could hold the key to producing accurate long-range (three- to five-day) weather predictions.

Violent Weather

Violent storms are probably the most frightening events in nature. Whether it is a severe thunderstorm, a winter blizzard, a massive hurricane, or a powerful twister, violent weather reminds us how powerless we are against the forces of nature. Modern technology allows meteorologists to understand violent storms better than ever before, but this will not allow us to prevent them. All we can do is learn to predict when they are coming and prepare as best we can to meet them.

Thunderstorms

The most common violent storms are thunderstorms. On hot summer days, the temperature increases and convection currents form as the hot, humid air starts to rise. In time, giant storm clouds build, and before you know it a full-fledged thunderstorm is rumbling across the landscape. Try the true/false quiz below to see how much you know about thunderstorms. (The answers are on page 270.)

An interesting feature of thunderstorms has to do with the intensity of the rainfall. The sky just seems to open up and pour rain. This is because so much moisture is held aloft by the warm updrafts, which carry water droplets up into the sky. Enormous quantities of moisture are held in suspension in the cloud, which explains why thunderclouds are so dark. Eventually, the water is too heavy for the rising air to hold up, and the rain starts to pour. The raindrops themselves are often huge because each drop has increased in size as more and more droplets have joined with it. Often the droplets are actually melted hailstones. If hail does make it to the earth's surface, the damage to crops and other property can be devastating.

Frontal Depressions

A **frontal depression** forms when two air masses meet and the warm air rises over the cooler air along the front, causing an area or **trough** of low pressure. When a frontal depression stalls over one place for an extended period of time, the damage can be extensive. These storms don't tend to be as violent as thunderstorms, but they are dangerous because of the sheer volume of precipitation they release. In early June of 2000, for example, southern Saskatchewan received 330 mm of rainfall in six hours during one such storm. Considering that

---

DO YOU KNOW THE FACTS ABOUT THUNDERSTORMS? (Answers are on p. 270)

1. There are about 2000 storms going on at any one time around the world.   T   F
2. There are no detection systems available for tracking thunderstorms.   T   F
3. The CN Tower is frequently hit by lightning.   T   F
4. Lightning causes about 4000 forest fires a year in Canada alone.   T   F
5. Lightning always causes death when it strikes someone.   T   F
6. All regions of Canada experience thunderstorms.   T   F
7. The static electricity in a lightning bolt comes from air molecules rubbing together.   T   F
8. A lightning bolt is almost as hot as the surface of the sun.
9. You can tell how far away a thunderstorm is by counting the seconds between the   T   F
   thunder and the lightning.   T   F
10. Staying inside your car is safer than being in an open field in a thunderstorm.   T   F

Figure 16.7
What patterns do you notice on this map?

Lightning flashes
per square kilometre per year

☐	0 – 0.25
☐	0.25 – 0.5
☐	0.5 – 1
☐	1 – 2
☐	2 – 3

Measured cloud-to-ground strikes
1998-1999 figures
△ Lightning sensors
(Canadian Lightning
Detection Network)

this is an arid zone where annual totals are usually below 250 mm, that is a lot of water! Farms were completely flooded. A more devastating storm took place in southern Quebec and southeastern Ontario in 1998. This time, the storm was in the winter, and therefore took the form of freezing rain. The rain was relentless for several days, forming a thick layer of ice on every exposed surface. Trees gave way, hydro lines collapsed, and the region suffered immensely. Some communities were without power for a month, livestock died by the hundreds, schools and hospitals shut down, and people froze to death.

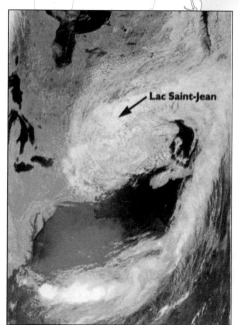

Figure 16.8
This satellite image shows a frontal depression over the Saguenay River, Quebec.

ANSWERS TO THUNDERSTORM QUIZ

1. True: While it may seem hard to believe, thunderstorms are common occurrences.
2. False: In the past, the only way lightning was detected was through direct observation. In 1998, however, Environment Canada initiated a system of 81 stations with computers, sensing antennas, GPS receivers, and satellite dishes. The map on page 269 was derived from data collected by this system.
3. True: The CN Tower, the highest structure in Canada, takes about 200 hits a year. Steel reinforcing rods are grounded so that the electric current is safely channeled into the bedrock on which it sits.
4. True: When Smokey the Bear says, "Only you can prevent forest fires," he is not being completely truthful. Each year in Canada, over 2 million hectares (an area about the size of Lake Ontario) is burned because of lightning.
5. False: Many people actually survive being struck by lightning. Survivors often have serious health problems, ranging from heart problems to memory and hearing loss. There is even a web site for lightning survivors <www3.bc.sympatico.ca/light-ningsurvivor>.

6. False: If you check the map on page 269, you will see that southern Ontario and the south-central Prairies are the most affected areas. B.C. and northern Canada get practically no thunderstorms.
7. False: Thunderclouds are so tall that the water droplets freeze. Some fall down because of gravity, but others are thrown higher into the air by convection currents. The rubbing of these ice crystals is what causes a cloud to become electrically charged.
8. False: At an estimated 30 000°C, air in a channel of lightning can be five times the temperature of the surface of the sun.
9. True: If you count the seconds between the lightning and the thunder clap, and divide by three, you will get a pretty good idea of how many kilometres away the storm is. If your count is less than 3 seconds, take cover!
10. True: Cars are relatively safe as long as you don't touch any metal in the car. The car tires ground the electric current, and most cars have a fairly low profile so they are relatively safe. If you are in an open field, you are in serious danger. Lie flat on the ground as far away as possible from trees or other objects that protrude above the earth.

Figure 16.9
The Quebec Ice Storm of 1998

Hurricanes

Hurricanes, or tropical cyclones, are by far the most destructive of all storms. Each year, between 75 and 90 hurricanes form in the Atlantic, the Pacific, and the Indian oceans. The annual damage caused by hurricanes is estimated at over $5 billion (US) on average. As many as 15 000 people a year lose their lives during these violent storms.

Hurricanes form when the hot, sunny weather over the Tropics heats the ocean all summer long. By late summer or early fall, the seawater is so warm that convection currents develop, forming low-pressure cells in source areas far from continental land masses. Winds blow in to replace the

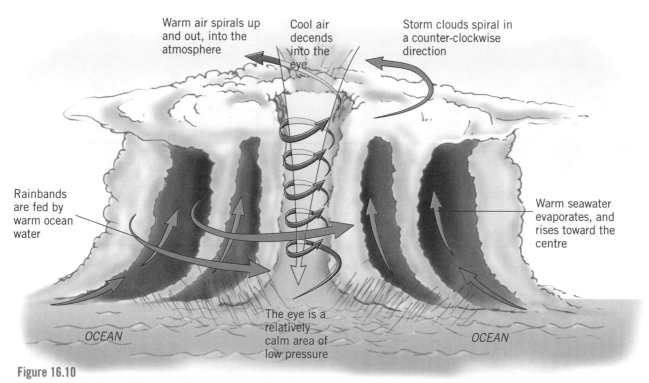

Warm air spirals up and out, into the atmosphere

Cool air descends into the eye

Storm clouds spiral in a counter-clockwise direction

Rainbands are fed by warm ocean water

Warm seawater evaporates, and rises toward the centre

The eye is a relatively calm area of low pressure

OCEAN

OCEAN

Figure 16.10
Anatomy of a Hurricane. What would the weather conditions be in the "eye" of this storm? Why?

unstable air that has risen high into the troposphere. The Coriolis effect starts the system rotating in a counter-clockwise direction. As more and more energy from the ocean flows into the atmosphere, convection currents intensify and the storm grows into a **tropical depression**. The air pressure drops in the centre, winds pick up, the dew point is reached high in the cumulonimbus clouds, rain starts to fall, and wind speeds increase. A **tropical storm** is thus formed. At this stage, the storm is named so that severe-weather forecasters can distinguish it from other tropical storms. The first storm of the year starts with the letter "A", and each subsequent hurricane is given a name with the next letter of the alphabet.

If such a storm developed over land, the temperature would drop once rain started to fall and it would likely remain just a thunderstorm and quickly die. This does not happen with hurricanes. These major storms continue to grow in intensity over several days. The super-heated seawater continues to pump energy into the atmosphere. Even though it is raining, the earth's surface is not cooling off, and so the vertical development of massive clouds above the ocean continues.

The characteristic eye of the hurricane develops as the system matures. Air gently descending from high altitudes warms in the centre of the eye. Because the air is descending, there is no wind within the eye, nor are there any clouds in the eye since the hot, moist air is rapidly sucked to the edges of the storm where condensation occurs, forming thick clouds. However, air spirals out from the inside wall of the storm at speeds of between 120 and 200 km per hour. The trade winds blowing steadily from the east, day after day, intensify the counter-clockwise spinning of the storm. This spinning vortex of clouds develops into spokes, like those of a pinwheel, extending from the eye of the storm.

The trade winds slowly move the system to the west so that it approaches continental land masses. Once it reaches land, it quickly loses the

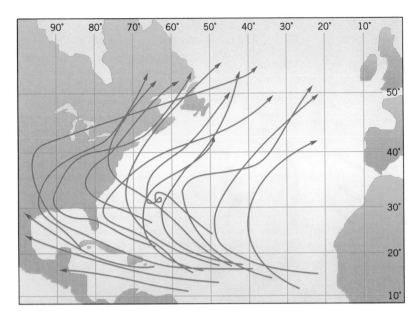

Figure 16.11
Tracks of Some Typical Hurricanes in August
Notice that the storms follow the prevailing winds.

source of its power and degenerates into a tropical storm. Sometimes it makes landfall, loses intensity, and then veers over water again where it redevelops into a hurricane. This happened to Hurricane Andrew as it moved over southern Florida and then redeveloped over the Gulf of Mexico. If the storm travels north up the eastern seaboard, westerly winds take over from the trade winds and often turn the hurricane onto a northeasterly track. This is what happened to Hurricane Floyd in 1999.

Meteorologists use satellite images to track hurricanes. The speed and direction of hurricanes is monitored hourly. The position of the eye is plotted on a map, and the distance the hurricane has moved is calculated by using the scale on the map. Computer programs determine where the storm is headed, using statistical programs that analyse the air-pressure gradients along projected trajectories. Direction is not always easy to predict because storms frequently take unexpected turns as the air pressure fluctuates wildly over the tropical waters. Meteorologists also study hurricanes using airplanes that actually fly at low altitudes

Figure 16.12
Satellite Image of Hurricane Andrew

Figure 16.13
Satellite Image of Hurricane Mitch

Name	Date	Affected Area	No. of Deaths
Hazel	Oct. 1954	Eastern US, Ontario	347
Diane	Aug. 1955	Eastern US	400
Hilda	Sept. 1955	Mexican coast	200
Janet	Sept. 1955	Caribbean	500
Audrey	June 1957	Louisiana, Texas	430
Hattie	Oct. 1961	Belize	400
Flora	Oct. 1963	Cuba, Haiti	6000
Inez	Sept. 1966	Caribbean, Florida, Mexico	293
Camille	Aug. 1969	Mississippi, Louisiana	256
Fifi	Sept. 1974	Honduras	2000
David	Sept. 1979	Dominican Republic, Dominica, Florida	1200
Allen	Aug. 1989	Caribbean, Texas	272
Gilbert	Sept. 1988	Jamaica	318
Andrew	Aug. 1992	Bahamas, Florida, Louisiana	62
Mitch	Nov. 1998	Honduras, Nicaragua	11000+
Floyd	Sept. 1999	Florida, North Carolina	68

Figure 16.14
Significant Hurricanes of the Last 50 Years

right through the storm! They measure wind speed, atmospheric pressure, rainfall, and, if possible, wave height. This is a dangerous assignment, but one that provides vital information for forecasters.

Meteorologists study satellite images for potentially dangerous storms in the eastern Atlantic, off the coast of Africa. Storms are tracked as the trade winds blow them westward. Since most storms follow the same path more or less, forecasters can predict with some degree of certainty where storms will come inland. Once a storm appears to be a threat, a storm alert is issued and broadcasters advise people of what actions to take.

Sometimes the forecasts are wrong, as with Hurricane Floyd—a massive storm that swept up the Atlantic Seaboard off the Carolina coast, but which never came ashore and caused only minimal damage. The storm was so huge that authorities evacuated the entire coastline. It was a massive undertaking, the largest evacuation of people anywhere during peacetime. Residents, tourists, and resort operators were very upset with the disruption. Millions of dollars were lost in tourist revenues and many vacations were ruined. Some people vowed that they will not leave when there is another warning. For these reasons, it is important that forecasters try to be as accurate as possible in their hurricane path projections.

Storms that remain over the ocean for long periods of time are usually the strongest storms. Fortunately, however, they cause little damage unless they make landfall. Then, of course, the scale of the tragedy can be immense. Such was the case in 1998 when Hurricane Mitch hit Central America.

The cost, the devastation, and the incredible impact on the people were immense. Mitch was a Category 5 monster of a hurricane, with average wind speeds of 290 km/h and gusts well over 320 km/h. This storm was so intense that at least 11 000 people died and thousands more were never found. The storm took shape off the coast of South America and spun northward toward Honduras. The original rainforest had been cleared along the coastal plain of Honduras and Nicaragua to make room for banana plantations. This is where Mitch made landfall. The storm ripped apart the coastline and caused massive flooding and mudslides. As it moved inland, it downgraded quickly to a tropical storm, but the damage had only just started. As much as 600 mm of rain fell in a week. The deforested mountain slopes melted away, filling the valleys with mud. Thousands of villages were buried, roads and bridges were obliterated, and the countries' economies were ruined.

While Hurricane Andrew devastated the United States, earning it the distinction of being the most expensive disaster in history, the number of people who died was minimal

Figure 16.15
Rainfall from Hurrican Mitch caused a mudslide on the Casitas Volcano, killing 2,069 people.

compared to the Central American tragedy wrought by Mitch. The Americans had **geotechnologies**, which allowed forecasters to predict the storm and warn the public of Andrew's approach. People evacuated the area, boarded up buildings, and prepared for the worst. However, developing countries like Honduras have neither the technologies nor the infrastructure to survive against such a force.

American agencies warned Central American authorities, but the region lacked the transportation and communications infrastructure of the United States, making evacuation impossible. In fact, many residents of Nicaragua were not even aware that Mitch was coming. In addition, the buildings were flimsy compared to American buildings, so property damage was greater even though the structures were worth less money. Another significant reason for the extensive damage in Central America was poor land use practices. The Caribbean coastline of Central America consists mainly of low-lying coastal plains and mangrove swamps. The region has been extensively cleared and drained to allow for huge banana plantations. In the past, storms did not cause the extensive damage that Mitch did because the forests and swamps acted as buffers

geo.web resources

<www.ns.ec.gc.ca/weather/hurricane/ index_e.html>

This is the Canadian Hurricane Centre. Click on "Current Conditions" and report on any storms being tracked. Click on "The Canadian Connection" and find out what happens when tropical cyclones near Canada.

Storm Category	Wind Speed	Barometric Pressure	Storm Surge	Damage
Tropical Depression	37 – 63 km/hr	N/A	N/A	N/A
Tropical Storm	64 – 119 km/hr	N/A	N/A	N/A
Category 1 Minimal Hurricane	12 – 152 km/hr	980 mb or more	Up to 1.6m	- Wind damage to unanchored mobile homes - Some flooding
Category 2 Moderate Hurricane	153 – 176 km/hr	965 – 970 mb	1.7 – 2.8 m	- Wind damage to roofing, doors, and windows - Significant damage to mobile homes and small craft
Category 3 Extensive Hurricane	177 – 209 km/hr	945 – 964 mb	2.8 – 4.1 m	- Structural damage to homes, mobile homes destroyed, flooding below 1.8 m msl
Category 4 Extreme Hurricane	210 – 250 km/hr	920 – 944 mb	4.2 – 6.4 m	- Major structural damage to homes, extensive beach erosion with flooding below 3.5 m
Category 5 Catastrophic Hurricane	Over 250 km/hr	Under 912 mb	more than 4 m	- Massive structural damage to homes, complete building failures, flooding below 5.3 m

Figure 16.16
Saffir-Simpson Hurricane Classification Scale

to the inland regions. The rain and wind would attack the coast, but the damage would be minimal. When Mitch came inland, unabated by the plantations on the coast, the rain and wind hit communities with full force. In order to lessen the damage of future hurricanes, more sustainable agricultural practices are needed.

Tornadoes

Tornadoes are like hurricanes in that they are violent storms with high winds and heavy rains; however, that is where the similarities end. For example, both move with the prevailing winds, but since tornadoes are mid-latitude storms, they move from the southwest (following the westerlies), instead of from the east (with the trade winds). Hurricanes cause tremendous damage over large areas—whole countries can be devastated by their fury. Tornadoes, on the other hand, have their enormous power confined to a relatively narrow band, so damage, while usually extensive, is concentrated on a small strip of land. Houses may be completely destroyed on one side of the street and untouched on the other. Hurricanes form over tropical seas in late summer or early autumn, whereas tornadoes form over

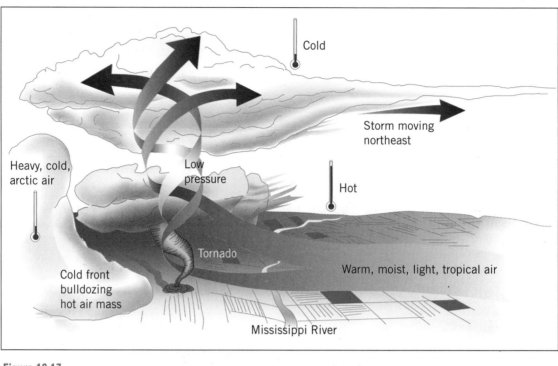

Cold

Storm moving
northeast

Low
pressure

Heavy, cold,
arctic air

Hot

Cold front
bulldozing
hot air mass

Warm, moist, light, tropical air

Mississippi River

Figure 16.17
How Tornadoes are Formed

land during spring or early summer. The trade winds determine the direction a hurricane travels. **Wind shear** caused by a cold front moving through a low-pressure cell starts a tornado spinning. Tornadoes, because they are different than hurricanes, require people to take different precautions. Tornadoes move along the ground at the speed of a car—between 50 and 100 km/h. If you see a "twister" coming, get out of the way!

Tornadoes are more difficult to track than hurricanes because they cannot be detected by way of satellite images. The cloud cover is so great that the characteristic funnel clouds are obscured. In the past, the only way to detect a tornado was through human observation from the ground. Severe-weather watchers are volunteers who report violent storms to the Ministry of the Environment.

When a tornado is coming, the sky turns greenish grey, the air changes from a hot, humid

condition to become cooler and fresher, and winds become very strong. Today, Doppler radar and **global positioning systems** (GPS) are used to track these storms (see p. 287 for more details on how the Doppler radar works). The Atmospheric Environment Service issues a **tornado watch** when conditions are right for a tornado. When a dark, funnel-shaped cloud is observed either visually or on radar, a **tornado warning** is issued. When this happens, people should immediately seek a safe place to sit out the storm.

The path a tornado will take is unpredictable. It does do not follow a straight line and will sometimes disappear altogether before reforming and touching down elsewhere. It skips and hops across the countryside, destroying some structures and sparing others. Whenever it touches the ground, everything not held down is drawn up the funnel just as if it were a giant

F-Scale Number	Intensity	Wind Speed (km/h)	Damage Evident
F0	Gale	64 – 115	Damage to chimneys, broken tree branches, small trees uprooted, damage to sign boards
F1	Moderate	116 – 170	Shingles peeled off, mobile homes pushed off foundations, cars blown off roads
F2	Significant	171 – 265	Roofs torn off buildings, mobile homes destroyed, large trees uprooted
F3	Severe	266 – 330	Roofs and walls torn off well-constructed buildings, trains overturned, most trees in forests destroyed
F4	Devastating ·	331 – 400	Well-built houses leveled, cars thrown, missiles made from blown objects
F5	Incredible	401 – 500	Houses carried considerable distance, car-sized missiles fly in excess of 100 m, trees debarked, steel-reinforced concrete buildings damaged
F6	Inconceivable	501 – 600	Not experienced yet

Figure 16.18
The Fujita Tornado Scale. Do you foresee any problems with scientists trying to classify tornadoes according to this scale? Explain your answer.

vacuum cleaner! The storm seldom lasts more than a few minutes at most, but the death and destruction left behind are remembered for a lifetime.

Wind speeds can be estimated after the fact by studying the damage. Engineers are able to determine the amount of force required to cause certain types of damage. From this data, it is possible to ascertain the amount of energy created by the whirlwind, using the **Fujita Scale**. With regard to forecasting tornadoes, however, the best meteorologists can do is to study the atmospheric conditions that have caused tornadoes in the past and assume that the same conditions will cause tornadoes in the future.

Two conditions are needed for the formation of a funnel cloud. First, there must be strong convection currents due to surface heating. This causes vertical cloud development in the form of cumulonimbus clouds to fill the sky with enormous amounts of moisture and energy. Second, a cold front must move into the area, usually from the southwest. The result is a body of unstable, rising, hot, moist air with a cold front bearing down on it from the southwest. When the cold front hits the convectional cell, the difference in the atmospheric pressure triggers the swirling funnel cloud we associate with tornadoes.

Figure 16.21 on page 279 reveals that tornadoes are not evenly distributed across North America. The most prone areas are in the American south-central states and the states bordering the Gulf of Mexico. Kansas, Oklahoma, and Iowa experience storms in the early spring as air masses originating over the Gulf of Mexico move north. If they meet cold arctic air masses flowing south from Canada, tornadoes are often the result.

The Pine Lake Alberta Tornado

July 16, 2000, was a day that will never be forgotten in Green Acres campground, located southeast of Red Deer, in central Alberta.

The vacation community was just finishing supper when the hailstones started. Everybody rushed for their motorhomes and trailers and took cover. Melvin Lindeman, who lived in a house across from the campsite, described what happened next: "To the southwest we saw what looked like a solid wall of water coming at us. As it moved forward the fields literally disappeared."

A huge grain bin bounced across the yard and smashed through the Lindeman family's living-room window. The force of the wind sucking the air through the window was so great that the bedroom ceiling collapsed and every door in the house slammed shut. Lindeman and his family climbed into a bathtub and covered their heads. Next, most of the roof of their home blew off. The worst part, he said, was the four minutes during which the tornado ravaged his house. He did not know if he would live or die.

With winds approaching 320 km per hour, the Pine Lake Tornado is classified as a category F3 on the six-level Fujita Scale (see page 277). While it was not the strongest tornado on the scale, it was relatively powerful for the Canadian Prairies. By the time the storm had passed through the campground and surrounding area, 11 people had died, 136 people were hospitalized, and most of the 429 trailers and motorhomes in the campground were destroyed. The total of the damage was set at $12 million.

Figure 16.20
Tornado Damage at Green Acres Campground

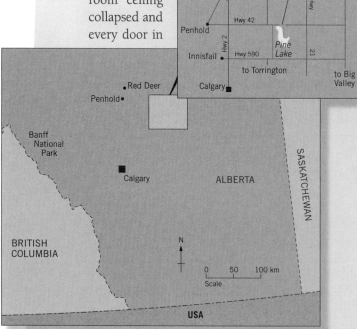

Figure 16.19
Map Showing the Location of Pine Lake Disaster

QUESTIONS:

1. Why are tornadoes of this size less frequent in Canada than they would be in the United States, further south?
2. What recommendations would you have for the owners of the trailer park to ensure better safety when they rebuild?
3. Describe what the family in this story did when they saw the tornado approaching. What would you have done?

Province/State	Tornadoes	State	Tornadoes
Alberta	0.3	Maryland	0.4
British Columbia	0	Massachusetts	0.5
Manitoba	0.1	Michigan	1.5
New Brunswick	0	Minnesota	1.8
Newfoundland	0	Mississippi	1.0
Nova Scotia	0.5	Missouri	1.4
Ontario	0.2	Nebraska	0.9
Prince Edward Island	0	Nevada	0.7
Quebec	0	New Hampshire	0
Saskatchewan	0.5	New Jersey	0
Montana	0.8	New Mexico	0
Alabama	0.8	New York	0
Alaska	0	North Carolina	0.8
Arizona	0.1	North Dakota	0.9
Arkansas	1.0	Ohio	0.7
California	0.4	Oklahoma	3.9
Colorado	2.8	Oregon	0.2
Connecticut	0	Pennsylvania	0.6
Delaware	0	Rhode Island	0
Florida	4.0	South Carolina	1.3
Georgia	1.1	South Dakota	1.7
Hawaii	0	Tennessee	0.8
Idaho	0.5	Texas	2.8
Illinois	2.1	Utah	0.1
Indiana	1.5	Vermont	0.4
Iowa	3.7	Virginia	0.2
Kansas	5.5	Washington	0.1
Kentucky	0.8	West Virginia	0.2
Louisiana	3.1	Wisconsin	0.7
Maine	0.1	Wyoming	0.9

Figure 16.21

Tornado Frequency per 10 000 km² by Province/State. Where in Canada are tornadoes most common? Why?

Coastal regions also experience tornadoes in the United States. The frequency of tornadoes in the winter and very early spring is becoming much more common in Florida, Louisiana, and Texas.

In Canada, tornadoes are particularly common in Saskatchewan and Alberta. Cold, dry air descends from the Western Cordillera on the western flank of Alberta. If it meets hot, humid air on the plains, funnel clouds are often the result. While the figures for the whole of Ontario are fairly low, Southern Ontario between London and Barrie is frequently hit by violent storms, while much of the north practically never sees them. The figures for Ontario are thus distorted, as it is a big province.

Blizzards

Blizzards are severe winter storms that most Canadians have experienced first-hand. The Atmospheric Environment Service describes blizzards as having a temperature of -12°C or less, wind speed of 49 km/h or more, visibility of less than 1 km, and duration of no less than three hours.

Blizzards are really just severe mid-latitude storms that occur in winter. They're not a significant problem when they occur in the Far North, where population densities are small and people are more or less used to them. But they become killers when they dip far south into southern parts of Canada and into the United States. A blizzard can happen when the jet stream loops far to the south, causing cold, dry air to come in contact with moist, tropical air from the southern United States.

Such was the case in January 2000, when Maritimers awoke to the second major storm in a week. New Brunswick experienced the worst conditions, with 70 centimetres of snow and record low temperatures. The snow was whipped into gigantic drifts by the 100 km/h winds. The province was virtually closed down until the cleanup was finished. However, just as the streets were made passable again, another storm hit.

Four days later, an even larger storm hit the entire eastern seaboard from North Carolina to Newfoundland. As the warm front travelled up the coast, heavy snowfall and whiteout conditions were replaced with freezing rain, sleet, and then heavy rains.

The January 2000 storm caused five deaths in the US, buried cars, closed schools, cut power to thousands of customers, and caused the shutdown of major airports.

Sometimes referred to as "nor'easters," these freak blizzards seem to be hitting with more regularity than in the past. Warmer than usual seawater off the coast of the southern states is heating maritime air masses. The energy contained in these volatile systems is released when confronted with cold, dry air from Labrador. The colder air is drawn south by the intense low-pressure cells that develop in the southeast.

Figure 16.22
Toronto's mayor called in the Canadian military to help the citizens dig out from the blizzard that buried the city in 1999.

ACTIVITIES

UNDERSTANDING CONCEPTS

1. a) Explain what happens to temperature, water vapour, and cloud cover when two air masses come into contact.
    b) Describe the weather conditions associated with each of the following cloud types: cirrus, cumulus, stratus, and nimbostratus.
    c) Why are storms more common in the mid-latitudes than elsewhere?
    d) Describe the characteristics of cyclones and anticyclones.
    e) Outline how studying jet streams could facilitate long-range forecasting.

2. a) Prepare an organizer comparing the different storms using the following format:

Storm	Description	Time and Location	Causes	Type of Damage	Safety Precautions
Thunderstorm					
Frontal Depression					
Hurricane					
Tornado					
Blizzard					

    b) Analyse the effects of atmospheric hazards (e.g., thunderstorms, tornadoes, hurricanes, and blizzards) on human activities.

3. a) Prepare a comparison organizer showing the differences between the damage caused by hurricane Mitch in Honduras and the damage caused by hurricane Floyd in the United States.
    b) Why do the rates of loss of life and property during hurricanes tend to be lower in developed countries than in developing countries?
    c) Describe the different forms of damage hurricanes can cause.

4. Assess the Saffir-Simpson Hurricane Scale and the Fujita Tornado Scale.
    a) How are they useful in studying hurricanes and tornadoes?
    b) What shortcomings do you foresee the scales having?
    c) How could these classification systems be improved?

DEVELOPING AND PRACTISING SKILLS

5. Study Fig. 16.2.
   a) Prepare a sketch map of North America. Indicate the location of source regions for each air mass. Shade the area between source regions and label it "Mid-latitude Storm Belt."
   b) Prepare a comparison organizer to describe each air mass. Include such criteria as name (continental Polar, maritime Tropical, etc.); symbol (cP, mT, etc.); source region; relative temperature (hot, warm, cool, cold); and relative humidity (moist, dry).

6. Study the satellite image showing the Saguenay Flood (Fig. 16.8).
   a) Locate the centre of the storm (where the clouds are thickest), and on a tracing of the image label this with an L for low pressure.
   b) Draw a line showing the frontal depression flowing out from the low.
   c) Where is the warm, moist air coming from?
   d) What pattern of precipitation did you notice as your analysis moved out from the centre of the storm?
   e) What factors could have resulted in the storm remaining stationary over the valley?

7. a) Prepare a graded shading map using the data from Fig. 16.14. Use one colour. Each time a place is mentioned in the organizer, lightly colour that place. If a place is mentioned more than once, it will have a darker shade of the colour because you have coloured it more than once. When you have finished, you will have a map that shows locations that are most prone to hurricanes.
   b) What generalizations can you make about where hurricanes occur?
   c) On a world map, show other locations where hurricanes could occur.
   d) Explain why hurricanes do not form over land, in mid-latitudes, or over the equator.

8. Try this simulation. Get two 2-L plastic soft drink containers. Fill one almost to the top with water. Attach the top of the second bottle to the top of the first, using two large washers and strong duct tape. Invert the bottles so that the empty one is on the bottom. Rotate the bottles to the left so that the water in one flows down into the other one. What you have created is a "tornado in a bottle."
   a) How is this simulation like a tornado?
   b) How is it different?
   c) Explain how tornadoes are formed using Fig. 16.17 and this simulation.

9. Prepare a graded-shading map using the data in Fig. 16.21 to show the distribution of tornadoes across North America.
   a) Explain why the organizer doesn't just list the number of tornadoes sighted by state or province, but instead shows the number of tornadoes per 10 000 km^2.
   b) What generalizations can you make about where tornadoes are most commonly found?
   c) Explain why tornadoes are most common in the regions shown on your tornado graded-shading map.

10. Compare the satellite images of Hurricane Mitch and Hurricane Andrew on page 272. Hurricane Andrew was called the "storm of the century."
    a) How does it compare to Mitch?
    b) Why was Andrew nowhere near the kind of problem Mitch was?
    c) What can you infer about the size and strength of hurricanes in recent years?

LEARNING THROUGH APPLICATION

11. a) Prepare a list of planning regulations that a town in a hurricane-prone, a blizzard-prone, or a frontal depression-prone region should follow.
    b) What precautions should individuals take for each type of storm?
12. Visit the National Oceanographic and Atmospheric Administration web site (www.noa.gov) (an American site), or use another web site of your choice to get information about recent disasters in the atmosphere. Make a display, which includes the following:
    a) Maps and air photos of an actual storm, with an analysis of the structure of the event.
    b) A timeline of events leading up to and following the storm.
    c) Photos of the damage after the storm, with a chart showing the damage.
    d) Recommendations for how the community could have been better prepared for the disaster.

Chapter 17

FORECASTING THE WEATHER

FOCUS QUESTIONS

1. What are the current methods and technologies used to track and predict dangerous weather phenomena such as hurricanes, thunderstorms, and tornadoes?
2. How do we observe weather patterns and collect weather data in the field?
3. How are written, oral, and visual communication skills used to present the results of weather-related inquiry and analysis effectively?

Key Terms

geostationary satellite

chaos theory

radiosondes

general circulation models

Doppler radar

Have you ever experienced a "surprise" snowstorm because the meteorologist on the news the night before had forecasted rain? Even with all the modern satellite technology at their fingertips, forecasters have always been and will always be wrong on occasion. But this isn't for lack of trying—weather is simply so complex it is often difficult to predict. However, if we understand the processes that operate in the atmosphere, then we will be better able to forecast weather.

Forecasting is very important in many ways. Extreme weather like floods, thunderstorms, and hurricanes can be predicted so that people can take appropriate action to protect themselves and their property. Daily weather forecasts advise people about what to wear and how to plan their day. Farmers plan when to harvest, filmmakers decide when to shoot, and vacationers make travel plans based on weather reports. Knowledge about the weather is increasingly important for modern society.

Collecting Weather Data

There is a wide assortment of instruments used to gather data about the weather: thermometers, rain gauges, barometers, wind vanes, and anemometers, to name just a few. Thermometers are thin tubes of glass that hold a liquid. The liquid expands or contracts depending upon the temperature, and therefore moves up or down the tube. By calibrating the tube, temperature can be determined. Rain gauges are simple cylindrical containers that hold precipitation. Barometers measure air pressure by using a variety of mechanisms. Wind vanes measure wind direction, and anemometers measure wind speed by counting the number of rotations a device makes and converting that information into kilometres per hour. These simple instruments are used by the many volunteers who operate the hundreds of weather stations across Canada, the United States, and the other developed countries of the world.

Sensor	Purpose	Mode of Operation
Liquid Precipitation Accumulation Sensor	Measures rainfall	Precipitation falls into the upper collector. The collector is heated to melt frozen precipitation. A mechanical device measures the rainfall in centimetres and tips out the water when it is full.
Visibility and Day/Night Sensor	Measures the horizontal distance a person can see	A flash of light is emitted by the sensor through a portion of the atmosphere. The scattered-light level is measured and the visibility is determined.
Freezing Rain Sensor	Measures freezing rain	An ultrasonic vibrating probe is used to detect icing. The frequency of the vibration changes with the amount of ice accumulated on the sensor.
Ceilometer	Measures cloud height (ceiling)	A pulse of laser light is shot into the sky. It is reflected back by clouds. By measuring the time it takes, the distance to the clouds can be determined.
Wind Sensor	Measures wind speed and direction	A three-cup rotating device and a vane measure speed and direction. An anemometer also provides wind power to operate the equipment.
Temperature Dew Point Sensor	Determines the temperature at which water vapour condenses (dew point)	A mirror is chilled so that a fine mist appears on it. The amount of energy needed to chill the mirror allows the computer to determine the dew point. A thermal sensor in the mirror measures the temperature.

Figure 17.1
Recent Technologies in Weather Data Collection

However, there is a problem with the instruments and the data they show. Variations between instruments and differences in the accuracy of readings have caused inconsistency in data collection. To overcome this problem, new, more accurate analogue sensors are now being used in automated weather stations. The sensors are self-contained even in remote regions and can be operated without human intervention, often by using solar or wind energy as a power source. Data is sent regularly by radio communication to satellites from which it is relayed to Environment Canada computers on the ground. Because there is no human factor, there are no variations of interpretation in reading the data, and the sensors can be located in remote regions where there are no people, thus providing complete readings across the country. The only drawback is that automated weather stations cannot replace the need for some types of human observation.

Building and maintaining weather collection stations is one of Environment Canada's main functions. In November 1999, for example, the department installed an automated weather station at the Forks in downtown Winnipeg. This new weather station is one of over 160 automated stations throughout the Prairie

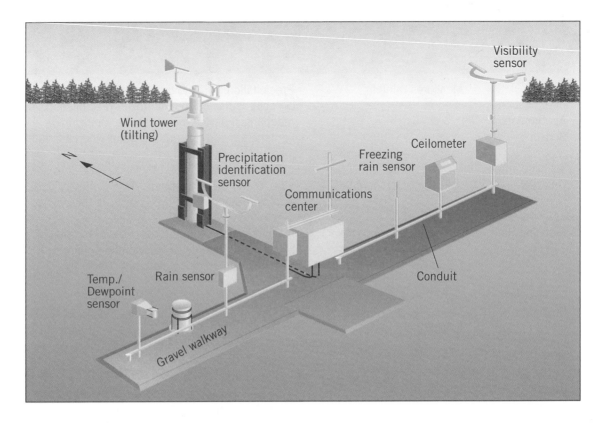

Wind tower
(tilting)

Visibility
sensor

Precipitation
identification
sensor

Ceilometer

Freezing
rain sensor

Communications
center

Conduit

Temp./
Dewpoint
sensor

Rain sensor

Gravel walkway

Figure 17.2
Automated Surface Observing System (ASOS) Sensors

provinces. However, weather stations perform only a part of the data-gathering process. In addition to the automated stations, Environment Canada operates 15 upper-air stations, 9 weather radars, 21 aviation weather stations, 80 staffed observing stations, 9 weather buoys, and 600 volunteer climate stations in the Prairies and the North.

Upper-air observations are provided by **radiosondes**—balloons with instrument packs attached. About a hundred balloons are released twice each day in a number of locations across North America. Information about air temperature, turbulence, dew point, and air pressure is sent back to the weather offices.

Weather radar locates and monitors cloud patterns up to 400 km away. This analysis helps meteorologists keep track of severe storms. Microwaves are emitted in a cone-shaped beam

from a slowly rotating antenna. The beam passes through cloud but bounces back as an echo when it hits objects in the sky such as rain, snow, or hail. The amount of precipitation in an area can be determined by the amount of scattering that takes place in the returned beam, while the location of the precipitation can be determined by measuring the length of time it takes the microwave to hit the object and return to the tower. From this, maps are drawn showing the location and intensity of storms.

As we learned in Chapter 16, satellites cannot predict certain dangerous storms such as tornadoes because the cloud cover is too thick to see the typical funnel formation. So, forecasters use the Doppler Radar system in conjunction with a global positioning system (GPS) to identify and warn the population about tornadoes.

Weather satellites have become important in

CHANGING TECHNOLOGY: Doppler Radar

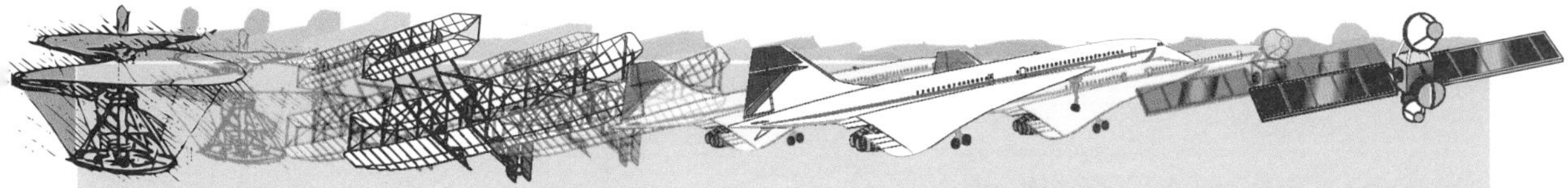

Doppler radar is a special form of radar that analyses the movement of individual raindrops in storms. It is better able to predict violent weather than regular radar.

The radar antenna sends radio waves out into space, and raindrops and other objects in the sky reflect the radio waves back to the receiver. From this information, it is possible to determine whether storms are moving towards the radar or away from it. Objects moving toward the scanner register increasingly higher frequencies as they move closer because there is less distance between the scanner and the storm. Conversely, if the storm is moving away, the frequency decreases. The reflected radio waves are converted electronically into pictures showing the intensity of the rainfall in the storm.

Environment Canada is establishing a national Doppler weather network (due to be completed in 2003). The $35 million project will see the installation of 29 Doppler radar stations across the country. These advanced systems help forecasters to determine such weather conditions as squalls, thunderstorms, and tornadoes. Previously, the only way these weather phenomena could be forecast was when they were observed and reported to the agency. However, that was usually too late!

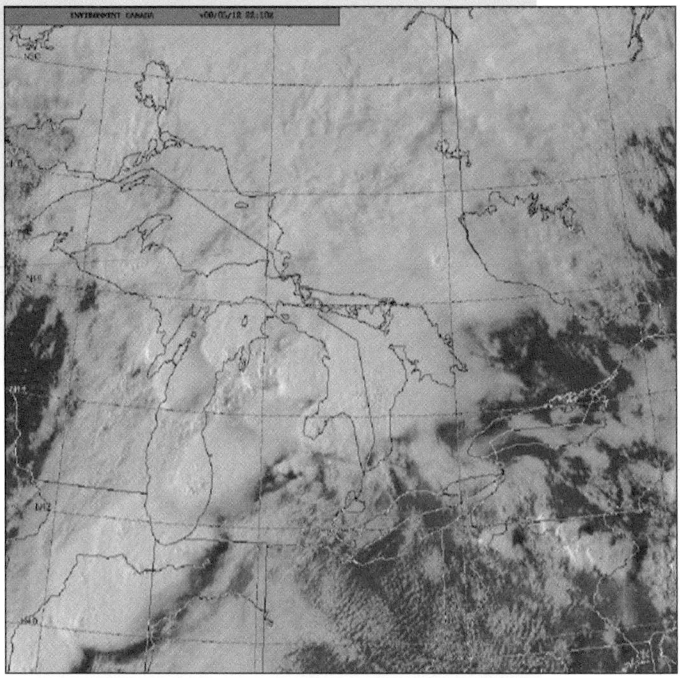

Figure 17.3
A Doppler Radar Image

This new system allows for more accurate forecasting and improved safety for those threatened by severe storms.

Question:
Draw and colour an illustration to show your understanding of how the Doppler radar works.

weather forecasting over the past 20 years. In May 2000, GOES-11, the newest weather satellite, was launched by the United States. Like other satellites, it monitors clouds over large areas of the country. The images you see on the nightly television weather forecast come from satellite sensors. While this new satellite will not actually be operational, it is a back-up system to be used if either GOES-8 or GOES-10 fails. Being **geostationary**, the satellites orbit the earth at the

Figure 17.4
Locations of Canadian Weather Stations

same speed that the earth rotates, so they are always over the same part of the planet. GOES-8 monitors the east coast of North and South America, while GOES-10 monitors the west coast. When hurricanes start to build from tropical storms, forecasters will see the formation through satellite data and be able to warn people of the potential disaster.

In addition to locating and monitoring cloud cover, satellites have other sensors that send back a steady stream of data to meteorologists. The sensors used in the satellites are Advanced Very High Resolution Radiometers (AVHRR). As solar energy is reflected off the earth, the AVHRR sensor picks up radiation in the visible and infrared portions of the electromagnetic spectrum over a 300 km-wide swath of the earth. These sensors monitor cloud, pollution, severe storms, fog, fires, volcanic eruptions, moisture content of clouds, and sea-surface temperature. This information not only allows technicians to monitor weather, but is also used to analyse climate change over long periods of time. (The satellites have been sending back data for over 20 years.)

In addition to geostationary satellites, **sun-synchronous** satellites orbit the earth, following the daylight so that they do not have to stop photographic analysis at night and are able to maintain power in their solar panels.

Conducting a Weather Field Study

Doing original research is not only an important exercise in expanding your understanding of natural systems; it is also an important aspect of higher education. Most university programs expect students to discover new knowledge. It is not enough just to restate the ideas that other people have expressed. This geographic inquiry provides you with opportunities to develop a hypothesis about the atmosphere, gather data about it, and determine whether your hypothesis is correct.

1. **Focusing**

   Decide on a question about the weather that you would like to research. Perhaps you have noticed that it usually rains when the wind blows from the east, so a possible question could be, "How do different weather variables such as wind direction and relative humidity affect each other?" You will gather evidence to answer your question and determine if your original hypothesis is correct.

2. **Organizing**

   Determine the type of data you will need in order to answer your question, and prepare an organizer to collect the information. Consider making a template for a spreadsheet by using either a computer or a sheet of paper. For the above example, a chart like the one below in Figure 17.5 could be used to collect weather statistics each day for a two-week period.

3. **Data Collection**

   Gather the data needed to complete your study. Depending on the question you chose, the data could be climate statistics for your city, weather forecasts from the newspaper or also from Internet web sites, long-range forecasts from an almanac, or original data that you have collected with weather-measuring instruments. In this case, you could get the data from your own observations using a wind vane and a hygrometer. Make sure you collect the information at the same time and place each day in order to keep your variables comparable.

   Often, it is necessary to refine your data-gathering technique so that the information you collect is measurable. In other words, give the description a numeric value. In this case, relative humidity expressed as a percentage would be a better input than "wet" or "damp." Likewise, with wind direction, it would be a better idea to use bearings (north is 0°, east is 90°, south is 180°, and west is 270°) instead of the description "west" or "north." Therefore, data for the example may look something like Figure 17.6.

Week 1	Wind Direction	Relative Humidity	Week 2	Wind Direction	Relative Humidity
Monday			Monday		
Tuesday			Tuesday		
Wednesday			Wednesday		
Thursday			Thursday		
Friday			Friday		
Saturday			Saturday		
Sunday			Sunday		

Figure 17.5

Week 1	Wind Direction	Relative Humidity	Week 2	Wind Direction	Relative Humidity
Monday	275°	20%	Monday	88°	75%
Tuesday	10°	28%	Tuesday	30°	40%
Wednesday	20°	65%	Wednesday	350°	50%
Thursday	182°	95%	Thursday	100°	65%
Friday	90°	100%	Friday	285°	50%
Saturday	92°	100%	Saturday	80°	75%
Sunday	95°	90%	Sunday	90°	80%

Figure 17.6

4. **Synthesizing**

Represent the data from your organizer on a map and comparison table or on a graph in order to show whether or not there are any patterns, trends, or correlations visible.

If you are using a graph to represent your data, be sure to choose the correct type for the job. A time-series line graph is great for showing trends, bar graphs and circle graphs are good for comparing information, and scattergraphs show correlations, which are useful if you want to determine how one variable affects another. (However, a scattergraph cannot be used in this example because wind bearings do not measure magnitude; they are simply numbers used to represent a location on a circular scale—a compass).

Be creative and come up with an original way of representing your data. For the example, a circle representing a compass with bars radiating out from it to represent relative humidity values would show the pattern. This is not a typical graph, but it works for this example (see Fig. 17.7).

5. **Applying**

Answer your focus question, based on your findings, and determine if the data you collected supports your original hypothesis or refutes it. Then decide if there are any recommendations you could make based on your findings. For example, in the sample

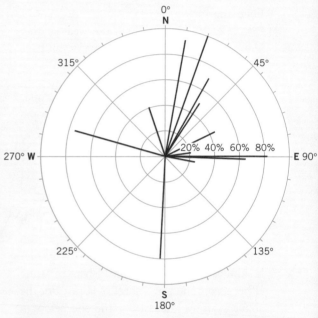
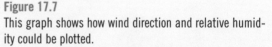

Figure 17.7
This graph shows how wind direction and relative humidity could be plotted.

question it was determined that when the wind blows from the east, the relative humidity is greatest. Therefore, you could suggest that architects erecting buildings in the area could design them to protect eastward-facing entrances from rain.

6. **Communicating Your Findings**

Prepare a presentation to show others what you have discovered. Your presentation should include the following:

- The focus question
- Your organizer showing all data collected from publications and/or your own measurements
- A map showing the location of the study area relative to the school and (where necessary) other study areas
- Graphs, tables, and/or maps used to represent the data
- A conclusion, written in paragraph form, answering the focus question, with supporting evidence
- A written explanation accounting for conclusions that were either expected or unexpected.

   The presentation could be in the form of a display, a bulletin board, a booklet, or even a video.

TRY IT!

1. Choose one of the following questions and conduct your own weather study, using the model described in this skill.

   - How accurate are weather forecasts?
   - How does the weather vary within a community?
   - How is the weather different this year from what it is usually like (i.e., climate)?
   - How does weather vary in different parts of Canada?
   - What relationship exists between air pressure and precipitation?
   - What relationship exists between air pressure and temperature?

Figure 17.8
This satellite image shows a storm off the Atlantic coast. Such images are the tools of the trade for meteorologists predicting the weather.

Weather Analysis and Interpretation

While the forecasters are only responsible for weather in their own particular regions, they need to be aware of a variety of weather fields around their area. Weather in the mid-latitudes generally moves from west to east, but occasionally storms will develop and move from the south and east. For forecasters, knowledge of weather in adjacent regions is therefore essential.

Analysis consists of studying a variety of current surface-weather fields. These include air pressure, three-hour air-pressure tendency, wind velocity and direction, air temperature, dew point, present weather, and visibility. The forecaster must also analyse what is going on in the upper atmosphere by using weather balloons. Clouds are studied to determine their height and type, and temperature and humidity changes are monitored. These conditions in the upper atmosphere give the forecaster an idea of how stable the air is. Lightning detection imagery is also studied. It is important to note that all of this data must be continually updated, as it can become stale very quickly.

Now that the meteorologist has a firm grasp of what the weather is like, an analysis of what is causing the weather begins. Is it due to a large-scale low-pressure system or to local effects like rain showers off the Great Lakes? Shorter range forecasts (e.g., for the purposes of aviation) rely heavily on knowledge of local weather conditions and those **upwind**. Longer term forecasts (for up to five days) rely heavily on a variety of computer models. The meteorologist must be aware of how well the model has been performing and how to adjust the output in a positive manner.

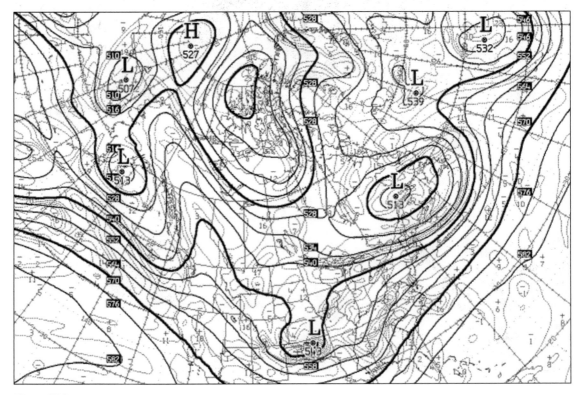

Figure 17.9
This is an example of an isobar map, which could be used by forecasters to produce a weather map.

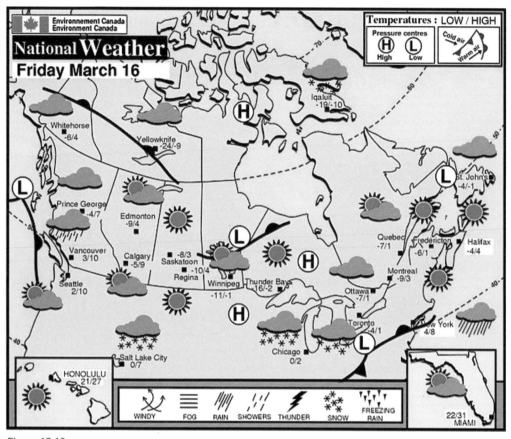

Figure 17.10
This weather map was produced for the same day as the isobar map on page 292.

Chaos Theory and Forecasting

Predicting the weather can be frustrating! So many variables affect the weather that a small change in any one condition can cause an abrupt and complete change in the big picture. Scientists are beginning to realize how incredibly complex natural systems are. **Chaos theory** is a scientific philosophy as important to modern scientific thought as the theory of relativity. Scientists study random events to determine patterns even when none seems possible.

The originator of this theory was a meteorologist named Edward Lorenz. In the late 1960s, Lorenz was working on his weather model at the Massachusetts Institute of Technology when he had a remarkable insight: minute changes in data changed his results radically. Applied to the real world, this suggested that a minute change in one region could affect weather the world over. For example, if a volcano erupts in Asia, temperature and rainfall patterns could be affected in Canada. Similarly, a change in ocean currents in the South Pacific could influence the weather in Europe. In the extreme, you could theorize that a butterfly flapping its wings in China could influence the weather in Winnipeg! The **butterfly effect** sounds farfetched, but there is some truth to the view that atmospheric disturbances can affect weather thousands of kilometres away. This is why weather forecasting is an extremely complex process. So even though computer programs such as **General Circulation Models** (see page 294) are very sophisticated, it is unlikely that anyone will ever be able to accurately forecast more than a few days into the future on a consistent basis.

CHANGING TECHNOLOGY: General Circulation Models

In the past, meteorologists made predictions based on historic patterns and their understanding of how pressure cells moved across the face of the earth. Today, the largest databases on earth contain weather data, and advanced computer programs called **General Circulation Models** (GCMs) help with the analysis. The Canadian Meteorological Centre houses a supercomputer that produces the Canadian weather model, called the GEM (Global Environmental Multi-scale) model. These sophisticated computers have revolutionized the study of the atmosphere.

Most of the processes that occur in the atmosphere can be measured. Temperature, humidity, wind speed, soil moisture, and many other measurements can be input for innumerable points on the earth's surface. Through the study of fluid physics, we know that there are relationships among these statistics, which can be shown with mathematical expressions. Once the statistics are fed into the computer, it can forecast the weather. The mathematical expressions simulate how weather conditions change from place to place.

Ten years ago, GCMs were crude and unreliable. Today the forecasts they produce are remarkably accurate. To verify the accuracy of the models, researchers input known variables from periods in the past and allow the computer to simulate what the future would be like. The computer's prediction can then be compared to what actually happened, and the accuracy of the model can be ascertained. Often the algorithms need to be modified and refined so that the simulation more accurately approaches reality. Unfortunately, there is no way that results can be verified 100 per cent. In fact, the same simulation run using the same data often results in very different results because chaotic systems have so many variables that no two simulations will be exactly the same. It is like dropping a ball out of a second-storey window: You can predict more or less how the ball will bounce, but it will never bounce exactly the same way twice. Such is the nature of chaotic natural systems.

Another problem lies in the **resolution** that GCMs use. Computer screens are divided up into tiny squares called **pixels**. The more squares there are on a screen, the higher the resolution will be. GCMs measure the atmospheric conditions for the whole planet; therefore, the image is so large that the resolution is naturally very low. Yet for the measurement to be accurate, even small changes in surface albedo, humidity, and a hundred other variables that can affect global climate must be accounted for. However, the resolution of the best GCM models is so coarse that one pixel with one set of values represents an area about equal in size to Israel— a small country that has amazing climatic diversity. This being said, however, there is value in using GCMs to get a sense of how climates are changing on a continental scale.

Question:
Why is it important that scientists continue to develop accurate ways to predict long-term weather and climate change?

ACTIVITIES

UNDERSTANDING CONCEPTS

1. a) Describe advances that have been made in weather instruments.
    b) Why are the new instruments superior to older methods?
    c) Explain the role of radar, weather balloons, and satellites in forecasting.
    d) Why are automated weather stations better than weather stations that are staffed by human observers?
2. Study the map showing the locations of Canadian weather stations (Fig. 17.4).
    a) Why is there an uneven distribution of weather stations?
    b) How could the use of satellites, automated weather stations, and radar overcome this limitation?
3. a) What are the advantages and limitations of GCMs?
    b) What is Chaos Theory and how does it relate to weather forecasting?
    c) Explain the process that forecasters use to predict the weather.

DEVELOPING AND PRACTISING SKILLS

4. Make a copy of Fig. 17.9 or print an iso-map from the Atmospheric Environment Service at http://weather.ec.gc.ca/cmc_htmls_reg_4panel_e.shtml.
    a) Draw arrows to show where you would expect winds to be flowing, using isobars to help.
    b) Shade in areas where you would expect cloud.
    c) Locate the isobars that have the highest air pressure. Shade in these **ridges** on your map.
    d) What characteristics would you expect along these ridges?
    e) Locate the isobars with the lowest air pressure. Shade in these **troughs** on your map.
    f) What general patterns can you determine from the air pressure map?
    g) How do these types of maps help forecasters predict the weather?
5. Examine Fig. 17.10.
    a) On a copy of the figure, colour the different types of precipitation.
    b) Label the air masses.
    c) Draw the wind direction for cyclones (lows) and anticyclones (highs).
    d) In an organizer, describe the weather (temperature, precipitation, wind direction, and air pressure) for the following places: Yellowknife, Seattle, Chicago, New York, Montreal, St. John's, and Vancouver.
    e) Predict the weather for the day *after* this map was made. Justify your forecast.
6. Make a photocopy of the satellite image in Figure 17.8 or download a similar one from the Internet.
    a) Label the cyclone in the image as a "low."
    b) Draw in the fronts and use arrows to indicate the wind direction around the cyclone.
    c) Label areas where "highs" might be.

LEARNING THROUGH APPLICATION

7. In an organizer, keep a daily record of the clouds that pass overhead for one week. Make weather predictions based on what you observe. Study the satellite images on TV weather broadcasts to verify the accuracy of your forecasts.

8. Clip the weather map from the newspaper or download maps from the Internet each day for a week to predict the weather for the following day. Record the accuracy of your predictions.

9. Prepare a report summarizing the information provided in each of the following web sites. Use the organizer to help in your analysis.

Web site	Agency	Summary of Information	What you liked or disliked about the site	Rating out of 10
www.weatheroffice.com/sky	National Sky Watchers			
www.weather.ec.gc.ca	Environment Canada			
www.cmc.ec.gc.ca	Canadian Weather Service			
www.ccrs.nrcan.gc.ca/ccrs/ homepg.pl?e	Canadian Centre for Remote Sensing			
www.tornadoproject.com	The Tornado Project			

Chapter 18

ACID DEPOSITION: A REGIONAL ISSUE

FOCUS QUESTIONS

1. What are the impacts of acid rain on your community and on your country as a whole?
2. Why does the acid deposition produced in one country also affect other countries?
3. How can industrialization create acid rain?

As this cartoon depicts, acid deposition is a problem that has people worrying about the safety of their environment. Many people are familiar with the term "acid rain," but are unfamiliar with the term **acid deposition**. Acid rain is rainfall that has been altered by pollutants to form a mild sulphuric or nitric acid. Acid deposition is a more all-inclusive term that includes acid rain, acid snow, and the dry fallout of acid dust from the atmosphere. You don't have to worry about pure acid falling on you, though, since the acid in the atmosphere is so weak that it will not cause burns to your skin. However, acid is a serious problem that disrupts ecosystems, affects public health, and causes surface damage to building materials.

HERMAN®   by Jim Unger

11-23   © 1982 Jim Unger

"He wasn't always bald. It's acid rain."

Figure 18.1

Key Terms

acid deposition

smelting

coking coal

crown die-back

pH scale

An Issue That Won't Die

Acid deposition was one of the most contentious issues of the 1980s in North America. The issue pitted environmentalists against mining corporations, sport fishers against electric utilities, and governments against each other. Over half a billion dollars—the most ever spent on an environmental issue—was spent on acid deposition research in the United States and Canada. In the end, Canadian and American legislation cleaned up the heavily polluting northern mining companies, implemented automobile emissions controls, and forced electric utilities companies to reduce pollution caused by the burning of high-sulphur coal. By the late 1990s, legislators, automakers, and other industrialists had basically agreed that the problem had been solved (at least in North America). Sport fishers, scientists, and environmentalists weren't so sure.

In 1999, the highly respected periodical *Nature* printed a comprehensive study of European and North American lakes. This study showed that while some lakes are becoming less acidic, those in the Canadian Shield, the Western Cordillera, and parts of New England have shown no sign of recovery, and likely won't for decades. The study involved extensive fieldwork that went beyond the computer models and theories employed by other studies. Twenty-three scientists from nine countries monitored acidity levels in 205 lakes and streams from 1980 to 1995.

In addition, a 1996 Environment Canada study found that only one third of the acidified lakes in eastern Canada are showing signs of recovery, 11 per cent are still becoming increasingly acidic, and 56 per cent have not improved. While there have been greatly improved technologies to reduce sulphur emissions by industries, the United States still produces close to 20 million tons of sulphur oxide each year. The expansion of electric power generation, increase in vehicular traffic, and growth of industrial output have combined to maintain the high sulphur levels of the 1980s. The American government has committed itself to reducing sulphur emissions to 14.4 million tons by 2010. Canadian emissions are significantly lower, at less than 3 million tons per year.

The Location of Acid Deposition-Prone Regions

North America and Europe are not the only places where acid deposition can be found. This form of pollution is becoming a serious problem in many emerging industrial nations. China, Brazil, and Eastern Europe are becoming increasingly affected by acid deposition as coal-burning power plants come on stream, automobile traffic increases, and heavy industry expands.

Although acid deposition is widespread, its distribution is uneven because specific environmental characteristics must exist for it to be a problem. First, **smelters** and large urban centres must be **upwind** from sensitive areas; and second, the underlying parent material that the soil is formed from must be acidic. By studying the map in Fig. 18.2, you can see that there are many isolated regions where acid deposition is a problem; however, it seems to be most significant in industrialized areas. Northern Ontario, southern Quebec, and the Atlantic Provinces (extending down the eastern seaboard of the United States) form one major problem area. A second problem area includes much of central and northern Europe. Regions in Africa, Southeast Asia, and northern South America are also becoming seriously polluted today, as these developing regions industrialize.

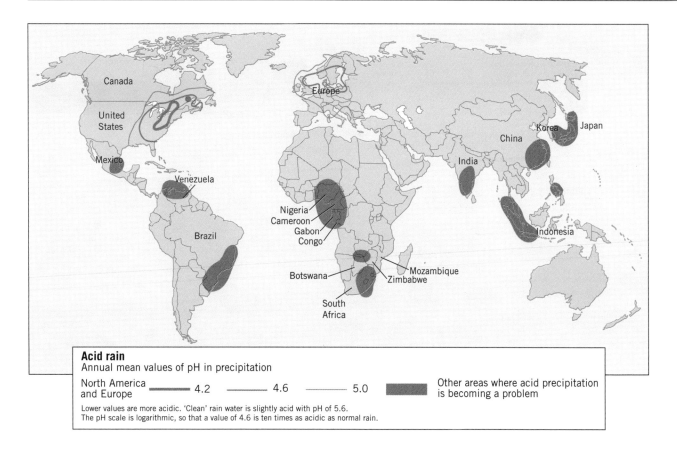

Acid rain
Annual mean values of pH in precipitation

North America | ——— 4.2 ——— 4.6 ——— 5.0   [dark band] Other areas where acid precipitation
and Europe | is becoming a problem

Lower values are more acidic. 'Clean' rain water is slightly acid with pH of 5.6.
The pH scale is logarithmic, so that a value of 4.6 is ten times as acidic as normal rain.

Figure 18.2
Using atlas maps determine what characteristics these areas have in common in terms of industrial development, geology, and wind patterns.

How Acid Deposition is Formed

Precipitation is normally a bit acidic since carbon dioxide is dissolved in raindrops to form a very mild carbonic acid. Acidity is measured on a **pH Scale**, shown in Fig. 18.3. The term "pH" refers to the activity of hydrogen ions within a solution. The lower the solution's pH, the more acidic it is. Lemon juice and vinegar have very low pH values, and so are quite acidic. By contrast, alkaline chemicals such as ammonia are at the other end of the scale, while baking soda is practically neutral with a pH of 8. The pH scale is a logarithmic scale like the Richter Scale. Every one-point drop in the scale represents ten times more acid than the point above it. So if a lake went from a pH of 5 to a pH of 4, it would be ten times as acidic. Many lakes in Southern Ontario and Quebec have had pH levels drop from 6.0 to as low as 4.5 over the past 50 years.

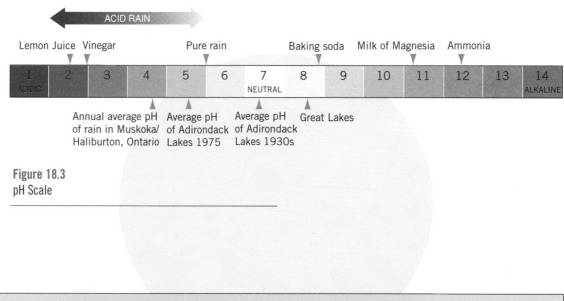

Figure 18.3
pH Scale

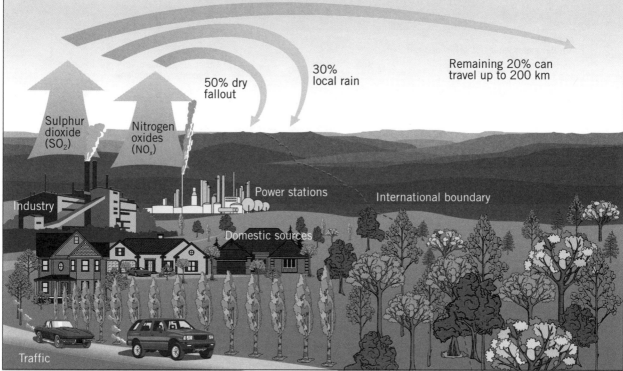

Figure 18.4
Flow Chart of Acid Deposition Cycle

Activities That Cause Acid Deposition

Acid rain comes from many sources. It can be caused by natural processes such as volcanic eruptions, and even by meteor impact. It is likely that the last mass extinction 65 million years ago was caused when a meteor hit the earth, creating huge amounts of acid rain a hundred times more acidic than what we have today. When most of the plants died out, the animals that depended on them died also. Thus ended the age of the dinosaurs. Another example, the Permian extinction of 230 million years ago, likely happened because of massive volcanic activity in what is now Siberia. Eighty per cent of all life was wiped out as sulphur dioxide rained upon the land.

Today, human actions are responsible for most of the acid deposition that is plaguing the planet. Industrial processes like **smelting** and the burning of fossil fuels release sulphur and nitrogen into the air. The use of automobiles also causes acid deposition as nitrogen oxide is released into the atmosphere. Natural systems often either intensify the problem or reduce its effects. For example, limestone bedrock can neutralize acid rain, whereas acidic bedrock can make the effects of the acid even worse.

Acid Deposition from Smelting

Smelting is the process whereby impurities are removed from ferrous ores using heat. When a ferrous metal like iron or nickel is mined, the resulting ore is so full of impurities that it has little value until it is purified. To make it useful, the metallic mineral is separated from the other unneeded material called **slag**, through mechanical processes that do not create much air pollution. These waste products litter mining towns everywhere. While this may be an unsightly waste management issue, it does not pollute the atmosphere. But the next step does. Smelting is the process used to get the sulphur (which is difficult to remove) out of the ore. Coking coal is burned with the ore. As the ore is smelted, sulphur atoms combine with oxygen atoms to form sulphur dioxide. From there, the ferrous metal continues on its way to becoming your next car.

The pollution produced by the sulphur dioxide is what causes the problems. This gas goes up the chimney and seems to disappear into the atmosphere. Of course it does not disappear—it becomes part of the atmosphere. When the SO_2 molecules rise into the atmosphere, they attach themselves to dust particles. When the dew point is reached, water vapour condenses on the dust. A chemical reaction occurs whereby the SO_2 combines with the H_2O to form H_2SO_4 (sulpheric acid). If there is no water vapour in the air, the dust can fall to the ground as acid dust. If the temperature is below freezing, the result is acid snow.

Figure 18.5
The Smelting Process

Acid Rain in Taiyuan China

Twenty years ago, this case study might have been about a small town outside of Sudbury. At that time, most of the trees in the area were dead, not a bird could be seen, and beautiful, but lifeless, crystal-blue lakes stretched for kilometres around the major nickel and copper mining belt in North America. Today, things are getting better for communities in Northern Ontario. New trees have been planted and are growing well because of reduced emissions. The lakes are still dead, but the cloak of forest has improved the appearance of the place, and animals are starting to come back.

Figure 18.5
The pollution hanging over Taiyuan creates a desperate acid rain problem in the area.

Figure 18.6
Locator map for Taiyuan

However, the situation in China's industrial heartland is worse than it ever was in Northern Ontario. The smoggy sky is filled with the sulphurous smoke of dozens of factory chimneys. Taiyuan is China's most polluted city. Dust from the surrounding coal fields and power plants blankets everything. The noonday sun cannot be seen because of the filth in the air. With 600 micrograms of suspended particles per cubic metre, the pollution registers at four times the World Health Organization standard. Nothing grows naturally anywhere. Streams are covered with soot, trees all died years ago, and there has not been any wildlife for a generation.

But Taiyuan is no longer the only badly polluted city in China. Now the capital, Beijing, 400 kilometres to the northeast is also suffocating in the industrial pall. A national holiday was declared during the period leading up to the fiftieth anniversary of Communism, on October 1, 1999. All the factories closed for 10 days. For the first time in a generation, people could see the sun and wonder at how blue the sky was. The Environment Minister, Zhou Jian stated, "…there should be a bright sky and clean air to celebrate the holidays." Since China has nine of the ten most polluted cities in the world, its government's policy of clean air clearly does not extend into the regular working part of the year.

The World Bank estimates that 300 000 Chinese die every year of air pollution. The country has such a giant population and such a high rate of economic growth that there is an insatiable need for power. The need for electrical power comes from the rapidly growing industries of the north. Gasoline is needed for the smelly two-cylinder motor bikes and tiny cars that a new, more prosperous working class is starting to buy. Furthermore, 200 million city dwellers need coal to heat their homes. And diesel power is needed to fuel the trucks and barges that have no catalytic converters. All these sulphur-producing, nitrous-oxide-spewing abominations make China the most unhealthy place to live in the world.

Liang Congjie, a 67-year-old environmental journalist, has formed China's first private (non-governmental) environmental organization. Inspired by the wildly successful Green Peace Organization, Liang hopes to embarrass the government into action. He writes articles constantly, telling people that they deserve better—that they should have clean air and safe water. His task is difficult in a country where critics are often treated acrimoniously. But the government is starting to listen. As another environmental activist says, "Before, they (the government) preferred to drink poisoned water in order to make money. Then they wanted to be healthy and wealthy. Now they would rather be healthy than rich."

QUESTIONS:

1. What is causing the acid pollution in China, and what evidence is there to show how bad the situation is?

2. Why do you think the authorities are starting to listen to environment critics?

3. What suggestions would you have for Chinese authorities?

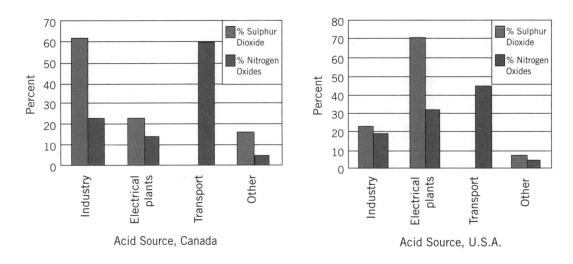

Figure 18.8
Graphs Show Acid Emissions by Canada and the United States. List the sources of sulphur dioxide and nitrogen oxides in order from highest to lowest percentages for each of the US and Canada. How are the lists different?

Acid Deposition from Power Plants

Sulphur dioxide is also released when sulphur-rich fossil fuels are burned to produce electrical power. Natural gas and oil give off some sulphur and nitrogen, but the worst offender of the fossil fuels is low-grade coal. While this hydrocarbon is not used as much as it once was in North America (due to the stringent pollution controls implemented in the 1980s), it provides much of the electrical power in the highly industrialized northeastern United States. In regions where these controls are less restrictive, sulphur emission problems are becoming very serious.

The main energy source in India and China is low-grade sulphur-rich coal. This fuel is abundant in these countries which have few other energy sources. It is being burned to generate the industrial expansion in these emerging economic powerhouses. China, for example, expects to build a hundred coal-fired power plants by 2020. As a consequence, these two nations—which collectively account for more than a third of the world's population—have developed serious acid deposition problems.

Acid Deposition from Cars

Cars are also responsible for acid deposition. Nitrogen is emitted as a by-product of combustion in car engines. This has been a particular problem in the Swiss Alps, where many transport trucks use the mountain passes between industrial regions in Italy and Germany. The truck exhaust is trapped in the mountains by **temperature inversions** and the acid deposition has killed off the forests on the mountain slopes. The beauty of the mountains is ruined, but more importantly, public safety is endangered. The heavy winter snows that used to be contained by the forests are now free to slide down into the valleys as avalanches. To remedy the situation, the Swiss now require truck traffic to move through the susceptible valleys on electric trains.

The problem of emissions from cars is much improved, as the mandatory emission controls in some developed countries has resulted in the use of catalytic converters in automobile exhaust systems. The catalytic converter forces exhaust to travel through a bed of platinum coated beads. Instead of NO_x coming out of the tail pipe, the exhaust is in the form of water, carbon dioxide, and nitrogen gas. These gases do not form acid deposition; however, CO_2 is a greenhouse gas.

CHANGING TECHNOLOGY: Coal's Improved Image

For years, coal has been blamed for acid deposition, increasing greenhouse gases, and air pollution. However, a group called the World Coal Institute (WCI) wants to change attitudes about the product it markets. One of its main opponents, an environmental group called the Worldwatch Institute, released figures in August 1999 showing that coal releases 29 per cent more carbon than oil and 80 per cent more than natural gas when it is burned. In addition, it contributes sulphur dioxide (SO_2), nitrous oxides (NO_x), and aerosols such as fly ash and soot. The WCI countered by stating that sulphur dioxide and nitrous oxides have been greatly reduced through the use of the new technologies listed in the chart below.

Unfortunately, many of these processes are expensive and are often not employed by emerging industrial countries where environmental controls are limited. Where they are used, it is sometimes the case that the pollution not going into the air is still present in some other form, which must be disposed of. Nevertheless, the new technology has provided a cleaner environment in North America.

Question:
Explain why the coal industry has developed and is continuing to develop new processes to remove sulphur from coal.

Process Name	Process Description	Benefits and Disadvantages
coal washing	Coal is crushed and placed in a water tank that jiggles from side to side. Some of the sulphur is contained in a mineral called pyrite, which is heavier than the coal. It therefore sinks to the bottom and can be removed mechanically.	30 – 40% of the pyrite (sulphur) is removed from high sulphur coal and 10 – 20% is removed from low sulphur coal. The process is inexpensive but further treatment is needed.
microwave desulphurization	Crushed coal is heated by microwave energy for 30 – 60 seconds. The remaining pyritic sulphur is converted to hydrogen sulphide gas that is recovered as a chemical by-product.	Most of the remaining pyritic sulphur is removed.

Figure 18.9

chart continued on next page

Process Name	Process Description	Benefits and Disadvantages
chemical desulphurization	Organic sulphur in the ore is removed by adding calcium hydroxide to the crushed coal. Calcium sulphate results and can be mechanically removed.	Up to 70% of the organic sulphur is removed. However, the calcium sulphate must be disposed of.
hydrothermal desulphurization	Crushed coal is mixed with sodium and calcium hydroxides and cooked under pressure. Sulphur compounds can be removed mechanically.	Most of the remaining sulphur is removed. The waste chemicals must be removed.
coal liquefaction	Through the process of hydro-genation, coal can be converted to high-grade liquid fuels like gasoline, which are less polluting than coal.	Coal made into a liquid is easier to use and transport and produces less sulphur. There are toxic by-products.
coal gasification	Coal is converted to gas fuel underground before it is mined. Two holes are drilled into the seam. Air is injected in one hole and the coal seam is ignited. The CO_2 and water vapour produced form methane gas, which is collected at the second hole.	There is no surface pollution, but under-ground fires are hard to control and groundwater can be polluted. The process has been used in Eastern Europe for decades.
fluidized bed combustion	Crushed coal is fed into a bed of limestone that floats in a stream of air blown through it from below. The coal is ignited and as it burns the sulphur combines chemically with the limestone to produce calcium sulphate, which is mechanically removed.	90% of sulphur is removed. The waste product can be used to make building materials. Less nitric oxide is produced because combustion temperatures are kept low.
flue gas desulphurization (scrubbing)	Exhaust fumes are treated with limestone, which is sprayed through the fumes as they go up the smokestack.	It has high energy demands and causes corrosion to the equipment. Chimneys become clogged with calcium sulphate.
staged combustion	Nitrogen oxides are controlled by regulating the temperatures at which the coal is burned.	NO_x emissions can be reduced by 50%.

Underlying Acidic Rock

Regions where **sedimentary** rocks, such as limestone or dolomite, are common are not susceptible to acid deposition. These rocks are made of the shells of ancient sea creatures and so contain calcium carbonate, a base material that neutralizes the acid. When the calcium reacts with acidic lakes, carbon dioxide is generated as a by-product. This is a greenhouse gas that has its own environmental problems. Of course, the limestone is dissolved in the process. This can be a concern where buildings are made of limestone or marble.

If, on the other hand, the region is made up of acidic **igneous rocks**, such as granite and quartz, then the acid is not neutralized and the effect could be exacerbated. Most of the Canadian Shield, much of interior Australia, parts of the Alps, the Western Cordillera, regions in Scandinavia, and Kazakstan are particularly prone to the problem because they have igneous bedrock. Of course, these complex geological formations also tend to have sedimentary structures in which acidity is not a problem. For example, in Muskoka, north of the Greater Toronto Area, there are many acid lakes. The waters are crystal clear because nothing grows in them. Lake Joseph is different, however. It was formed in a limestone basin, so it is not acidic even though it experiences the same acid fallout as the lakes all around it. Consequently, it is one of the few lakes in the area that have really good fishing.

Prevailing Winds

In the Northern Hemisphere, where most industrialization and large cities are located, the winds usually blow from the west. Consequently, natural areas downwind from big cities and industrial facilities are particularly prone to damage from acid deposition. In Sudbury, people started noticing damage to the ecosystem in the 1950s. International Nickel decided the best thing to do was to build a "super smokestack." Then the acid deposition would dissipate into the atmosphere and cause no more damage to the

Figure 18.10
This photo shows the smokestacks at International Nickel in the 1950s, before the company installed their Super Stack.

local region. Super Stack, the tallest smokestack in the world, was built in the 1960s. Rather than solve the problem, Super Stack just spread the pollution around more. Satellite images show a plume of devastation spreading out from Sudbury in an eastward direction (the direction in which the prevailing westerlies blow).

geo.web resources

< http://www.city.vancouver.bc.ca/
  commsvcs/pandl/enviro/agenda.htm>

This British Columbia government site outlines many of the environmental issues facing the City of Vancouver at this time. Go to the "Air Quality" page and summarize the city's plan to reduce its acid rain problem.

Damage Caused by Acid Deposition

As well as being harmful to natural systems, the problem of acid deposition is responsible for damaging many ancient buildings and statues around the world. The Parthenon in Greece is so affected by the acid deposition from the traffic of nearby Athens that the monument to human ingenuity is being eaten away by side effects of

Figure 18.12
The Pitted Surface of the Parthenon in Greece

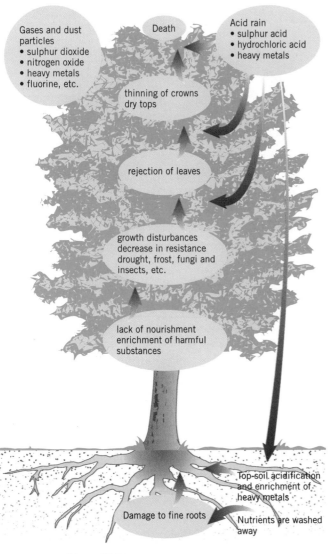

Gases and dust particles
• sulphur dioxide
• nitrogen oxide
• heavy metals
• fluorine, etc.

Death

Acid rain
• sulphur acid
• hydrochloric acid
• heavy metals

thinning of crowns
dry tops

rejection of leaves

growth disturbances
decrease in resistance
drought, frost, fungi and
insects, etc.

lack of nourishment
enrichment of harmful
substances

Top-soil acidification
and enrichment of
heavy metals

Damage to fine roots

Nutrients are washed
away

Figure 18.11
The Effect of Acid Deposition on Trees

our modern technology. Acid deposition is also a human health risk. The acid is so diluted that it will not hurt you directly, but the acid dissolves heavy metals in the soil and water. New chemical compounds containing heavy metals collect in animal tissue. The more you ingest, the more your body absorbs. These metals can cause horrible neurological diseases like Minimata Disease—a rare disease first witnessed near a paper mill in Japan, and which has shown up in northern Ontario. Fish ingest the heavy metals, and when people eat the fish, the metals accumulate in the human tissue. That is why there are restrictions on the amount of fish you can eat from some Ontario lakes. Agriculture is also threatened by acid deposition, but farming is not done extensively in most acid-prone regions.

The main damage, however, is to plants and animals in the wild. In the Canadian Shield, its signs are common. **Crown die-back** occurs when the leaves at the top of a tree die and fall off because nutrients do not reach them. The acid in the soil reduces the tree's ability to metabolize nutrients from the soil. Acid dissolves heavy metals in the soil, which become absorbed into the tree, thus reducing the tree's ability to fight off disease and fungal infections. Damage to the fine root hairs of the tree reduces its ability to absorb life-sustaining water and diminishes its capacity to make carbohydrates through the process of photosynthesis. This affects our economy as well, since the reduced rigour of the boreal forests has a negative impact on the forestry industry in Canada. It is also responsible for reduced maple syrup yields in Quebec.

In Atlantic Canada, acid fog is a problem. Pollution from large American cities along the eastern seaboard blows to the northeast. As the air passes over the Maritimes, the nitric and sulphuric acids are deposited. Small aquatic animals are also greatly affected by the problem. In the winter, the acid accumulates in the snow. When the snow melts in the spring, the shock from all the acid entering rivers and lakes at the same time creates havoc—especially since this is also the time when fish and amphibians are most vulnerable. Tadpoles and fish fry cannot cope with the acid shock, and they die before they have a chance to mature and develop a tolerance to the situation. Adult fish and amphibians accumulate heavy metals in their tissue, as discussed earlier, and could become too poisoned to eat.

Solving the Problem of Acid Deposition

There are two approaches to solving the problem of acid deposition: the first approach has to do with rehabilitating lakes, while the second relates to prevention. Limestone, like you see on driveways, can be dumped into lakes to neutralize the acidity so that life can return. Unfortunately, so much limestone would be necessary that the cost would be prohibitive. Furthermore, the forests and land animals would not be helped.

A better solution has to do with prevention. International Nickel, Falconbridge Mines, Ontario Hydro, and other acid-producing companies have worked hard to change the way they purify their ore. From 1980 to 1998, the Copper Cliff smelter owned by International

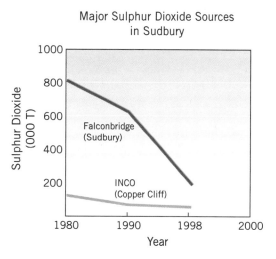

Major Sulphur Dioxide Sources in Sudbury

Figure 18.13
Graph Showing SO$_2$ Emissions Reductions by Falconbridge and Inco

Nickel reduced emissions by 75 per cent, from 820 kilotonnes per year to 200 kT. In the same time period, Falconbridge reduced its emissions from 123 kT to only 54 kT. Much of the sulphur is taken out of the ore by mechanical processes prior to smelting and limestone is added in the smelting process to neutralize the acid. Scrubbers are used to remove the sulphur from the smoke before it goes up the chimney. Much of the reform has been the result of clean-air legislation in Ontario, and there is no doubt that the Sudbury of today is much prettier than the bleak moonscape the city displayed in the 1950s and '60s.

Even if a place is not producing its own pollution, it can still be the recipient of acid deposition created elsewhere. Ontario, for example, is downwind from the huge steel mills and coal-burning power plants of industrial Indiana, Ohio, and Pennsylvania, all in the US. Acid deposition is obviously not held in place by political borders, making the problem an international issue that must be solved by countries working together.

ACTIVITIES

UNDERSTANDING CONCEPTS

1. a) Outline the human activities that have caused acid deposition.
   b) Evaluate the impact your community has on acid deposition.
2. Describe how the following factors contribute to acid deposition.
   a) smelting and industrial processes
   b) power plants
   c) automobiles
   d) prevailing winds
   e) underlying geology and soils
   f) volcanoes and meteorites
3. Explain the impact that acid deposition has on natural vegetation, animals, public health, and structures.
4. a) Evaluate the ways the problem of acid deposition has been dealt with in Canada.
   b) Why is acid deposition still a serious problem in some parts of Canada?
   c) What problems can you see with implementing the solutions?
   d) What can you do as an individual to help solve the problem?

DEVELOPING AND PRACTISING SKILLS

5. Using the map in Fig. 18.2, identify the cities and towns in the Canadian Shield that would be susceptible to acid deposition.
6. a) Use an atlas to prepare a map showing how the prevailing westerlies would blow pollution from industrialized American cities into Ontario.
   b) Prepare a similar map showing how pollution from the Ruhr Valley (i.e., Dusseldorf) would affect forests in southern Germany (i.e., the Black Forest) and the Swiss Alps. Try using GIS programs (Arcview) to help in your map preparation.
7. Explain the specific problems associated with acid deposition for each of the following regions.
   a) Canadian Shield
   b) Atlantic Canada
   c) Switzerland
   d) China
8. a) Study the different diagrams and visuals in this chapter. Explain what each shows and evaluate how the visual representation is preferred over a written description.
   b) Prepare a flow chart to show how acid deposition is created and how it affects ecosystems and human geography.

LEARNING THROUGH APPLICATION

9. Analyse the different ways that sulphur can be removed from coal.
   a) Prepare a decision-making organizer like the one below to assess which methods would provide the best alternatives. Use the "Total" column to rate the methods numerically.

Alternatives/ Criteria	Effectiveness of Process	Cost of Process	Side Effects	Ease of Process	Total
Coal Washing					
Microwave					
Hydrothermal					
Liquification					
Gasification					
Fluidized Bed Combustion					
Scrubbing					
Staged Combustion					

   b) Explain why the use of several processes in combination would likely yield the best solution.
   c) Explain why the coal industry is developing new processes.
   d) Why are these processes lacking in China?
10. a) Assume one of the roles in one of the following groups.
    - cottage owner, sports fisher, environmentalist.
    - labour union president, bank manager in a mining town, president of a mining company, oil company executive.
    - nuclear physicist, pollution specialist, biologist, chemical engineer, medical doctor specializing in neurological diseases.
    - Minister of Natural Resources, Minister of the Environment, Premier of the Province, Minister of Finance.
    - Leader of the Opposition, Provincial Natural Resources Critic, Provincial Environment Critic, Provincial Finance Critic.
    b) Prepare a report summarizing how you feel about acid deposition.
    c) Non-politicians should present their reports at a simulated public hearing.
    d) Get together with other people who have similar attitudes and develop an action plan that will solve the problem.
    e) Return to the public hearing with your proposal.

f) Those in the Government and those in the Official Opposition should each produce a position paper and present it to the group, outlining ways to solve the problem while simultaneously satisfying all parties as much as possible.

g) After both parties present their ideas, hold a vote for the party with the best plan and declare a winner.

h) Explain why it was difficult attaining consensus in the debate.

11. Conduct a field study in a local wetland, lake, or river.

a) Determine the pH of the water in your test site, using an acid deposition kit.

b) Decide whether the river is acidic or not.

c) Study local factors, such as crushed limestone on riverbanks, to determine whether they affect acidity.

d) Conduct an assessment of aquatic life to see if the water body is alive or dead.

e) Develop strategies to improve the water quality of the site.

Chapter 19

CLIMATE CHANGE: A GLOBAL ISSUE

FOCUS QUESTIONS

1. What are the difficulties involved in predicting climate change?
2. What are the potential impacts of climate change on the economic feasibility of industries that are based on renewable resources?
3. What are the potential effects of long-term climate change on different parts of the world?

Climate change is one of the most controversial issues of our age. Some people believe that the planet is warming up because the human population is increasing the supply of greenhouse gases. They have strong evidence to support their case, and contend that action must be taken immediately to change virtually every aspect of human activity in order to avert environmental destruction. On the other hand, there is also a group of people who believe that climate change is a natural process that will occur no matter what people do, and that its dangers are being wildly overstated by environmentalists. This group also has strong evidence to support its contention.

There is a lot of confusion about terms related to climate change. Climate change, global warming, the greenhouse effect, greenhouse gases, and ozone depletion all have to do with the changing atmosphere, but they each mean different things.

Look at the chart on page 314 to see how the terms could easily be confused.

Many scientists and environmentalists believe that global warming is caused by people's abuse of the environment. If we did not use cars so much, or turned off the lights when we left the room, we would not be adding such a large amount of greenhouse gas to the atmosphere. Often, we are encouraged to conserve resources. On the other hand, other scientists, industrialists, and economic policy advisers oppose action against global warming. These people want to continue the current economic prosperity we are experiencing and do not deem it necessary to spend the billions of dollars it would take to dramatically change the way we live. Who is right? In this chapter, both sides of the debate will be presented in an unbiased way so that you can decide where you stand on the issue.

Key Terms

global warming

greenhouse effect

carbon sinks

hydrocarbons

soil respiration

Term	Definition	Possible Reasons for Confusion
Climate Change	Any change that occurs in climate over a long period of time. We are currently experiencing a warming trend, but climate change can also mean a reduction in global temperatures, a change in precipitation patterns, or any other change in the atmosphere.	Because there is so much talk about global warming, we tend to think of only one type of climate change. In fact, increased greenhouse gases may not necessarily increase temperatures for all parts of the planet.
Global Warming	This is climate change that relates to an increase in world temperatures likely due to the build up of greenhouse gases in the atmosphere (although other factors may also be involved).	Because greenhouse gases are the most likely cause of global warming, the term "greenhouse effect" is often erroneously used interchangeably with the term "global warming."
Greenhouse Effect	The greenhouse effect is the special property of the atmosphere that allows it to reradiate reflected energy from the earth's surface back to the earth. Because of the greenhouse effect, Earth has a climate that supports life.	Because the greenhouse effect is the most likely cause of global warming, it is often used to describe a warming climate.
Greenhouse Gases	These are the gases that cause the greenhouse effect. They include carbon dioxide, methane, nitrous oxide, water vapour, chlorofluorocarbons (CFCs), and tropospheric ozone.	This term is confused with the greenhouse effect. However, we have a very limited understanding of how greenhouse gases affect climate change. Many environmental variables affect how they operate. So global warming could be at work despite, not because of, greenhouse gases.
Ozone Depletion	This term has to do with increased ultraviolet radiation entering the lower atmosphere because the ozone layer is being destroyed by CFCs. It really has very little to do with global warming, but the rate of ozone depletion can be affected by temperatures in the ozone layer.	The fact that CFCs are greenhouse gases that also affect ozone depletion does not mean that other greenhouse gases affect ozone depletion or that ozone depletion results in global warming. To further complicate the matter, tropospheric ozone (near ground level) is also a greenhouse gas: Stratospheric ozone (high in the atmosphere) is what blocks UV rays.

Figure 19.1

Consequences of Global Warming

If the planet does warm up significantly, there will likely be catastrophes the severity of which we have never seen. There are already significant signs that global warming has become a serious problem; for example, the rising sea level has worsened problems associated with coastal flooding. As continental ice caps melt, the sea level rises. Since most of the world's people live within 100 km of the ocean, the consequences of these coastal regions becoming inundated with seawater could be severe. Island nations like the Bahamas, off the coast of Florida, could disappear altogether. The entire eastern seaboard of the United States, including New York, Washington, Baltimore, Miami, and New Orleans, would be destroyed. Cities built along estuaries, like London, Montreal, and Buenos Aires, would be submerged. Rich farmland in deltas and along coastal plains from China to Egypt would all disappear. Mass migrations of people inland to higher ground would ensue around the world.

The damage would not be confined to the coasts, however. Continental regions far from the oceans would also be affected as higher temperatures caused evaporation rates to increase, especially in summer. The hotter, drier weather could reduce crop production in what is today some of the best farmland in the world. The Midwestern United States, the Ukraine, Central Europe, and the Pampas of South America produce most of the world's exported wheat, as well as huge amounts of beef, soybeans, and other crops.

ENVIRONMENT WATCH

Deaths from Urban Heat Waves on the Rise

Deaths from heat waves in big cities worldwide are expected to double over the next two decades if nothing is done to curb global warming. This was the prediction of the United Nations weather agency during the November 2000 meeting of the United Nations in the Hague to reach a global strategy against climate change.

"Heat waves are expected to become a major killer," World Meteorological Organization Secretary General Godwin Obasi said. Small increases in global temperatures, believed by some to be due to growing amounts of greenhouse gases, are amplified in big cities, he added.

In the 15 biggest US cities an average of 1,500 people collapse and die from heat waves each year, a significant increase over the past decade, Obasi said, without giving previous comparative figures. Cities around the world he expects to see burgeoning deaths from heat include Toronto, Shanghai, Athens and Madrid. The problem is expected to be more acute in sprawling so-called megacities in poor countries, which have more difficulty informing people about how to prevent heat stroke and where infrastructure is lacking.

Carbon dioxide and other gases, scientists say, will boost global temperatures by 1.5 to 6.0 degrees Centigrade during this century. U.N. scientific experts say a warmer world is likely to spread disease in tropical regions, cause sea levels to rise and increase the rate of severe storms. Globally, the 1990s was the warmest decade on record and 1999 the hottest year.

Land surface temperatures are showing the highest rises in winter and at latitutes greater than about 50 degrees, the WMO said.

(REUTERS NEWS SERVICE)

Question:
Why will the increasing global temperatures be amplified in major cities such as Toronto? What can urban dwellers do to combat the problem?

However, if evaporation rates increased, rainfall in these regions—while currently sufficient for crops—would be less than the minimum needed to grow food, resulting in possible famine and hunger on a scale unknown throughout history.

In addition, because there is more energy trapped in the atmosphere, it is likely that more violent storms will be common in the future. Cyclones off the coast of India, hurricanes and tornadoes in the United States, blizzards in Europe, and vicious ice storms in Canada seem to be more common and more severe now than they used to be, and could become even more so in the years to come. If Hurricane Andrew was the "storm of the century," what was Hurricane

Mitch? This tempest caused so much damage to the coast of Central America that it will take many years for Honduras and Nicaragua to recover. While it did not cause much damage because it did not come ashore, Hurricane Floyd, in 1999, was the biggest hurricane ever recorded and resulted in the largest peacetime evacuation in American history. In Canada, we had a freak ice storm that shut down Quebec and Eastern Ontario for a month, caused tremendous misery,

Figure 19.3
Snow Blizzard in Toronto, 1999

Figure 19.2
Flooding in China, 1999

Figure 19.4
Hurricane Damage in Honduras, 1998.

Because more energy will be trapped in the atmosphere as global temperatures increase, occurrences of violent storms such as these could also increase.

and cost billions of dollars. And what about Europe? In the fall of 1999, northern Europe was hit with freak storms that created the most expensive natural disaster in the continent's history. Trees hundreds of years old in the grounds of the famous Versailles Palace were uprooted as if they were mere seedlings. Typhoons have plagued southern Asia, and severe flooding in 1998 forced 100 million Chinese out of their homes. How many "storms of the century" can take place in one decade?

Of course, some regions would stand to benefit from higher annual temperatures. Countries such as Canada and Russia, with their long, bitterly cold winters and their enormous Arctic wastelands could enjoy economic as well as environmental rebirth. The northern extent of agriculture would increase so that previously marginal farming regions could become "bread baskets" to make up for those lost in the south. The northern extent of the boreal forest would also expand, allowing forestry to develop in areas where it was previously impossible. Permafrost would melt, and as the peat decomposed, more nutrients would be available for a greater diversity of plants and animals in the large bogs of the Far North.

Of course, this process would take hundreds and even thousands of years. Much of the Arctic is still recovering from the last glacial period that took place 10 000 years ago. In the meantime, people and other animals living in the Arctic will experience major changes. In the coastal areas, the melting of sea ice would make traditional hunting impossible. New species of fish and sea mammals would arrive as other cold-water animals died out. This process is already occurring, in fact: In the summer of 2000, Inu fishers reported seeing salmon in Arctic water but not sea lions because there was no sea ice—a condition that extended even into the autumn. And inland, melting permafrost would result in a quagmire of mud that would take years to drain off and dry out.

Further south, agricultural regions that currently grow temperate crops could begin to grow more lucrative plants such as grapes, peanuts, and cotton. This would enable farmers to improve crop yields and increase the variety of crops they grow.

Longer Growing Season in Europe

Europe's growing season has increased by 10.8 days since the early 1960s and is getting longer every year, scientists said. Thanks to global warming, spring is coming earlier. Trees are unfolding their leaves and plants are flowering six days earlier than they did three decades ago, while leaf colouring and other signs of autumn have been pushed back 4.8 days. The scientists used data collected since 1959 at the International Phenological Gardens, a Europe-wide network of sites growing identical plants, allowing a controlled comparison of their growth patterns.

"Our phenological modelling indicates that the changes are caused by a temperature increase, which is one of the effects of global warming," Annette Menzel and Peter Fabian, of Germany's Munich University, said in a letter to the science journal *Nature*.

Their findings could be bad news for Europe's ski resorts because they show winters are getting shorter, but music to the ears of farmers hoping longer summers will boost harvests. However, the effects of lengthening the growing season have yet to be quantified and the researchers said a longer season would not necessarily translate into greater crop yields and much of the benefit would depend on water supplies, rain and snow falls.

The results were consistent with regional studies showing a shift towards earlier flowering and a previous report on seasonal change and carbon dioxide, one of the greenhouse gases blamed by some scientists for global warming.

(REUTERS NEWS SERVICE)

Question:
In your opinion, do the benefits that global warming could bring to Europe outweigh the drawbacks? Explain your answer.

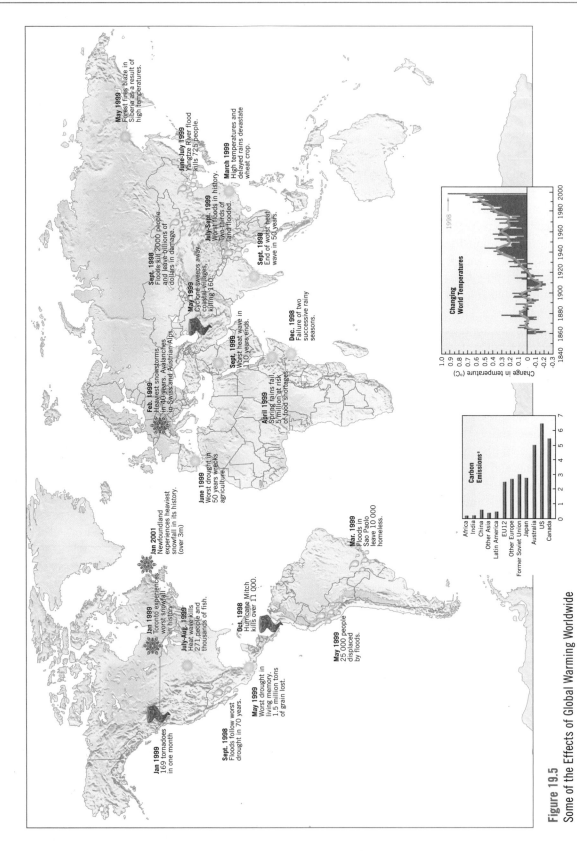

Figure 19.5
Some of the Effects of Global Warming Worldwide

May 1999
Forest fires blaze in Siberia as a result of high temperatures.

June–July 1999
Yangtze River flood kills 725 people.

March 1999
High temperatures and delayed rains devastate wheat crop.

July–Sept. 1999
Worst floods in history. Two-thirds of land flooded.

Sept. 1998
End of worst heat wave in 50 years.

Sept. 1998
Floods kill 2000 people and leave billions of dollars in damage.

May 1999
Cyclone sweeps away coastal villages, killing 160.

Dec. 1998
Failure of two successive rainy seasons.

Feb. 1999
Heaviest snowstorms in 40 years. Avalanches in Swiss and Austrian Alps.

Sept. 1999
Worst heat wave in 110 years, ends.

April 1999
Spring rains fail, 5 million at risk of food shortages.

June 1999
Worst drought in 50 years wrecks agriculture.

Jan 2001
Newfoundland experiences heaviest snowfall in its history. (over 3m)

Jan 1999
Toronto experiences worst snowfall in history.

July–Aug. 1999
Heat wave kills 271 people and thousands of fish.

Oct. 1998
Hurricane Mitch kills over 11 000.

Mar. 1999
Floods in Sao Paolo leave 10 000 homeless.

May 1999
25 000 people displaced by floods.

May 1999
Worst drought in living memory. 1.5 million tons of grain lost.

Sept. 1998
Floods follow worst drought in 70 years.

Jan 1999
169 tornadoes in one month

Changing World Temperatures

1998

Change in temperature (°C)

1840 1860 1880 1900 1920 1940 1960 1980 2000

Carbon Emissions*

Africa
India
China
Other Asia
Latin America
EU12
Other Europe
Former Soviet Union
Japan
Australia
US
Canada

In cattle-ranching regions, farmers might be able to winter their animals outside without expensive barns and the need to grow and store hay for the cold seasons. In fact, Canada could fare better than most countries, at least financially, if global warming occurs. It is obvious that our climate is changing, but it is impossible to know what the future holds, save one thing: The human species is going to have to be prepared to adapt in order to survive.

Greenhouse Gases and the Greenhouse Effect

The so-called "greenhouse effect" is really an unfortunate term. It gives the impression that there is a layer of greenhouse gases like the glass on a greenhouse. While the glass and the gases do both trap heat, greenhouse gases do not form a layer in the atmosphere, but rather are spread throughout. While the term may cause some misconceptions, the end result of the greenhouse effect is the same as in an actual greenhouse—the atmosphere is made warm enough for plants and other life forms to exist.

Greenhouse gases are one of the characteristics that make this planet habitable. When sunlight strikes the earth's surface, some of the energy is changed from light energy to heat energy. The heat is then radiated out from the surface into the atmosphere. The heat would dissipate quickly into space if greenhouse gases did not trap it around the planet. Each molecule of greenhouse gas re-radiates the energy back down to the earth. At night, when there is no sunlight, the energy from the daytime is stored in the atmosphere until the energy source is restored when the sun rises. In this way, the atmosphere remains warm enough for plants and animals to survive through the night.

Greenhouse gases are therefore essential to life. The problem is that the amount of greenhouse gases in the atmosphere is increasing because of human activities, and many people fear that this increase will cause a dramatic elevation in global temperatures over the next hundred years. There is no question that greenhouse gases have increased. Monitors around the world have proven that, but the planet has many mechanisms that reduce the impact of increased greenhouse gases, so the effect may be less severe than expected.

Carbon Dioxide

Carbon dioxide is the best known and understood of the greenhouse gases. The flow chart in Fig. 19.6 shows that carbon exists in many different states in the environment, and moves freely between the atmosphere, the biosphere, the lithosphere, and the hydrosphere. In the atmosphere, carbon appears as carbon dioxide. The amount depends on natural and human processes. In the biosphere, enormous amounts of carbon are contained in plants and animals. Called **carbon sinks**, the world's forests contain an enormous amount of carbon. The United Nations Framework Convention on Climate Change (UNFCCC) defines a sink as "any process, activity or mechanism which removes a greenhouse gas, an aerosol, or a precursor of a greenhouse gas from the atmosphere."

Of course, the carbon is released into the atmosphere when the trees (and all other vegetation) are burned or when they decompose. The number of forest fires is on the rise either because of lightning strikes or because people are burning down forests to free up land for agriculture. Not only is the carbon released into the atmosphere, but the amount of carbon dioxide being converted by vegetation is also reduced. If there are fewer trees, then less CO_2 is absorbed by biosphere sinks. Other carbon sinks in the biosphere include life forms in the world's oceans. Phytoplankton, coral polyps, fish, and other forms of sea life store enormous amounts of carbon just as the forests do on land. There is a growing body of evidence to suggest that phytoplankton is in decline in southern oceans because ozone depletion has caused an increase in UV radiation in these regions. Coral reefs are also in decline because of increased pollution and other environmental factors. In addition, fish

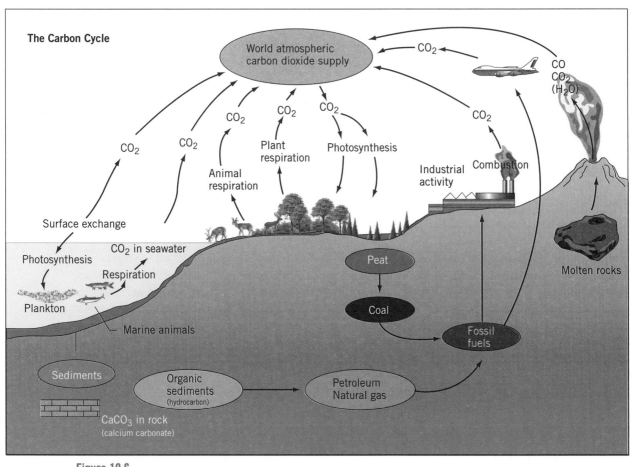

Figure 19.6
The Carbon Cycle

populations are diminishing as a result of over-fishing. The reduction of these carbon sinks in aquatic ecosystems increases the amount of CO_2 in the atmosphere.

The movement of carbon between the lithosphere and the atmosphere is another feature of the carbon cycle. When plants and animals die, they decompose. When this happens, carbon returns to the atmosphere as CO_2, but substantial amounts are also deposited in the lithosphere. Marine sediments are rich in carbon because the constant rain of dead and decaying plants and animals forms a thick layer on the sea floor. Over time, these sediments form into rock such as limestone. On land, dead and decaying life

becomes part of the soil and provides nutrients for new plants and animals. Some of the carbon is returned from this sink when microscopic plants and animals feed off the organic matter in the soil. Organic litter that covers the forest floor also gives off carbon dioxide as it rots. This return of carbon to the atmosphere is called **soil respiration**.

When plants die in wetlands where there is little or no oxygen in the water, peat bogs form. These wetlands cover enormous parts of Canada and northern Europe (including Asiatic Russia). Over time, these deep deposits of peat store huge quantities of carbon. If peat layers become buried through sedimentation or tectonic processes, coal is formed. Coal fueled the Industrial Revolution.

By burning coal, steam engines were able to produce goods on a massive scale for the first time without using human muscle energy. The world economy boomed, the human population exploded, and the modern age was born. Some scientists believe that another factor contributing to global warming was carbon that had been locked in rock layers for millions of years, which, through burning, was released back into the atmosphere as CO_2. Today, coal is still being burned in increasingly large amounts in recently industrialized China and India.

In the developed world, oil and natural gas have, for the most part, replaced coal as the fuels of choice. These fuels run our cars, heat our homes, and create much of the electricity we use. While oil and natural gas burn more cleanly than coal, they are still **hydrocarbons**, which when burned release CO_2 into the atmosphere. While carbon from Chinese and Indian power plants may be increasing carbon dioxide concentrations in Asia, oil and natural gas consumption is adding carbon dioxide to the atmosphere over Europe and North America. And most alarming is the increase in oil consumption in the developing world as populations grow and human prosperity develops worldwide.

The world's oceans are perhaps the largest and most volatile of the carbon sinks. Covering over 70 per cent of the earth's surface, and extending to great depths in many places, these features absorb a massive amount of carbon. As CO_2 concentrations grow in the atmosphere, increasingly larger quantities of carbon dioxide are being dissolved in seawater. Scientists still do not fully understand the processes that occur within the oceans, and so cannot predict how much carbon the oceans can hold, but there is no doubt that they have reduced the impact of increased carbon in the atmosphere.

Changes in Atmospheric Concentrations of Carbon

In 1997, data collected from 40 monitoring stations worldwide indicated that average atmospheric concentrations of CO_2 had increased to 364 parts per million by volume (ppmv). The rate of increase has been about 1.5 ppmv (or .5 per cent) per year since 1980. This may seem like a slow rise on a human scale, but it means that in a hundred years the concentrations will be 50 per cent higher!

Scientists from the transnational Intergovernmental Panel on Climate Change (IPCC) monitor carbon sinks using a variety of sensing devices and methodologies. The *Spring 2000 CO_2 /Climate Report* issued by Environment Canada summarizes over one thousand scientific studies. The evidence provided in this publication shows that the processes whereby carbon moves in and out of the atmosphere do not always support the view that carbon will continue to increase in the atmosphere. One of the findings states that the global carbon **flux** between terrestrial ecosystems and the atmosphere is balanced. In other words, just as much carbon is being taken out of the atmosphere by plants and animals on land as is entering it. Even though deforestation is occurring at an alarming rate, ecosystems (especially in southern parts of North America, Eurasia, North Africa, and the Amazon) are compensating by increasing plant growth. On the other hand, rapid increases in temperature will likely increase soil respiration. Microbes are more active when it is warmer, and produce more carbon dioxide. So a rise in temperature will increase carbon dioxide emissions from soils.

Studies also show that carbon dioxide emissions from industrial processes are not as significant as one might expect. About 35 per cent of the carbon emissions generated by industrial processes in the 1980s have since been absorbed by seawater. Up to 85 per cent of the carbon from industrial processes could be removed over time, as deep-water carbon is neutralized through its absorption by sediments under the oceans. This implies that only 15 per cent of the increased carbon would remain in the atmosphere. The problem is that these processes take place on the geologic scale, over thousands of years, not in the very short time span (a dozen or so years) that would be required for oceans to fix the problem before it adversely affects human systems.

Of course, many greenhouse gases, including CO_2, are added to the atmosphere through natural processes. For example, when volcanoes vent, they emit greenhouse gases. In fact, the atmosphere was likely first made by these subterranean emissions. But volcanic activity is relatively low at present, compared to the end of the Permian period 230 million years ago. At that time, vast regions of what is today northern Russia were buried under huge lava domes.

Methane

Methane (CH_4) is another greenhouse gas. As the chemical formula shows, it is a carbon compound. It is produced in wetlands when the biomass decomposes **anaerobically** (without the presence of oxygen), and is also produced in rice paddies in much the same way. In addition, it is produced by the bacteria found in the intestines of animals during digestion, and is thus also present in animal excrement. Human activity has also increased the amount of methane in the atmosphere. When organic wastes like lawn clippings are deposited in landfills, they produce methane gas. Furthermore, the increasing demand for meat and dairy products to feed an ever-growing world population results in more cattle that produce methane gas.

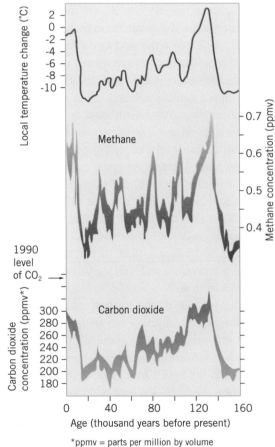

Figure 19.7
This graph compares the temperatures as well as atmospheric methane and carbon dioxide levels in Antarctica over the past 160 000 years.

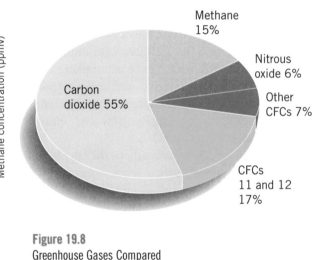

Figure 19.8
Greenhouse Gases Compared

Studies of ice cores compare past atmospheric methane concentrations to totals calculated today. From the year 1000 to 1800, the average amount of methane in the atmosphere was a steady 695 parts per billion by volume (ppbv). There was no apparent increase in methane concentrations from year to year. However, with the development of the Industrial Revolution (from 1800 onward), there was significant growth in methane production. The rate of increase peaked at 17 ppbv per year in 1981 and then began to decline. Methane concentrations are still growing in the atmosphere, at a rate averaging between 5 and 6 ppbv per year. However, there is good news. A methane molecule only stays in the atmosphere for 7.9 years, so a decrease in methane production could eventually stabilize methane concentrations. Studies conclude that this equilibrium could be reached with a 5 per cent reduction in methane production. The current rate of increase is faster than the rate for carbon dioxide, but there is much less methane—only 0.5 per cent as much as there is carbon dioxide. However, one molecule of methane absorbs 29 times as much heat as one molecule of carbon dioxide. So, control of this gas is very important.

Chlorofluorocarbon

Chlorofluorocarbon is linked to ozone depletion, but it is also a potent greenhouse gas. Comprising only a small part of the atmosphere, it is significant because it absorbs up to 300 times more heat than carbon dioxide. Unlike natural greenhouse gases that readily leave the atmosphere, chlorofluorocarbons remain for many years. However, since the implementation of the Montreal Protocol (see page 226) the chlorofluorocarbon growth rate has been declining. But CFC replacements, while less hazardous than the older synthetic chemicals, are growing rapidly.

Historic Climate Change

Studying past climates helps scientists understand how climates could change in the future. We have statistical records dating back over 100 years, but that is not far enough to get an accurate understanding of long-term cycles.

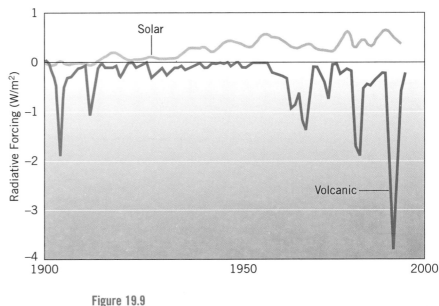

Figure 19.9
This graph shows how solar energy and volcanic activity have affected global warming. Notice solar energy has been increasing over the past century.

Computer climate models, ice core measurements, plant pollen, tree rings, air bubbles in ice caps, and sediment analysis detail what past climates were like. We know, for example, that there is usually a period of global cooling every 100 000 years. This pattern has repeated itself at least eight times over the past 800 000 years. Between each glacial period, there is a time when temperatures rise 4° to 6°C. We are currently experiencing one of these interglacial periods, but we are due for a new ice age to begin.

A thousand years ago, the earth was about 1°C warmer than it is today, sea level was higher, and rainfall patterns were different. In the Little Ice Age of the Middle Ages, temperatures were .5°C cooler than today. Tree ring studies in Siberia indicate that the twentieth century was the warmest in the past 500 years. Indeed, the end of the century confirmed this warming trend, as nine of the ten warmest years in the twentieth century were between 1987 and 1997.

Recent climate changes are attributed by some in the scientific field to increased greenhouse gases, but past climate changes in this millennium were brought about by other natural phenomena. For example, the earth's supply of solar energy is not constant, but rather varies over time. Over the past 300 years, solar intensity has increased to the level it was at a thousand years ago.

Another factor related to greenhouse gas production is the amount of dust in the atmosphere. If a lot of dust is sent into the atmosphere by a massive explosion, the amount of solar energy that reaches the earth's surface is reduced. This was particularly evident in 1991 when the eruption of Mount Pinatubo reduced global temperatures by 0.5°C. When there is another volcanic explosion, or if a comet hits the earth and covers the planet in a pall of dust that blocks out the sun, global temperatures will drop again. Sixty-five million years ago, a comet with a 20-kilometre diameter and a speed of 180 000 km/h slammed into southern Mexico. More than 25 000 cubic kilometres of rock flew out of the crater, raining down for 5000 kilometres in all directions. The skies in the Americas were alight with molten debris, and the killing heat burned the forests of both South and North America to the ground. The comet has been widely accepted as the cause of the extinction of the dinosaurs. If another similar comet hits the earth's surface, global warming will be the least of our worries!

Predictions of global warming are based almost entirely on climate models called general circulation models. (To review GCMs, go to page 294.) In the past, they gave wildly divergent projections because they could not possibly replicate the earth's atmosphere. However, their results are becoming more accurate as scientists improve their understanding of atmospheric systems and as the capabilities of computers develop.

Scientists at Environment Canada are convinced that projections made by their new 1999 GCMl are accurate. This is very important to the people who are warning the world's populations about the problems of global warming, since climate models are really all they have to prove that this situation is a crisis. During a GCM test run, the following observations were made about the system's accuracy.

- Mean global temperatures and sea-level pressure were close to those observed in reality. (See Fig. 19.12, Projected and Observed Twentieth-Century Temperature Trends.)
- Global precipitation patterns were realistic when compared to actual results.
- Ocean circulation and salinity were similar to observations, although there were discrepancies in polar regions.
- Ice extent is reasonably accurate, but was underestimated in the Arctic.
- Global snow cover agreed well with observations.

Of course, these test runs were for relatively short periods of time. Reliability decreases as projections are made further and further into the future.

The results of Canada's GCM are reinforced by the results of other models. If we compare the results of GCMs in Canada, the US, Britain, Germany, and Australia, they all show a great similarity. Indeed, Fig. 19.11 indicates that the results are all quite similar for six selected locations. The only results of the CGCM1 that show slight discrepancies are Ellesmere Island's mean summer temperature for 2050 and Summer Precipitation for Florida and California in 2050. These comparisons imply that the accuracy of the GCM is very strong, since all the models made similar projections even though the methodologies used were different.

geo.web resources

<www.climatechange.gc.ca>

Contact the Government of Canada's Climate Change web site to find out more about how the Government of Canada is committed to reducing greenhouse emissions. Summarize your findings.

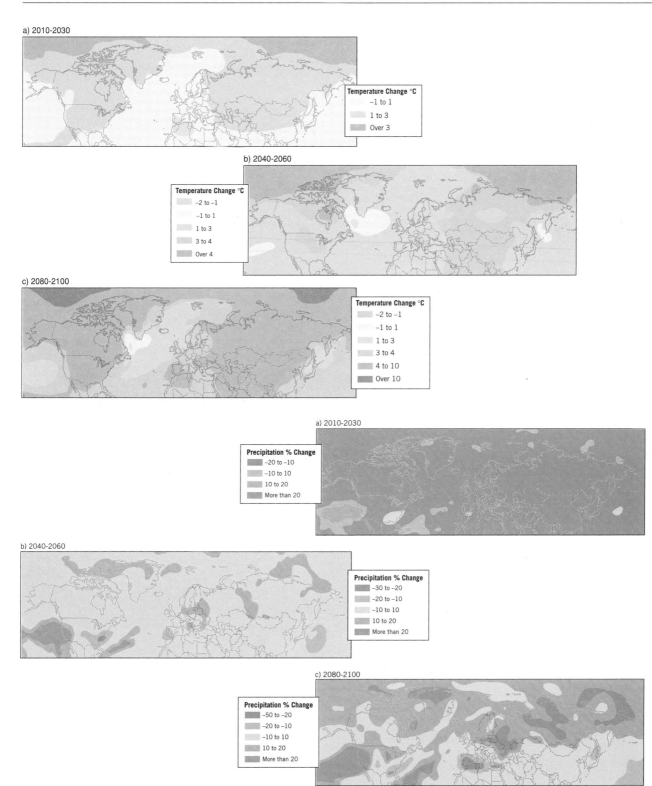

Figure 19.10
Based on GCM tests, these maps show the projected changes in annual temperature and precipitation.

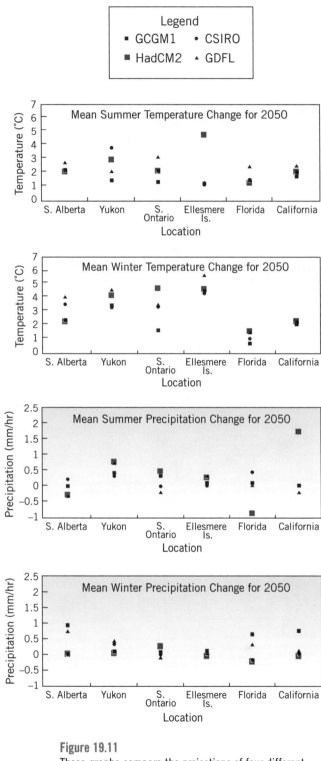

Figure 19.11

These graphs compare the projections of four different climate models.

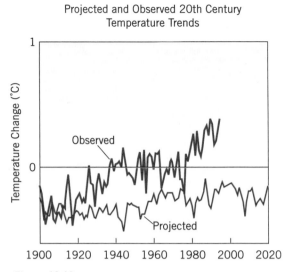

Figure 19.12

Trends and variations in average global surface temperatures shown in the computer-simulated control run (blue line) are compared with observed climate trends (black line).

Reducing Carbon Dioxide Emissions

Canadians use more fossil fuels than almost any other country in the world. Cold winters require us to burn tremendous amounts of oil. It is also dark for long periods of time during the winter, so we use more electricity for lighting. In summer, of course, it is often uncomfortably hot in many parts of the country, so we use air conditioners that consume vast amounts of electricity. All of these factors contribute to the amount of energy we use and the amount of carbon dioxide we produce. We also use a lot of gasoline to travel and move goods around this vast nation. Whether we are flying across the country or driving to school, we are all contributing to increased carbon dioxide levels and possibly to global warming.

There are many ways we can reduce our carbon dioxide emissions. Instead of commuting to work, people could try to find jobs closer to home or move closer to work. Carpooling saves money and reduces the amount of fossil fuels being consumed by cars. Public transit is also a good idea since buses and subways produce less carbon dioxide per passenger than cars. Skateboarding, in-line skating, and cycling are also healthy and economical alternatives to driving a car. For those who must drive, choosing a fuel-efficient vehicle and having it regularly tuned minimizes fuel use. Here are some additional suggestions.

- Use caulking and weather stripping around windows to help reduce the amount of home heating needed.
- Turn down the thermostat during the day, when everyone is out of the house, to reduce heating fuel usage.
- Do not allow a car to idle unnecessarily. Drive at or under the speed limit to reduce energy consumption.
- Use passive solar energy to heat your house.

Governments are doing their part, too. In the late 1990s, representatives from the Canadian federal government met with representatives from 160 other countries in Kyoto, Japan. At this pivotal conference, participants agreed to take action to reduce greenhouse gas emissions. Canada committed itself to reducing greenhouse gases to 6 per cent below 1990 levels for the period between 2008 and 2012. This can be seen as a fairly ambitious commitment because it will require major changes in the way Canadians produce and use energy.

Furthermore, the federal government has committed itself to increasing public awareness and understanding of global warming. It also supports further scientific research into climate change and the development of cost-effective, energy-efficient consumer products. In addition, the federal government has committed government departments to reducing greenhouse gas emissions by 20 per cent by 2005. The Government of Canada is working with provincial, territorial, and municipal governments; industrial groups and corporations; and environmental groups and scientists to try to meet this commitment. One provincial initiative to improve emissions was the Ontario Government's "Drive Clean" program. Every vehicle in Ontario is now tested to ensure that its emissions of greenhouse gases are at acceptable levels.

Certain corporations have also begun to produce more energy-efficient products on their own. Honda and Toyota, for example, have recently developed alternative-fuel cars that are considerably more fuel-efficient than conventional models. The Toyota Prius uses a regenerative braking system. When the driver steps on the brake, the electric motor that drives the car becomes a generator. This generator converts the energy produced in the deceleration into electricity that is stored in the battery. Thus, some of the energy normally lost during braking is recovered and used to power the motor.

Investors are starting to realize that climate change is the next great investment opportunity. The amount of venture capital invested in alternative-fuel inventions and energy-alternative engineering is increasing rapidly. Money is available for inventors with good ideas. The Ballard Fuel Cell is a case in point. This ingenious Canadian invention uses hydrogen from water to power automobiles. Not surprisingly, the share price of the stock has risen astronomically. The main advantage of the fuel cell is the complete lack of greenhouse gases in the emissions of vehicles powered by this technology. Considerable energy is still needed to remove hydrogen from water or natural gas, however.

Waste management is another area in which innovation is occurring. Because rotting refuse produces methane, garbage dumps are major greenhouse gas contributors. A German company has exploited this factor and developed a system of utilizing garbage as an energy source. After all the recoverable waste such as aluminum and newspaper is removed, the biotic material in the garbage is reduced by bacteria, and the resultant methane is harnessed. The methane is then used to generate electricity, using a natural-gas turbine. The residue that is leftover is used as fertilizer. Canadian Composting Inc., the company that brought the German invention to Canada, forecasts that we could reduce greenhouse emissions in our country by 4 to 10 per cent if major cities used the technology. As added bonuses, cheap energy would be produced and waste management sites could become a thing of the past.

ACTIVITIES

UNDERSTANDING CONCEPTS

1. Explain why global warming is a serious issue.
2. Prepare an organizer comparing the various greenhouse gases, using the following criteria: rate of increase per year; heat absorption compared with carbon dioxide; proportion in the atmosphere compared with carbon dioxide; natural and human sources; controls.
3. a) Outline how global warming is expected to affect natural and human systems.
   b) Describe how climates have changed over the past 160 000 years. (See Fig. 19.7.)
   c) How do these historic climate variations compare to short-term changes in weather?
4. a) List the factors, past and present, that have caused and are causing climates to change.
   b) Determine whether each factor causes temperatures to increase or decrease.
5. a) What are GCMs?
   b) Outline the reasons why these models are limited in their ability to predict future climate conditions.
   c) Explain how analysts improved the forecasting capabilities of the CGCM1.
   d) Summarize the projections that the CGCM1 made about climate changes that will take place in Canada by the year 2100.
6. Describe how climate change would likely affect the following resource-based industries in Canada:
   a) agriculture
   b) forestry
   c) fishing
7. Describe the initiatives to reduce greenhouse gases that have been made by Canadians in each of the following groups:
   a) governments
   b) automakers
   c) waste-management companies.

DEVELOPING AND PRACTISING SKILLS

8. a) Explain why people may be at least partly responsible for global warming.
   b) Prepare a world map showing areas that would benefit and areas that would suffer from an increase in global warming.
9. a) Study Figure 19.11. What trends do you notice in the graphs?
   b) Use the map in figure 19.5 to describe the unusual weather that has occurred throughout the world.
10. Summarize the information in the chapter that supports each of the following contentions.
   a) Global warming is a serious issue caused by increased greenhouse gases.
   b) Global warming is a serious issue caused by natural systems that operate independently from human systems.
   c) Global warming is not a serious issue and has been blown out of proportion.

11. Present an argument supporting one of the positions listed in Question 10. Support your argument with facts from this book as well as from other sources.

12. Collect articles on global warming from the Internet or other sources. Decide whether the articles support the notion that global warming is a problem or reject it as a fallacy. Based on your survey, decide if you feel that the Canadian population is very worried about the problem or relatively unconcerned.

LEARNING THROUGH APPLICATION

13. a) Describe the processes whereby carbon moves through natural systems.
    b) Evaluate the impact of deforestation and the burning of fossil fuels on the carbon cycle.
    c) Describe the difficulties involved in predicting climate change.

14. Explain how global warming could make the lifestyle of your grandchildren significantly different from the one you enjoy today. Consider each of the following aspects: clothing, leisure activities, housing, transportation, food, and vacations.

15. For each of the following economic activities, determine if global warming will have a positive or negative effect. Explain your answers.
    a) owning a ski resort in Quebec
    b) shrimp fishing near the Mississippi delta
    c) running a theme park in central Florida
    d) farming in southern Saskatchewan
    e) farming in northern Saskatchewan
    f) living in London, England
    g) owning a home in Calgary
    h) paying for snow removal in Winnipeg

16. a) What predictions have been made about climate change in Canada?
    b) What impact would these changes have on the Canadian environment and people? Consider such things as settlement patterns, permafrost, trees, wildlife, water resources, tourism, etc.
    c) Which regions of Canada could benefit from increased global warming? Which regions would be adversely affected? Explain.
    d) Debate whether overall global warming will be an advantage or a disadvantage to Canadians.

17. a) Describe how new technologies have enabled scientists to better assess the impact of increased greenhouse gases on global climate.
    b) Describe new technologies that have been developed to reduce emissions of greenhouse gases.

18. Study each of the following choices. Prepare a decision-making organizer to determine which choice is best from an environmental point of view. Use at least six criteria, including such aspects as carbon dioxide produced, waste produced, convenience, cost, peer image, etc. Rate each criterion according to how important you feel it is in relation to the others.
    a) Driving, walking, biking, or busing to school
    b) Using a paper/plastic lunch bag, a lunch box, or buying lunch
    c) Shaving with an electric razor, a straight razor, or a disposable razor
    d) Using disposable diapers, cloth diapers, or a diaper service
    e) Using natural gas, oil, wood, coal, or solar energy to heat your home.

Culminating Activity: Plannning to Reduce Greenhouse Emissions

Several international planning meetings to reduce greenhouse gas emissions have taken place in recent years. The process began at the 1992 Framework Convention on Climate Change, in Rio de Janeiro. The 167 United Nations countries that attended developed a plan to allow for economic development while still addressing the critical issue of global warming. In 1997, the Kyoto Protocol followed up on the Rio de Janeiro climate plan by establishing binding legal limits on greenhouse gas emissions in developed countries. The protocol set a target of a 5 per cent reduction in emissions by 2008–2012. Countries producing the most gases were expected to cut more than members who had lower rates, and some countries were

actually allowed to increase emissions if their rates were low. Fig. 19.13 summarizes the rates for major countries.

One highly controversial feature of the Kyoto Protocol was the permission it granted for United Nations countries to "trade" emissions with each other. For example, a country that has met its emissions-reduction objectives can sell credit emissions to another country that can use the credit in seeking to reach its target. Canada and the US have been particularly active in this strategy. Opponents argue that this practice goes against the intent of the protocol: to reduce emissions worldwide. If a member nation does more than meets its required reduction, then so much the better. On the other hand, proponents of the

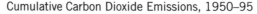

Cumulative Carbon Dioxide Emissions, 1950–95

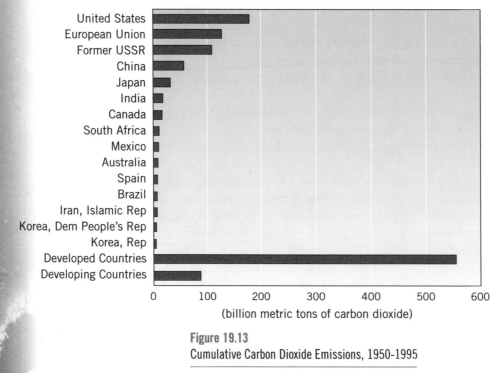

Figure 19.13
Cumulative Carbon Dioxide Emissions, 1950-1995

concept argue that it is cheaper to reduce emissions in some countries than in others.

In 1998, the United Nations met again in Buenos Aires to develop an implementation plan. Several proposals were presented that did little to further the progress of the plan. The group's exclusion of key emerging industrial nations such as India, China, and Brazil was thought to be a major drawback since these three nations account for over 40 per cent of the world's population. As these nations rapidly industrialize, emissions are expected to grow enormously over the next decade. Other members complained that hard evidence that global warming is caused by human activity was lacking. However, environmentalists thought that these nations were simply trying to avoid meeting their targets for emissions reduction. The European Union representatives upset those from the United States and Canada by suggesting the setting of limits on emissions trading.

As this book is being written, the United Nations ended their year 2000 meeting at The Hague without any resolution to these issues. Many politicians are committed to cutting emissions but will not sacrifice economic growth. Yet 2012 keeps getting closer, and little is being done!

Activity

Use an inquiry model like the one below to plan how to reduce greenhouse emissions in one of the member nations listed in Fig. 19.13, or in newly developing industrial nations like China, India, Brazil, or South Korea.

a) FOCUS:
Assume that you are a member of a national Task Force charged with the responsibility of reducing emissions for your country. You have been allotted $500 million for a 10-year investment. Choose one country or a region and prepare a strategy to solve this geopolitical problem.

b) ORGANIZE:
Prepare a needs-assessment organizer using the model on the next page.

c) LOCATE/RECORD:
Use the library/resource centre, the Internet, or other resources to obtain as much of the information and as many of the statistics as you can on the country you selected in order to fill in the "Present Situation" column.

Next, using your knowledge of how greenhouse gases are produced and the solutions and methods developed by businesses and governments to address particular emissions problems, fill in the "Action Plan" column with initiatives to better the current situation.

Finally, fill in the "Vision for the Future" column with the ideal results you hope to obtain through your action plans.

d) SYNTHESIZE/EVALUATE:
Rank the criteria based on the significance of each to reduce emissions and, with your budget in mind, decide which criteria should be selected for the development project. It doesn't matter if the costs you assign to each of your initiatives are accurate—just make your best guess and record the amounts you spend. (The budget limitation has been imposed on you so that your solution will be more realistic.)

e) APPLICATION:
Using your chosen criteria, produce a development plan that will maximize results over the 10-year period. For each initiative, give explanations of any new technologies used, cost factors, difficulties you anticipate with its implementation, and possible negative consequences, if any, that may result. Include both short-term and long-term projects in your plan.

f) COMMUNICATION:
Communicate the results of your plan to your class or group in a multimedia presentation that might make use of maps, charts, illustrations, graphs, models, videos or web sites. Make sure to include what the decisions were, how the decisions were made, and what the expected results will be.

Criteria	Present Situation	Action Plan	Vision For The Future
POWER PRODUCTION			
Amount of power from burning fossil fuels			
Amount of power from sustainable alternatives			
Potential for alternative power generation			
INDUSTRY			
Major industries that produce emissions (i.e., steel production)			
Major industries that produce few emissions (i.e., computer software)			
Agriculture that produces emissions (i.e., cattle farming)			
Agriculture that produces few emissions (i.e., organic farming)			
TRANSPORTATION			
Number of people per vehicle			
Number of vehicles			
Emissions control standards			
Public Transit			
Alternative transit (bicycles, walking)			

Criteria	Present Situation	Action Plan	Vision For The Future
ENVIRONMENT			
Area (in km^2) of forested land to absorb CO_2			
Area (in km^2) of swampland (methane producers)			
Area (in km^2) of urban land			
LIFESTYLE			
Housing types			
Home heating			
Consumer spending			
Other			
GOVERNMENT			
Political stability			
Government policy on greenhouse gas emissions			
Other			
ENVIRONMENTAL MOVEMENT			
Major groups			
Amount of support			
Other			

UNIT 5

ALL THAT IS LIVING: UNDERSTANDING THE BIOSPHERE

Human Drama

In Logged Forests, Hunting of Wildlife Becomes Deadly "Second Harvest"

Not only are trees being removed from the world's rainforests, but staggering numbers of gorillas, elephants, and other wildlife are being killed and sold as "bushmeat," according to a report by the Wildlife Conservation Society (WCS), published in the journal *Science*.

WCS says that increased logging in tropical forests has spiked markets for wild game by providing access to more than 23,000 square miles of formerly inaccessible areas each year through new logging roads.

In the Congo for example, hunting of wild game was 3–6 times higher in communities adjacent to logging roads than in roadless areas. Even recent policies that seek to protect rainforests through "sustainable forestry," rather than outright protection, have unintentionally added to the bushmeat problem.

In tropical Africa, WCS estimates that the annual harvest of bushmeat exceeds one million metric tons—much of it the result of increased access to forests being logged.

"Logging has pulled the plug on tropical forest wildlife," says the study's lead author, Dr. John Robinson, WCS vice president for international programs. "Animals are now being sucked out along the newly constructed roads."

Hunting by the logging companies themselves has also contributed to the slaughter of wild game, according to WCS. In 1996, workers in just one logging camp in Sarawak killed over 1,100 animals, totalling 29 metric tons.

This loss of wildlife threatens the very forest itself, says WCS. Removing wildlife such as elephants and tapirs that help regenerate trees through seed dispersal jeopardizes the forest's ability to sustain itself. Other effects include loss of protein sources for local people who have relied on subsistence hunting of wild game for centuries.

According to the report, the ability of the industry to sustain its logging activities will depend on its acknowledging that current logging practices are rarely sustainable in terms of trees themselves, let alone in terms of the forest animals, and that the industry will have to change its current practices.

Continued on next page.

WCS has called on the logging companies—often the only institutional presence in remote forests—to provide leadership by reducing their role in the explosion of bushmeat in logged areas, as well as national legislation to limit hunting of wild game. Some laws have already been enacted. Last year, working with WCS, Sarawak passed legislation that involved logging companies by banning the commercial sale of bushmeat.

"The situation is critical, but collaboration between logging companies and conservationists offers a way forward," Robinson said.

At a market in Cameroon, a vendor sells illegal elephant meat.

Unit Focus Questions

1. What are the sources and nature of energy flows through the biosphere?

2. How does the earth provide both a habitat for life and a resource for human society?

3. Why are stewardship and sustainability important guiding principles for human use of the physical environment?

INTRODUCTION

Of all the earth's spheres, the biosphere is perhaps the most amazing, for it is the one in which life occurs. Life evolved in a very complex but balanced food web in which even in death, plants, animals, and other organisms contribute to the living world. Human beings dominate the food chain and often stand outside this web of life. We alone have the means and the will to cause great changes in many natural systems. Some of these changes, however, have negative consequences for us and for other life forms on this planet.

Human activities in specific ecozones have frequently disrupted natural systems to the point that plants, animals, and humans are unable to thrive. The grasslands of North Africa are an example. Overgrazing and other unsustainable agricultural practices have made these once fertile lands into wastelands where nothing can grow and animals can no longer prosper. In Canada, vast regions have been degraded through acid rain and unsustainable forestry practices. The situation is even worse in some tropical rainforests where soils and climates have changed through the elimination of forest cover.

Although the earth provides both a habitat for life and a resource for society, this dual benefit will last only if humans can learn to reduce their impact on natural systems while continuing to extract the resources they need and desire. This idea that people are responsible for the life-support systems of the planet is sometimes called "stewardship." Just as a steward is a person appointed to keep watch over and supervise another's property, people are responsible for looking after planet Earth and ensuring that all creatures have an opportunity to thrive. By developing resources sustainably, people can use the raw materials society demands while ensuring that natural systems are not destroyed.

By the end of this unit, you will be able to do the following:

Geographic Foundations: Space and Systems
- Demonstrate an understanding of the principal features of the earth's biosphere;
- Explain the sources and nature of energy flows through the biosphere;
- Explain the physical processes that create soils and vegetation.

Human-Environment Interaction
- Explain how the earth provides both a habitat for life and a resource for society;
- Evaluate the impacts of natural systems on people and their activities;
- Evaluate the impact of human life on natural systems;
- Demonstrate an understanding of the importance of stewardship and sustainability as guiding principles for human use of the physical environment.

Global Connections
- Analyse the global distribution of soils and vegetation to determine reasons for the observed distribution patterns;
- Describe selected ecosystems in different parts of the world and explain the processes that shape them;
- Analyse local, regional, and global issues related to physical geography.

Understanding and Managing Change
- Explain how human uses of the earth, including uses involving technology, such as airborne laser terrain mapping, cause changes in natural systems.

Methods of Geographic Inquiry
- Describe careers related to physical geography, such as forestry and ecology;
- Use geographic skills, such as graph-making, and technologies such as satellite images to analyse ideas and information.

Contents

Chapter 20

ENERGY AND LIFE IN THE BIOSPHERE

FOCUS QUESTIONS

1. How are food pyramids, food webs, and food chains used to show energy flows through a given ecosystem?
2. How do environmental changes affect plants and animals within the biosphere?
3. Why it is important that people use the planet sustainably and act as stewards of the planet?

Key Terms

photosynthesis

evapo-
transpiration

net productivity

mutants

biomass

Whether we are referring to a giant beech tree in an ancient forest, human beings working in a vast cityscape, or a tiny amoeba in a mud puddle, all living organisms on this planet are part of the biosphere. The variety of organisms occupying this sphere is astounding. Close to 1.75 million species have been classified, close to a million of which are insects and myriapods, 100 000 are fungi and lichen, 270 000 are plants, and 22 000 are fish. Human beings are just one of the many (4 500) mammal species that inhabit the earth, and the populations of mammals are relatively insignificant when compared to the populations of all other species. Yet humans are the only creatures in the history of the world that have so dominated the planet that they possess the capacity to destroy all other species. No other creature has even come close to having this amount of power.

Features of the Biosphere

Plants and animals have specific needs that are met by both living (biotic) and non-living (abiotic) elements in the planet. For example, animals need plants or other animals for food. Whenever you have a hamburger and a glass of orange juice, you are ingesting biotic elements of the biosphere. The hamburger meat, the bun, and the orange juice originated from living organisms. Abiotic essentials needed by organisms include sunlight, heat, air, water and certain minerals. The combination of biotic and abiotic elements is infinitely complex, but both types of elements are needed for all the different species to survive and for energy to flow through the biosphere from one species to another.

We know that energy flows through the biosphere because plants and animals are constantly changing. Whether we see it in trees forming new buds in spring, leaves turning colour in fall, a puppy growing into a dog, or the flight of a seagull overhead, change in the living world is ubiquitous and constant. Some movements are easy to see; others are more gradual. For example, no matter how closely you watch, you cannot see the tree on your front lawn grow, but you know that it is indeed happening because it is now bigger than it was when you were a young child.

Chemical Energy in the Biosphere

The biosphere is made up of plants and animals. Plants are called **producers** because they can actually produce living tissue through chemical reactions generated by solar energy. Chemical processes within the plant allow it to grow leaves, stems, roots, and all the other essential living material that makes up the plant. Because animals consume nutrients created by producers, they are called **consumers**. They are unable to use solar energy to produce animal tissue and must rely on the living tissue of plants and other animals for food.

Primary consumers, or **herbivores**, eat plants directly. For example, horses, elephants, and many different insects graze on grass or browse on the leaves of small bushes and trees. Spiders, snakes, and wolves are examples of **secondary consumers**, called **carnivores**, which live by eating other consumers. A third category of consumers, **omnivores**, eats both plants and animals. Humans, along with other primates, dogs, and pigs all belong to this category. No matter what consumers eat, they are all dependent on other life forms for sustenance.

The process by which plants use solar energy to convert carbon dioxide and water into **carbohydrates** is called **photosynthesis**. The following chemical equation shows the process:

Figure 20.1
The biosphere is dynamic and constantly changing.

$$H_2O \text{ (water)} + CO_2 \text{ (carbon dioxide)} + \text{sunlight} \rightarrow CHOH \text{ (carbohydrates)} + O_2 \text{ (oxygen)}.$$

The term "carbohydrate" comes from the two words, *carbon* and *hydrate* (water). When carbohydrates are produced, the carbon from the CO_2 is used, but the oxygen is a waste material that is released into the atmosphere. The radiant energy from the sun that triggered the process is stored in the carbohydrates. This energy remains locked in the plant tissue until it is released in any of a number of ways. These ways include the plant being eaten by a consumer, in which case the energy becomes part of the tissue of that animal, or the plant being burned, which releases the energy along with waste gases such as CO_2 into the atmosphere.

If the plant dies and decomposes, carbon dioxide and methane are also produced; but if it becomes buried, the plant can then become part of the lithosphere. Many shales and limestones are the remains of ancient plants and animals that have been locked in stone. Some of these layers of stone contain oil and natural gas while others are made of coal. These ancient sources of solar energy are stored for millions of years and not released until natural and artificial processes free them.

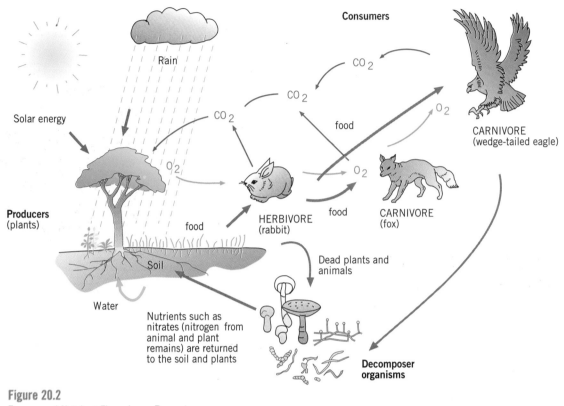

Figure 20.2
Energy and Nutrient Flows in an Ecosystem

Plant Respiration

Plants use energy from the sun to convert water, air, and nutrients from the soil into living tissue and the organs needed for reproduction. Plants convert the energy stored in carbohydrates into other forms of chemical energy by using oxygen and nutrients that they obtain from the soil and atmosphere through their roots and leaves. The chemical energy from the carbohydrates can then be used to build tissue such as buds and leaves, or to carry on other metabolic processes.

Figure 20.3 shows the nutrients that plants need. If just one of these chemical elements is unavailable, the plant will not grow. Carbon and oxygen are the only elements that come from the atmosphere, and the rest come from the soil. Although nitrogen is found in abundance in the atmosphere, most plants absorb it from the surrounding soil, through their root systems.

By-products of Photosynthesis

Water and oxygen are by-products of photosynthesis. Water that the plant no longer needs is expelled through a process called **transpiration**. The water diffuses from leaf cells as water vapour and then either enters the atmosphere or condenses on the surface of the leaf. The moisture then evaporates and re-enters the atmosphere. Together with evaporation, transpiration ensures that water is returned to the atmosphere. Often, the term **evapo-transpiration** is used to describe the combined evaporation from the surface of the earth and the release of water vapour from plants.

A full-grown tree can pump hundreds of litres of water into the atmosphere everyday. If all the plants are removed from a region, the climate can be completely changed. For example, when forest cover is removed from tropical rainforest

Nutrient	Amount Needed (mg/L)	Function	Sources
oxygen	–	respiration	atmosphere
carbon	–	photosynthesis	atmosphere
nitrogen	15	protein and vitamin creation	soil bacteria
sulphur	1	protein and vitamin creation	minerals from soil (pyrite, gypsum)
calcium	3	cell membrane formation	minerals from soil (limestone, feldspar)
potassium	5	protein creation, phosphorus synthesis	minerals from soil (clay, mica, feldspar)
magnesium	1	chlorophyll, enzymes	minerals from soil (dolomite, clay)
phosphorus	2	organic molecules, energy source	iron, aluminum, calcium phosphates in soil
iron	0.1	respiration	iron oxides in soil
trace minerals*	0.2	enzymes, respiration, cell division, nitrogen synthesis, cell function	igneous rock, sea spray (boron, sodium)

*includes manganese, copper, zinc, boron, molybdenum, cobalt, sodium, silica, chloride

Figure 20.3
Essential Plant Nutrients

regions, local precipitation norms decline. In the Tropics, air masses do not travel far from their source. Convection currents move the air up and down in a relatively narrow band, so incursions of humid air from outside the cell are unlikely. Thus, if the forests are burned or cut down in these areas, the moisture supply is often lost. As a result, parts of the Amazon that were once rainforest have been replaced with secondary-growth savanna—a scrub forest with much lower biodiversity.

Oxygen is another by-product of photosynthesis. If it were not for plants, oxygen levels would likely be too low on Earth for terrestrial animals to survive. When deep oceanic sediment cores are analysed, it becomes clear that oxygen levels were once very low in the atmosphere. Sediments that have a small amount of organic matter are also devoid of oxygen. However, sediments containing plant remains show increasingly higher levels of oxygen. As plants colonized much of the earth's surface, the proportion of the atmosphere comprised of oxygen increased to its current level of 20 per cent.

Figure 20.4 shows that oxygen, like other elements, flows through the earth's spheres. Substantial oxygen sinks are present in the calcium carbonate layers of sedimentary rock that cover much of the earth's surface. Whenever a metal is **oxidized**, it combines with oxygen to form a compound of the metal. Enormous quantities of O_2 are stored in these oxidized sinks. Oxygen is also stored in plant and animal tissue.

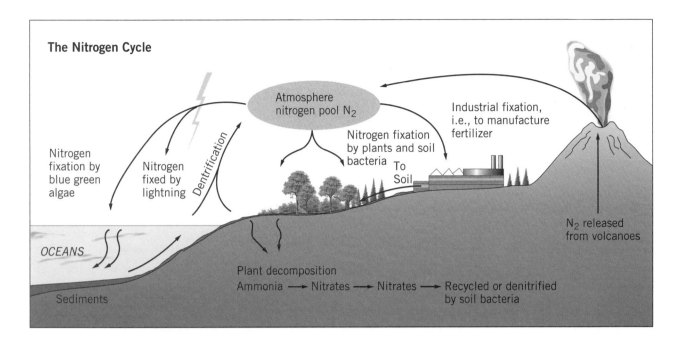

The Nitrogen Cycle

Atmosphere nitrogen pool N_2

Nitrogen fixation by blue green algae

Nitrogen fixed by lightning

Dentrification

Nitrogen fixation by plants and soil bacteria

To Soil

Industrial fixation, i.e., to manufacture fertilizer

N_2 released from volcanoes

OCEANS

Sediments

Plant decomposition
Ammonia ⟶ Nitrates ⟶ Nitrates ⟶ Recycled or denitrified by soil bacteria

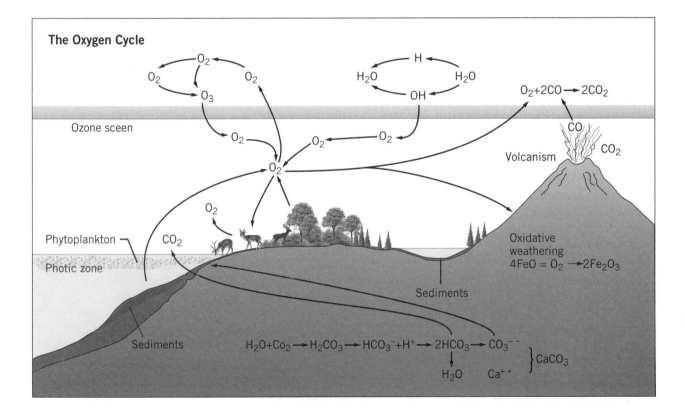

The Oxygen Cycle

O_2 O_2 O_2 O_3

H H_2O H_2O OH

$O_2 + 2CO \rightarrow 2CO_2$

Ozone sceen

O_2 O_2 O_2

CO CO_2

Volcanism

O_2

Phytoplankton CO_2

Photic zone

Oxidative weathering
$4FeO = O_2 \rightarrow 2Fe_2O_3$

Sediments

Sediments

$H_2O + Co_2 \rightarrow H_2CO_3 \rightarrow HCO_3^- + H^+ \rightarrow 2HCO_3 \rightarrow CO_3^{--}$

H_2O Ca^{++} $\Big\} CaCO_3$

Figure 20.4
The Oxygen and Nitrogen Cycles. Describe the flows shown in each diagram.

The Carnivorous Plants of Newfoundland

Newfoundland is affectionately called "The Rock" by its inhabitants. This is an apt title since the island province has little soil and is, in fact, mostly rock. The thin soil and the relatively cool temperatures result in much of the island being covered with infertile peat bogs. Few varieties of plants are able to overcome the lack of nutrients available; however, the pitcher plant and the sundew plant grow in abundance in these peat bogs despite the limitations. These unique plants obtain the nitrogen they need by trapping insects.

Pitcher plants have leaves in the shape of tubes, which collect and hold rainwater. Insects are drawn to the plant by its slightly rotten smell and by the sweet nectar that the plant secretes around the rims of its leaves. As a further enticement, the leaves are red and have markings on them that make the pitcher look like rotting flesh, so bugs may be drawn to the plant just as

they may be attracted to a dead animal. Once an insect descends into a leaf-tube, it is trapped there by tiny hairs on the inside wall of the leaf. In time, the insect falls into the water held in the tube and drowns. The plant does not actually digest the insect; instead, other tiny insects— which live out their whole lives in the mini-ecosystem of the water held in the tube—eat the remains of the dead captive. The excrement and other debris resulting from this microscopic feeding provide the nutrients for the plant that are lacking in the surrounding soil.

The sundew plant is more actively carnivorous. Although it is very tiny—standing just a centimetre or two above the surface of the bog— and has leaves only about a centimetre in diameter, it is a killer! The leaves of the sundew plant are covered with hairs that are coated with a sticky substance. If an insect crawls onto the surface of a leaf, it is instantly snared by the hairs. The hairs secrete a substance that actually works to decompose the insect and provide nutrients for the plant. Thus, these two amazing plants have overcome the limitations of their environment by becoming consumers.

QUESTIONS:

1. Carnivorous plants are found in other ecosystems also. What characteristics would you expect those ecosystems to have?
2. Do some research to find an example of another species of carnivorous plant living in a country other than Canada. How does this plant obtain nutrients from its environment?

Figure 20.5
The Carnivorous Sundew Plant

Thermal Energy in the Biosphere

Since oxygen is the only atmospheric gas that supports combustion, materials like wood burn more easily at lower temperatures if the percentage of the atmosphere that is oxygen increases. A mere rise to 22 per cent could result in the spontaneous combustion of many of the world's scrub brush and dry forests. Oxygen is in perfect equilibrium, so the chances of a major conflagration are relatively low. This being said, however, there has been a tremendous increase in the incidence of forest fires in recent years. This is attributed not to increased levels of oxygen, but to higher temperatures and drier weather in certain regions, especially in the continental interiors.

People have long used fire to clear land for farming since this practice instantly transfers carbon from the biomass into the atmosphere and makes other nutrients contained in the biomass available to crops. The increased fertility after the burn provides a false assessment of the soil's long-term capabilities.

In the past natural fires as well as accidental fires set by humans were discouraged. As a result, there was nothing to get rid of the annual rain of dead branches and leaves on the forest floor. Today we know that forest fires are essential to the health of the forest, since periodic fires clear away the accumulation of flammable vegetative litter on a regular basis. Fires burn through the forest, but they do not have enough fuel to gain the intensity needed to reach the canopy where the leaves are. Many trees even have fireproof bark to protect them. Some trees, such as the Douglas fir, need fire to open seed cases before germination can occur.

If there are no periodic burns, when fire finally does come, so much flammable litter is lying on the forest floor that the intensity of the fire is increased and the hot flames reach into the canopy and completely destroy the trees. These types of "**fire storms**" can be so great that local weather systems occur within them and the effects can be felt thousands of kilometres away. To overcome the problem, foresters often help nature by purposely burning off the litter on the forest floor. These **prescribed burns** prevent harmful fires from obliterating entire forests.

Kinetic Energy in the Biosphere

Kinetic energy is the energy of movement. When you walk to school, your body converts carbohydrates into muscle energy. The tissue has the energy to propel an animal forward or allow a plant to grow higher. Living tissue stores the chemical energy from the food that has been consumed, so that it can be used later.

In a daily struggle for survival, plants and animals strive to get the energy they need to make it from day to day and to reproduce. Over the long term, plants and animals evolve so as to utilize energy as efficiently as possible. If a gradual change occurs in the environment, then plants and animals evolve to make the most of the new situation.

If you like the outdoors and prefer country living, are good at geography and biology, and don't mind being isolated in rural surroundings, **forestry** may an excellent career choice for you. There are many aspects to the job. Some foresters are remote-sensing specialists who, until several years ago, would have analysed air photos to determine the characteristics of forest stands. Today foresters use more advanced remote-sensing technologies such as lasers (see Changing Technology pp. 396) to analyse the moisture content, health, species type, height, and age of trees. This data can be used to determine tree-stand inventories and prospective harvest sites.

If you are more of a hands-on person, you may wish to work in the field. Ground truthing remotely sensed data, conducting surveys, working in public relations, supervising work teams, and replanting trees are some of the many field jobs that foresters do. Forestry programs are offered at most universities, but are more common in areas where forestry is practised. The program usually takes five years, and post-graduate specialization is normally required for senior forestry positions.

CHANGING TECHNOLOGY: Global Fire Monitoring

Satellites enable scientists to monitor forest and brush fires. Infrared images allow scientists to identify where a fire is burning when its precise location is obscured by smoke. Firefighters can then be directed to exactly where the fire is. By monitoring infrared images, the water content of vegetation can also be ascertained, which is especially important because it allows authorities to predict "hot spots." If the forests are very dry and temperatures are high, the Ministry of Natural Resources declares the area a "No Fire Zone." Warnings to campers about the use of campfires and the cancellation of prescribed burns can often be enough to reduce the likelihood of fire.

When water content is low and thunderstorms are imminent, forest fires are often beyond the control of the authorities. People are warned about the potential risk, and are asked to be ready for possible evacuation, while firefighters wait on standby.

Satellite images can also be used to monitor masses of hazardous blowing smoke. For example, in May 1998, portions of Mexico and Central America were covered with violent brush fires. Farmers traditionally clear the land with fire in these regions, but the extremely dry weather brought on by a severe ENSO (El Niño Southern Oscillation) made the area more susceptible to fire than usual. Smoke plumes entered the upper troposphere and

made it as far north as the US-Canada border. Smoke and haze caused health alerts in Texas, and airports in Texas and northern Mexico closed because of poor visibility. The left image in Fig. 20.6 is from the Sea-Viewing Wide Field of View Sensor (SeaWiFS). Three visible wavelengths show clouds, vegetation, and seawater. Smoke and haze may be seen over the western half of the Gulf of Mexico and the south central United States. The GEOS-8 image has been enhanced to show smoke and air-blown particles (aerosols). The red and green portions of the images show the concentrations of aerosols over Mexico and the central US.

Question:
How were forest fires and "hot spots" monitored before the use of satellites?

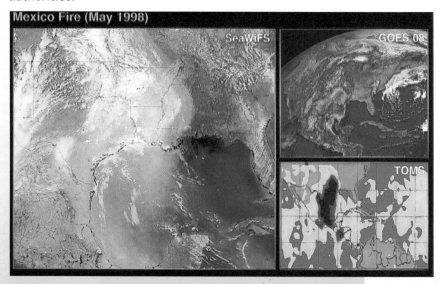

Figure 20.6
These images show the massive fire that took place in Mexico and the United States in May 1998.

Contrary to what many people may think, evolutionary change is not a gradual process. Fossil evidence shows that it occurs rapidly (within several generations) and sporadically, as opposed to evenly, over millions of years. Fossils of a species remain virtually unchanged over thousands and even millions of years. We see significant changes in fossil remains only when there is evidence of an environmental change having occurred. This is because adaptation occurs when there are mutations in the regular form of the species.

Mutations are constantly occurring in plants and animals. **Mutants** are individuals with characteristics that are different from their parents' or siblings'. Usually, the mutated organisms die out because they are not as well-suited to their environment as their siblings are. However, sometimes the mutated offspring is better suited to its surroundings. When this happens, the mutant has a competitive advantage over its siblings and so has a better chance of survival. Such a situation can be seen clearly in the evolution of the zebra. Originally, these horses did not have stripes. However, as predators adapted and

Figure 20.7
Why has the sabre-toothed tiger become extinct?

became better at hunting them, those animals that had camouflaged coats were harder to see in the tall grasses of the African savanna. When mutants were born with the classic stripes we associate with zebras, they had a competitive advantage over their non-striped siblings who could be seen more easily by lions and hyenas. As a result, the striped horses had a higher survival rate.

The same process can occur in trees. The evergreens of the boreal shield tend to have very short, resilient branches. They evolved this way because long, brittle branches would snap in the winter under heavy snow loads. In contrast, further south, in the southern United States, similar species of evergreens have much longer branches than their northern cousins do. The snow load is less of a problem in the coastal plains of Georgia, so there is no competitive advantage to having short branches there.

However, if there is a significant environmental change over a relatively short period of time, a mutant that is sufficiently adapted to survive in the new environment may not be born. This is usually the case. Over 90 per cent of the plants and animals that have evolved throughout the history of planet Earth are now extinct. This is why there are no longer any woolly mammoths in northern Canada, giant tree sloths in South Africa, or sabre-toothed tigers in India.

When change is rapid, plants and animals may become **extirpated** in one region, but still survive elsewhere. The polar bears in the western Hudson Bay area may become extirpated as sea ice forms later and breaks up earlier each year. The lack of ice will mean they cannot hunt for long enough to get the energy requirements to sustain them through the summer when no sea ice exists and opportunities to hunt seals are no longer available. Either they will evolve so that they can hunt without sea ice, or they will die out in the Hudson Bay region. However, they will likely survive further north where the sea ice lasts longer.

Some animals migrate in order to find conditions that are suited to their needs. When much of the old-growth forest was cut and the swamps drained in Southern Ontario, the indigenous moose moved further north. At the same time, white-tailed deer moved into the region. The smaller species thrives on young saplings and prefers solid ground to wetlands. Today deer are abundant in the mixed forest of Southern Ontario, but moose are rare until you travel into the northern marshes.

Even plants migrate. Of course, they cannot pick up their roots and walk from place to place like animals, but their seeds do float on the winds, flow down rivers, and hitch rides on unsuspecting couriers. Often, the seeds end up in an inhospitable environment, where if it does sprout, it likely will not last long enough to reproduce. If the environment is well-suited to the seed's growth, then the plant will thrive and extend its range into a new region.

Potential Energy in the Biosphere

The fibres and biomass of the biosphere store a great deal of energy. Solar energy is stored in tree trunks, leaves, grass, and even the tiny plankton that inhabit the oceans. Animals convert plant energy into animal tissue when they eat plants, thereby storing even more potential energy. However, when an animal eats another animal, a much smaller percentage of the original plant energy is gained. The rest of the energy is converted by the first animal into body heat, respiration, and incomplete digestion. So, a

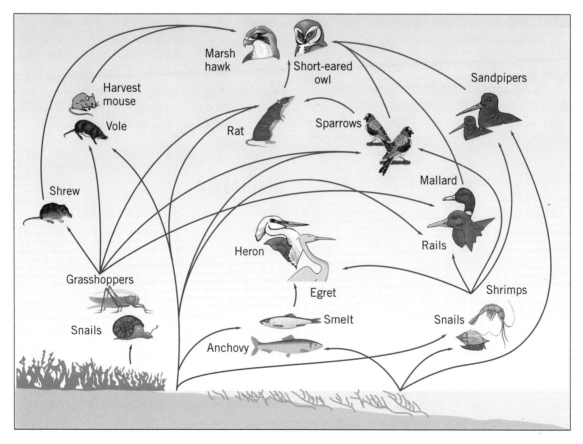

Figure 20.8
This example of a salt marsh food web shows the movement of energy through this ecosystem. It was made by linking several food chains together. Identify one such chain in this illustration.

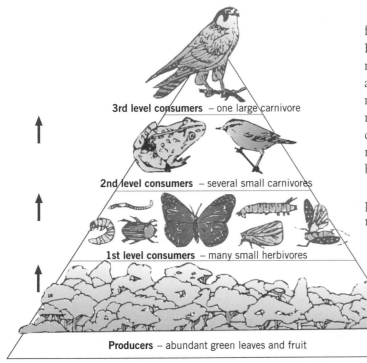

3rd level consumers – one large carnivore

2nd level consumers – several small carnivores

1st level consumers – many small herbivores

Producers – abundant green leaves and fruit

Figure 20.9
A food pyramid graphically illustrates the comparative populations of consumers and producers needed to support each level of a vertical food chain.

A **food pyramid** is a diagram that shows a food chain as a vertical stack of horizontal bars. Each bar shows the number of plants or animals needed to support the species of plants or animals on the level above. Generally, the number of organisms at each bar decreases as one moves up the levels, from producers to consumers. At the top of the pyramid, a small number of individuals is supported by a massive base of many different plants and animals.

The further energy flows up through a food pyramid, the less each successive consumer receives of it. For example, if a coyote were to eat a rabbit, the predator would receive less than 10 per cent of the rabbit's potential energy. Therefore, it would require a lot of rabbits to fulfill the food requirements of one coyote. You can look at the concept this way: 1 g of coyote fibre requires 10 g of rabbit fibre, which requires 100 g of plant fibre. As a result, the population of consumers decreases with each level of the pyramid. So, there might be several families of rabbits but only one pack of coyotes that range through a particular meadow.

rabbit would need to eat 100 g of grass to produce 10 g of rabbit tissue.

Three interconnected terms are often confused when talking about the movement of energy through ecosystems. The term "**food chain**" refers to a simple, linear diagram, showing the sequence of producers and consumers that are dependent upon each other for food. For example, an osprey may swoop down on an unsuspecting fish in a coastal region of Georgia. That fish likely ate smaller fish, which in turn ate even smaller fish or microscopic plankton. When an animal dies in the food chain, the nutrients that made up the tissue of the animal are returned to the ground, where new plants recycle the nutrients back through different interdependent plants and animals. The term "**food web**" refers to several food chains joined together, as seen in Fig. 20.8.

Biomass

The biosphere has tremendous diversity, although some areas are better suited to life than others. The regions well-suited to life become sinks for enormous amounts of potential energy. Plant and animal tissue—either alive or dead—is collectively called **biomass**. This is the amount of mass produced by all the plants and animals living in a region, per square metre, per year. This amount is approximated by conducting field surveys of different ecosystems.

A strong relationship exists between the amount of biomass in an area and the energy and nutrients available in that area. The lithosphere provides nutrients from the regolith (weathered bedrock). The biosphere contributes recycled nutrients from dead and decaying plant and animal material. The hydrosphere provides the water necessary for photosynthesis and nutrient transport through plants and animals. The atmosphere provides heat, light, and carbon for photosynthesis to occur. When a lot of energy and nutrient inputs occur, the amount of biomass is high; when inputs are low, the biomass is also low. Fig. 20.13 shows the differences in biomass for the major ecosystems. It is interesting that rainforests have the most biomass and are found where solar energy is most concentrated. On the other hand, desert and semi-desert regions have high energy inputs from the sun but are poor biomass producers. Obviously, the lack of water reduces the capacity of the plants and

animals to produce biomass. Likewise, the Nile Valley, which is in the Sahara Desert, is one of the most productive agricultural regions in the world. The artificial infusion of water makes it an anomaly.

Plants on land and in the ocean (phytoplankton) contain chlorophyll, a green pigment they use during photosynthesis. Using satellite sensors, we can measure chlorophyll concentrations on land as well as in oceans, lakes, and seas to indicate the distribution and abundance of vegetation. Since most animals rely on vegetation for nutrition, directly or indirectly, scientists refer to these images as snapshots of Earth's biosphere.

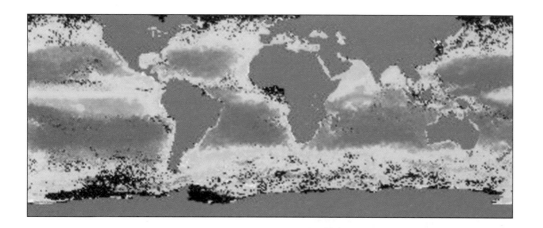

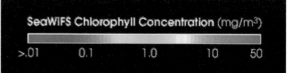

Figure 20.10
These images show chlorophyll concentrations in June and January around the world. Which areas have the highest levels of chlorophyll in each map? What factors could explain this pattern?

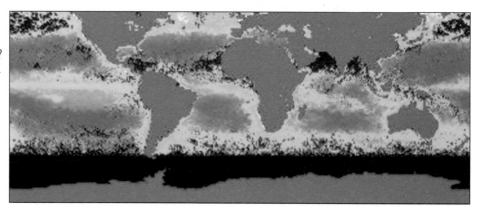

Using Graphs Effectively

Nothing shows a statistical pattern better than a graph. There are essentially four types of graphs:

- Line graphs are good for showing trends over time. For example, if you want to show how CO_2 levels have changed over a period of time, a line graph displays the information effectively. The x-axis shows the dates and the y-axis indicates the levels for the period. Depending on what a presenter wants the data to show, the scale can be manipulated such that the change appears to be either great or minute.
- Pie graphs are useful for showing the percentage of a feature with specific characteristics. The components of the atmosphere could be shown using this graph.
- Bar graphs are useful when comparing data from different regions, even though you do not have the values needed to show the complete picture. Carbon dioxide production by country is a good example. All regions of the world contribute CO_2, but only the most significant contributors are included in a bar graph. Small, non-industrialized countries such as Nepal may be excluded.
- Scattergraphs are good for showing whether a relationship exists between two variables, and if so, whether that correlation is positive or negative. If you wanted to see the correlation between carbon dioxide levels and global warming, for example, this graph would be appropriate.

In addition to these graphs, there are many modifications and combinations that can be used for specific purposes.

- Multiple line graphs are useful for comparing variables over time. They can also show correlations effectively. If both lines follow more or less the same trend, then the two variables have a positive correlation. If they seem to show exactly opposite patterns, a negative correlation is indicated.
- Combination graphs show line and bar graphs together. Climate graphs are commonly of this

type. They are useful for showing the characteristics of one region.

- Graphs can also be used in combination with maps. Proportional circles and proportional arrows showing comparisons of regional characteristics are combined with locational factors shown by a map.

Computers have vastly improved the way we can make graphs. Spreadsheet programs are fast and easy ways to produce accurate, attractive graphs of excellent quality.

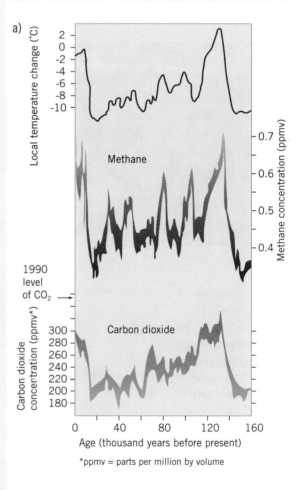

a)

*ppmv = parts per million by volume

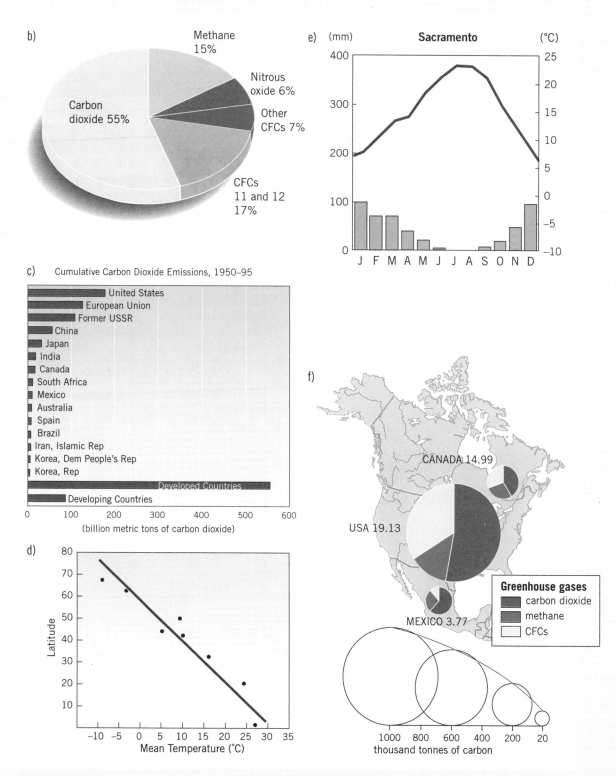

Figure 20.11
Give examples of data or different types of situations that could be represented by each of these types of graphs.

TRY IT!

Study the data contained in Fig. 20.12 and the map in Fig. 20.13.

1. In order to compare the mean net productivity per unit area of the ecozones given,
   a) What type of graph would be best?
   b) Which data would you input?
   c) Prepare the graph.

2. In order to show the area distribution of each terrestrial ecosystem,
   a) What type of graph would be best?
   b) Which data would you input?
   c) Create the graph.

3. Create a new graph that shows the Normal Range for each ecosystem.
   a) What type of graph would be best?
   b) Which data would you input?
   c) Prepare the graph.

4. a) Using an appropriate spreadsheet-type software program, construct graphs for questions 1-3. For each, decide what headings would be used for the columns, what headings would be used to represent each row, and which data you would input.
   b) Print out your completed graphs and colour them if you do not have access to a colour printer.

Type of Ecosystem	Area (106 km²)	Net Productivity per Unit Area (dry grams/m²/year) Normal Range	Mean Net Productivity per Unit Area
Tropical Forest	17	1000 – 3000	2200
Temperate Deciduous Forest	7	600 – 2500	1200
Temperate Evergreen Forest	5	600 – 2500	1300
Boreal Forest	12	400 – 2000	800
Savanna Grassland	15	200 – 2000	900
Temperate Grassland	9	200 – 1500	600
Tundra	8	10 – 400	140
Semi-desert	18	10 – 250	90
Desert	24	0 – 10	3
Arable Land	14	100 – 4000	650
Total Terrestrial Ecosystems	129		
Lake and Stream	2	100 – 1500	400
Estuaries	1.4	200 – 4000	1500
Upwelling Ocean Zones	0.4	400 – 1000	500
Open Ocean	332	2 – 400	125
Continental Shelf	27	200 – 600	360
Total Aquatic Ecosystems	**362.8**		

Figure 20.12
Net Primary Productivity of Major Ecosystems

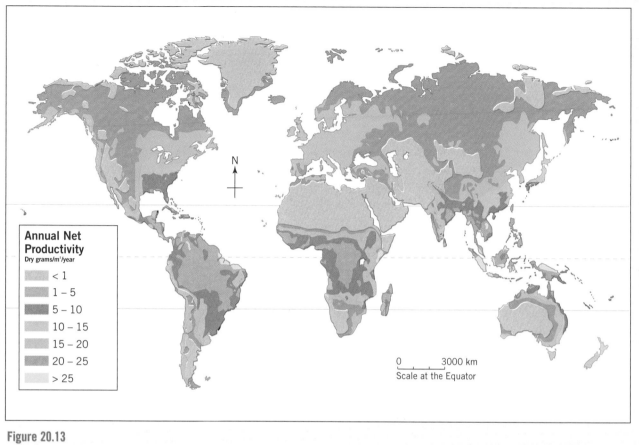

Figure 20.13
Annual Net Primary Productivity

ACTIVITIES

UNDERSTANDING CONCEPTS

1. a) List the essential needs of plants.
    b) Classify each need as biotic or abiotic.
2. a) Describe the relationships that exist between secondary consumers, primary consumers, and producers.
    b) When can plants become consumers?
    c) Describe the inputs needed and the outputs produced through the process of photosynthesis.
3. a) Explain how oxygen and water levels affect forest fires.
    b) Describe the technology used to monitor forest fires.
    c) Describe forest practices that encourage tree development and discourage destructive forest fires.
    d) Describe the job characteristics and educational requirements of a forester.
4. a) List the different ways in which plants and animals show kinetic energy.
    b) How do plants differ from animals in the way they migrate?
    c) How do plants and animals respond to environmental change?
5. a) State the hypothesis made in the chapter regarding evolutionary changes in life forms.
    b) What evidence is given to support the hypothesis?
    c) What is your opinion of the idea? Explain, giving a detailed analysis.
6. a) Explain what a food pyramid is.
    b) Why does the amount of energy received from each species decrease as you go up the pyramid?
    c) What is biomass?
    d) How is biomass a good measure of ecosystem productivity?
    e) Why is there such a wide range of biomasses for different areas of each ecosystem?
    f) How do each of the following variables affect ecosystem productivity?
        – Water
        – Soil nutrients
        – Solar energy
        – Latitude
        – Elevation

DEVELOPING AND PRACTISING SKILLS

7. Study Fig. 20.3 on page 341.
    a) Prepare a pie graph showing the values of nutrients needed for plant growth. Combine all fractional elements under the title "Trace Minerals."
    b) Identify the different soil components that provide essential nutrients and list those nutrients under each.

8. Study Fig. 20.4.
   a) Explain how nitrogen and oxygen flow through natural systems.
   b) Give examples of nitrogen and oxygen sinks and explain their significance to natural systems.
   c) Do human activities have an impact on the oxygen and nitrogen cycles? Explain your answer.
9. a) Make a flow chart to illustrate a food web in one of the following ecosystems: tundra, rainforest, ocean, temperate forest, or prairie.
   b) In the food web you created in part a), eliminate one of the levels. What effect would this have on the food web?
10. Describe what is shown in Fig. 20.10 on page 349.
    a) What is the relationship between chlorophyll and photosynthesis?
    b) Which areas seem to be particularly high in chlorophyll production?
    c) What impact does this have on biomass production?
    d) How is the image different in January as compared to June?

LEARNING THROUGH APPLICATION

11. Go on a field study to measure the impact of biotic and abiotic elements in two or more different ecosystems. Consider studying a small section of a flood plain, a field or meadow, a forest, or a north-facing slope, etc.
    a) Measure the following abiotic elements: temperature, humidity, soil moisture, wind velocity, and soil type.
    b) Make an inventory of the different biotic elements (plants, animal droppings, insects, worms in the soil, etc.) in each ecosystem.
    c) Identify where differences occur.
    d) Make assumptions about why the ecosystems are different, based on abiotic differences.
12. a) Explain what stewardship is and why people need to help preserve life in the biosphere.
    b) Assess the ecoregion you live in to find examples of people either destroying or preserving natural systems.
    c) Would you consider people in your community to be stewards of your local ecoregion? Explain.
13. a) Provide examples to show how people modify the nitrogen cycle.
    b) How can human intervention be both positive and negative?
    c) Create a strategy whereby the negative impact of human intervention can be reduced.
14. For the food web you created in question 9,
    a) Explain how people interrupt the food web.
    b) Outline the repercussions this could have on the ecosystem.

Chapter 21

CLIMATE, SOILS, AND NATURAL VEGETATION WORKING TOGETHER

FOCUS QUESTIONS

1. What are the relationships among global patterns of landforms, climates, soils, and natural vegetation?
2. How do patterns in your local bioregion compare with global distribution patterns of landforms, climates, soils, and natural vegetation?
3. What are the interconnections among natural systems (e.g., natural vegetation, climate, wildlife) within selected ecosystems?

Key Terms

ecosystem

ecoregion

natural vegetation

soil horizon

pedologist

Ecology is a relatively new branch of science that focuses on the study of **ecosystems**—complex communities of plants and animals. Earth's ecosystems develop distinct characteristics because of the interactions among climate, landforms, soils, natural vegetation, and animals—including people. Examples of ecosystems include the equatorial rainforest, tropical desert, tropical savanna, and mixed forest.

When the characteristics of these different natural systems are similar, life within them tends to evolve in similar ways. This is why the plants and animals of the equatorial rainforest of Borneo are so similar to the plants and animals of the Amazon and the Congo. They are thousands of kilometres apart, yet giant trees, huge snakes, and tree-climbing monkeys have evolved in all three locations. (The three regions were, in fact, once joined together in a great land mass called Pangaea, but the continents separated before mammals started evolving, so they could not have had a common mammal ancestor.)

Examples also exist of people responding to like environments in similar ways. The San, a Stone-Age people of the Kalahari Desert, have developed in many ways like the Aborigines of the Great Australian Desert. Both peoples have similar tools, hunt animals in much the same way, and even have similar animist religions. However, human societies also respond to similar environmental challenges in dissimilar ways because they have different technologies. The term "technology" refers to the tools and processes a society has acquired through its people's own knowledge or the knowledge they have adopted from others. Paleo-Indians in North America hunted horses to extinction because they did not know to use them as beasts of burden. By contrast, Mongolian tribes living in similar conditions domesticated the horse and developed an equestrian culture that did not emerge in the American plains until the horse was re-introduced in the seventeenth century.

Often, the technology improves a society's environment, making it more productive and better able to meet human needs in a sustainable way. However, human modifications to the environment are sometimes destructive and cause natural systems to break down. This chapter provides background material on how natural systems work together to create unique ecosystems. The following chapters explore the intricacies of specific ecosystems.

The Gaia Hypothesis

One interesting hypothesis concerning living systems on Earth was developed in the late 1960s by James Lovelock, a British atmospheric chemist. He had been researching the reasons why the earth's atmosphere was so different from that surrounding the other planets in our solar system. While walking in his Devonshire garden, where all the plants and animals lived in such harmony, he was struck by a new way of looking at natural systems. Lovelock hypothesized that instead of life evolving to fit the conditions that the planet presented, life has changed the environment so much that it has become more suitable for new, more complex forms of life to evolve.

The early forms of life on the planet were extremely primitive algae and bacteria. But over untold hundreds of millions of years, this primitive ooze transmuted into the vast variety of life we have today. Early single-celled plants and animals could exist on an inhospitable planet where no other life forms could survive. In time, these simple life forms so changed the atmosphere that more advanced plants and animals were able to evolve. In other words, the planet developed at the same time as the plants and animals evolved. And the process is still occurring.

The name for the hypothesis is an apt one. It is derived from the ancient Greek goddess Gaia, who was believed to have delivered the world from chaos by creating ordered natural systems on a planet that was a living entity. Lovelock contended that the entire planet is like a single, self-regulating, living entity. If you damage one

small part of the planet, the whole being is affected. His idea is still highly controversial, and some in the scientific community claim that it is too simple or too general to test. However, the Gaia hypothesis has since become accepted by a good number of scientists, especially in the field of ecology.

People who study ecosystems are called ecologists. Their area of expertise is larger than that of biologists, as they study the impact of inorganic or non-living things on natural systems. Ecologists observe natural systems and determine how healthy the environment is by cataloguing different plants and animals and assessing the relationships that exist among them. If you love nature and are good in science and geography, the field of ecology may provide an exciting career for you. Generally, students study biology, ecology, geography, and organic chemistry in an undergraduate program. Post-graduate programs often require students to specialize in one specific type of ecosystem.

Natural Systems

Natural systems include climate, natural vegetation, and soils, among other things. Because natural systems are infinitely complex, they are difficult to study. To simplify the process, the spatial distribution of each element of a natural system is presented separately in this chapter. Once we understand how each of climate, natural vegetation, and soils are spread over the surface of the earth, specific case studies can be undertaken.

Places with similar characteristics are called **regions**. If you study the maps showing natural vegetation and soil (on pp. 364, 370), you will notice that they look very similar. This is because regions with the same or similar climate characteristics usually have the same or similar natural vegetation and soils. Interestingly, there is tremendous variation in the terms used to describe regions having the same natural characteristics. Environment Canada uses the term "ecozones," but this term is not widely used internationally. The term "ecosystem" is often used to describe small ecological units within larger ecological units (e.g., a wetland in a mixed forest). In this book, the term "ecoregion" is used to describe large ecological units on a global scale.

Climate Regions

Ecoregions develop partly because of the climate a region has. In turn, the ecoregion determines, to some extent, what the climate is like. For example, when forest cover is stripped away from an ecoregion, rainfall often decreases because there is less water vapour in the air due to reduced evapo-transpiration.

Soils and other elements of the lithosphere are also affected by climate. If a region has heavy rainfall, soils are often **leached**. If the precipitation is low, salt deposits may develop on the surface of the soil. The amount of precipitation and the amount of surface heat determine how surface rocks weather. If the climate is hot and wet, chemical weathering is prevalent. But if it is cold and dry, mechanical weathering is more common.

The hydrosphere is intimately bound to climate. Precipitation patterns, ocean currents, and other aspects of the hydrosphere greatly affect climate and are in turn affected by it. Human activities are also influenced by climate. To study the climate of a place is to attempt to understand many of the essentials for studies in ecology.

Ancient Greek philosophers distinguished three types of climate regions, basing their ideas on temperature difference. The Far North was home to the "frigid zone." This land of ice and snow has a mean monthly temperature that stays below 10°C all year round. In the "tropical zone," the temperature never goes below 18°C. The Greeks, being somewhat ethnocentric, believed that the region where they lived, the "temperate zone," was the best; it was not too hot like the

region further south, yet it was warmer than the land further north. They reasoned that their culture evolved into an advanced form because the climate allowed for the accumulation of abundant food without undue labour, leaving them with more time to dedicate to the creation of art and technologies and to debate ideas. Of course, what they failed to realize was that there were similarly great cultures in tropical zones. Mayan, Indus, and Inca cultures are but three examples. The Vikings came later, but contrary to the Greeks' beliefs, they thrived in sub-polar ecoregions. Even though the Greeks' assumptions about the influence of climate on human activity were too narrow, they did form the basis for later ideas about climate regions.

The system developed by the Greeks needed to be refined and further developed to be more accurate. Here is an example that shows how much of an over-generalization it is: The climates of Moscow and Ottawa are both temperate, but so are the climates of Miami and Athens. Yet, the first two cities are noted for their long, bitterly cold winters, while the latter two cities are brutally hot in summer and mild in winter. Obviously, the temperate zone must be further subdivided to make the system more specific and meaningful. Indeed, climatologists have subdivided the category into mid-latitude and subtropical. Mid-latitude coincides with climate zones between about 35° and 65°. Polar was similarly divided into subpolar and arctic for those regions in the high latitudes that are cold and very cold.

What was also needed was a classification system that took precipitation into account. Regions can be classified as arctic, subpolar, midlatitude, subtropical, and tropical, but they can also be wet, seasonally dry, and dry all year. If you combine all the possible temperature and precipitation characteristics, you come up with the climate regions described in the table below. Some combinations don't occur in nature, and so are omitted.

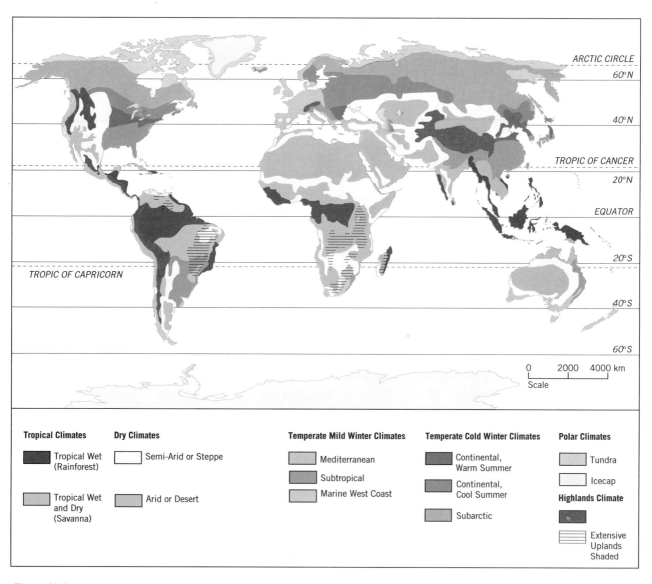

Figure 21.1
Climate Regions of the World
One group of climatologists has recognized six general climate regions, each of which can be divided into two or three sub-regions.

Figure 21.2
Study the pictures and try to determine which climate zone each represents. Give evidence to support your choice.

Soil Development

Soil provides a good example of the complex inter-action between biotic and abiotic elements. One soil ingredient, **humus**, is made up mainly of decomposing plant material such as leaves and twigs. It is therefore a biotic element because it is made from material that was once living. Soil is part of the **regolith**—weathered bedrock. The particles of rock of varying sizes from minute to huge that make up the regolith are abiotic since they are not living. Soil also contains moisture, which is an abiotic element. The (abiotic) water found within the pores of the soil is essential to the photosynthesis that occurs in green plants and to the movement of nutrients from the soil into plants' structures through intricate root systems. Air, another abiotic element found in the soil, is essen-tial because it is used by tiny animals and bacteria that live in the ground. Soil fauna are biotic elements that break down minerals and organic matter. Ants, worms, and other burrowing crea-tures mix the soil and make passageways that water and air move through. Biotic bacteria convert nitro-gen from air pockets in the soil into a form of nitro-gen that plants can access. Together, all these elements, both biotic and abiotic, provide the essential nutrients plants must have in order to live.

Variations in climate, natural vegetation, and regolith result in the enormous variety of soil types that cover the earth's surface. Soils need several conditions to develop, one of which is stability—long periods of time without tectonic, atmos-pheric, or human interference. It is estimated that many of the fully developed **soil horizons** in our most fertile agricultural regions are thousands of years old. In addition to a long period of stability, there must also be an abundant source of rocks and minerals. Water and air are also essential ingredients in soil creation since they support the mechanical and chemical processes that break down the regolith into increasingly smaller parti-cles. Tiny plants and animals are also needed to mix and break up the different ingredients of the soil and add organic compounds.

Soils develop three layers that are called **hori-zons** by **pedologists**. At the surface, where soils interact directly with natural vegetation, a layer of humus-rich topsoil called the **A horizon** is formed. At the bottom of the soil horizon, where the soil interfaces with the bedrock, there are accumulations of broken up rock of different sizes and shapes. This **C horizon** is made up of **parent material** from which the soil is made. The transitional **B horizon** is found between the A and C horizons. Nutrients are often leached (washed) from the topsoil into the B horizon, where plants cannot access them. To compen-sate, some types of plants grow dispropor-tionately long root systems.

Pedologists are scientists who specialize in the study of soils. They work for agencies such as the Ministry of Agriculture, the Ministry of Natural Resources, Parks Canada, and Environment Canada. If you are interested in chemistry (especially organic chemistry), biology, and geography, this field could be of interest to you.

Farmers send soil samples in for analysis by pedologists, who are able to determine nutrient levels and make recommen-dations as to what fertilizers and other additives are needed in order to grow specific crops. They can also make recommenda-tions regarding which crops would grow best in particular soil samples and which residual chemicals are found in the soil. With crop farming becoming such a scientific field, the use of government scientists is widespread. University training in organic chemistry and soils is required for this type of work.

Soil formation is a complex process. Water from a gentle rainstorm filters through the soil and changes the soil chemistry. Plant roots and burrowing animals mix soil materials together. Shifting caused by freezing and thawing as well as mass-wasting action also contribute to the devel-opment of soil.

Soil is also affected by the regolith over which it develops. Mechanical and chemical weathering reduce particle size and change the chemical composition of the C horizon. The action of water, oxidation, and other chemical processes in this "active zone" releases nutrients that plants need. However, the vegetation cannot benefit from these nutrients until they have migrated (through **capillary action**) up in the soil to where

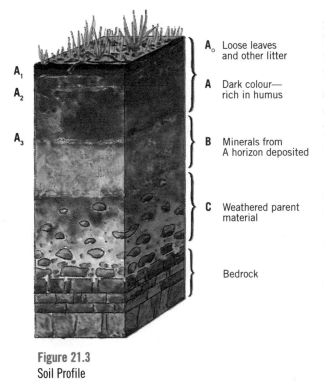

Figure 21.3
Soil Profile

A₀ Loose leaves and other litter

A Dark colour—rich in humus

B Minerals from A horizon deposited

C Weathered parent material

Bedrock

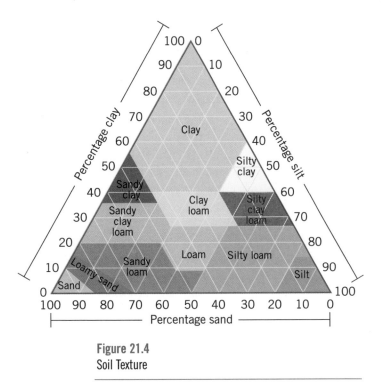

Figure 21.4
Soil Texture

most roots are. At first, simple mosses and lichens cling to the nutrient-poor rock particles. In time, these **pioneer plants** decompose and leave organic matter in the form of humus. As the soil develops, more varied and advanced plants can **colonize** the area. After many hundreds of years, **climax vegetation** may evolve in a fully developed soil horizon.

The characteristics of landforms also influence the soil's characteristics. Soils that develop from soft, easily eroded rocks are often deep and fertile. It is no accident that many of the most productive agricultural regions of the world are located where the bedrock is made up of relatively soft limestone. Rocks such as the granites and shales found in the Canadian Shield and the Western Cordillera are so hard that weathering is slow and soils have shallow horizons. Sometimes the parent material comes from another region. Running water, wave action, glaciers, and other processes carry parent material far from the bedrock where it originated. Soils that form in river valleys are called **alluvial soils**. They usually develop from materials that come from weathered rock high upstream, and develop unique ecosystems within larger ecoregions.

Most soils contain significant amounts of air and water. Up to half of a soil's volume can be made up of these two substances. Air is essential for plants because it provides nitrogen. Nitrogen-fixing bacteria on the roots enable plants to synthesize this vital nutrient. As soil moisture fills up the spaces between the solid ingredients of the soil, the volume of air decreases. The amount of air and water a soil is able to hold is determined by how porous it is. **Permeable** soils, such as sand, have large particles that do not stick together. There is plenty of room for air and water, so water flows straight down through the soil, leaving it dry and fairly useless for plants. Soils that contain clay are porous, but when wet, they create an impermeable structure that holds a lot of water rather than allowing the liquid to flow straight through. These soils are hard for farmers to work in the spring because they may be waterlogged; but, if they have sand or humus cultivated into them, they can be the most fertile soils available for agriculture. Clay soils hold water received in the spring well into the summer, when evapo-transpiration is at its greatest in many continental climates.

The best agricultural soils have a combination of particle sizes. Loam is made up of approximately one-third sand, one-third clay, and one-third silt (which has a particle size in between that of clay and sand). The clay particles hold the moisture needed for plant growth, while the sand and silt facilitate drainage and aeration.

Temperature, precipitation, and the rate of evaporation all influence soil development. If the rate of precipitation exceeds the rate of evaporation, soluble nutrients are leached out of the upper layers of the soil. **Alkaline** elements such as silica, magnesium, calcium, sodium, and potassium are washed out of the soil and deposited in a hard layer some distance down in the C horizon. Soils in the Tropics are usually red because most minerals have been leached out, leaving behind iron oxide as the dominant substance.

In areas where the rate of precipitation is less than that of evaporation, **translocation** occurs. The movement of water in the soil is upwards instead of downwards, so this process is the opposite of leaching. Minerals that are dissolved in the water are carried to the surface of the soil rather than being washed out of it. The minerals form deposits when the moisture reaches the surface and evaporates. **Salt pans** or **alkaline flats** are common features in deserts where rainfall is low and evapo-transpiration rates are high.

In Southern Ontario and other regions with continental climates, both leaching and translocation operate, depending on the **water balance**. "Water balance" is a term used to describe the relationship between precipitation and evapo-transpiration. In continental climate zones, soil is leached in the spring as snow melts and frost leaves the ground. Surface water washes minerals lower in soil horizons. In late summer, the rate of evaporation exceeds precipitation, and translocation occurs as soil moisture carries nutrients up to the surface. It is no wonder that some of the world's best farmland is found in this climate zone, where there is adequate rainfall and leaching is compensated for by seasonal translocation.

Temperature affects soil development in two ways. Chemical and bacterial activity are greatest

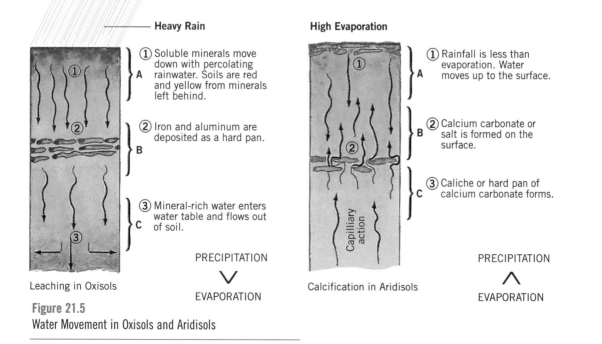

Heavy Rain

① Soluble minerals move down with percolating rainwater. Soils are red and yellow from minerals left behind. **A**

② Iron and aluminum are deposited as a hard pan. **B**

③ Mineral-rich water enters water table and flows out of soil. **C**

Leaching in Oxisols

PRECIPITATION
∨
EVAPORATION

High Evaporation

① Rainfall is less than evaporation. Water moves up to the surface. **A**

② Calcium carbonate or salt is formed on the surface. **B**

③ Caliche or hard pan of calcium carbonate forms. **C**

Capilliary action

Calcification in Aridisols

PRECIPITATION
∧
EVAPORATION

Figure 21.5
Water Movement in Oxisols and Aridisols

when it is hot. These activities decrease as the temperature drops, until they cease altogether when the soil is frozen. Therefore, in hot climates, parent material is chemically altered so rapidly that there is practically no C horizon. Bacterial activity is also so great that forest litter is consumed almost immediately, so there is virtually no litter or humus in the Tropics. As a result, tropical soils are composed of red oxide clays with little horizon development.

In cooler climates, parent material is converted to soil so slowly that temperate soil horizons often have thick C horizons containing rocks of varying shapes and sizes. In addition, organic matter takes longer to decompose into humus and become part of the soil because bacterial action is slower. The lack of chemical action and the virtual absence of bacteria result in little horizon development. The lack of vegetation means that there is little humus and the A horizon is poorly developed. However, mechanical weathering such as frost action causes the bedrock to break into jagged rocks of varying

shapes and sizes. Without warm temperatures, with little vegetation, and with moisture frozen for most of the year, polar soils are the least developed of all. Parent material is often exposed at the surface.

Temperate climate zones are located between the Tropics, where chemical weathering is dominant, and polar regions, where mechanical weathering predominates. As a result, soils that form in temperate climate regions have three well-defined horizons: a thick A horizon containing lots of humus, the transitional B horizon, and a C horizon containing parent material awaiting chemical decomposition by weathering agents.

Soil Classification

Russian soil scientist V.V. Dukuchaev provided an early soil classification system in the late 1800s. In recent years, the American Soil Conservation Service has developed a classification system based on detailed chemical analyses from extensive field studies. Fig. 21.7 details soil regions under the Soil Conservation Service system.

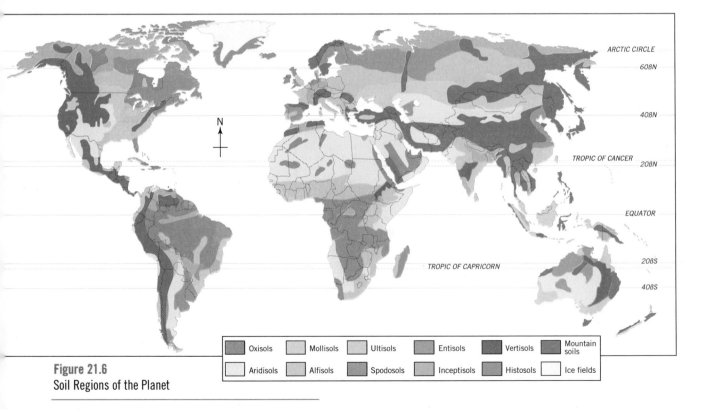

Oxisols	Mollisols	Ultisols
Aridisols	Alfisols	Spodosols

Entisols	Vertisols	Mountain soils
Inceptisols	Histosols	Ice fields

Figure 21.6
Soil Regions of the Planet

Order	Derivation of Prefix	World Land Area [%]	Description
Oxisols	Oxide (compound of oxygen)	9.2%	• red, yellow, and yellow-brown A horizon • heavily leached with iron/aluminum accumulations in B horizon • low mineral and humus content, but soaked with water • thin A horizon, but deep C horizon—ancient soils
Aridisols	Arid (dry)	19.2%	• the A horizon is thin—little humus due to lack of vegetation • salt and calcium concentrations on surface and in B horizon • movement of moisture is toward surface • parent material is coarse-grained sands and large particles
Mollisols	Mollis (soft)	9.0%	• black or dark brown A horizon • deep and fertile with much humus from accumulations of grass • well-structured horizons—soft and easily ploughed
Vertisols	Inverted	2.1%	• clays expand more than 30 per cent in rainy season • black and grey-brown A horizon—fertile but heavy with clay • huge cracks develop in dry season and humus falls through to B horizon, so the soil seems inverted
Ultisols	Ultimate	8.5%	• red-yellow and yellow A horizon due to leaching • more fertile than oxisols due to seasonal rainfall • heavy clay in B horizon—tropical forest cover
Alfisols	Alfalfa (hay crop)	14.7%	• grey or grey-brown slightly acid A horizon • moderately leached but fertile due to forest cover • high clay content
Spodosols	Ash wood (latin)	5.4%	• highly leached, acidic A horizon due to needle-leaf litter • sandy parent material—thin soils • low in fertility—ash-grey colour
Inceptisols	Beginning (latin)	15.8%	• weakly developed, early soils • little development of horizons • infertile, little weathering • shallow—found on new land (lava flows)
Entisols	Recent	12.5%	• sandy, porous soils • tidal mud flats, sandy deserts, marshland, alluvium • poor structure, infertile • underdeveloped horizons
Histosols	Tissue (Greek)	0.8%	• muck soils with heavy humus and clay • no horizons
Rocky Out-crops and Other Surfaces		2.8%	

Figure 21.7
Soil Taxonomy

Natural Vegetation

If you look out the window, it is unlikely you will see any *natural* vegetation. What you will likely see is vegetation that people have planted around the school—green lawns, a few trees, some shrubs, and maybe some flowers. The term "natural vegetation" refers to plant life that would grow in a region without any human interference.

Climate determines, in no small way, the type of natural vegetation that a region can support. Plants found on different continents often evolve with similar characteristics because they develop under similar climate conditions. For example, towering evergreens grow along the wet temperate coastlines of British Columbia. In New Zealand, similar conditions have resulted in the kauri pine, a tree noted for its immense size.

The close relationship between climate and natural vegetation is based on the things plants need in order to grow. The atmosphere provides air, sunlight, and heat, and the hydrosphere provides water. This is why the climate regions map and the natural vegetation map on pages 359–370 look so much alike. Air is abundant in virtually every ecosystem, but the availability of water does vary from climate to climate. Those plants that do not require large amounts of water

thrive in desert regions. They often grow well in more humid regions also, but other varieties with higher water needs are stronger and choke out the less dominant **xerophytic** plants.

The amount of radiant energy also varies from place to place. Sunlight is essential for photosynthesis. A negative correlation exists between the amount of direct sunlight that a place receives and its total precipitation. Places with heavy rainfall are gloomy because clouds block the sun. Plants that grow in these wet climates evolved to compensate for the lack of sunlight by having bigger leaves and developing ways of climbing up other plants to reach what sunlight there is. Most seedlings that start out under the forest canopy never grow to great heights. Instead, they wait until a bigger tree falls, giving them the opportunity to reach up to the daylight.

Heat is unevenly distributed because of variations in latitude, altitude, ocean currents, and moderating water bodies (see page 245). Plants have minimum heat requirements that must be met in order for them to survive. Most trees, for example, must have at least one month with a mean temperature above 10°C.

Other plant requirements—nutrients, support, and space—are all related to the lithosphere. Soil provides such essential nutrients as nitrogen, potassium, and phosphorous. When a plant dies, **decomposers** quickly break the organic matter down into nutrients that other plants use. Soil is also important because it supports root systems and holds up the plant. Thin soils provide poor support for some types of trees, while deep, well-drained soils enable forest giants to climb into the air. While it is easy to overlook space as a plant need because it is so obvious, it is in short supply in some ecosystems. In the rainforest, plants such as lianas and orchids have adapted to the crowded conditions by climbing up other plants or growing in crooks between branches high in the forest canopy.

Each ecoregion fulfils a unique mix of plant needs. The natural vegetation responds by evolving so that it can take full advantage of available resources while compensating for deficiencies in

Figure 21.8
Decomposers Working on a Felled Tree

other areas. Consider the deciduous trees of Southern Ontario. The continental climate of much of southern Canada provides abundant heat and moisture during the summer, but in the winter it is so cold that the water freezes and becomes unavailable. As a consequence, the tree goes into a period of dormancy when moisture is stored in the root system, and the tree appears to be dead because its leaves are shed to reduce transpiration. When the spring sun melts the snow, and water becomes available, moisture in the roots moves by **capillary action** up to the branches, where buds sprout and leaves eventually appear once again.

Change and Natural Vegetation

When you go for a walk in a forest, you can see rapid and gradual changes taking place everywhere. A tree may have been struck by lightning and crashed to the ground. As the tree slowly rots, the soil is enriched by nutrients that were once part of the tree. Mushrooms and other fungi sprout along the tree trunk while termites, milli-pedes, and other decomposers move in. Thus, the death of one plant provides opportunities for many other life forms. In nature, nothing is wasted.

When there is a change in the climate, drainage patterns, or soil fertility, new species move into an area. Increased competition for essential needs may cause individual plants or even whole species to die out. If all the essentials are provided, then the new species will thrive. But if just one essential element is reduced to a point below the minimum requirements of the plant, then the plant will die. Other plants will take over if they can tolerate the change in environmental conditions.

New, non-vegetated surfaces are often created either naturally or by human intervention. When this happens, natural vegetation soon covers the bare land. After a forest fire, hardy plants such as fire bush sprout even while the ground is still smouldering. Over time, the natural vegetation changes. At first, only flowering plants such as golden rod and ragweed spring up. In time, these

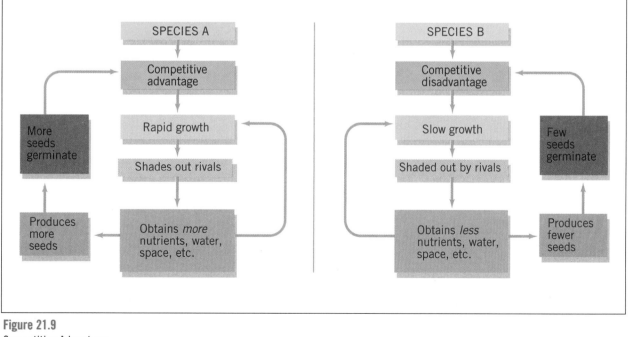

Figure 21.9
Competitive Advantage

pioneer species give way to trees that grow well in open sunlight. Trees such as Manitoba maple and white pine start to colonize the area. Later, there is no room for the pioneer species, and they give way to new plants.

In many of the remaining forests in Southern Ontario, massive white pines tower over the maples, beeches, and red pines. These large pines are remnants of a much earlier time when there was no forest. White pine seedlings will not sprout in the deep gloom of the mature forest, but they will grow if they are carried to open ground where there is ample sunlight. Because of its high commercial value, the white pine is often the tree of choice for clear-cut areas that are being reforested. As the trees start to shade the ground,

Figure 21.10
Purple loosestrife is a pretty flower that is growing in increasing numbers along Canadian riverbanks. The problem is that one plant produces hundreds of thousands of seeds, which the river water then carries downstream. Because the plant is so prolific, it supplants many indigenous **riparian** plants.

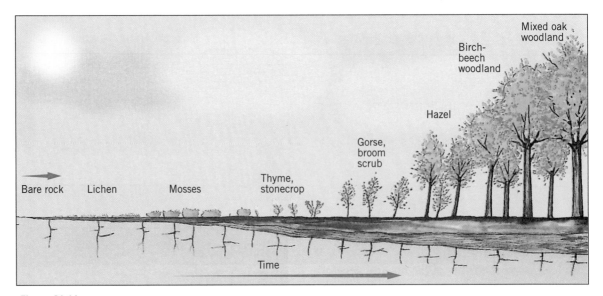

Figure 21.11
How an Ecosystem Develops from Pioneer Species to Climax

the climate close to the ground changes: the amount of sunlight reaching the soil decreases, humidity increases, and soil moisture rises. New shade-loving plants such as trilliums, lady slipper, and mosses grow in the shade. Trees that like moist, cool ground such as red pine, cedar, and birch take over from pioneering tree species. Eventually, the area reaches **climax vegetation**—that is, it becomes fully developed and no new plant species move into the area.

The concept of climax vegetation simplifies chaotic natural processes. Natural systems seldom reach climax because climate, hydrology, and soils are in constant flux. It is, however, a level to which all ecosystems evolve if left undisturbed. The rainforests of the world are excellent examples of climax vegetation. Untouched by recent glaciation (i.e., 12 000 years ago), with stable soil profiles and constant climate norms, these regions (except for the areas harvested by humans) are much the same today as they were a thousand years ago.

Natural Vegetation Regions

Just as there are climate regions, there are corresponding natural vegetation regions. The chart on page 371 summarizes these plant communities.

While a particular vegetation type may dominate a region, there is often considerable local variation. If you go for a walk along the Bruce Trail in Ontario, for example, you will encounter many different vegetation types. Along a river valley, water-loving plants such as willow and hawthorn may be dominant. On a dry upland, grassy meadows may occur; while on northern slopes where the wind is strong, only rugged shrubs may cling to rocky surfaces. It is not possible to show these local ecosystems on a world map.

While it is conceivable that a map showing the types of animals in regions could be developed, these are not found in most atlases. The only classification that **zoogeographers** use is based on continental regions, so it bears no relationship to climate, soils, and natural vegetation. There is no doubt, however, that animals have evolved in response to specific vegetation and climate characteristics. For example, animals of the savanna are significantly different than animals of the Subarctic region. The characteristics of specific animal communities are examined in ecoregion case studies later in this unit.

Figure 21.12
British Columbia belongs to the coniferous-forest natural vegetation region, as does much of Canada. However, the extremely moist climate of parts of this province has produced unique rainforests containing magnificent cedar stands.

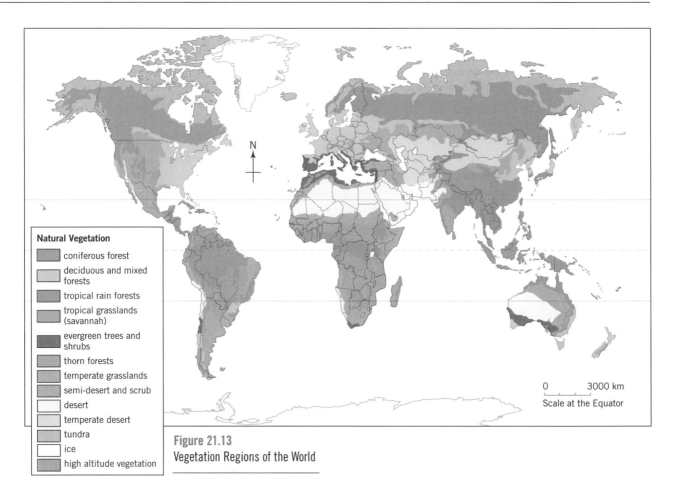

Natural Vegetation

- coniferous forest
- deciduous and mixed forests
- tropical rain forests
- tropical grasslands (savannah)
- evergreen trees and shrubs
- thorn forests
- temperate grasslands
- semi-desert and scrub
- desert
- temperate desert
- tundra
- ice
- high altitude vegetation

0   3000 km
Scale at the Equator

Figure 21.13
Vegetation Regions of the World

Agronomists are consultants employed by the Ministry of Agriculture to assist farmers. They are less specialized than pedologists and work mainly in the field rather than in laboratories. Their advice relates to all forms of agricultural practice: from cultivation to pest control, from animal husbandry to manure management. They also provide advice regarding the use of water resources. It is ideal work for people who are interested in farming, have good people skills, and like to solve problems. Educational requirements are varied but often include biology, pedology, hydrology, rural economics, and geography.

Figure 21.14
An Agronomist Surveying a Field

COMMUNITIES OF NATURAL VEGETATION

Community/ Vegetation Regions	Examples	Location
The Forest Community:		
Coniferous forest	Pine, cedar, fir, larch	Northern Canada and Eurasia
Deciduous forest	Oak, maple, linden	Southern US, western coastal Europe, southern coastal Brazil
Mixed forest	Both coniferous and deciduous – maple, ash, spruce, pine	Southern Ontario and Quebec, the Maritimes and New England, south central Europe, and China
Tropical and subtropical dry forest	Acacia, eucalyptus, baobab	Venezuela, India, and Indo-China
Tropical rainforest	Teak, mahogany, rosewood	Amazon, Central America, the Congo, Indonesia, Indo-China
The Grassland Community:		
Temperate grassland	Red oat grass and other short grasses	American Great Plains, south central Russia
Tropical grassland	Elephant grass, other tall grasses, acacia trees	Central Africa between the rainforest and desert, western Australia, south central, northwest India-Pakistan, Brazil, Uruguay, and Argentina
The Scrub Community:		
Semi-desert and scrub	Maquis, lemon, cork, grape, dry grasses, spinifex and thorn brush	Mediterranean Europe and North Africa, central California, southern Australia, and southwestern US
Marsh and swamp	swamp grasses, bulrushes, cypress, mangroves	Flooded areas
The Desert Community:		
Hot desert	Cactus, Joshua tree, date palm	North Africa, Saudi peninsula, central Australia
Temperate desert	Cactus, short grasses, creosote bush	South central Asia
High altitude vegetation	mosses, sedges, stunted willows, lichen	Mountain summits
Tundra	Mosses, sedges, lichen, stunted willows and larches	Northern Canada, Alaska and Eurasia, mountainous regions

Figure 21.15
Vegetation Communities

Ecoregions

Ecoregions are natural regions defined by climate, soils, natural vegetation, and surface features. Because the term "region" is an amalgam of different classification systems, it is a broad generalization. However, although there is wide variety within ecoregions, the classification of these areas allows for some understanding of how each ecoregion functions as a single living entity.

The environment around us influences everything we do. For example, people in colder climates must insulate and heat their homes and wear warm clothing, while people in warmer climates may have developed sleeping and working patterns that accommodate the extreme heat at midday. However, humans are unlike most animal species in that they change the natural environment to suit themselves. Instead of relying on wild plants and animals for food, people have developed **hybrid** plants and animals that are produced on farms. We also modify the environment when we extract metals to make into tools, build vast cities, remove natural vegetation, and modify the soil so as to grow crops.

Often, the changes we make to the environment and the resources we harvest improve our lifestyles. Sometimes, however, these changes are

ECOREGIONS OF THE WORLD

Ecoregion*	Location
Arctic	Near the poles
Subarctic	Northern Canada, Russia, Alaska, and Scandinavia
Moderate Continental	Great Lakes Region, eastern Europe, northeastern Russia
Warm Continental	Just south of Moderate Continental
Marine	Western Europe, west coast of Chile, east and west coasts of Canada, Oregon and Washington states
Humid Subtropical	Southeastern US, southern Brazil, China, eastern coastal Australia
Prairie	Southern Alberta and Saskatchewan, south central US, eastern Australia, Rio de la Plata estuary
Mediterranean	Mediterranean Europe, north Africa and the Levant, California, southern tip of Africa, southwest Australia, and central coastal Chile
Tropical Steppe	Surrounding tropical deserts
Temperate Steppe	Great Plains states, central interior Asia
Tropical Desert	North Africa, Saudi peninsula, central Australia, west central South America, southwest Africa
Temperate Desert	Central Asia, Patagonia, western interior US
Savanna	Surrounding tropical rainforests in Africa, South America, and southeast Asia
Tropical Rainforest	Equatorial Africa, South America, and southeast Asia

Figure 21.16

*The names of each ecoregion are based mainly on climate; however, they reflect more than just climate characteristics. Create a world ecoregions map using the information in this chart to guide you.

so disruptive that we can destroy entire ecosystems. For example, when farmers over-fertilize and over-irrigate their fields, these processes can result in contaminated water supplies. Whenever we change natural systems to meet our needs, we must be careful that we do not cause irreparable damage to the environment, and, indirectly, to the quality of our lives. Human overpopulation and unsustainable resource development are the root causes of most ecological problems. We need to understand the patterns and processes of physical geography so that we can avoid making mistakes that could destroy the ecosystems that plants and animals need in order to survive.

ACTIVITIES

UNDERSTANDING CONCEPTS

1. a) Describe the Gaia hypothesis.
   b) Do some research and explain the major criticisms of the Gaia hypothesis.
   c) Analyse the arguments you have researched and decide whether or not you accept the hypothesis, or if there is not enough information available for you to decide.
2. a) Define the term "region."
   b) Explain how climate regions are created.
3. Describe how, within natural systems, change occurs between
   a) climate and soils,
   b) vegetation and soils,
   c) soils and vegetation,
   d) vegetation and climate,
   e) climate and vegetation.
4. a) Explain how soils are the result of long-term processes acting upon parent material. Consider the effects of water, air, soil, flora and fauna, temperature, evaporation, and tectonic processes acting on soils.
   b) Analyse the importance of soil texture to soil fertility.
5. a) Explain how the atmosphere and hydrosphere supply plant needs.
   b) Explain how the lithosphere and soils supply plant needs.
   c) Explain what climax vegetation is and why it is seldom found in natural systems.
   d) Study Fig. 21.10. Explain how competitive advantage and competitive disadvantage affect ecosystems.
6. a) Define the terms "ecoregion" and "ecosystem."
   b) What components of natural systems are included in ecoregions?
   c) How are the classifications of ecoregions gross over-generalizations?
   d) Despite these generalizations, why is such classification a useful exercise?

DEVELOPING AND PRACTISING SKILLS

7. a)   Prepare a comparison organizer like the one shown below. Show how well plant needs are met in each of the natural vegetation zones by indicating G for good and P for poor in each category. The Tropical Rainforest category has been completed for you.

Vegetation Zone	Air	Water	Light	Heat	Nutrients	Support	Space
Tropical Rainforest	G	G	P	G	P	G	P
Tropical and Subtropical Dry Forest							
Mixed Forest							
Coniferous Forest							
Tropical Grassland							
Temperate Grassland							
Schlerophyll Scrub							
Hot Desert							
Temperate Desert							
Alpine							
Tundra							

Legend   G = Good   P = Poor

b)   Based on the information in the organizer, rank the Natural Vegetation Zones in order from "Best Provider of Plant Needs" to "Worst Provider of Plant Needs."

c)   Using the Natural Vegetation map found on page 370 and old geographic magazines, make a collage illustrating vegetation patterns for a continent of your choice. To do this, make a large cut-out map of the continent and identify the different natural vegetation zones. Select representative pictures for each zone and glue them on the appropriate places on your map.

8.   Study the climate, natural vegetation, and soils maps, and the ecoregions chart on pages 359, 364, 370, 372.

a)   Prepare an organizer showing the types of climates found in each ecoregion.

b)   Expand the organizer to include soils found in each ecoregion.

c)   Further expand the organizer to include natural vegetation found in each ecoregion.

9. a) Draw a cross section at 30°E longitude, marking the latitude in 15° intervals. Estimate the profile of the land along this meridian using a relief map. Use symbols to illustrate the different ecoregions.

    b) Determine the limits in latitude for each ecoregion.

    c) Relate the patterns you found for Africa and Europe to the Americas. Account for differences between these continents.

10. Study the Soil Texture Graph (Fig. 21.5 on page 362).

    a) Determine the approximate breakdown of clay, silt, and sand for loam, sandy clay, and silty loam.

    b) How is soil texture important to farmers and gardeners?

GIS Assignment on Soils and Agriculture

11. You are a consultant for the agricultural industry. Use ArcView to prepare a GIS map to determine areas where farming is successful in Canada. Also determine the type of agriculture best suited to specific soil types. (For detailed instructions, download the exercise from the ESRI web page — http://www.esri.canada.com/k-12/)

    a) Prepare a **layer** showing the Canadian provinces, using the ArcCanada CD-Rom (/canada/canprov.shp). Next, load the Land Potential Database (/canada/lpdb.shp) and prepare a layer showing the suitability of land for agriculture.

    b) Which regions of Canada are mapped in detail?

    c) What assumptions can you make about farming in Canada?

    d) Create a dot-density map of census farms in Canada to determine the correlation between soil suitability and farm location. Make canprov.shp **active**. Join the agriculture **attribute file** to the attribute file for canprov.shp. Follow the detailed instructions from the web site.

    e) How important is soil suitability for farm location?

    f) What other factors affect agricultural output? Can these be mapped?

    g) How would these maps be useful for planners?

    h) Prepare a map showing soils and agriculture, along with a report that includes the answers to the above questions. Include these in a layout that displays the soil layers.

LEARNING THROUGH APPLICATION

12. Find and describe examples in your community of

    a) climax vegetation

    b) pioneer species colonizing "new" land

    c) changes in natural vegetation.

13. a) Find newspaper articles about people modifying ecosystems in your community.

    b) Discuss whether the change is positive or negative.

    c) Display your results on a bulletin board or in a scrapbook.

14. a) What are the climate zone, natural vegetation region, soil zone, and ecoregion where you live?

   b) What variations in your local community deviate from the descriptions of each of the natural regions in a)?

15. Determine the educational requirements, current opportunities, and future prospects for the three careers discussed in this chapter.

16. Conduct a field study of a local ecosystem. Each member of your group should select a different location within the study area. For example, if your site is a river valley, suggested sites might include: marshland that is frequently flooded, part of the flood plain, a forested northern slope, a forested southern slope, or a grassy meadow above the river valley.

   a) Map the site.
   - Measure off an area about 10 m by 10 m.
   - Make a grid of 1 m squares using string and stakes driven into the ground. (This may be difficult to do in forested areas.)
   - Draw a map to a scale of 2 cm to 1 m [1:50]. Show the location of major features. Use a legend to help.
   - Use GPS to geo-reference significant plants such as large trees.

   b) Study the plants and animals.
   - Take an inventory of every plant and animal in each grid and indicate its location on your grid map.
   - Use a field manual to identify each life form.
   - Include evidence of creatures no longer on the scene. Evidence may be in the form of **scat**, footprints, nests, spider webs, and so on.
   - Find evidence of food webs in your study plot.
   - Describe the litter of dead material directly on the ground.
   - What decomposers are noticeable?
   - Take photographs or video of significant features (use a digital camera or video-camcorder if possible).

   c) Study the soil.
   - Carefully clear away some of the natural vegetation and litter. Dig a hole or pit 50 to 100 cm deep.
   - Look for layers in the soil. Make a scale drawing to show where each layer occurs in the profile. Colour each layer appropriately, trying to copy the differing textures of the soil. Indicate the locations of pebbles and larger stones.
   - Alongside your soil profile, write a description of each soil layer. Include the following details:
      i) *Particle size or texture (sand, clay, or silt)*: For large particles, use a ruler and sieve to measure exact size.
      ii) *Water content*: When you are back in the classroom, weigh some of the material you excavated. Bake the soil to remove as much moisture content as possible. Weigh the soil again and estimate the percentage of the soil that was water.
      iii)*Humus content and colour*: Describe the litter on the surface and the humus in the A horizon. Estimate the amount of the A horizon that you think is organic material.

iv) *Parent material*: Use a field guide to determine the type of rock the regolith is derived from.

v) *Soil Flora and Fauna*: record the number and type of bugs and insects in the soil (i.e., beetles, worms, ants, etc.)

- Use clues such as natural vegetation to determine the fertility of the soil. Make recommendations of inputs that would improve soil fertility.
- Fill in the hole and restore the natural vegetation as best you can to its original state.
- Account for differences in natural vegetation and soil for each of the study sites in your group.

d) Report your findings.
- Prepare an organizer like the one below, summarizing the characteristics of plants and animals in your study site. The first row has been done as an example.

Number	Species	Description	Notes
16	Maple trees	1 with a 32 cm diameter trunk 4 with 10 – 30 cm diameter trunks 5 with trunks 5 – 10 cm diameter trunks 6 seedlings with trunks less than 5 cm	Evidence of disease in older tree Fungus growing in holes in bark Young trees have tent caterpillars in branches

- Prepare a flow chart showing interactions among elements of your ecosystem.
- Prepare a report summarizing your findings. Use photographs to illustrate ideas. If using digital technology, embed photos within your written work.
- If available, use computer presentation software to prepare a presentation or poster of your study site. Consider embedding GIS map layers, digital photographs, video clips, and sound effects captured with a digital video camera.
- Back in the classroom, compare your results with students working in other study plots.

Chapter 22

THE TROPICAL RAINFOREST ECOREGION: LIVING IN PARADISE

FOCUS QUESTIONS

1. How do convection currents distribute energy and moisture through tropical rainforest ecosystems?

2. What are the characteristics of the tropical rainforest ecoregion and what are the interrelationships that exist among climate, plants, soils, and animals?

3. How do human activities, such as resource development, impact on natural systems in tropical ecosystems?

Key Terms

biodiversity

ALTM Sensor

ecotourism

diurnal temperature range

Tropical ecosystems are among the most fascinating and diverse on Earth. While all tropical climates have warm to hot temperatures all year, there is considerable variation among them based on rainfall patterns and local landform features. These climatic differences are reflected in the plants and animals that inhabit tropical regions. They also affect how people respond to environmental challenges.

The tropical rainforest climate is hot and wet all year, but local variations occur because of drainage and elevation. Some areas are poorly drained, swampy regions, and others are highland jungles. At the other extreme are the tropical deserts. The picture of such regions that most of us have in our mind's eye is of unending sand dunes, but deserts can also be rocky pavements and upland plateaus. These vast regions may look at first glance like wastelands, but they are actually very much alive, with a huge variety of specially adapted plants and animals. The tremendous diversity of life here depends on local features.

The Tropical Rainforest Climate

The tropical rainforest climate is typically characterized as having mean monthly temperatures above 18°C every month of the year in addition to precipitation totals of at least 60 mm every month, on average. However, it is difficult to find climate stations that have these exact characteristics, and often the amount of rainfall slips below 60 mm during one or two months. This is because the climate data is a broad generalization, which is not often supported by on-site studies of the region. However, one look at the vegetation of such a place will tell you that it is tropical rainforest: the dense jungle forms a canopy over the land that makes it unmistakable.

The high temperatures occur because of the region's location on or near the equator. Because the sun's rays shine more directly on the equator than anywhere else, solar energy is more concentrated there, making temperatures hot most of the time. The high temperatures result in considerable instability in the atmosphere. Convectional currents develop most afternoons and, as a result, heavy rainfall occurs at that time almost every day as a result. Because the trade winds blow from the east and warm ocean currents run along the east coast, the hot, wet climate zone often extends as much as 20° latitude north and south of the equator. Known as the tropical rainforest **littoral**, it is exemplified along the southern coast of Brazil, where places such as Rio de Janeiro have a tropical rainforest climate even though they are a considerable distance from the equator. Tropical rainforest ecosystems are also found on the east coast of Central America, some Caribbean islands, and in southern Mexico, as far north as 20°N latitude.

Figure 22.1
The lush canopy of leaves makes the tropical rainforest unmistakable.

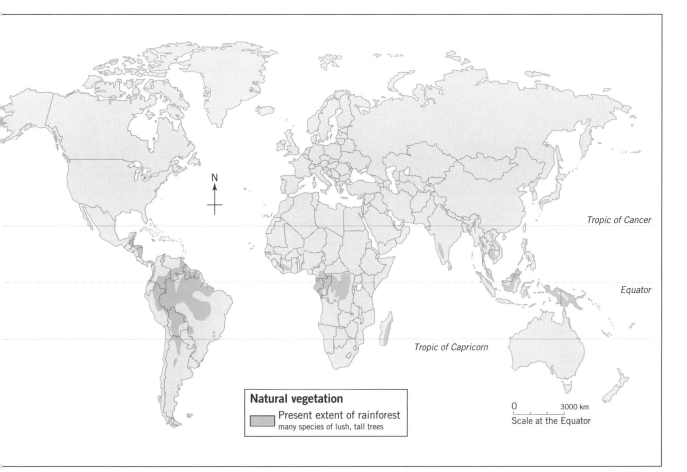

Figure 22.2
Map Showing the Location of the Tropical Rainforest Ecoregion

Figure 22.3
Tropical Mangrove Swamp in Brazil

Figure 22.4
Highland Jungles of New Guinea

Figure 22.5
Coastal Littoral Zones in the Philippines

ecosystem in low-lying regions from Mozambique to Kenya. The reason they do not show up on the map is that the land rises abruptly from the east coast. The higher elevations result in the lower temperatures and seasonal rainfall that are characteristic of the savanna region. Rainforest ecosystems are also found in Indonesia and the Philippines. These island nations have developed incredible genetic diversity within their forests because they are cut off from the mainland and influenced by coastal waters. While animals on the mainland and on different islands may have had the same ancestors with the same genetic structure, years of isolation result in differences that manifest themselves in different physical characteristics from island to island.

Although tropical rainforest climates are hot all year, daily maximums are cooler than the incredibly high temperatures found in the hot desert climate. The heavy cloud cover of this

On the west coast, cold ocean currents limit the region's poleward boundary. Africa does have a significant west coastal rainforest zone, however. The shape of the coastline has resulted in the region being extended further north than would normally be the case. On the east coast of Africa, a rainforest littoral shows up along the coast of Madagascar. The mainland seems to be devoid of rainforest, but there are pockets of the region acts as insulation and reduces the amount of solar radiation reaching the lower atmosphere. Therefore, daytime temperatures are lower than you would think. In addition, the processes of photosynthesis and evapo-transpiration use up much of the solar energy that does reach the forest canopy, which results in less solar energy being available for heating the air than if the region were devoid of plants. Interestingly, areas of the rainforest that have been cleared are often significantly hotter because of the lack of protective vegetation. Significantly different ecosystems develop where the jungle has been cleared because of this temperature difference.

Even though the rainforest region may not be the hottest of the tropical climates, the temperature feels hotter than it is because of the extremely high moisture content of the air. It is so hot and sticky that the heat is almost unbearable until the daily thunderstorm lowers humidity and cools the air slightly. The **diurnal temperature range**, or difference between the daily maximum and daily minimum, is slight because the humidity and cloud cover keep the heat from escaping even during the nighttime.

Strong convection currents cause heavy precipitation all year. The equatorial low is a feature of the region. As the hot, moist air rises, water vapour condenses and violent thunderstorms result, usually in late afternoon. Moving away from the equator, however, a slightly drier climate prevails. Some months receive much less rain than others. Consider Monrovia, Liberia, for example. Located at 6°N, it has two months when the rainfall drops significantly (see Figure 22.6). Entebbe, Uganda, which is right on the

	J	F	M	A	M	J	J	A	S	O	N	D
Georgetown, Guyana												
T [°C]	26	26	26	27	27	27	27	27	28	28	27	26
P [mm]	203	114	175	140	280	302	254	175	81	76	155	182
Entebbe, Uganda												
T [°C]	22	22	22	22	22	21	21	21	21	22	22	22
P [mm]	66	91	160	257	244	122	76	74	75	94	132	116
Monrovia, Liberia												
T [°C]	26	26	27	27	26	25	24	24	24	25	26	26
P [mm]	31	56	97	216	516	973	996	373	744	772	236	129
Singapore, Singapore												
T [°C]	26	27	27	27	28	27	27	27	27	27	27	27
P [mm]	252	173	193	188	173	173	170	196	178	208	254	257
Belize, Belize												
T [°C]	23	24	25	27	27	27	27	27	27	26	24	23
P [mm]	137	61	38	56	109	196	163	170	244	305	226	185

Figure 22.6
Climate Statistics for Selected Tropical Locations

equator, has much less monthly variation in rainfall. The reason for this has to do with seasonal changes in wind patterns. Moving away from the equator, rainfall patterns become increasingly seasonal until monthly totals drop well below 60 mm. At this point, the region is becoming more like a savanna. The transition between rainforest and savanna is a gradual change that takes place over hundreds of kilometres, the shift occurring as natural vegetation reflects long-term changes in monthly mean precipitation totals.

Tropical rainforests are exotic and beautiful, but the high temperatures, heavy rain, and constant humidity can make living conditions uncomfortable. However, many coastal areas in this region are densely populated. The strong trade winds increase evaporation. The energy expended evaporating moisture reduces the heat of surfaces, thus making the hot climate more bearable.

The Tropical Rainforest Ecozone

Tropical rainforests have the greatest diversity of plants and animals of all terrestrial ecosystems. Researchers did an inventory of plants and animals living in the rainforest of Ecuador and found 473 different tree species in just one hectare! In Canada, there are often fewer than 10 different species in a forest a hundred times larger. A study of a single tree in Peru yielded 43 distinctly different ant varieties. This is roughly equivalent to the total number of ant species in all of Britain. Biologists have barely scratched the surface of the **biodiversity** of these natural genetic laboratories. Less than 1 per cent of all the plants and animals in the rainforests of the world have been studied. In addition to the diversity of the region as a whole, each hectare of the rainforest is different from any other area in the forest. Some species of plants and animals found in a given location are found nowhere else.

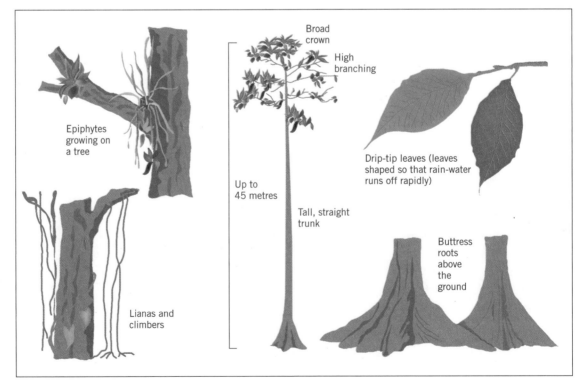

Figure 22.7
Vegetation of the Equatorial Rainforest

Strong **symbiotic** relationships develop between the plants and animals in these regions. Plants depend on animals and animals rely on plants so much that the disappearance of one interdependent species will result in the elimination of the other. Animals evolve to take advantage of very specific vegetation characteristics such that one animal may have a **niche** no other animal fills. For example, an insect may feed off a fungus that grows only on a particular type of tree. If the tree stops growing or if the fungus is eradicated, the fungus-feeding insect becomes extinct. On the other hand, if the insect dies out, the tree may become extinct because it will have no protection against the fungus. Even the fungus benefits from the insect indirectly since, if the insect dies out and the tree is killed off by the fungus, the fungus will also become extinct because there will no longer be any host trees available for it. These complex symbiotic relationships are very common in rainforest ecosystems.

Not only is there a broad diversity of species from place to place within the rainforest, but there are also considerable variations in plants and animals inhabiting layers at different heights above the forest floor. In this way, the tropical rainforest ecosystem is very similar to that of coral reefs, in which the biodiversity present in a reef-layer depends on its proximity to the water's surface.

While the rainforest has heat and moisture in abundance, the essential plant needs that are in short supply are sunlight, space, and nutrients. Plants overcome the lack of sunlight and the cramped quarters by growing upward, toward the top of the forest canopy. Giant trees called **emergents** grow higher than all other plants in order to reach the sun. Rainforest soils are often marshy and water-logged, so these giant trees have developed buttress roots that support the mass of the tree by spreading the trunk and root system over a large area of ground.

Vines and lianas use other plants for support in their search for sunlight. They lack the trunk that larger plants have, so they compensate by

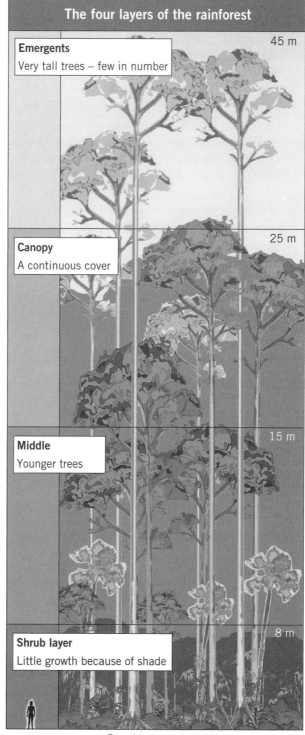

The four layers of the rainforest

Emergents
Very tall trees – few in number

45 m

Canopy
A continuous cover

25 m

Middle
Younger trees

15 m

Shrub layer
Little growth because of shade

8 m

Broad butress roots

Figure 22.8
The Layers of Vegetation in the rainforest

wrapping themselves around the host plant and growing up the giant trees to reach the sunlight. **Epiphytes** such as orchids reach sunlight by growing where tree branches join the main trunk high above the forest floor. **Parasitic** plants are those that sap the nutrients from the host plant while receiving life-giving light. While all vines, epiphytes, and parasites may destroy the host plant, there are plenty of other potential hosts in the form of seedlings, waiting in a semi-dormant stage for enough light to enable them to grow up through the gloom. Importantly, symbiotic relationships prevent one species from dominating others, resulting in a kind of balance that has evolved over thousands of years. When people introduce **exotic** species, the delicate balance can be lost and ecological disaster can result.

Below the canopy, types of vegetation such as the banana plant have adapted by having huge leaves that make the most of whatever sunlight gets to the jungle floor. Because the leaves are so big, they allow the plants to transpire larger quantities of water than the smaller leaves of trees in drier zones. Moisture is needed to bring nutrients from the soil to the plant cells. On the ground, decomposers such as fungus, as well as mosses and ferns, grow wherever there is space. Contrary to what many people may believe, the floor of the rainforest is largely free of plant material. The lack of sunlight is such a limiting factor that dense underbrush exists only around clearings and along riverbanks, where sunlight can penetrate the gloom. Tropical plants are uniquely suited to this diverse ecosystem, whatever layer of the rainforest they inhabit.

Many species of animals have adapted to the rainforest by evolving to live in trees. Because they are **arboreal**, such animals have many physical features to facilitate living in this habitat. While most birds and insects have developed limbs that enable them to fly, mammals, reptiles, and amphibians have developed specially designed climbing appendages. Monkeys have an opposing thumb, which enables them to grasp branches. Long, flexible arms and legs further help them perform their acrobatic feats high in

the canopy. Apes are larger primates, and while they may spend some time on the ground, many large apes do live in trees as well. Like monkeys, apes have opposing thumbs and flexible limbs. The orangutans of Borneo have arms and legs that are structured almost identically, an evolutionary development that enables them to swing from their legs as easily as they swing from their arms. Monkeys and apes are usually vegetarian, or omnivorous but there are carnivorous mammals that also live in the trees.

Big cats such as lions and cheetahs are more at home on land than in trees and are found in the open savanna that surrounds the rainforest. Rainforest cats are often smaller and adapted for climbing trees. Tigers found in the rainforests of India and Southeast Asia are the largest predators in this ecozone. They are equally at home in trees and on the ground; but because of their size, they tend to remain in the lower layers of the forest. In other rainforest regions, panthers, leopards, and jaguars all have similar adaptations including long, flexible limbs for climbing; sharp, retractable claws; and flexible toes that help them to hold on. Long tails provide balance as they stealthily glide through the lower branches in search of monkeys and other small animals. Their coats are often camouflaged in the forest gloom, so their quarry does not see them coming. With slow precision, they stalk their prey in the shadows, but in a flash they can spring and catch an unsuspecting animal in their powerful jaws or flesh-ripping claws.

The adaptations made by rainforest creatures in order to thrive in this environment are fascinating. For example, tree frogs have specially adapted suction cups on their feet to help them climb trees, and chameleons have long toes that help them cling to tree surfaces. Bats are mammals that have developed the ability to fly. While not confined to the rainforest, there are many different varieties of bats in this ecozone. One of the most interesting is the giant fruit bat. These African natives are so big that they are sometimes called flying foxes. They look fearsome, but are vegetarian and thus quite innocuous.

Figure 22.9
Fruit Bat

Figure 22.10
Lemur

Figure 22.11
Chameleon

often shown in the media eating a wayward animal in a matter of seconds. Other ferocious water animals include caiman, crocodiles, and alligators. These reptiles are amazingly camouflaged to look like harmless floating logs, but they can move with lightning speed and have powerful jaws and flesh-ripping teeth. Their muscular tails propel them rapidly through the swamps where they seize their prey below the waterline. With nostrils and eyes on the tops of the their heads, they can lie almost completely submerged until opportunity provides the next meal.

The hippopotamus is considered one of the most dangerous animals that people can encounter in African lakes and river systems. With incredible speed, this "river horse" can easily capsize a large boat. Its powerful jaws can destroy a canoe in one crunch! While the hippo is vegetarian, it also has a reputation for being bad-tempered and is to be avoided at any cost.

The variety of creatures and the number of predators in this ecozone means that the smaller, weaker animals must have ways of protecting themselves. **Camouflage** is one of the defense mechanisms they use. By looking just like the surrounding plants, they blend in and are not detected by their predators. This is particularly true of insects and reptiles that cling to the tree branches or roam the forest floor.

The rainforest's trees are not the only places where large numbers of animals live. There are also many aquatic animals living in the swamps, bogs, and rivers of this ecoregion.   Perhaps the most legendary for its ferocity is the piranha. These little fish with their voracious appetites are

Soils of the Tropical Rainforest Ecoregion

The vegetation of the rainforest is so lush and green that people may easily come to the conclusion that the soil there must be very fertile. In fact, the oppostie is true. Water-soluble nutrients are leached from the A horizon, and it is only at the active layer in the C horizon—where the agents of weathering are in contact with the bedrock—that there are nutrients available.

Plants have adapted by growing incredibly long root systems that may travel as deep as 5 m to reach the nutrients released from the decomposing bedrock. Many rainforest plants have disproportionately large fruit that encases a substantial seed. When the seed sprouts, the fruit provides the energy needed to send a root many metres down to the active layer.

Saving Bolivia's Rainforest Reserve

Hunted almost to extinction for their beautiful coats, jungle cats are making a slow comeback in protected game reserves. However, the pressures against the establishment of these reserves are considerable. As with other rainforest animals, the main problems jungle cats experience are poaching and the destruction of habitat. It is difficult to prevent poaching in protected areas, since many of the people who live in these regions have limited economic opportunities and an ocelot pelt or a tiger skin is worth the equivalent of several years' income. Furthermore, as the rainforest is cleared for farms, the indigenous animals are displaced from their natural environment. They continue to hunt in their old haunts, but if their quarry becomes domesticated goats, cattle, or—even worse—small children, then residents have an even greater incentive to hunt these "dangerous" predators.

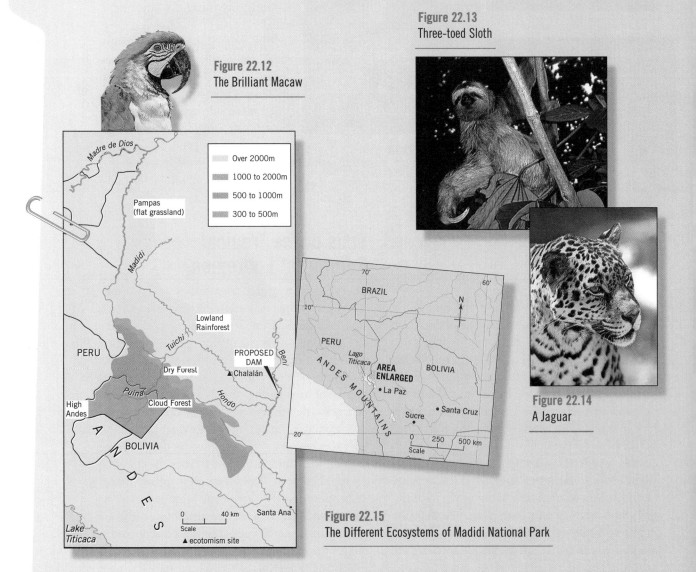

Figure 22.12
The Brilliant Macaw

Figure 22.13
Three-toed Sloth

Figure 22.14
A Jaguar

Map legend:
- Over 2000m
- 1000 to 2000m
- 500 to 1000m
- 300 to 500m

Pampas (flat grassland)

Lowland Rainforest

PROPOSED DAM
▲ Chalalán

Dry Forest

Cloud Forest

Puina

High Andes

PERU

BOLIVIA

Madre de Dios

Madidi

Tuichi

Hondo

Beni

Lake Titicaca

Santa Ana

0   40 km
Scale
▲ ecotomism site

BRAZIL

N

PERU

Lago Titicaca

AREA ENLARGED

BOLIVIA

• La Paz

Sucre

• Santa Cruz

ANDES MOUNTAINS

0   250   500 km
Scale

70°   60°

10°

20°

Figure 22.15
The Different Ecosystems of Madidi National Park

Organizations such as the World Wildlife Fund, government agencies, biologists, ecologists, and concerned citizens are working hard to establish wildlife sanctuaries throughout the Tropics to protect rainforest ecosystems from human intrusion. One such park is Madidi National Park, a 2 million-hectare wilderness area about the size of Vancouver Island, B.C. It is located in the South American country of Bolivia and was created by the Bolivian government in 1995.

Since opening, the park has faced such intense pressures that it may not survive much longer. Park director Ciro Oliver has an annual budget of under $200 000 (US) to protect the vast region. With two boats and fifteen guards, he is up against poachers, unscrupulous lumbering companies, and those who hunt endangered animals for bushmeat or capture animals and sell them as exotic pets. When his office opened in 1997, nobody was in favour of the park because 90 per cent of the residents lived by cutting down rainforest trees. Forty-eight logging camps were closed down and much of the more blatant poaching ended. However, many problems still exist.

Birds, snakes, monkeys and other animals continue to be captured live for sale as pets in the cities of South America. And in March 2000, an illegal logging camp cut 100 000 board feet of mahogany worth about $50 000 (US). As a result, the forest continues to shrink, and the habitat of big cats and other animals is slowly disappearing.

Nevertheless, some of the residents are hoping to make improvements by developing **ecotourism** in the area. The townspeople of San José de Uchupiamonas, with help from an international conservation group, built Chalalán

Ecolodge. This facility opened in June 1998, and already four other lodges are planned for the more accessible lowland regions of the park. With this type of enterprise, the residents can generate a good income while simultaneously protecting the rainforest that is part of their heritage.

However, despite the action taken by the local people to preserve the region, the future does not look promising for the park. In August 1998, the Bolivian National Congress announced plans to build a gigantic hydroelectric dam at Rurrenabaque. The dam will flood over 1600 km² of rainforest, displacing native peoples, destroying the new tourist lodges, and causing the extinction of untold thousands of species of plants and animals. The government realizes that the forest is important, but so too is the economic prosperity of this impoverished country. Since hydro sales to Brazil can increase national income and employment, the government has chosen to support the economy over the animals of this forest. Despite the protests of international as well as local environmental groups, the project is still in development as this book is being written.

QUESTIONS:

1. Summarize the different development strategies for the rainforests of Bolivia.

2. Assess which strategies are sustainable and which will cause ecological damage.

3. Do you agree with the Bolivian government's decision to go ahead with the proposed dam? Explain your answer.

Oxisols are the predominant soil type in rainforests, although **entisols** and **inceptisols** are also common. Oxisols develop in a tectonically stable region where the parent material has remained the same for hundreds of thousands of years. High temperatures and moisture allow for rapid chemical weathering of the bedrock, with the result that the soil is extremely deep and made up mainly of A horizon. Heavily leached, the red or yellow colour comes from the iron and aluminum oxides that are left behind when water-soluble nutrients are removed. A hardpan layer often develops deep in the soil, where iron and aluminum deposits are concentrated.

Since most rainforests have evolved in lowland regions, limestone parent material is common. The regolith is so weathered that tiny clay particles make up the soils. These waterlogged soils are deep and muddy, but if allowed to dry out, they can be easily cultivated. The constant rainfall makes this almost impossible, however. While the soil can be tilled, the lack of nutrients in the upper horizon is the main problem with farming in the region.

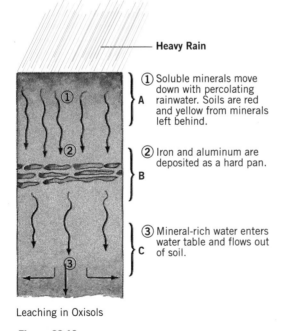

Leaching in Oxisols

Figure 22.16
Tropical Rainforest Soil Horizons

Local variations in soil fertility are caused by differences in drainage and underlying bedrock. Entisols form where rivers have laid down fresh deposits of alluvium. While these soils are often infertile, in some regions they are relatively nutrient-rich compared to the more prevalent oxisol soils. A horizons are poorly developed, especially if seasonal flooding adds new deposits each year. The Amazon River delta is made up of these soils. The region often has a poorly developed forest structure because of constant flooding; however, grassland meadows fringed with trees are common and have been exploited for cattle ranching.

Histosols are also found in swampy areas such as the Okovango Wetlands in southeast Africa. The deep muck soils are very fertile and support a rich diversity of plants and animals. If they are allowed to dry out, they make good farmland. With little horizon development, the soils are mostly made up of decaying organic matter. Ultisols develop in regions on the edge of the rainforest where there is greater seasonal variation in rainfall. These soils are less leached than oxisols but they have the same characteristic red colour and a heavy clay subsoil.

Drainage and rainfall patterns are not the only causes of soil variability in the rainforest. Underlying bedrock also affects soil and plant development. If the bedrock is mainly made up of silicates such as quartzite or sandstone, the soil is usually infertile and plant growth is limited. In these regions, the forest looks unhealthy and lacks the vitality associated with the tropical rainforest ecoregion. The southeastern portion of the Amazon basin is characterized by this kind of soil and vegetation.

Peoples of the Tropical Rainforest Ecoregion

Forest peoples have lived in harmony with nature for thousands of years. Economic systems evolved that were sustainable yet effective. With the invasion of rainforest wilderness areas by external human forces, indigenous peoples have come in contact with people from the outside world. Since this initial period of contact, the indigenous peoples have often been encouraged to change their ways and adopt different lifestyles.

In the past, peoples of the rainforest took only what they needed in order to live from day to day. The extreme climate, tropical diseases such as malaria, and the limited food resources kept Aboriginal populations low. The accumulation of wealth was not a part of the various cultures, so their impact on natural systems was minimal. In fact, they were as much a part of the natural environment as the plants and animals of the region where they lived.

These forest dwellers developed lifestyles that were appropriate for the extreme atmospheric conditions. Heavy clothing is unnecessary because of the heat and humidity, but biting insects are a nuisance. It is no surprise, therefore, that the people often painted their skin with organic dyes that acted as insect repellents, and wore very little clothing. Exposed to the air, the body can freely perspire, thus reducing body temperature. Housing is made from readily available materials including leaves, sticks, and mud. Open walls allow for ventilation and steep-sloping roofs shed the heavy rainfall. Many dwellings are built on stilts to reduce the impact of flooding. Even though indigenous peoples are separated by thousands of kilometres and have never been in contact, the lifestyles of many groups are similar.

Slash and burn agriculture (Fig. 22.18) is the traditional economic activity in rainforest regions. Foods such as corn, manioc, and cassava can be grown close to the home once the trees have been felled. This diet is sometimes supplemented with bushmeat, which includes favourite foods such as monkeys and wild pigs. In addition to what is grown and hunted, wild fruits, nuts, honey, and roots are gathered from the forest. Although large-scale agriculture does not usually succeed in the rainforest, the small-scale **horticulture** that is practised by most rainforest peoples is sustainable. This type of farming begins a year or two before the land is needed, by

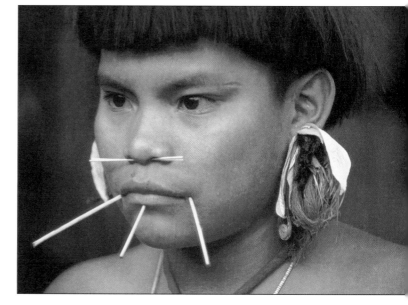

Figure 22.17
The Yanomami people live deep in the rainforest of South America.

removing the bark of the larger trees around the whole trunk. When the tree dies, it can be set on fire, usually in the dry season. Sunlight can now reach the forest floor, and crops can be planted in the ashes between the tree stumps. The ashes provide enough nitrates to compensate for the poor soils. When the land becomes infertile after two or three years, it is abandoned, and a new site is selected. The clearing soon recovers and the forest is restored. Most forest dwellers do not appreciate the concept of land ownership. When the land they are using is exhausted, they move on to a new forest plot.

In the past, these indigenous peoples had little contact with the people from regions outside the rainforest. When foreign cultural products, values, and ideas were introduced to these societies, the effects on some of the people were dramatic. T-shirts and shorts, portable radios, and western languages have become ordinary sights and sounds in some of these once-isolated groups. Changing attitudes are evident as well. Some indigenous people now undervalue their traditional ways and have begun to acquire the trappings of wealth so admired by mainstream Western society. Today many of the sustainable traditions and the rich cultural values of some indigenous groups have been replaced by the values of modern, materialistic society.

Economic Development in the Tropical Rainforest

Just as Canadians look to the great northern wilderness for natural resources, emerging industrial nations such as Brazil, Indonesia, and the Congo look to their tropical rainforests for the raw materials of industry. The assets locked up in the thousands of hectares of forest are too valuable to leave undisturbed. The wood from the forests, the minerals buried deep underground, the oil and natural gas reserves, the rich diversity of animals, the huge water resources, and the potential agricultural capacity of the region are all viewed as available commodities by those who wish to convert them into money to fund economic expansion.

Brazil is one country that is doing its best to make its forest resources finance its emergence as

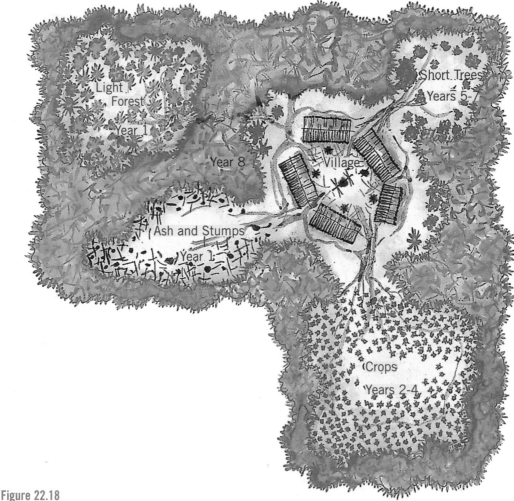

Figure 22.18
Slash and Burn Agriculture
This illustration shows a village clearing and four garden patches in the jungle. This method of agriculture allows people to grow crops such as corn, manioc, and cassava sustainably on a small scale.

an economic power. It has been developing its jungles for generations, but the wealth of the forests is elusive. Just when Brazilians think they have their hands on a rich resource, an ecological disaster takes away the lustre of the new development. The problem lies in the fact that sustainable practices must be utilized if the forest is to provide resources over a long period. Also, the forest resources need to be utilized in such a way that the rich biodiversity is not lost. This has not been the practice in Brazil or in many other developing countries with rainforest resources. However, one country that has developed a model for sustainable development in the rainforest is Costa Rica. Today some nations are starting to use the ideas and practices that this Central American country has instituted.

Location	Description	Time
Amazon	• Over 600 000 hectares burned	March 1998
Amazon	• New studies show that half the precipitation in the Amazon results from evapo-transpiration; therefore, if trees are removed, reduced precipitation won't allow the rainforest to grow back	1999
Bolivia	• Hydroelectric dam at Rurrenabaque will flood Madidi National Park, destroying 1600 km² of rainforest	August 1998
Central America	• Wood from rainforest trees provides 70% of energy demand	Study 1999
Democratic Rep. of the Congo	• Bonobo chimpanzee threatened by rainforest destruction • Mountain gorilla in decline because of revolutionary war and the deterioration of its ecosystem	1998
Dominica, Jamaica, St. Lucia	• New government initiatives to develop ecotourism following the Costa Rican model are being implemented	Late 1990s
Indonesia	• Resettlement programs have moved thousands of poor farmers from overcrowded islands to Kalimantin (a wilderness region)	Late 1990s
Philippines	• Three insect varieties—which could not have spread widely in the original forests because of the diversity of species—are destroying plantations and secondary forests that lack biodiversity	1998
Sumatra	• Habitat fragmentation and hunting places the Sumatran rhinoceros on the endangered species list	1999
Vietnam	• In Tam Dao National Park, residents sell endangered insects, butterflies, and snakes to tourists for as much as $100 each • Restaurants serve endangered species to tourists for supper	June 1999

Figure 22.19
Recent Developments in Rainforest Resource Management

Ecotourism in Costa Rica

The Central American country of Costa Rica has developed a strategy through which to utilize its forest resources sustainably, provide jobs for its people, and earn significant foreign income without exporting anything. The idea is to promote Costa Rica as a tropical paradise and have tourists from the United States, Canada, and Europe pay to come and experience it. The idea has caught on and the people, the plants, and the native animals are all benefiting.

While other Central American countries were spending millions on their armed forces, Costa Rica disbanded its military in 1949. The government believed (correctly) that Costa Rica's allies would never allow another country to invade the tiny nation. Because they saved so much money, they could afford to develop education and health services, as well as conserve their natural heritage. A quarter of all the unoccupied land was protected in national parks, biological reserves, wildlife refuges, and private reserves. Today the country of 3.5 million has one of the best standards of living in the Western Hemisphere. Economic growth has taken off and employment is improving after a period when banana exports provided the only employment for many.

More than 800 000 tourists visit the country each year. They spend money for accommoda-

Figure 22.20
Costa Rica is a popular tropical destination for both the active outdoors enthusiast and the ecotourist, who wants to witness undisturbed ecosystems.

tion, food, entertainment, and souvenirs. Tourist accommodation ranges from five-star, all-inclusive resorts, to more economical hotels, to homey bed and breakfasts. The activities visitors can participate in are seemingly endless. With many tourists wanting more than just a week in the sun, Costa Rica offers activities ranging from bird watching to hiking, from snorkeling to whitewater rafting. Some of the amazing adventures available are as follow:

Arenal Volcano

On July 29, 1968 Volcán Arenal exploded violently. Clouds of superheated gas and rivers of lava destroyed the forested slopes of the mountain. Since then, this classic cone-shaped volcano has been continuously active. While tourists are advised not to climb the treacherous mountain, it is accessible by four-wheel-drive vehicle. In the town of Nuevo Arenal there are many inexpensive restaurants and small hotels to host tourists. In the summer of 2000, the volcano erupted again. Tourists were safely evacuated, nobody was killed, and damage was light.

Isla del Coco

Isla del Coco provided the setting for the movie "Jurassic Park." Located 600 kilometres southwest of the mainland, it is the largest uninhabited island in the world. Tourists can charter a boat to the island and explore the thick, coniferous forests full of springs and rivers. The 100-metre-high cliffs that encircle the shoreline are covered with incredibly thick tropical vegetation. Majestic waterfalls plunge into the sea from the jungle inland. Visitors are not allowed to camp on the island, but can sleep in their boats at night. This ensures that the ecosystem is left as undisturbed as possible.

Monteverde Cloud Forest

The Reserva Biologica del Bosque Nuboso de Monteverde is located 180 kilometres northwest of San José. The main attraction of this biological reserve is the amazing quetzal, the most spectacular bird in the Tropics. While the bird is extirpated in other parts of Latin America, it has recovered significantly in this forest. It is estimated that as many as one thousand quetzals live in the biological reserve. Other exotic animals in the cloud forest include hundreds of different species of butterflies, an incredible diversity of plant life, and many mammals not found anywhere else. Even jaguars have been spotted in the jungle.

Parque Nacional Manuel Antonio

This is the main beach area of the country. There are three long strands of white sand fringed by jungle on one side and the Pacific on the other. Above the clean, wide beaches are tall cliffs covered in thick rain forest. The forest comes right down to the shoreline in places, which allows tourists to swim in the shade of the jungle. The number of people in the park is restricted, to prevent too much impact on the ecosystem.

QUESTIONS:

1. How has Costa Rica developed the rainforest differently than other countries in rainforest regions?
2. What activities would you like to participate in if you went to Costa Rica? Explain.
3. What has the country done to reduce the impact of tourism on natural areas?
4. What suggestions would you have for Costa Rica and other rainforest nations regarding ecotourism?

Figure 22.21
Large-scale burning of rainforest causes soil degradation, and the destruction of plant and animal species.

Rural Development in Rainforest Countries

Many rainforest countries are populated with large numbers of landless peasants. Improved health care and high birth rates resulted in a population explosion in the 1980s and 1990s. Existing farmland was already occupied by

geo.web resources

<www.pbs.org/tal/costa_rica/>

This site, organized by the Public Broadcasting Service, contains a wealth of information and photos of tropical rainforests. Click on the "Rainforest Issues Forum," choose an issue from the list, and research it before adding your opinion to the discussion.

farmers, but even their children suffered from the population increase, as not all the children in a large family could inherit and farm the same land. In addition, transnational corporations were buying up vast farm areas outside of the rainforest during the same period. With no land to farm, the people were forced to either relocate to the slums surrounding the cities or move to marginal lands to try farming there. City planners and politicians discouraged the massive migration to the outskirts of the overpopulated cities since infrastructures were hard-pressed to support the city dwellers who were already crowded into the urban areas.

The building of highways into the forest and the resulting mass migration of poor families into the newly accessible lands was encouraged as a way of developing what planners perceived as an underutilized resource and providing a new life for these people without having to expand the already overtaxed urban infrastructures. The model has a precedent in the expansion of the American frontier. When land in the eastern United States became fully utilized in the 1800s, Americans moved west and populated the Midwest. This same model is being used in countries such as Brazil, Indonesia, Malaysia, and the Philippines. The difference is that the Great Plains was a rich agricultural area, whereas the rainforests are not. What sounded like a great idea in theory has turned out to be an ecological disaster.

Large tracts of the Amazon were made available free of charge to Brazilians who wanted to clear the land, set up a homestead, and grow a crop. In the Philippines, farmers moved into the mountains, displacing indigenous tribes. Similar developments are occurring in Indonesia, as people from overpopulated Sumatra and Java are resettled in the rainforests of Kalimantan.

The problem with these resettlement programs has been that planners do not fully understand the complex nature of the rainforest. Once the forest is removed, the infertile soil is exposed to more intense leaching and erosion. For the first year or two of farming, the land seems quite productive as the plants take advantage of the nitrates released from burned forest cover. By the fourth or fifth year, however, the land is so infertile that seeds, fertilizers, and other farming costs outweigh the value of the crops produced. The settlers move further up the highway, clear new land, and begin the cycle all over again.

The shifting cultivation typical of the indigenous peoples was sustainable because there were so few forest dwellers practising this form of farming. With thousands of farmers now doing it, the impact on the forest is devastating. The secondary growth that moves into the cleared land is usually less vigorous than the original vegetation and lacks its genetic diversity. Often, the land is not allowed to return to its naturally vegetated state, and is converted instead into land for cattle ranching. While grass does grow on the land, rainfall starts to decline and a type of impoverished savanna replaces the forest.

Lumbering goes hand in hand with farming. The marketable trees are cut and removed before the land is put to the torch and its underbrush is burned off. The rainforests are so extensive that they are considered by some to be an inexhaustible source of wood. This belief is, of course, a fallacy. The annual loss of rainforest indicates that the forests will soon disappear completely if current rates of clear-cutting continue. An area roughly the size of Greece is eliminated every year. At this rate, it is certain that the world's most accessible rainforests (those located along coastal regions and rivers) will be wiped out within the next 20 years. Some remote regions of the forest will likely never be destroyed because they are too far from transportation routes and the terrain is too difficult to travel through.

Many rainforest trees possess unique qualities that put them in high demand. Teak, mahogany, rosewood, and ebony are easily made into furni-

Figure 22.22
With no land to farm, poor families in tropical Brazil relocate to favelas surrounding urban centres.

ture, and yet are durable and attractive woods. However, there is so much species diversity that very few trees are actually of any use as marketable materials on global markets. The one thing that consumers want is consistency—they do not want to buy kitchen cabinets in which the wood of each door is slightly different from the others. The diversity of rainforest vegetation makes uniform materials a problem. Because of this, only one tree in a hundred may be suitable for market. The rest are burned to make charcoal or are just left as forest litter. Harvesting the trees of the Amazon is therefore much more difficult and wasteful than in the more genetically uniform forests of Canada.

With only about 5 per cent of the trees in the rainforest having any commercial value, **selective cutting** is the preferred logging technique. This sounds like an ecologically viable practice; however, much of the other vegetation is destroyed even though only the marketable wood is being removed. Methods are becoming less wasteful today, although much of the forest is still disturbed. Modern techniques allow the non-commercial wood to be ground into chips, which are then made into pulp for use in the manufacture of paper.

CHANGING TECHNOLOGY: Airborne Laser Terrain Mapping

One of the main problems with forestry in the past was a lack of knowledge of what the ground was like under the tree cover. Recently, however, aerial photography has allowed foresters to prepare detailed inventories of the types of trees growing in a forest, their relative health, and even an idea of the volume of wood a given stand will provide. Previously, the exact height of the trees and the nature of the ground where the forest grew were not known until forestry crews went into a region. But in the rainforest, the terrain can be virtually impassable if the forest is flooded or if the underbrush is too dense. It is therefore worthwhile understanding the surface conditions before a crew is sent in to harvest a forest.

Airborne laser terrain mapping (ALTM) is a new Canadian technology that is increasingly being used internationally to map regions that are impossible to assess because of forest cover. The system operates using a combination of laser, radar, and GPS technology. A plane flies over the study site with an ALTM sensor attached where the aerial camera would normally be mounted. The sensor measures the distance between the ground and the airplane at a rate of 33 000 pulses per second. A primary pulse bounces off the top of the forest while a secondary pulse goes right through the vegetation and does not bounce back to the sensor until it hits the hard surface underneath. GPS and ground receivers record the exact location for each second of operation. After the flight, post-processing software combines all the information to produce an accurate terrain map showing forest cover and topography. The system has been successfully used in mapping forests in Canada, the US, and Europe. A project is planned for the winter of 2001 to map Toncatins State in the southeastern Amazon Basin of Brazil so that forest resources in this region can be better exploited.

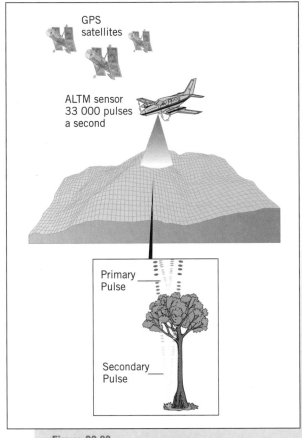

Figure 22.23
How Airborne Laser Terrain Mapping Works

Question:
What will the effect of this technology be on rainforest ecosystems and on the economies of rainforest countries?

Small-scale cottage industries are often the best way to utilize the trees of the rainforest. Small villages in Central America are going into the furniture-making business. Chairs and tables are made using local woods. Instead of sending large machinery into the forest, the carpenter goes into the forest and selects the trees needed to make the furniture. A small amount of wood is removed at a time. Some trees would not normally be marketable, but the local carpenter uses different trees for different purposes, depending on their unique properties. The inner bark of one tree may be used to weave the seat of a chair; another light-coloured tree may be used for inlaid accents on a table made from a darker wood. Using simple hand tools, craftspeople are able to turn each piece of furniture into a masterpiece. These chairs and tables become highly prized consumer goods in North American stores, which cater to eclectic tastes. The people of the village also benefit more than they would have if the wood had been sold wholesale to a lumbering company. Because labour has been put into the product, it has a higher value. So, much more money is made from a very small amount of wood. The harvesting of the wood is so slow that it is sustainable—the trees grow back faster than they are removed. All in all, everyone benefits from this selective type of harvesting.

Forest resources are not the only valuable commodities found in rainforest areas. Vast mineral deposits including gold, diamonds, and industrial metals are frequently found in equatorial regions. Hidden from view by dense jungles, these resources are only beginning to be exploited. When mines open in the area, they create ecological disaster. First, the vegetation is cleared away; next, the soil and overburden are removed; then, tailings and other waste products are littered across the land. Often, dangerous chemicals are used in the extraction of the mineral. Some of these chemicals tend to accumulate in the living tissue of animals downstream and cause neurological diseases.

Getting the mined materials out of the forest also causes extensive damage. As railways are cut through the landscape, they sever migratory

Figure 22.24
This ebony sculpture was made for sale in North America by a rainforest artisan.

routes through the jungle and separate species that may be dependent on one another. The air pollution and the increased noise also have a devastating effect on solitary animals that need to be left undisturbed. The needs of wild animals are seldom seen as being as important as jobs and economic development in these often economically depressed regions. So, mining continues to expand in rainforest regions.

Valuable Resources of the Extractive Reserves

A hundred years ago, rubber tappers collected latex from rubber trees indigenous to the Amazon Basin. They went from tree to tree collecting a little of the precious sap each day, just like Canadians collect maple sap in the spring. The practice is sustainable because the sap can be taken without causing any harm to the tree.

Because synthetic rubber has replaced natural latex, Amazonian rubber tappers had to develop other economic activities in order to survive. As they travelled along their daily paths, they started to notice many other things that were valuable in the forest. Brazil nuts, mangoes, chicle, herbs, and papaya all grew along the trail. In time, the rubber tappers encouraged the growth of some natural species such as bananas, cassava, and taro along the forest trails. Today these people sell what they collect from these extractive reserves to tradespeople who export them to the rest of the world.

The **extractive reserve** is one of the only modern development strategies that is truly sustainable, and it is the legacy of Chico Mendes, a rubber tapper murdered by cattle ranchers in 1988. After his death, the Brazilian government gave its support to extractive reserves. By the late 1990s, four extractive reserves had been established in the Amazon. These areas are reserved strictly for the gathering of forest products and

for small-scale horticulture. No mining, forestry, or other development is permitted. This type of small-scale, sustainable development ensures a better future for forest people since they are living harmoniously with their environment and not destroying it.

The main disadvantages of extractive reserves are that they are too small and too distantly located from each other to support the millions of homeless peasants in Brazil. Even for those people whom extractive reserves help, the rate of return is much lower than it is for other development projects. Farming, ranching, and particularly mining all provide more jobs and a greater income for a given area of land. Of course, in the long run, extractive reserves will be able to operate profitably long after the mines are closed and the farms are abandoned.

ENVIRONMENT WATCH

Fair Trade Practices

Increasingly, products are becoming available that treat people and the environment with respect. Products from lumber to coffee are currently being produced by workers who are better compensated for their labour. According to Oxfam, "fair trade is about giving workers a fair price for their work." You can find vendors of fair trade goods on the Internet by searching under "fair trade." Fair trade commodities are often produced on co-operative farms where farmers determine how the crops are grown. Because they have a vested interest in the land, sustainable production methods are used. Inspectors determine if methods are sustainable and if workers are being fairly paid. Often, the price of the product may be a little higher, but the consumer can rest assured that its purchase benefited the people that produced it and did not contribute to the nightmarish poverty that exists in many developing countries.

Figure 22.25
Fair Trade Logo

Question:
What effect, if any, could paying higher wages to workers in rainforest countries have on the health of tropical ecosystems?

ACTIVITIES

UNDERSTANDING CONCEPTS

1. a) Look at the chart in Fig. 22.6. Place the names of the climate stations along a continuum
        like the one below, to show whether they are predominantly rainforest or savanna.

    b) Hypothesize the relative latitude of each location based on temperature and precipitation
        data.
2. a) Describe the characteristics of the tropical rainforest climate and explain how natural
        vegetation and other factors can affect these climate systems.
    b) Describe the characteristics of the tropical rainforest natural vegetation and explain how
        these trees and plants adapted to overcome limitations of soil and climate.
    c) Describe the characteristics of the tropical rainforest soils and explain how climate and
        other factors affect them.
    d) Describe the characteristics of the tropical rainforest animals and explain how this
        wildlife has adapted to the natural vegetation of these regions.
3. a) Explain what symbiosis is and provide examples of it from the text.
    b) Does the example of the rainforest ecoregion support or contradict the Gaia Hypothesis?
        Explain your answer.
4. a) Describe different human economic activities in the tropical rainforest ecoregion.
    b) Assess the impact each has on ecosystems.
    c) Explain how habitat destruction affects ecosystems using a flow chart diagram.
    d) List the resource management practices that are sustainable and describe the importance
        of such practices in industries within the tropical rainforest.
5. a) Explain how differences in terrain can affect local ecosystems within the tropical rainforest.
    b) Study the map of Madidi National Park on page 386. Describe the different ecosystems
        found in the park and explain why each is different from the others.
    c) Why are tropical rainforest ecosystems similar even though they may be thousands of
        kilometres apart?
6. How would the ALTM mapping technology help forestry companies in the tropical rainforests?

DEVELOPING AND PRACTISING SKILLS

7. a) Describe how solar energy flows through the tropical rainforest ecoregion.
    b) Explain the relationship of these energy flows to climate, soils, and natural vegetation.

8. a) Why is solar energy concentrated in equatorial regions?
    b) Outline how convection currents operate to affect equatorial climates.
    c) What impacts do ocean currents have on east coast rainforest littorals?
    d) How do variations in elevation affect climatic patterns, especially in equatorial east Africa?
9. a) Explain how
        • climate affects soil development in the tropical rainforest.
        • climate affects natural vegetation in the tropical rainforest.
        • soils affect vegetation in the tropical rainforest.
        • climate and vegetation affect animal adaptations in the tropical rainforest.
        • the removal of forest cover affects soil development.
        • the removal of forest cover affects climate.
    b) Summarize the ideas from a) in a flow chart.
10. Reread the chart in Fig. 22.19 on page 391.
    a) List all the developments that could lead to the destruction of sections of the rainforest.
    b) List all the encouraging developments.
    c) Assess whether the future looks bleak or promising for the tropical rainforest ecozone.
    d) What can Canadians do to encourage its preservation?

LEARNING THROUGH APPLICATION

11. a) Evaluate the role of airborne laser terrain mapping in changing human-environment relationships in the tropical rainforest.
    b) What other applications can you imagine for this technology?
12. Explain the effects of natural variations in climate on the structure and composition of soils of tropical rainforest ecosystems.
13. Identify geopolitical issues that face nations that share the tropical rainforest ecoregion.
14. Evaluate each of the ecological events in the chart in Fig. 22.19. Describe the implications of each action on forest ecology and global biodiversity.
15. Analyse the long-term effects of human use of the tropical rainforest ecozone in each of the following industries or methods.
    a) Forestry
    b) Mining
    c) Extractive reserves
    d) Farming
    e) Ecotourism
16. Study the section that describes ecotourism in Costa Rica.
    a) What are the ecological advantages of this type of development?
    b) How was Costa Rica able to develop ecotourism while other nations like Bolivia were not?
    c) Of the activities listed, state which ones would appeal to you and explain why.
    d) How successful will ecotourism be as a basis for economic development, in your opinion?
    e) What ecological challenges could result from tourism in ecologically sensitive regions?
17. Conduct a web search to find other countries with ecotourism programs.

Chapter 23

SUBTROPICAL AND WEST COAST ECOREGIONS

FOCUS QUESTIONS

1. How does location affect the different climates of the subtropical ecoregion?
2. How does climate affect the plants, animals, and soils of subtropical and west coast ecoregions?
3. How do human activities, such as resource development, impact on natural systems in the subtropics?

Figure 23.1
The subtropics contains some of the most highly populated regions on Earth.

While the subtropics and West Coast ecoregions represent less than 10 per cent of the earth's surface, more people live in these regions than in any other. So, what makes the regions so popular?

These regions are located approximately between 30° latitude and 35° latitude, (although the region extends as far as 40° on the western coast of continents) and contain a tremendous variety of climates and ecosystems. Hot summers, mild winters, and regular precipitation all year make this a favorite human habitat. Plants and animals thrive in the subtropics when the land is not so modified by people that their natural habitat is destroyed.

At this level of latitude, the climate on the west coast of each continent is different than the subtropical one on the east coast. Known as the Mediterranean ecoregion, the west coast zone has temperatures comparable to those on the east coast, but it also has a drought in the summer. The lack of rain in the growing season has a

Key Terms

Mediterranean climate

clear cutting

strip cutting

subtropical climate

sclerophyll shrub

profound effect on the plants in this ecoregion. Scrubby **xerophytic** plants like those of the desert make the region seem dried out and less verdant than the zone on the opposite side of the continent. Mediterranean Europe and Africa are not the only places where this zone is found; it also exists along the coast of California, in South Africa, and in southwest Australia.

Further away from the equator, temperatures drop and precipitation becomes more efficient as evaporation rates drop. On the west coast, rainfall patterns change from that of the arid Mediterranean lands, being characterized by a much higher level of annual precipitation. The Pacific west coast all the way from northern California to Alaska and much of western Europe

have this marine west coast climate. While much of the original forest was removed from Europe a thousand or more years ago, there are still remnants of the great temperate rainforests in British Columbia. Rivalling the tropical rainforests for their biodiversity, these ecoregions are quickly being degraded as people exploit the forest, fish the rivers, and mine the mountains.

Between the subtropical and Mediterranean zones lie the great temperate deserts of the United States, South America, and Asia. They share many of the characteristics of tropical desert ecozones but can be very cold in the winter because of their continental location and the often high elevation of the regions' physical features. Spectacular scenery abounds in these

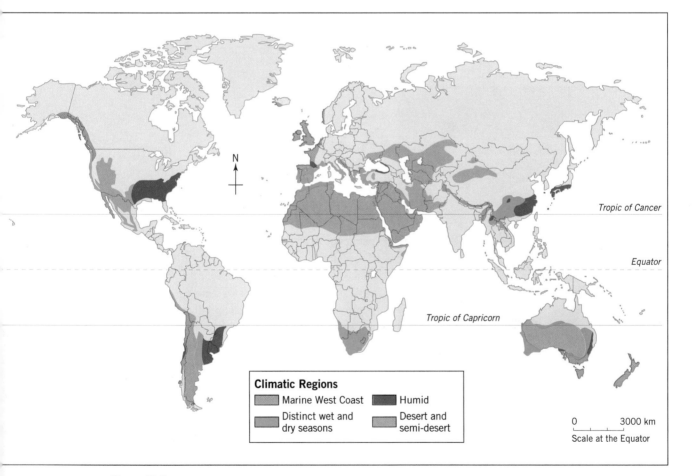

Figure 23.2
This map shows the different regions of the subtropical and west coast zones.

areas, and retirement communities have become common in such American desert states as Nevada, Arizona, and New Mexico. In central Asia, the remote regions of Tibet, Afghanistan, and other isolated nations are sparsely populated, partly due to the rugged relief and resulting inaccessibility. Of course, the largest expanse of uninterrupted desert is in North Africa. The enormous Sahara separates the Mediterranean lands that skirt its northern boundary and the vast savannas that stretch south to the equator.

The Subtropical Ecoregion

Some Canadians may already be familiar with the subtropics since such regions are popular "spring break" destinations. Being so much further south than Canada, South Carolina, Georgia, and especially Florida are warm and sunny in March while most of our provinces and territories are still buried under melting slush or still glazed with layers of snow and ice. In Asia, the subtropical zone is in southern China, the world's most populated region. With its salubrious temperatures and regular rainfall, this region is comfortable at all times of year. In addition, agriculture thrives in this area of China, where rich soils developed from the **alluvium** carried down the rivers to the coastal plains.

Two mechanisms result in regular rainfall in the region throughout the year. In winter, frontal precipitation occurs because maritime tropical and continental polar air masses come together over the region. Precipitation can take many forms, depending on the air temperature. Because the region lies close to the Tropics of Cancer and Capricorn the sun's rays are relatively direct during the summer solstice.

During summer, convectional rainfall is common, as it is in the savanna regions located between the subtropical zone and the equator. The wind blows from the sea across the land in a way similar to the monsoon winds of southern Asia. A low-pressure cell often forms over the land because of the high daytime temperatures. High-pressure cells offshore pump moist, cool air over the land, making heavy rains common on

hot afternoons. This region often experiences hurricanes or tropical cyclones in the late summer. Enormous amounts of energy stored offshore in the oceans create these violent storms, which can devastate coastal areas. (See Chapter 16 for more information on hurricanes.)

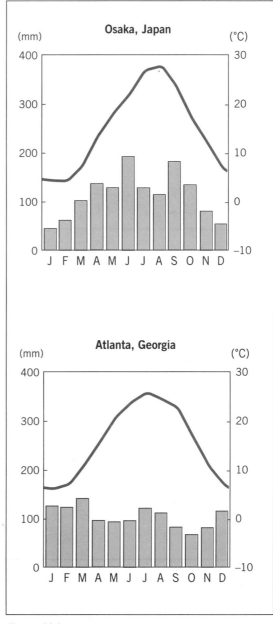

Figure 23.3
Climate Graphs for Atlanta, Georgia and Osaka, Japan

The Florida Everglades

The Florida Everglades is a unique wilderness area in danger of being destroyed. It has gained worldwide recognition for the diversity of its natural systems, has been designated a World Heritage Site by the United Nations, is an International Biosphere Reserve, and is the largest subtropical wilderness in the United States. The fact that millions of people are crowded along the edge of the park is causing irreparable damage to this unique, natural landscape.

Figure 23.4
Everglades Ecosystem

This subtropical zone has many of the characteristics of wetlands found in tropical regions. It has a definite dry season like the savanna and a wide diversity of plants and animals. However, its seasonal differences affirm its status as a subtropical ecoregion. Each summer, heavy rains supply an abundant source of fresh water, which is stored in shallow Lake Okeechobee and then drains southward to the Gulf of Mexico. The main river that drains the 1900-km² lake is as much as 80 km wide but only 0.3 to 0.9 m deep. As it slowly drains, at a rate of about 400 m per day, it provides sustenance for the different ecosystems within the park. In the winter season, the wetland dries out. Birds, alligators, and other predators feed on the aquatic feast that has become concentrated in deeper pools of water. In May, convectional rainfall starts to flood the region once again, and animals disperse for the rainy season. Plants and animals have adapted to the alternating dry and wet seasons, so any disruption in water flow affects the health of the region.

Moving from the ocean inland, the different ecosystems in the park include the estuarine zone, the mangrove swamp, the coastal prairie, the freshwater slough, the cypress swamp, the hardwood hammocks, and the pinelands. Along the shore, a 2000-km² area of seagrass provides habitat for shellfish, fish, and sponges. This estuarine zone acquires nutrients from the water as it drains off the land into Florida Bay.

Mangrove forests fill in the zone behind the estuary. Shrimp in abundance become food for wading shore birds that nest in the mangrove trees during winter. Sand dunes make up the coastal prairie. Drought-resistant grasses and cacti hold the sand in place, except when hurricanes blow ashore. Then the dunes are so eroded that vegetation has to begin its growth process all over again.

The main part of the Everglades is made up of a fresh water **fen**. Along the edges, limestone sediments restrict the flow of water, but in the centre of the wetlands, a broad marshy slough covers the land. When the summer rains come, an algae mat

Figure 23.5
Map of the Florida Everglades National Park

grows over the surface of the slow-moving water. The microscopic plants are eaten by tiny creatures, which are in turn used as food by small fish and frogs. The whole food chain is supported by this annual bloom of algae on the sloughs.

Dotted throughout the wetland are islands called hammocks. While they may rise only a few centimetres above the water's surface, they provide an entirely different habitat—one that supports deer, foxes, and panthers. In the dry season, these animals venture onto the sawgrass sloughs and feed on pools of stranded fish and other aquatic animals. Tropical trees such as mahogany and cocoplum, whose seeds blew in from Caribbean islands, intermingle with subtropical trees such as live oak and red maple.

In the dry season, fires are common in the Everglades, but they are welcome because they allow for the preservation of the ecozone. Slash pines, which are fire resistant and survive while all other species are destroyed, grow on higher ground where fire is more common. Forests that grow on the hammocks are protected from the flames by a wet moat created when acids from the tree roots and dead leaves dissolve the limestone around them. Where the water does not flow, cypress swamps develop. These majestic trees provide shelter for many aquatic animals and nesting sites for the ever-present osprey.

Unfortunately, this natural environment is becoming increasingly endangered. Nine hundred people take up permanent residence in Florida every day! In addition to this, another 12 million tourists arrive every winter in the dry season. It is no wonder that the Everglades is a threatened natural environment. Increased needs for municipal water and increased coastal development are disrupting fresh water supplies in the park. In addition, sewage and agricultural waste are reducing water quality. Pesticides are killing insects essential to the food web, and fertilizers are disrupting the growth of microscopic plants on Lake Okeechobee. As more and more water is taken from aquifers for municipal water needs, salinity increases. Seawater is flowing into the

sloughs and killing the fresh water plants and animals there. Sometimes, local residents flood the Everglades with their waste water. This can be especially disruptive in the dry season, when animals depend on stranded fish for food, and birds need dry land to nest.

As a way of alleviating the pressures imposed by too large a population around the park, the American government provided $20 million in 1999 as part of $1 billion Lands Legacy Initiative. The funds were used to acquire 6800 ha of land adjacent to the park, crucial for the restoration of fresh water flowing into the Shark River Slough. Park officials are optimistic that the purchase of this region will help the park to recover. In addition to the new funding, regulations at the local level have been enacted to ensure a steady flow of fresh water from Lake Okeechobee into the wetlands each spring. Municipal needs will now come second to the needs of natural systems in this preserve.

As evaporation rates continue to rise because of global warming and as the demand for water increases, it remains to be seen whether the good intentions of legislators will prevail for long. The steady growth of the population along the coast will continue to cause concerns for the health, and even survival, of such natural regions.

QUESTIONS:

1. Analyse the effects of slight variations in surface elevation and salinity on Everglade ecosystems.

2. How are people disrupting the different ecosystems of the Everglades?

3. Do you believe that the preventative measures implemented will save the Everglades from eventual destruction? Why or why not?

4. In your opinion, should the need to save the Everglades outweigh the needs of the growing Florida population? Explain your answer.

Figure 23.6
Vineyards in South Africa

The Mediterranean Ecozone

People have always enjoyed the climate of the Mediterranean region. This zone has warm to hot summers, unusually mild winters, and bright sunshine for most of the year. Even so, there is enough rainfall during the winter season to allow for farming and municipal uses. This is one of the few climate zones that experiences summer drought and winter rain. Snow and frost rarely occur, so crops tend to grow all year. It is therefore not surprising that the Mediterranean climate supports some of the densest populations in the world.

Named after the Mediterranean Sea (located between Africa and Europe), this region lies on the west coasts of continents between 30° and 40° north and south of the equator. In addition to the main region in southern Europe and North

Africa, a large Mediterranean zone is located on the west coast of the United States. Smaller examples exist in Chile, South Africa, and Australia. No matter where the region is found, it is always on the west coast, just north of the Tropic of Cancer or south of the Tropic of Capricorn, and extends into the middle latitudes. The region is at its largest extent around the Mediterranean Sea. This vast sea so moderates the climate that the zone extends far into the centre of the Euro-African land mass.

Dry tropical steppes border the side of each zone that is closest to the equator, while the sides closest to the poles are bordered by wet marine west coast climates. Generally, rainfall increases as one travels toward the poles. The latitude of the climate region explains why it has a summer drought and mild temperatures all year.

The movement of prevailing winds with the **thermal equator** results in the unusual rainfall pattern of this zone. During the summer, the region is under the influence of the trade winds. As the winds blow out from the middle of the continent, they are relatively dry and hot. Any surface moisture is quickly evaporated, creating

geo.web resources

<www.nps.gov/ever/home.htm>

This is an American National Park Service web site. Visit this site and summarize an update on the current health of the Florida Everglades.

Figure 23.7
Locator Map of California

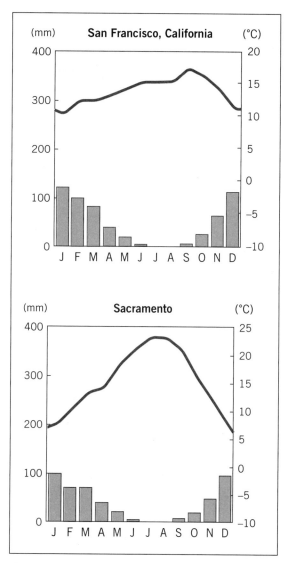

Figure 23.8
These are climate graphs for San Francisco and Sacramento, which lie at approximately 38° and 37° N, respectively. What differences do you notice in summer temperatures? Using the California locator map, explain why.

an almost desert-like region in summer. Although temperatures are often very hot, the dry air makes it feel less uncomfortable than the sticky heat of the subtropical region, where the trade winds pump a regular supply of moist air over the land all summer long.

Coastal areas can be much cooler than the interior because these areas are moderated by cold ocean currents off the coast. Fog is a common feature along coasts as the hot, dry air comes in contact with cool, damp air over the ocean. Many Californians travel to the coast around Santa Barbara to escape the summer heat. In winter, the migration reverses. Since the thermal equator has travelled away from the region, westerly mid-latitude winds take over. Westerlies blowing off the ocean bring cool, steady drizzle and fog inland throughout the winter. In Europe, occasional incursions of either bitterly cold polar air from northern Europe or dry, hot winds out of the Sahara occasionally cause variations in weather patterns from year to year. The presence of the Rocky Mountains in the United States blocks most arctic weather, preventing it from reaching "sunny California."

Temperatures in the Mediterranean region are warm all year. High summer temperatures occur

because the thermal equator is almost directly overhead. Mild temperatures in winter are caused by the moderating influence of the ocean currents and the low latitude.

The natural vegetation of the Mediterranean zone is interesting because it is both tropical and

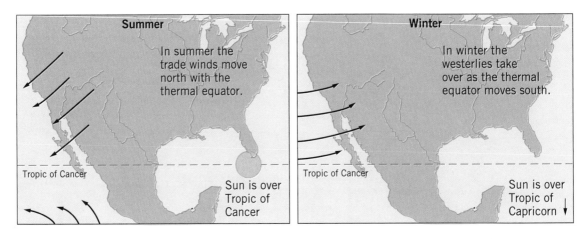

Summer

In summer the trade winds move north with the thermal equator.

Tropic of Cancer

Sun is over Tropic of Cancer

Winter

In winter the westerlies take over as the thermal equator moves south.

Tropic of Cancer

Sun is over Tropic of Capricorn ↓

Figure 23.9
Variations in seasonal winds can have a great effect on Mediterranean climates.

adapted to a dry growing season. **Sclerophyll** scrub has unique adaptations that allow it to flourish in the dry summer growing season. Plants need moisture during the summer, not in the winter when low temperatures limit growth. Scrub plants have adapted in several ways: their small leaves and waxy coverings reduce the amount of water lost through transpiration, and their small size allows them to cling to the soil and modify the microclimate. The temperature is much lower in the shade of a stand of bushes, and humidity is usually quite a bit higher, as water exuded by the vegetation is trapped by branches and leaves close to the ground.

Many parts of the Mediterranean region have been populated with people for so long that little is left of the natural vegetation in many places. Often, irrigation in the summer makes the region look greener than it would normally be. Undisturbed natural vegetation can usually be found only in areas where human access is difficult because of rugged topography.

Thousands of years of agriculture in the Mediterranean regions of Europe have led to the development of a variety of different foods. Many plants evolved to produce a succulent fruit around inner seeds. Fruits, such as oranges and lemons, are often covered with a thick skin to prevent moisture from seeping out when the fruit drops to the ground and to protect the seed as it uses the moisture to germinate in the dry spring-time. Once the seedling takes root, the autumn rains provide enough moisture for the plant to develop a strong enough root system to sustain itself during the dry summer. Of course, the oranges and grapefruit we are familiar with are much different from wild citrus fruit. For hundreds of years, farmers used only the seeds

Figure 23.10
Scrub Vegetation in the Hills of Southern Spain

from trees with sweet, juicy, meaty fruit so that trees with the characteristics people wanted therefore became the dominant species. In other words, farmers helped **natural selection** along a bit. The old Darwinian adage that the fittest species survive has been modified such that the "fittest" fruits are those that provide certain qualities that people value.

Other plants that developed in the gardens of the ancient Greeks, Romans, and Phoenicians include grapes, pomegranates, melons, cork, and olives. As with citrus fruits, they all need a long growing season, characterized by hot summers and damp, mild winters. While grapes lack the thick skin of the orange, they do have a moist fruit. Over the years, they have been modified so that their seeds are smaller and less plentiful than in their natural state. Seedless grapes do actually have seeds, but they are so small and soft that you don't notice them. Melons have a thick skin and moist interior. Cork is the bark of a specially adapted Mediterranean tree, which is used to make stoppers for wine bottles. This special type of stopper allows for the slow diffusion of gases over time, thus enabling aging wines to acquire subtle flavours and bouquets.

Viticulture has developed in other Mediterranean climate regions outside of Europe. South African, Chilean, Argentinean, and California wines are often as good as the wines produced in Italy or France. Wine is also produced in regions of Southern Ontario. The Niagara Region may not be Mediterranean, but it has a more salubrious microclimate than other parts of the country and produces excellent wines.

The Temperate Desert Ecozone

In North America, Asia, and South America, great temperate deserts occupy large regions in the interior of the continent. Like the deserts at lower latitudes, these regions are extremely arid. They are considerably cooler than tropical deserts, however. This is due to their location in the mid-latitudes, and also to the fact that many temperate deserts are found in high plateaus or upland regions where the **environmental lapse rate** reduces **daily maximums**.

Unlike tropical deserts, these regions are dry because of the location of mountain barriers between them and moisture-bearing prevailing winds. For example, in Patagonia the westerlies blow from the Pacific Ocean onto the Chilean coastline. As these winds rise up the Andes Mountains, the temperature drops below the **dew point**, and precipitation—in the form of rain on the lower slopes and snow higher up—falls on the western slopes. As the air goes over the summit and starts to descend, it expands, the temperature increases, and the humidity drops. **Dry adiabatic heating** and extreme dryness characterize the air that arrives over the mountains in Patagonia. This pattern of **rain shadows** also exists in North America in the Great American Desert, and in the deserts of central Asia, where the massive Himalayas block moisture-bearing winds.

Figure 23.14
Using a landforms map, analyse why this desert in Mongolia has the dry climate and lack of vegetation evident in this photo.

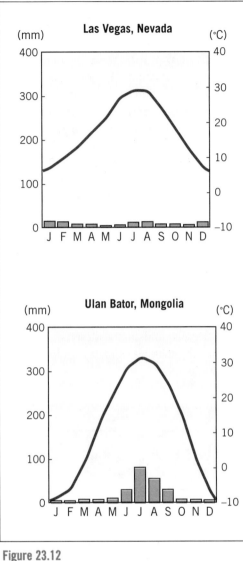

Figure 23.12
Climate Graphs for Las Vegas and Ulan Bator

in central Asia because the climate is so severe, and southern Patagonia is therefore isolated and relatively unpopulated. For these reasons, ecosystems are fairly intact, meaning that natural xerophytic plants and desert animals continue to live much as they have for thousands of years. In this part of Asia, nomadic herders still graze their herds of horses, sheep, goats, and yaks.

The situation is, however, very different in North America. Because of their closer proximity to the equator, the American desert states of Nevada, Arizona, New Mexico, and Utah have warm temperatures in the winter. People in the area enjoy warm, sunny days, and overcome the lack of water by using deep wells, which tap into the aquifers underlying the region. As with population pressures in Florida, the increasing numbers of people in these states is causing a deep impact on water resources. Las Vegas is the fastest growing city in the United States, yet it relies on a finite supply of water. In Scottsdale Arizona, water resources are so squandered that most people have swimming pools and there are actually golf courses in the desert. The evaporation rates are so high that surface water practically disappears before your eyes. The use of the Ogallalla aquifer under much of the south central portion of the Great Plains has made much of this possible, although water is also derived from glacial meltwater carried to the ocean by the mighty Colorado River. The water in this aquifer is rapidly being used up as municipal, recreational, and agricultural water users keep drawing from it.

Many desert dwellers are heeding the warnings of environmentalists and hydrologists by modifying their lifestyles. In addition, municipal water wardens force people to conserve water by fining extravagant users. Many people have replaced the traditional front lawn with desert plants and stone patios. Water resources are precious and especially rare in the temperate desert of the United States. They need to be used carefully.

These remote temperate deserts can be extremely cold, as evidenced by the Ulan Bator climate graph. This Asian capital has the distinction of being the coldest nation's capital in the world (Ottawa is second). Not only is it fairly high in latitude at 48° but it is far from the moderating influences of large bodies of water and it is isolated from moderating winds by the mountains to the south. There are very few cities

Constructing a Climate Graph

Climate graphs are important tools for geographers and travelers. By studying a climate graph, geographers can determine much about the nature of a region. Not only do trained geographers find out about climate, but they can also make assumptions about a region's natural vegetation, surface water, agriculture, and the lifestyle of its people. Travellers use climate graphs to determine the best time to travel to a region so that, for example, they will not end up on vacation in India during the rainy season.

The climate graphs in this book were created using a computer software program, but they can also be done manually. However, if you have access to a computer, try using a data base or spreadsheet program to construct the graph.

1. Take a piece of graph paper (blank paper will also do). Using a ruler, draw a line where you want the bottom of the graph to appear. This is the **x-axis**. For blank paper, measure 12 cm along this line and mark each centimetre interval; for graph paper, use one or two grid intervals for the width of each column. Next, draw two **y-axes**, one at each end of the x-axis.

2. Label each column along the x-axis for the months (i.e. J, F, M, A, M, J, J, A, S, O, N, D). Label the first y-axis "Precipitation (mm)" and the second y-axis "Temperature (°C)."

3. Include a scale on the two y-axes. If you plan to compare this graph to another, it is important that the y-axis scales be the same on each graph. Try to keep the precipitation scale low so that the precipitation bars don't cover the temperature line.

4. Plot the temperature values in the mid-point of each grid column from J (January) to D (December). Connect the dots using a red pen. The temperature line should run from left axis to right axis and should enter the graph at precisely the same temperature it exits the graph on the right. The temperature line should be smooth and continuous.

5. Draw a horizontal line across each grid column at the precipitation value for each month from J (January) to D (December). Lightly shade each bar from the horizontal line down to the x-axis in blue.

6. Complete your graph with a title.

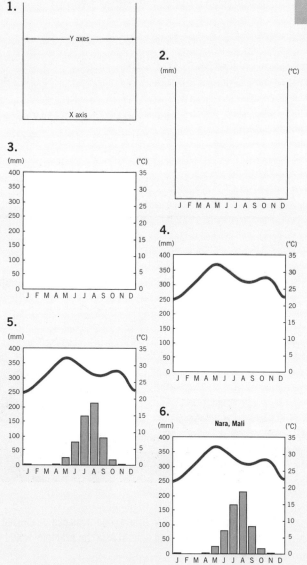

TRY IT!

1. Study the climate graph data below and prepare a graph for each station, as directed by your teacher. Classify each graph as representative of the savanna, monsoon, or steppe climate, and be prepared to explain why you categorized the graph as you did.

		J	F	M	A	M	J	J	A	S	O	N	D
Nara, Mali	P (mm)	3	0	0	3	25	74	160	211	99	20	3	0
	T (oC)	22	25	28	31	33	31	28	27	27	29	28	23
Cochin, India	P (mm)	23	20	51	125	297	724	592	353	196	340	170	41
	T (oC)	27	28	29	29	29	27	26	26	27	27	28	27
Karachi, Pakistan	P (mm)	13	10	8	3	3	18	81	41	13	0	3	5
	T (oC)	18	20	24	28	30	31	30	28	28	28	24	20
Broome, Australia	P (mm)	160	147	99	31	15	23	5	3	0	0	15	83
	T (oC)	29	29	29	28	24	22	21	22	25	27	29	30
Caracas, Venezuela	P (mm)	23	10	15	33	79	102	109	109	107	109	94	46
	T (oC)	18	19	20	21	22	21	21	21	21	21	20	20

Figure 23.13

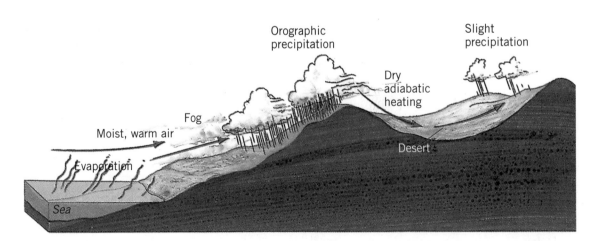

Figure 23.14
This illustration shows how desert conditions can be caused by the rain shadow effect. Climate graphs for locations in Nevada, Patagonia, and Central Asia, for example, would reflect this effect with low precipitation levels throughout the year.

The Marine West Coast Ecozone

As the name implies, the marine west coast climate is found on the west coasts of continents. It extends from the Mediterranean region well into the upper latitudes. It reaches much further north in the Northern Hemisphere than do temperate climates on the east coast or in the centre of the continents. This climate zone is not only found in coastal western Europe and British Columbia, but is also located in New Zealand and southern Chile.

Warm ocean currents moderate the climate zone so much that regions as far north as 55° never experience temperatures below freezing. What a difference from deserts in the interior, where temperatures can be unbelievably cold in winter! (See Ulan Bator's climate graph.) The Gulf Stream and North Atlantic Drift carry warm water all the way from the Caribbean to northern Europe. Westerly winds pick up moisture from the relatively warm ocean and dump it along the coast. Fog and rain are common all year, so the climate provides plenty of moisture for crops and pastures. Summers are characteristically cool, being moderated by offshore ocean currents. Overall, the marine west coast has a low temperature range, with mild winters and cool summers. As you would expect, the temperature drops as you move away from the equator.

Most of the natural vegetation in western Europe was removed centuries ago. In southern England, the raising of sheep on common lands destroyed much of the natural forest. The animals ate everything in their path, including grass and the leaves off small trees and bushes. When the larger trees were cut down for timber, seedlings could not replace the original forest because of the herds of sheep. The Norman king of England decreed that a new forest would be allowed to grow in Sussex. This forest was thus developed as a natural hunting ground for the king. The name "New Forest" gives the present-day student the impression that the forest is relatively young, but King William made the royal

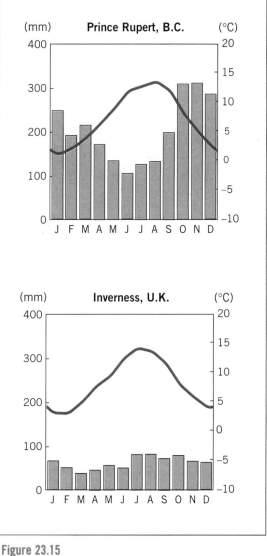

Figure 23.15
Climate Graphs for Prince Rupert, B.C., and Inverness, U.K.

decree in the eleventh century! This ancient New Forest has been protected from poaching and unauthorized grazing for almost a thousand years by game wardens called verderers. It is a delightful forest that is more like a garden than a wilderness area. Deer, wild ponies, and many smaller animals live in the sheltered preserve within an hour's train ride from the huge metropolis of London. William was not so much interested in preserving nature as he was concerned about

Figure 23.16
British Columbia

Figure 23.17
Coastal Britain

having hunting grounds nearby. Nevertheless, his bold decision led, over the centuries, to the formation of one of the most beautiful forests in Europe.

Canada is fortunate to still have virgin stands of temperate rainforest. These are found along the Pacific shoreline and on the offshore islands of British Columbia. The stands are truly magnificent: the majestic giant Douglas fir, Sitka spruce, and lodgepole pine soar higher than any other plants on Earth. The trees provide shelter and sustenance for a diversity of plant and animal life as rich as that in any tropical rainforest. The mild temperatures and the abundant rainfall allow these trees to grow all year. As in the tropical rainforest, soils are often heavily leached and lacking in nutrients. However, nutrients are locked in the vegetation, and when leaves and other organic matter fall to the ground, they quickly decompose, releasing these minerals into the soil, where they are recycled.

There is a delicate balance in the food web here. For example, the relationship between salmon and bears is essential to the health of the entire ecosystem. Each year, salmon travel up the mountain streams and rivers to spawn. They

have spent many months fattening up on the rich sea life found in coastal waters, and are returning to the lakes where they were born so that they can reproduce. The trip is perilous. They have to jump over rapids, run a gauntlet between human and animal fishers, and survive with virtually no food. But the salmon lay so many eggs that only a small percentage of those that begin the journey have to succeed in reaching their destination in order for the species to survive. Since only one in a thousand fish fry ever grows to maturity, the species compensates by being extremely prolific.

Grizzly bears wait for the annual salmon migration. They are extremely skilful hunters and have learned from their mothers how to catch fish. They wade into the streams with amazing alacrity, considering their large, ungainly appearance. One wrong step could mean that they would be swept away by the tumultuous mountain rivers. These animals become bloated on the dozens of salmon they catch, even though they often eat only the delicious belly meat and the roe (fish eggs). Birds, insects, and small mammals lower on the food chain feast on the bears' left-over meals. Leftover scraps and animal droppings enrich the soil so much that even the forest benefits from the annual event. After the fish reach their destination and reproduce, they die. Their remains wash downstream and provide another feast for scavengers in the rivers, along the shore, and in river estuaries. In the spring, billions of hatchlings become a banquet for predators in mountain streams and all along the rivers. Remember: only one in a thousand will make it back to the ocean.

Adding to the problems caused by forestry, some other industries pose threats to the preservation of natural systems along Canada's west coast. Not only does the region have fish and lumber, but it also has running water. In an energy-hungry continent where nuclear power has lost public support and the burning of fossil fuels is unpopular with people who want to reduce greenhouse gases, hydroelectric power provides a sustainable, clean, and safe alternative. However, harnessing this type of power has drawbacks. When rivers are dammed to create hydroelectric sites, water levels downstream are lowered considerably, increasing the potential for ecological disaster.

The Kemano 2 Power Diversion Project is one development that has been targeted by Aboriginal peoples and environmentalists for the negative impact it would have. In 1952, Alcan Aluminum built the Kemano I Dam on the Nechako River. Water flow was reduced by two-thirds and the environment suffered. In the 1990s, the company wanted to build another dam on the river, which would block the flow of water by 88 per cent. Twenty per cent of British Columbia's salmon spawn up the Nechako River. As a compromise, the company intended to build artificial spawning beds, but biologists were not convinced that the fish would accept the change. In the late 1990s, the B.C. government cancelled the project even though the company had already spent 500 million dollars on the development and the government stands to lose millions in tax revenues.

Figure 23.18
King William's New Forest is one of the few remaining areas of natural vegetation in England.

Figure 23.19
Bears gorge themselves on salmon every spring.

Resource Management in British Columbia

Figure 23.20
Disputes between those in the forestry industry and environmentalists are common in B.C.

The complex food web of British Columbia has existed for thousands of years. Aboriginal peoples in the area celebrate the interdependence of nature in beautifully carved house-posts. They also fish for salmon, hunt whales, and live in harmony with natural systems. However, modern demands for timber, hydroelectricity, and salmon are destroying the balance. The forests of British Columbia have long been exploited for their beautiful and strong wood, which makes excellent construction material for furniture, decks, and housing. This wood's natural ability to withstand the rotting that occurs in moist environments makes it a very valuable commodity. The workers of British Columbia want the jobs and the wealth that the industry provides, but the province is under constant pressure to find a compromise between the needs of modern society and the preservation of an incredible wilderness area.

The foresters argue that allowing an old forest to die naturally is a waste. Thousand-year-old trees are worth a fortune and should be harvested. Environmentalists contend that nothing is wasted in nature and that old-growth forests should be allowed to exist as they always have. Aboriginal peoples are ambivalent; many want the jobs that the forestry industry provides, while others want to preserve the wilderness for spiritual and cultural reasons. In such disputes, the government tries to represent the views of the majority without completely neglecting differing minority opinions on the matter.

The approach so far has been to allow the forestry industry to continue harvesting, while also ensuring that sustainable forestry practices are used. In the past, **clear-cutting** was the usual way in which trees were harvested. Huge sections of land were cleared of all vegetation, which forced animals to migrate deeper into the forest. In areas of flat to rolling hillsides, the seed cones left after the clear-cut quickly germinated and grew back.

Animals could return in 20 or 30 years, and the region could be logged again in 80 to 100 years. Forestry companies even helped nature along by planting trees in cleared areas. However, the problem with this approach lies in the fact that natural regeneration is actually better than artificial plantings. If the forest grew back naturally, there would be greater genetic diversity as native species of all types took over the land. When people planted seedlings, only the most marketable tree species were used, and the resulting **monoculture** reduced the biodiversity of the area.

From the economist's and forester's point of view, reduced biodiversity is to be encouraged because it facilitates clear-cutting. However, environmentalists and hunters deplore the loss of biodiversity because it eliminates habitat, reduces the gene pool, encourages the development of pests, and generally decreases the biological vitality of the region.

When clear-cutting occurs on mountain slopes, the practice is especially harmful since the soil is exposed to the heavy rainfall. On flat to rolling ground, the heavy rain just sits in puddles and small pools, but on the sides of mountains, the water rushes down the slopes, picking up massive amounts of mud and forest litter. There are no trees to slow down the soil erosion. When the muddy water reaches streams and rivers, its load is deposited in the river. Imagine the impact this has on spawning salmon! As if their upstream struggle is not hard enough, they now have to swim through muddy water and negotiate silt and sandbars in the rivers. The silt also buries salmon spawning-grounds. Many species indigenous to specific watersheds have become endangered because their environment has been so greatly altered. Not only are the salmon at risk; but the whole food web could collapse if the annual migration ends. Bears and other land animals would suffer, but so too would scavengers, marine mammals in estuaries, other fish, and small mammals. The annual infusion of nutrients into the forest vegetation would also be missing if the remains of the salmon were no longer available.

A constructive approach from an ecological point of view is selective cutting. In this process, foresters select certain trees in a forest—often those that are diseased or dying—and carefully harvest these individual trees while leaving the rest of the forest intact. Unfortunately, the large machinery moving in to get the tree often destroys as many trees as are saved. Industrial helicopters could airlift trees out, but this is a prime example of the main drawback of this harvesting method—it is too expensive for companies to practice. With the increasing economic success of forestry companies in some developing countries where environmental controls are not a priority, Canadian forestry companies have to remain competitive. In addition, some major Canadian companies have been bought out by transnational corporations whose main concern is profitability.

One sustainable alternative that is economical for forestry companies is **strip-cutting**. This is a harvesting technique in which narrow strips of forest are removed on steep slopes. A buffer zone along river valleys allows for any eroded material to be trapped by the existing forest before it reaches the stream. Because the strips are relatively narrow, and extreme slopes are not harvested at all, soil erosion is minimal. While the harvesting

Figure 23.21
This air photo shows the erosion that can result from the clear-cutting of forests.

method is still intrusive, natural species are able to exist by migrating to adjacent forests. This forestry practice is being used increasingly in the coastal mountains of British Columbia.

An international movement to promote sustainable forestry practices has done the most to save the endangered old-growth forests. Consumers, especially in Europe, have lobbied the industry to label forestry products that are harvested with the health of the ecosystem in mind. Some major retailers like Home Depot carry only these specially labelled wood products. By expressing their concern for the environment, consumers can make a difference.

QUESTIONS:

1. Explain how the temperate-forest food web is dependent on salmon.

2. Assess different forestry practices from the point of view of profitability and sustainability.

3. Outline how political and consumer activism has helped to save old-growth forests on Canada's west coast.

ACTIVITIES

UNDERSTANDING CONCEPTS

1. a) Prepare an organizer like the one below and summarize the characteristics of the different subtropical and west coast regions.

Characteristic	Subtropical	Mediterranean	Marine West Coast	Temperate Desert
Temperature Patterns				
Seasonality of Rainfall				
Amount of Rainfall				
Reasons for Rainfall Patterns				
Location				
Other				

    b) Explain how local variations in elevation and drainage create different ecosystems within the Everglades.

    c) What patterns of seasonality occur as one moves north through Mediterranean and marine west coast regions?

    d) What patterns of seasonality occur as one moves east from the Mediterranean region, through the temperate desert region, and into the subtropical region?

2. Explain how human activities have affected each of the following
    a) Water resources in the temperate desert
    b) Ecological systems in the Everglades
    c) Forest management in British Columbia.

3. Describe the ways in which legislators and the public have dealt with environmental concerns in each of the situations listed in Question 2.

4. a) Identify global issues that relate to the ways in which people manage resources in temperate rainforests.
    b) What can we do to encourage sustainable practices in subtropical and west coast ecosystems?

DEVELOPING AND PRACTISING SKILLS

5. Analyse the reasons for the observed distribution patterns of subtropical and west coast ecoregions around the globe.

6. Using a flow chart(s) describe the flow of matter and energy through marine west coast ecosystems in relation to landforms, climate, soils, natural vegetation, and wildlife.

7. Explain how the following climatic controls act upon the elements of the atmosphere to produce the subtropical and west coast ecoregions.
   a) Latitude
   b) Elevation
   c) The modifying influence of major water bodies
   d) Ocean currents.

LEARNING THROUGH APPLICATION

8. a) Analyse the long-term effects of human use of vegetation in the Mediterranean and western Europe.
   b) Identify and explain two geopolitical issues that face nations that share subtropical and west coast ecoregions.

9. Assume one of the following roles: lumber executive, government agent, labour union leader, conservationist, hydroelectricity executive, or salmon fisher.
   a) Prepare a development strategy for the exploitation of old-growth forests in coastal British Columbia. The strategy should be suitable for the needs of the role you are playing.
   b) Form into groups with other members of your class who have chosen the same role, and together produce a list of arguments to support your development strategy from the point of view you have chosen.
   c) Elect one person from your group to debate the merits of your strategy with the elected members from the other groups.

GIS Assignment on Species Extinction

10. As a conservationist working for the IUCN (International Zoological Conservation Organization) your job is to create global policies to protect animal species threatened with extinction. This exercise focuses on the five categories of threatened species and the natural causes as well as the human activities that threaten their survival. In this activity, your job is to prepare thematic maps showing the relationship between endangered species and protected lands.

    The first step is to download the instructions for the exercise from the ESRI Canada web site at http://www.esricanada.com/k-12/lesson/threatened_species/index.html and then click on the version of software that your computer uses. The document is in PDF format, so it will be necessary to have Adobe Acrobat in order to read it. (Instructions for downloading this program are on the ESRI web site.)

11. Upon completion of the downloaded instructions, analyze the patterns of the thematic map on the Percentage of National Protected Lands by making statements about which regions of the world have adopted a National Protected Lands Policy.
    a) In general, which regions of the world have the highest percentage of protected land area?
    b) Which regions of the world need to establish a Protected Lands Policy?
    c) From this information alone, what would be your guess about the relationship between protected land area and the number of endangered species?

12. Create a thematic map that illustrates the region or countries where there is the greatest threat to a specific species.
    a) Copy the theme map from question 11 and paste it into a new view. Change the query in the Theme Properties to the appropriate species. For example: ([Mamlthrt89]>-99) for mammals)or ([Birdthrt89]>-99) for birds. Choose from mammals (Mamlthrt89), birds (Birdthrt89), reptiles(Reptthrt89), amphibians(Amphthrt89), fish(Ffshthrt89) or plants(Planthrt91).
    b) Describe the pattern of the highest concentrations of a threatened species from the thematic map.
    c) Which regions of the world or countries pose the greatest threat to the species you have chosen?
    d) Try comparing your results with any of the other species. Is there a generalized pattern that emerges? You may wish to experiment with the removal of the mid ranges through the legend editor. Remove the two middle ranges leaving the 2 lowest and 2 highest. Click on apply.

13. Human activities can be illustrated through thematic maps using a number of the other field headings in the database. What range fields impact on the survival of a species? An example would be to compare the maps created in question 11 or 12 to a thematic map showing the Percentage of Wilderness Area in the world ([Wilderns88]>-99) or the Percentage of Urban Population in each country ([Urbpop]>-99).
    a) Consider other fields. Copy the theme from question 11 and paste it into a new view. Choose one other field of human activity and compare it to the thematic map created in question 11 or 12. Use the appropriate query under Theme Properties.
    b) Conduct an inquiry into the human activities that contribute to the extinction of species. Organize group presentations based on the comparative analysis of all thematic maps constructed. Try focusing your comparison on a specific country.

Chapter 24

CONTINENTAL AND EASTERN MARITIME ECOREGIONS

FOCUS QUESTIONS

1. How does climate affect the plants, animals, and soils of continental and eastern maritime ecoregions?
2. Why are sustainable practices in resource-based industries, such as fishing, so important?
3. How has population growth and changes in human activities over the past one hundred years increased the ecological footprint of our species?

The provinces of Manitoba, Alberta, Saskatchewan, and Ontario are included in the continental region, as are vast parts of Russia and Eastern Europe, all the way from the Alps to the frigid wastelands of Siberia. The continental climate is one of extremes, noted for its cold winters, hot summers, and adequate precipitation patterns. Where rainfall and snow are abundant, great forests are found. In the south, the trees tend to be mainly deciduous but as one travels north, conifers take over. The farther an area is away from the influence of the oceans, the less precipitation it receives. In these more arid regions, trees are replaced with a vast grassland region. Such regions are known as the steppes of Russia and the Ukraine, the prairies of Canada, and the great plains of the United States. Rich soils and flat land make this region incredibly good for growing grain and cattle.

Heading toward the ocean, the climate becomes more moderate and receives greater amounts of precipitation. This eastern maritime region includes Atlantic Canada, New England, parts of north eastern Asia, as well as some coastal areas in the southern hemisphere. The three regions—the prairies, the eastern maritime zone, and the continental region—are all variations on the same temperate climate zone.

The Continental Ecoregion

In North America, the continental ecoregion is found throughout most of southern Canada, New England, and most of the American Midwest. A belt of continental climate is also found in eastern Europe, although it does not extend as far east into continental Asia because of the rain shadow caused by the Himalayas to the south. The nature of this climate zone is determined by its location on large continental land masses. There are no examples of continental climates in the Southern Hemisphere because there are no major mid-latitude land masses south of 40° latitude.

Key Terms

boreal forest

multi-spectral scanner

sustainable resource management

ecological footprint

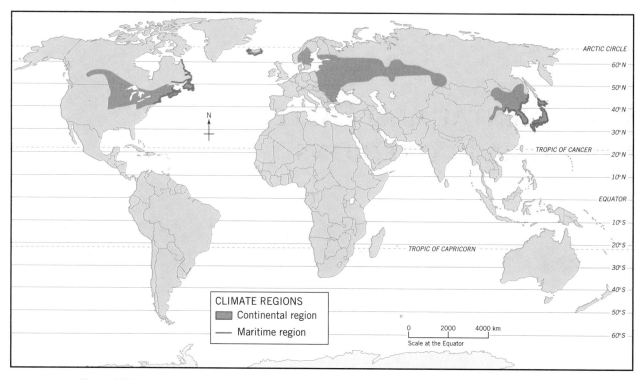

Figure 24.1
Continental and Eastern Maritime Regions

Temperature characteristics vary with distance inland and distance from the equator. Climate stations closer to the coast, such as Quebec City, have more moderate temperatures because of the influence of the oceans than climate stations further inland, such as Winnipeg. On the other hand, Pittsburgh, which is located at a lower latitude than Quebec City, has a mean annual temperature of 12°C while Quebec City's average is only 4°C.

Summer can be quite hot in the interior of the continent, even though this zone may be far from the equator. The sun's low angle on the horizon is compensated for by the long summer days (which may last for as many as 15 hours), thus making up for the sun's low intensity. Hot temperatures often trigger afternoon thunderstorms. In the winter, mid-latitude cyclones carry bitterly cold weather from the northern polar regions resulting in weeks of sub-zero temperatures. This can make the winter there seem unbearably long.

The combination of warm summers and plentiful summer rainfall provide the necessary ingredients for forests to grow. Deciduous trees such as maple, oak, and hickory are common in the south, while coniferous trees such as spruce, pine, and hemlock take over in the north. Between the hardwood forests of the south and the vast **boreal forests** of the north exists a transitional zone of **mixed forest**. On north-facing slopes, trees are often hardier conifers while southern slopes are covered with hardwood trees. Much of the forested land has been cleared in this region to make way for farms, industry, and cities.

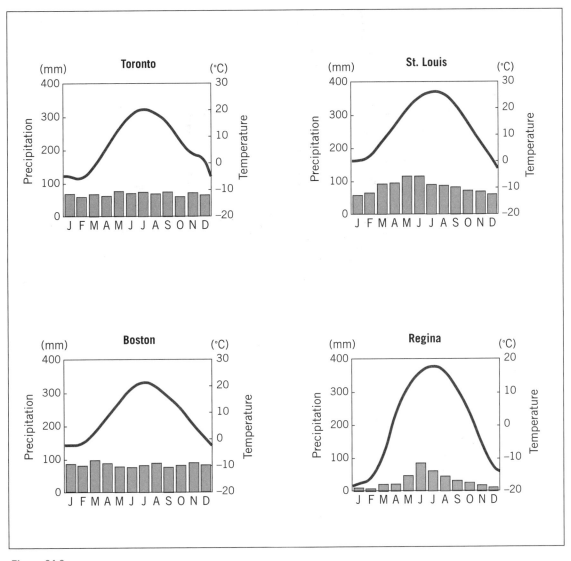

Figure 24.2
Which of these climate graphs is continental, which is inland, which is located in the north of the region, and which is eastern maritime? Give reasons for your choices.

Soils of Continental Lands

Soil fertility varies within the region, although most soils are good for farming. Water-soluble nutrients are washed out of the soil in the spring when the ground becomes sodden with melting snow and ice. **Spodosols** are moderately leached soils found in the northern part of the region where conifers are most common. Further south,

where summers are warmer, evaporation rates tend to be quite high, and the hot days dry out the topsoil horizons. Instead of the nutrients being washed out of the soils in the south, water-soluble minerals are drawn to the surface by capillary action, resulting in **alfisols.** These soils are less acidic and more fertile than the spodosols further north. Because deciduous trees are more common here, a nutrient-rich layer of forest litter

Figure 24.3
Some of the mixed forest areas have been cleared to make way for cities such as Montreal, pictured here.

Figure 24.4
Forested lands surrounding cities, such as Toronto, are usually greenbelt or agricultural areas.

rots to form humus. The climate and the natural vegetation work together to create a rich, fertile, forest soil that further increases the productivity of the land. When the region is cleared and crops grown, the land becomes highly productive for agricultural.

While farming is still very important, much of the region was cleared centuries ago and converted to other land uses. Today much of the ecoregion has been urbanized. From Pittsburgh to Chicago and north to Toronto and Montreal, the mixed-forest ecoregion has become one of the favorite habitats of the human species. In Eastern Europe similar patterns of urbanization and industrialization have taken over the land-

geo.web resources

<http://www.ccrs.nrcan.gc.ca/ccrs/imgserv/tour/toure.html>

Visit the Canadian Centre for Remote Sensing web site and take a tour of Canada via satellite. Choose a location by clicking on the map, then read the analysis alongside the image to interpret the colours and shapes.

scape. The indigenous animals such as raccoons, rats, field mice, and geese that have been able to adapt have become very successful at surviving in urban environments. However, most animals in the region are domesticated livestock such as cattle, hogs, chickens, and turkeys, which are grown in massive agricultural factories.

While many natural systems have been removed or seriously damaged because of human inhabitation, there is an increased effort among many urban dwellers to preserve some natural areas near their cities. As a result, national and provincial parks are becoming increasingly popular. Point Pelee is an example of a national park located in the most southerly region of Canada. Many migratory birds stop off at this nature reserve on their way north (in summer) or south (in winter), and it has become a bird-watcher's paradise for this reason. The preservation of greenbelts along the Niagara Escarpment and in the Oak Ridges Moraine are being fought for by local activists, town councils, and environmentalists alike. However, the pressure for low-cost housing and urban development in this highly sought-after area creates ongoing challenges for those who wish to protect such regions from urban sprawl.

Similar patterns of urbanization and agricultural development exist in other parts of the region. South of the Great Lakes, cities and farmland follow shorelines and river valleys. Less developed are the rolling Appalachian Mountains in New York State, Pennsylvania, Illinois, and Ohio. Remarkably, natural systems are present in many of these heavily populated states because landform features discourage development. The North European Plain—another continental region—also has similar patterns. Cities such as Berlin, Warsaw, Prague, and Minsk spread into the countryside and are surrounded by farmland, while forested regions dominate mountainous and inaccessible outlying regions.

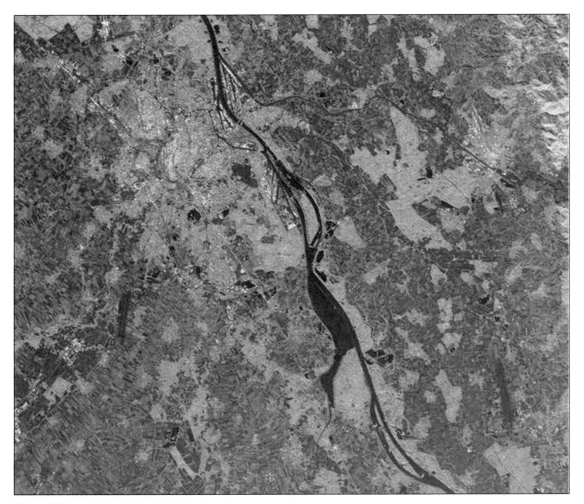

Figure 24.5
This satellite image shows the Rhine River where it forms a divide between the Alsace region of Northern France on the left and the Black Forest region of Germany on the right. The river valley is densely populated, as seen in this image, which shows the French city of Strasbourg (the light blue, orange areas in upper left corner) and the German cities of Kehl (across the river from Strasbourg) and Offenburg (the bright area in right, centre). The purple patches are vineyards and the light green areas are forests. Analyse the situation of the cities, forests, agricultural areas and landforms.

Analysing Satellite Images

Satellites launched over the past five decades provide scientists in many fields with a wide variety of pertinent data on all the spheres of planet Earth. For example, the first satellite devoted to remote sensing was launched by the United States in 1961 to monitor weather. Since then, weather satellites have provided a massive record of data showing climate patterns over a 40 year period. In 1972 the first of seven Landsat satellites was set in orbit over the north and south poles with the sole purpose of mapping the planet. The Geostationary Operational Environmental Satellites (GOES) that were initiated two years later orbit the earth at the same speed and direction as the earth spins, resulting in the satellites remaining stationary over the same place on the earth. While the resolution is lower than that of the Landsat satellites, this program is especially good at monitoring tropical storms.

In 1998, France launched the SPOT (*Satellite Pour l'Observation de la Terre*) 4 satellite, which was one in a series that was begun in 1986 to monitor global vegetation patterns. In 1995 Canada launched the RADARSAT series of space observers, which use microwave sensors (radar) to collect data through clouds, dust, smoke and other forms of air pollution. The EOS AM program was launched in 1998. With a polar **sun-synchronous** orbit, this satellite studies the planet as an integrated system combining images of ice, oceans, atmosphere, and the biosphere. The impacts of global warming can be studied via this satellite as the planet warms up.

Satellites act as platforms housing scanners that record images of the earth. Many people think that these images are photographs made

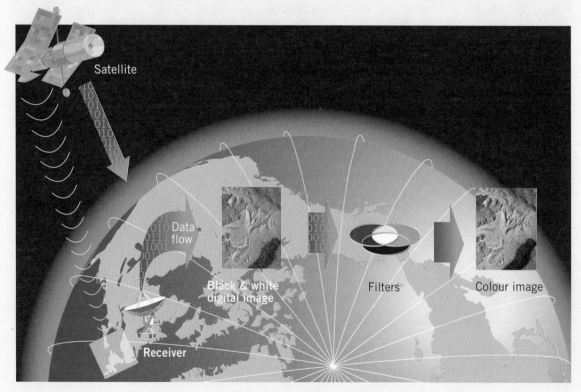

Figure 24.6
This illustration shows how satellite images come into being. Write a paragraph describing the process.

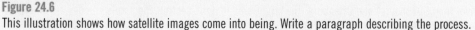

with cameras, but increasingly satellite images are made using sophisticated **multi-spectral scanners**, which enable the observer to see light reflected from the earth in many different colours of the spectrum. Each colour allows for different properties to be observed. Passive or thermal infrared systems are especially good for observing vegetation. The chlorophyll in the leaves absorbs all the green light in the spectrum leaving red. Wherever the image is green, vegetation is prolific. Microwave or radar systems are good for observing the surface of the planet through clouds and other atmospheric interference. Most sensors record their images in digital format. Computers and advanced communications equipment transfer the data to earthbound computers where the digital values are converted into pictures.

By studying the shapes and colours displayed in a satellite image we are able to identify features. The use of a map of the same area also aids in the analysis. Study the satellite image of Winnipeg and the accompanying map.

Follow these steps to help in the analysis.

1. Align the map and the satellite image in the same direction. Unlike maps, satellite images seldom have north at the top.
2. Prepare a tracing of the satellite image using tracing paper and a fine-tipped marker.

   Trace drainage patterns, which are shown as black thin often serpentine lines for rivers, such as the Red River. Often valleys can be seen because they have the serpentine shape of rivers but are a darker colour than the surrounding land. This indicates a **reparian zone** of natural vegetation growing along a flood plain.
3. Identify types of urban areas and transportation systems. Because colours vary with images, use the map to identify and trace one

Figure 24.7
Satellite Image of Winnipeg

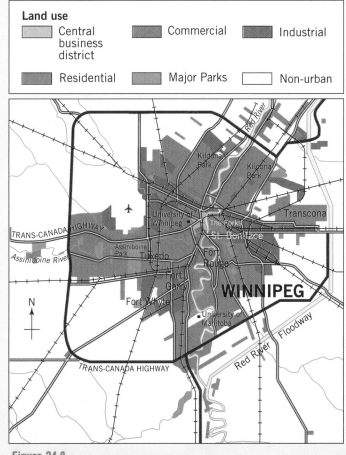

Figure 24.8
Map of Winnipeg

type of urban area and use the same colour to establish the locations of others. Transportation routes such as the TransCanada Highway and the railways are visible on the satellite image. Trace the ones you can see.

4.   Farmland usually surrounds urban centres. Since the example is an enhanced infra-red image, these areas are shown as a wine colour. Depending on the scale of the map and the time of year the image was taken, it is possible to identify individual farmers' fields. For this study we will trace only the broad regions where agriculture is the main activity.

5.   Forested areas appear in green or yellow. In the centre of the image is the purple and blue urban area. What do the darkest purple areas represent?

6.   Once your image has been completely traced, label all the features you located. Now that you have a detailed diagram of the region it is possible to analyse what the image shows.

TRY IT!

1.   Where is the Cetral Business District located in relation to natural features such as drainage and landforms?

2.   Describe the land surrounding the city. What do the various colours and shapes show?

3.   What suggestions would you have for urban planners in this region?

The Eastern Maritime Ecoregion

We often refer to New Brunswick, Nova Scotia, and Prince Edward Island as the Maritime provinces, but in physical geography the term "maritime" has a broader meaning. These are the places that are influenced by the ocean. Thus eastern maritime regions include not only the Maritime provinces, but also the coastal areas of Newfoundland, New England, Europe, eastern Asia, and island nations such as Iceland and Japan, to name but a few.

Winters in eastern maritime climates tend to be milder along the coast than in the middle of continents, while summers are usually cooled by moderating ocean breezes. The cold Labrador Current often carries icebergs past the coast of Labrador to the waters off eastern Newfoundland even in early July. The ocean also affects precipitation patterns. In the fall, tropical storms originating as far away as the subtropics sweep north into Canada's eastern provinces. Heavy rains and strong winds bring a quick end to a summer

Figure 24.9
Iceland's Coastline

that seems too short. In winter, arctic storms from Labrador sweep over the region. Pleasant weather is common in P.E.I., Nova Scotia, and New Brunswick in July and August, and even Newfoundland can have warm sunny days, especially in the interior.

Vegetation, Soils, and Landforms in Eastern Maritime Areas

As with the continental region, natural vegetation varies with local climate conditions, soil, and elevation. Mixed forest in the south gradually gives way to boreal forest in the north and finally to **tundra** in high altitude zones. Deciduous trees have adapted to the northern climate by growing mainly in sheltered valleys where temperatures are warmer. In winter, these trees shed their leaves to reduce water lost through transpiration during this dormant period. When spring comes, energy stored in the trunks and roots is used to produce the leaves needed for continued growth. Unlike deciduous trees, coniferous trees on the slopes of the Appalachian Mountains continue to grow all year, although their winter growth is slower because of the low temperatures and the lack of moisture. The thin needles of these trees reduce transpiration, especially in winter when so much of the moisture is frozen.

Spodosol is the dominate soil type in the mountainous inland regions where precipitation is plentiful and conifers prevail. However, Prince Edward Island and the adjacent shorelines of New Brunswick and Nova Scotia have deep, red soils unlike those found in the mountainous parts of the region. These unusual soils formed from red sandstone and shale, which developed during the Carboniferous period. Called **placosols**, these soils support a rich agricultural industry.

Landforms are also varied. In the south, broad coastal plains and wide valleys encourage urbanization and farming. The old fold mountains of the Appalachians dominate the inland landscape. These ancient mountains have been eroded for so many years they look more like rolling hills. Soils are often thin on the slopes but accumulations in the valleys are common. In Newfoundland and Labrador, the landscape becomes increasingly rugged as the Appalachians give way to the Canadian Shield. The thin soils and cold climate make agriculture a marginal activity here. Driving along the roads in Northern Newfoundland, one can see tiny garden plots, planted wherever there is a patch of soil on the rocky landscape.

Resource Development in Atlantic Canada

Resource developers from fishers to foresters are inventing new ways of harvesting renewable resources. **Sustainable resource management** is the idea that renewable resources are harvested at a slower rate than the resources can be replaced. Non-renewable resources are used sparingly and sustainable alternatives are developed wherever possible.

Although the eastern maritime regions provide a variety of natural resources, the one most commonly associated with the ecosystem is the fishing industry. Renewable ocean resources such as fish need to be carefully managed so that they will continue to be available for exploitation by future generations. Unfortunately, this lesson was learned the hard way through the loss of the cod fishery in the Atlantic provinces in the 1990s.

After 500 years of cod fishing off the east coast of Canada, the resource has been so depleted that some scientists do not believe it will recover in the foreseeable future. Even the government imposed **moratorium** on cod fishing, which was implemented in 1994, has not revived the cod stocks enough to allow the industry to even partially reopen. It apparently was too little too late. The reasons for the destruction of this once lucrative industry are many and include complicated political, biological, and technological factors. The Maritime economy went into a tailspin as fishers lost their livelihoods and fish plants closed. Today, the lessons learned from the cod fishery are being applied to other renewable ocean resources.

Lobster Fishing in the Maritimes

After the economic devastation caused by the collapse of the cod industry, fishers along Canada's East Coast have had to cast their nets in new directions to earn a living. As a result, lobsters replaced cod as a source of income for many coastal families. Though it is not undertaken on a scale as large as the cod fishery once was, the lobster fishery has taken over as the most lucrative fishery in Atlantic Canada. In 1996 approximately $400 million worth of lobster was caught. This level of resource exploitation could not continue, however, without threatening the future sustainablity of the industry.

In 1995 the Fisheries Resource Conservation Council revealed alarming findings: lobster stocks had been in steady decline throughout the early 1990s and would continue to shrink unless something was done. Council members stated that the vast majority of lobsters—up to 90 per cent—were being taken from the water before they had a chance to reproduce even once. This resulted in the egg production level dropping to 0.3 per cent—which is well below the level needed for lobsters to maintain their population. Basically, too many lobsters were being fished, leaving too few in the water each season to replenish the stocks.

But the government learned a valuable lesson in sustainable resource development through the loss of the cod fishery, and it was not about to let history repeat itself with the lobster fish-

Figure 24.10
Maritime Lobster Fisher

ery. In 1998, the Minister of Fisheries and Oceans, David Anderson, developed a conservation plan through consultations with fishers and scientists to double egg production in waters off the Atlantic provinces over a four-year period. The solution involved increasing the minimum size of the lobsters being harvested so that younger lobsters would have a chance to reproduce at least a couple of times before they were caught. In addition, fishers were asked to tag 50 per cent of reproductive-age females they caught by notching a V into their **carapaces**. The tag makes the sale of these individuals illegal. As well, the government began holding workshops on resource issues, while fishers volunteered to collect data for scientific study.

Government officials indicated that there appeared to be a greater spirit of co-operation among fishers, scientists, and themselves to save the lobster fishery than there had been during the cod fish crisis. In a statement issued by the Department of Fisheries and Oceans, Minister Anderson said, "The response and advice I have received from the fishing community demonstrates that there is widespread and strong support for lobster conservation... We must all work together to protect this valuable resource." However, the need for legal enforcement of the new rules was still necessary. The RCMP and Revenue Canada imposed fines of up to $10 000 and jail terms of no more than 90 days for fishers selling undersized or "V-notched" females.

The conservation measures put in place in 1998 continued to be implemented into 2001, while scientists continued to evaluate the effect of the plan on egg production levels.

QUESTIONS:

1. Why does there appear to be a more co-operative attitude with the lobster fishery than there was with the cod fishery?
2. How has the lobster fishery been unsustainably managed?
3. What can we learn from this case study regarding the sustainable management of resources?

The Prairie Ecoregion

The temperate grasslands, although called by different names in different countries, are known globally as the "breadbaskets" of the world.

Precipitation determines the location of these regions, which are mainly found in the mid-latitudes in the dry interiors of large continents. The only exceptions are the pampas of Argentina and the veldt of South Africa, which are on east coasts where rain shadows occur. The region, which is too dry for trees, is a transition zone between mixed forest and desert. The temperate grasslands are important agricultural regions. It is therefore important to understand how human modifications have changed them.

Figure 24.11
The Canadian Prairies are one of the "breadbaskets" of the world.

Prairie Climate

The continental growing season is short with frosts occurring in early to late fall and lasting well into the spring. This greatly affects the ecosystem because plants and animals must cope with frozen soil for much of the year. In winter most of the precipitation falls as snow, but when the spring thaw occurs, the water is released into the ground, providing moisture for germinating seeds.

Like the tropical grasslands, the mid-latitude prairies are made up of two vegetation zones—short grasslands and tall grasslands. The short-grass region, which is the semi-arid zone that borders the temperate deserts, receives between 250 mm and 500 mm of precipitation. Moving east away from the interior of the continent, precipitation increases and taller grasses flourish. This tall grassland region ranges from the low latitude subtropics to continental and even subarctic climates. As with all ecoregions, there is a great deal of variation from one region to the next.

Plants and Animals

As the name states, grasses are the main form of natural vegetation in the region. In their natural state, the tall grasses of the American Midwest reach heights of over 2 metres. Today, however, agriculture dominates the entire ecosystem, and the original tall-grass prairie is difficult to find.

The natural grasses were well adapted to the climate. Buffalo grass, a short steppe variety, and various types of blue-stem grasses predominated. They had extensive root systems that could reach deep into the rich soil. These plants grew rapidly when it was warm and there was rainfall, and seeded quickly before frosts came in the fall. Most were **perennial**, meaning that they were dormant in the winter but came back to life when growing conditions returned. Trees are seldom found in the region. The only exceptions are in sheltered places where there is abundant groundwater close to the surface and protection from dry winter winds. As a result, river valleys and springs often have small deciduous forests.

Some of the large indigenous herbivores that used to live on these grasslands, including bison, pronghorn antelope, and deer, have also vanished, except where they are protected in parks and game preserves. Long legs and hard hoofs allowed these animals to migrate in search of fresh pastures. The bison's long matted fur protected it from the severe winters, while its heavy bearded head was well suited to pushing through snow to reach the grass in winter. Smaller animals such as prairie dogs and gophers, as well as numerous insects live off the grasses. The coyote, the only major predator, preys on these smaller animals.

Soils and Landforms

There are three main soil groups in this ecozone: aridisols, mollisols, and alfisols. In the steppe around temperate deserts, aridisols are common. Low water content, a thin layer of humus, and concentrations of salt in the A horizon make aridisols—in their natural state—unsuitable for most field crops. As a result, the region makes up the range-country of the western prairies. If the soil is irrigated and well drained, the salts and other mineral deposits can be washed away, leaving sections of arable land where ranchers can grow alfalfa—an excellent cattle feed. Water is either pumped from rivers or tapped from aquifers deep underground.

Mollisols are found in the core of the grasslands. These are some of the most fertile soils in the world. Extremely deep, with well developed horizons, these black soils have a high humus content. They absorb water when it rains yet do not pack down tightly like clay soils. Litter accumulates in deep layers because decomposition of the annual buildup of grass is slow in this temperate climate. When it rains, the mat of dead grasses and roots retains moisture and allows it to slowly percolate through the soil. It is this soil that makes the region a good agricultural area.

To the east lie the alfisols. These soils share many of the characteristics of the rich mollisols, but they have a higher water content because of the relatively higher level of precipitation in the region. Like mollisols, they are deep and easily ploughed once the natural vegetation is removed. Alfisols are moderately leached and slightly acidic, but the addition of lime and fertilizers makes them excellent agricultural soils.

While there are some exceptions, these temperate grasslands have developed on flat or gently undulating plains. The absence of trees and the level ground make it possible to see great distances in this vast, uniform landscape. In North America, the region was a shallow inland sea during the Cretaceous and Tertiary periods. Sediment carried by rivers from the Canadian Shield and the newly formed Rocky Mountains was deposited in the shallow water. Over millions of years, layer upon layer of sediment accumulated until the sea was virtually filled in. When sea level dropped as polar ice caps expanded, the region was exposed above the surface of the water and today's soils formed from the limestone regolith that remained. Present-day rivers erode through the plains, creating some variety in the flat prairie.

Indigenous Peoples

In North America, many Aboriginal peoples lived sustainable lifestyles on these grasslands. The populations were relatively small, so their main economic activities of hunting and gathering had little impact on the land. The people relied on the abundant herds of bison and deer to meet most of their needs. Meat was eaten, skins were used for clothing and shelter, and bones were substituted for wood to make implements in this virtually treeless ecosystem. Berries, grains, and other wild foods supplemented their diet. The people lived in harmony with the environment and were well adapted to it.

Figure 24.12
This Peter Rindisbacher painting, completed around 1824, shows members of the Assinniboine people hunting bison with bow and arrows.

For centuries the herds of bison were so large that hunting had no negative impact on animal populations. This changed, however, once the European settlers introduced foreign technologies into the equation. In the mid-1600s, Europeans brought horses to the plains. These animals provided hunters with greater mobility. Later, guns enabled both the settlers and the Aboriginal people to hunt more efficiently. In the eighteenth and nineteenth centuries, Europeans initiated the hunting of bison for sport and the sale of their hides for profit, leading to a dramatic increase in the number of animals being killed. As a result, what had once seemed like an inexhaustible resource was almost completely wiped out in the nineteenth century. Today, the North American bison can be found only in protected reserves. With the demise of the bison, the traditional lifestyle of many Aboriginal peoples could no longer be sustained.

Resource Development on the Prairies

To appreciate how the grasslands of North America became the great agricultural regions they are today, it is important to understand the historical geography of these regions. In Europe and eastern North America, the best farmland was forested. Because the plains lacked trees, European settlers believed the region to be a wasteland, unsuitable for farming. In addition, the sod was so thick that ploughs could not break through it. Even cattle ranching was difficult since the lack of trees meant there was not enough wood for building large enclosures. Cattle roamed the grasslands freely, identified by the ranch's brand burned into the animal's hide. Because it seemed so inhospitable, the region came to be known as the "Great American Desert."

Revolutionary agricultural inventions provided the technology needed to open the land

Figure 24.13
Threshing machines and new wheat strains were two of the new technologies which led to the wheat boom on the Canadian Prairies.

to development. In 1825, John Deere invented the self-scouring steel plough. Now that the deep prairie sod could be turned, the ploughing of the American West began. The invention of barbed wire allowed the range to be fenced with a minimum of wood. Animals could now be contained and crops protected. Drilling equipment allowed water wells to be dug deep into aquifers that lay beneath the farmland. This provided settlers with an abundant supply of water.

In Canada, the Prairies were developed after the American West was settled. The Canadian Pacific Railway opened the prairies to settlers from eastern Canada, Europe, and the United States. However, the first crops grown here weren't always successful because the new settlers imported wheat strains that were not appropriate for the shorter growing season of these northern lands. In the 1840s an Ontario farmer named David Fife successfully developed a new strain of wheat from some seeds he received from a friend in Glasgow, Scotland. This new wheat, which became known as Red Fife, matured 10 days earlier than previously used strains. This enabled the farmers to harvest the crops before the first fall frosts destroyed them, usually. A Canadian

botanist named Charles Saunders solved the problem by crossing the Red Fife with a variety of wheat from India. The result, which he called Marquis wheat, took only 100 days to ripen. This innovation allowed farmers to plant crops farther north in areas that had an even shorter growing season. The pioneers were able to use the naturally fertile soils effectively because of the newly developed technologies. Today the grasslands support two main economic activities, farming and livestock ranching.

People who specialize in the study of plants are called botanists. In recent years such professionals have become very important because of the cutting-edge research that is being done on cloning and other forms of genetic engineering. These scientists have for centuries bred plants with desired qualities to produce offspring with highly valued characteristics. For example, wheat varieties with strong resilient shafts were bred with wheat types that have big, full seed heads. The result was a new **hybrid** wheat with shafts strong enough to support the bigger seed heads. Today botanists are splicing genes from one species into another, totally different plant. Improved tolerance to fungus, better growing features, and even improved taste are sometimes the result. If you are good in science, enjoy solving problems, and are interested in living things this could be the field for you.

Farming

The temperate grasslands are the most modified rural landscapes in the world. Virtually every aspect of the region has been changed. The natural vegetation has been replaced with farm crops. The native animals have disappeared, while domestic herds have claimed their territory. The soils have been ploughed, treated, and irrigated. Drainage patterns have been controlled. Even the aquifers are being changed as ever-increasing numbers of wells remove water from them. Only the climate remains the same, and even this could be changing as a result of global warming.

Much of the world's population is being supported by the breadbasket regions of North America, Argentina, Russia, and the Ukraine. But can we continue to use these grasslands without destroying them?

Whenever crops are harvested—whether it is a grain crop or cattle—nutrients are removed from the soil. To bring the soil fertility back to its previous level and keep crop yields high, nutrients must be added to the soil. By the 1930s, the soils of the Canadian Prairies and the American plains were much less fertile than they were before intensive farming began. In addition, the region was plagued by droughts. Marginal areas that were only suitable for farming when rainfall was good became **dust bowls** as wind storms ripped away millions of tons of topsoil. Crop yields dropped and the region's economy suffered.

These problems continued into the 1940s. After the Second World War, chemical fertilizers were added to the soil to increase fertility. The soils recovered and so did crop yields. However, populations around the world also rose, leading to an increase in the demand for grain and meat. Over the next 30 years, farmers experimented with fertilizers and relied increasingly on this chemical technology to revitalize soils in order to meet growing market demands. Sometimes too much fertilizer was applied to the land, especially in the spring when runoff is greatest, causing phosphorous and nitrogen to enter groundwater and eventually end up in streams and rivers. High concentrations of these chemicals stimulated the growth of algae, which in turn used up much of the oxygen in the water and damaged natural ecosystems as a result. Rising fertilizer costs and the need to constantly increase the amount of additives to the soil each year to maintain crop yields complicate the issue even further. Today, farmers have a better understanding of soil dynamics. Fertilizers are used in moderation to ensure a healthy crop with less harmful effects on natural ecosystems.

Another problem is pest control. Grain farming is an unnatural process. Planting one or two species over thousands of hectares enables insects or plant fungi to travel from plant to plant until the entire crop is destroyed. In a natural ecosystem, a variety of plants is interspersed throughout the region. It is difficult for pests to spread across vast areas because some plants are naturally resistant to them. To compensate for this lack of diversity, artificial pesticides must be used.

Unfortunately, pesticides often kill beneficial creatures, too. For example, the praying mantis eats grasshoppers, which feed on grain crops. If the praying mantis is inadvertently killed by pesticides, then more grasshoppers will survive to destroy the crop. Pesticides may also destroy organisms in the soil that are responsible for breaking down litter and weathering parent material—two processes that allow nutrients to re-enter the soil. Without these organisms, soils suffer.

In the 1950s, toxic sprays such as DDT (dichlorodiphenyltrichloroethane) were used on farms worldwide. This insecticide not only built up in the soil but also in animal tissue and groundwater. DDT takes more than two years to break down naturally. Each year more and more of the poison was added to the soil, thereby increasing the residual amount in the ecosystem. Animals high in the food chain, such as hawks, fish, and even people, had concentrations of DDT in their bodies. The substance is now banned in many countries and, as with fertilizers, more ecologically responsible practices are being followed today. New pesticides break down in several weeks and are much more toxic, so smaller amounts are needed and there are few residual chemicals.

Another common farming practice, especially in the southern plains, is irrigation. Higher evapo-transpiration rates make rainfall less effective here than in the cooler north. Field irrigation produces higher yields and allows farmers to grow crops of greater value. Water for irrigation often comes from aquifers. When evaporation is high, water is taken out of the aquifer: in the spring, when meltwater swells streams, the aquifer is replenished. The Ogallala aquifer stretches from Wyoming to Texas and holds about the same volume of water as Lake Huron.

Figure 24.14
Drought on the Prairies caused precious topsoil to dry up and blow away creating the "dust bowl" of the 1930s.

This seemingly endless supply of groundwater has been tapped for over 40 years. Today, however, advanced pumping systems are removing the water faster than it can be replenished. There is a danger that so much of the water will be removed that the aquifer will no longer be able to provide water for irrigation. This water supply can be sustained only if people do not over-exploit it.

Sustainable agricultural methods are being rediscovered by many farmers. Crop rotation is one example. It involves growing a different crop on a particular field each year. This method improves soil fertility because legumes such as soy beans or alfalfa actually increase soil fertility since bacteria on their roots fix nitrogen directly from air in the soil. (Nitrogen is a natural fertilizer that encourages plant growth.) Leaving a field fallow for a year allows the soil to recover lost nutrients. Allowing crop stubble from harvests to remain in fields until new seeds are planted maintains soil moisture and reduces wind erosion. **Zero tillage** takes this idea one step further as seeds are planted on the fields without any ploughing. Whichever methods are used, sustainable agricultural practices are essential if the breadbaskets of the world are to remain productive.

Cattle Ranching

Cattle ranching in the temperate grasslands today relies on modern technology. Ranches are often immense, covering thousands of hectares. Although still used, horses are no longer as feasible as they once were because of the sheer size of the farms. Trucks and even helicopters are often necessary to monitor operations. Farmers use all-terrain vehicles to carry feed out to animals stranded in winter blizzards. ATVs are also used to assist in rounding up cattle and to maintain fences, pumps, and other farm equipment that may be in remote locations.

Marginal lands unfit for field crops are usually reserved for cattle and sheep ranching. As long as there is enough land for the pasture to regenerate itself, this type of farming is sustainable. Problems result when too many animals are kept on too little land. If the land is over-grazed, grass cover is reduced and wind erosion increases. The microclimate is altered and the process of **desertification** is launched. This has not been a serious problem in North America, but over-grazing has caused ecological problems in Australia where rainfall is less reliable.

Cattle ranching is a huge industry in North America because people in the United States and Canada consume large amounts of beef per capita. This product is only one of many products we use to meet our needs and wants. However, every resource we take from the environment, whether it be a cow or a tree, has an impact on the planet over time. Geographers call this human impact our ecological footprint.

geo.web resources

<http://www.unccd.int/main.php>

This is the web site of the United Nations Secretariat of the Convention to Combat Desertification. Visit the site and summarize the UN's current efforts to halt the problem of land degradation in arid, semi-arid, and dry sub-humid areas.

Your Ecological Footprint

If you step into some soft earth, you leave a footprint. The idea of an **ecological footprint** is a metaphor to indicate how big of an impact you have on the planet. Everything you do and everything you consume affects nature. When you drive a car, you use gasoline that was processed in a refinery and you produce greenhouse gases and acid rain from the emissions. The materials that went into making the car were taken from the natural environment. Even watching TV has an impact. The material used to make the TV and the electricity used to run it came from natural systems.

The ecological footprint estimates all food, oxygen, water, fuel, and other resources you have consumed in terms of land area. For example, your footprint considers the amount of land needed to grow all the food you eat, to produce the fibers from which your clothes are made, to accommodate the waste material you create, to produce the clean drinking water you need, and to supply the resources to produce the electrical energy you use. The more land you need, the bigger your ecological footprint.

If you divide the number of people on Earth into the amount of land area of the planet you will find that each person is entitled to 1.5 hectares of land. This is an area 150 meters by 100 meters. Since much of the earth is unproductive land, your ecological footprint should be even less than that. However, most Canadians have ecological footprints three to four times what the earth can provide. Our current average ecological footprint of 4-5 hectares is immensely large compared to that of the average East Indian at 0.4 hectares. If everyone on the planet lived the way we do, we would need three planet Earths to live sustainably. A hundred years ago Canadians had ecological footprints more in keeping with what the earth could provide. While it is not possible to return things to as they were in 1900, it is possible to live a more sustainable lifestyle.

ACTIVITIES

UNDERSTANDING CONCEPTS

1. Prepare an organizer summarizing the characteristics of the temperate grasslands under the following headings: location, climate, plants and animals, soils and landforms, indigenous peoples.
2. a) Describe the interrelationships that exist among the soil, climate, and vegetation for the temperate grasslands by explaining how
    *   climate affects soils.
    *   climate affects vegetation.
    *   vegetation affects soils.
    b) Show the results in a flow chart.
3. Outline the geographic factors that led to the economic success of the North American temperate grasslands.
    a) List the technical innovations that led to the agricultural development of the region.
    b) Explain how each innovation allowed people to develop the resource base.
    c) Determine the negative environmental effect of each innovation and suggest strategies that could minimize these effects.
4. Prepare an organizer summarizing the characteristics of the eastern maritime region under the following headings: location, climate, plants and animals, soils and landforms.
5. Explain how the lobster fishery is being handled differently than the cod fishery.
6. People have a significant impact on their local environment. Prepare a research paper on the impact people are having in your community. It may be a development scheme such as the building of a new quarry or a new housing development. It could even relate to government legislation such as the relaxation of environmental standards to allow a new factory to make a profit, or the expansion of the bear hunt into the breeding season. Choose a topic that is local and is of interest to you.
    a) Evaluate the impact of the human activity on your local environment.
    b) Identify and create maps of the areas in the local community that could be rehabilitated.
    c) Develop an action plan to rehabilitate your problem area.
    d) Present your findings to the class and act on your plan to help restore balance to your local community.
7. a) Explain why our ecological footprints were so small 100 years ago even though people did not practice sustainable lifestyles.
    b) How do you account for the fact that people in developing countries have such small ecological footprints?
    c) What would be the result if people around the world acquire ecological footprints more approaching the size of North Americans'?

DEVELOPING AND PRACTISING SKILLS

8. a) Trace your footprint on graph paper.
    b) Describe your footprint quantitatively and qualitatively.
    c) Make a collage of photos and illustrations within the outline you drew of some of the things that make up your ecological footprint.

d) Write a paragraph describing the items in your collage.

9. The extraction of minerals such as potash, natural gas, and oil are other human activities that take place on the temperate grasslands of North America. Conduct research to determine how mineral extraction affects grassland ecosystems.

10. Survey some web sites to find satellite images of different regions of the world that are found in the middle latitudes. You could use the following site, which is a collection of recent NASA images, as a starting point <www.visibleEarth.nasa.gov>.

   a) Select an image and analyse the impact people are having on that specific area by studying how the land has been modified.

   b) Locate the image on an outline map of the world.

   c) Trace the image, showing significant physical and human features.

   d) Describe a possible environmental problem that could result from continued, increasing human use of the area.

LEARNING THROUGH APPLICATION

11. a) Assume one of the following roles: fisher, biologist, fish plant worker, government official.

   b) Prepare an argument for or against the lobster conservation strategies and role-play a debate these different people might have over the issue.

12. Research three other resource-based industries currently operating in Canada's Atlantic provinces. Assess each in terms of its impact on the natural ecosystems of the region. Some suggestions for research include **aquaculture** industries (mussels, salmon, etc.), pulp and paper, and tourism.

13. a) Research an eastern maritime region outside of Canada and compare its physical geography (climate, natural vegetation, soils, and natural resources, etc.) to Atlantic Canada.

   b) Assess whether or not physical geography has been central to the development of industries in your chosen region.

14. While the regions studied in this section are remarkably diverse, there is a common theme that runs through the chapter—the sustainable development of resources. Compare the three regions stating what has been done correctly, what has been poorly done, and what changes need to be made in each in order to improve sustainable management practices.

15. a) Your ecological footprint is much larger than your actual footprint. Go out onto the schoolyard and measure 4.5 ha to get an idea of the impact one Canadian has on the land. One hectare is 100 m by 100 m, so 4.5 hectares is 450 m by 100 m or 225 m by 200 m. One stride is about 1 metre. Pace out the area on the schoolyard.

   b) After this is done, pace out 1.5 ha. This area represents the amount of productive land currently available to support each person on Earth.

   c) Assume your actual footprint is 4.5 ha. Outline it on a piece of paper. Draw another footprint at a third of the size of your original to show the 1.5 ha. of land currently available to support each person on Earth. Place the smaller print on top of the larger.

   e) What conclusions can you make from this activity?

Culminating Activity: Producing a Sustainability Case Study

The food we eat, the homes we live in, the water we drink and the resources needed to create all of our other needs and wants are provided for us by natural systems on Earth. Yet humans continue to abuse and overuse the very things that are necessary for our continued existence. Two hundred years ago British philosopher Thomas Malthus warned that there was a limit to the number of people the earth could support. While Malthus was concerned about food production keeping up with population growth, his idea about the earth's maximum capacity for life is gaining wide acceptance.

What is the earth's **carrying capacity**? Can the resources provided by this planet support the billions of human inhabitants of the earth? The answer, at least for present, appears to be yes. Many people in the developed world are more prosperous today than they have ever been. The majority of Canadians live in modern homes with numerous amenities. Electricity, indoor plumbing, central heating, basically limitless clean tap water, and appliances such as televisions, stoves, refrigerators, and stereos are things many of us take for granted. A mere 50 years ago things we think are basics today were unheard of luxuries. People in some developing countries are living better also. Higher incomes allow people in countries such as Mexico and China to buy consumer goods and accumulate material possessions to achieve a higher standard of living.

However, there is a limit as to how much we can take out of the environment without irreparable damage being done to the planet. It begs the question: Will there come a point when the earth can no longer provide for our needs and wants? The answer to this question rests, in part, with our ability to use the resources we have sustainably.

Assignment

Produce an independent case study in which you analyse the importance of stewardship and sustainability as guiding principles for human use of the physical environment.

STEP 1: Getting an Overview

1. Choose a renewable natural resource that interests you. A natural resource is anything in nature that can be used to benefit people, so the list of possibilities is huge: maple trees, rivers, oysters, coral reefs, fertile soils, gorillas, beautiful landscapes, bananas, etc.

2. Using atlas maps that show the locations of natural resources, find a country that is developing the resource you chose. If the resource is not shown on the maps, use the Internet, encyclopaedias, or other library resources to find such a country.

3. In a report describe the resource, it uses, and value to people. What benefit is the resource to the people of the country and/or other countries?

4. a) In detail, describe the method of exploitation being used by the country to develop the resource. Gather photos and/or diagrams to expand on your description.

   b) If the resource is being extracted from nature or manipulated in some way, how is this process undertaken? What technologies, if any, are being used in the development of the resource? Include diagrams, photographs, and maps in your explanation.

STEP II Analysis

5. a) Locate another country that exploits the same resource, but uses a different method to do so and describe that method in detail. For example, the first country you chose might tap maple trees for maple syrup, whereas the second country may chop down the trees for lumber to make furniture.

   b) Gather facts in order to compare the development of the resource in the first country to the second country. Create a chart like the example on the next page for your comparison. However, depending on the resource you chose, the criteria list may have to be modified to better suit the situation.

   c) Using the definitions of stewardship and sustainability given in this book and the facts collected in your chart, write a paper in which you argue why the method used by one of the countries can be considered more sustainable than the other. If you consider both methods unsustainable, do further research to determine if an option for sustainable development of the resource exists and explain it. In your paper include reasons why you feel it is important that this resource be sustainably developed.

STEP III Present Your Findings

6. Organize your research paper, the chart you created in question 5, maps, photos, and diagrams into a case study on bristol board.

7. Take part in a "Sustainable Development Fair" in which students examine each others' displays.

CRITERIA	COUNTRY A	COUNTRY B
Briefly describe the method of exploitation used		
Environmental impacts of the development process (both long-term and short term)		
Short-term and long-term impacts of the development on the resource itself		
Efficiency of the operation (i.e., how much waste material, if any, is produced through the development process)		
Remedial actions taken during or after the development process		
Other		

Glossary

A

above mean sea level the elevation above which the ocean never reaches on average

abrasion the erosive scraping and polishing that results from the action of wind, water or ice on the exposed surface of the earth

absolute time time that can be measured using units such as hours, days, years and millennia

acid deposition any form of precipitation (rain, dust, snow, etc.) that has a low pH due to natural or artificial causes

active layer the part of the permafrost that thaws and refreezes each year

aeolian landscape an arid region where the primary gradational process relates to wind action and flash flooding

agronomist a professional who specializes in soils and farming practices

air mass a body of air that takes on the characteristics (temperature and humidity) of the surface over which it develops—see also source region

albedo the percentage of incoming solar radiation that is reflected by the earth's surfaces—objects with high albedo are light coloured and often shiny such as snow; while dark objects like forests have a low albedo

alfisols a category of soils (under the American Soil Conservation Service classification system) that form under natural forest cover. It has a grey-brown, slightly acidic A horizon and a high clay content

alkaline flats deposits of high pH minerals (salts) that form on level, arid regions due to the evaporation of subsurface water—see also salt pans

alluvial fan a fan-shaped delta formed as sorted sediment is deposited in the river valley of an arid landscape

alluvial soil soil that develops from silt and sand carried by running water

alpine pertaining to mountains, as in alpine glaciation

altitude the distance a place is above sea level

anaerobically without the presence of air

angle of repose the highest angle from the horizontal that a slope can maintain stability without mass wasting occurring

anthropogenic contamination the poisoning or pollution of water or other resources due to human activities

anticlines an arch-shaped fold in rock strata—see also fold mountain

anticyclone a high pressure cell

aquifers large water deposits located underground in layers of porous rock

arboreal of, living in, or connected to trees

arches erosional features formed from the differential weathering of rock layers so that a natural portico is formed through a wall of rock

arête a sharp ridge between two cirques formed by the erosion of alpine glaciers

asthenosphere a plastic layer in the upper mantle which is thought to provide the base upon which crustal plates float

atmosphere the part of the earth that is made up of gases or vapors

aurora borealis commonly called the Northern Lights, these are lights in the skies of the upper latitudes created by charged particles sent by the sun

azimuth the angle that is formed between the horizon and highest point in the sky that a specific object reaches

B

balancing rock an erosional feature formed from the differential weathering of underlying rock layers so that a relatively large rock appears to be secured on top of a relatively narrow column—see also pedestal rock

barchan a crescent-shaped sand dune with the "horns" of the dune pointing downwind

basal slippage the forward movement of a glacier as a result of heat and friction melting the layer of a glacier in contact with the earth's surface

base level the level to which all surfaces erode, assuming tectonic stability does not interfere with gradational processes

batholith an intrusive structure created when magma fills a massive hollow or cavern, which could be hundreds of square kilometres in size

bayou a marshy area where flood water from a river accumulates in flood plains

big bang theory a widely held scientific theory that contends the creation of the universe, the Milky Way, and our solar system resulted from a violent explosion of matter

biodiversity the degree to which species are diverse and have tremendous variation in genetic structure

biogenic sedimentary rocks rocks formed from the accumulation of weathered materials that were originally living

biomass the total mass of all the organisms per hectare

biosphere the part of the earth that is made up of living organisms, such as plants, animals and bacteria

bog wetlands fed by precipitation, as opposed to rivers; usually low in nutrients

Boolean string a list of words that are logically connected and which are used to find information in electronic data bases (e.g. the Internet). For example, if you needed to find data on volcanoes that have erupted in the last 100 years you might use the following Boolean string volcano and erupt and "twentieth century"

boreal forest an ecological belt of coniferous forests that girdles the earth in the northern hemisphere from about 50° to 55° latitude.

butterfly effect the idea that random, inconsequential occurrences in the environment (such as the beat of a butterfly's wings) could affect weather patterns on the other side of the planet—see also chaos theory

C

camouflage an adaptation that allows animals to blend in with their surroundings so they are hard to see; used as a defense or hunting mechanism

cap rock a non-porous rock that prevents natural gas or oil from floating to the surface

capillary action the upward movement of water through the soil or thin tubes because of surface tension

carapace the upper shell of a lobster or other crustacean

carbohydrates organic compounds containing carbon, oxygen, and hydrogen

carbon sinks any natural feature, such as forests, oceans, or sedimentary rocks, which removes a greenhouse gas, such as carbon dioxide, from the atmosphere

carnivore a animal or plant that eats other animals

carrying capacity the number of people the earth's resources can support

cellular evolution the hypothesis that one-celled bacteria grew out of non-living amino-acids and simple chemical compounds

chaos theory the theory that natural systems, such as weather, can be dramatically and unpredictably influenced by what may seem like a minor variance in one or more contributing variable—see also butterfly effect

chemical sedimentary rocks rocks formed from the accumulation of weathered materials altered by processes such as evaporation

chemical weathering the wearing down of the earth's surface through such chemical actions as hydrolysis and oxidation

chlorofluorocarbons chemical compounds used in some refrigeration products and such industrial processes as air conditioning, the blowing of foams into molds, and the cleaning of electronic equipment. These gases, which destroy the ozone layer, are extremely stable and don't readily break down naturally

circle of illumination the line, separating day and night, that moves over the face of the earth

cirques semi-circular depressions formed in mountains as a result of the erosional action of alpine glaciers

cirrus clouds high-altitude, wispy clouds associated with warm fronts

civil engineers people who study the properties of structures such as dams, bridges and roads to ensure that they can be safely built in a given terrain

clastic sedimentary rocks rocks formed when weathered material is naturally cemented together

climax vegetation the state at which a forest reaches its maximum level of development and no new species will be naturally incorporated into the system

coking coal a compound that is formed by heating coal, and then used in the smelting process to extract iron from its ore

col a feature formed when alpine glaciers erode a depression or "pass" through a mountain ridge between two overlapping cirques

collision fault the structure created when one plate of the earth's crust slides up relative to the plate it is jamming into

colonize the act of a plant species becoming established in a new area

column a depositional feature of karst topography formed when a stalactite and a stalagmite join together to create a continuous pillar of calcium-rich stone

compound a combination of two or more elements

condensation the change of state from gas to liquid; the water that forms on cool surfaces

consumers life forms that derive the food energy they need by eating other consumers or producers

contact metamorphic rocks rocks that change because of the heat given off when intrusive igneous rocks are formed

continental climate a set of atmospheric conditions that result in winters that are relatively cold and summers relatively hot due to the absence of large water bodies

continental drift the theory proposed by Alfred Wegener that the continents float across the earth's surface on beds of molten granite; the precursor to the theory of plate tectonics

continental pertaining to continents as in continental glaciation or continental climates

contour interval the difference between lines of elevation on a contour map

contour mapping a mapping technique that uses lines of like elevation to indicate the relief and height of surface features

convection currents the movement that results when heated air or liquid rises and a cooler version rushes in to take its place

convectional flow see convection currents

convectional precipitation rain or snow that occurs as a result of the dew point being reached as warm moist air is forced up by cooler air in a convection current

coriolis effect the deflection of water and air currents to the right in the northern hemisphere and to the left in the southern hemisphere because of the rotation of the earth

crests the high point of a wave

crown die-back the degraded natural state that occurs when trees lose foliage due to acid deposition

cryosphere that part of the planet covered with ice, glaciers, and snow; pertaining to ice and snow

cumulonimbus clouds low-altitude, fluffy, gray, rain-bearing clouds associated with thunderstorms

cumulus clouds fluffy, white clouds associated with fair weather

cyclone a low pressure cell—see also anticyclone

D

daily maximum the highest temperature a place can expect for the day

decomposers plants and animals within food chains that break down other plants and animals into simple chemical compounds

delta a depositional feature found at the mouth of a river

dendritic drainage pattern a drainage pattern that resembles the branches of a tree

deposition the process whereby weathered material is laid down

deranged pattern a drainage pattern where there seems to be no organized pattern, as in regions that were recently glaciated

desertification the process whereby arable land turns to desert because of climate change

dew point elevation the altitude at which water vapor condenses at a given humidity

dew point the temperature at which water vapor condenses at a given humidity

diastrophism gradational forces acting within the earth

differential weathering the process whereby different layers of rock erode faster or slower than others because of their relative hardness

dike an intrusive structure created when magma fills a vertical crack within a geological structure

discharge rate the amount water flowing through a river; usually measured in m3 per minute

discharge the emptying of aquifers as water is removed from them

distributaries smaller rivers that flow out of larger rivers

diurnal temperature range the difference between the coldest and the warmest readings on a thermometer in a 24 hour period; if the maximum temperature was 12°C and the coldest reading was –2°C, the diurnal temperature range would be 14°C.

diurnal having to do with a 24-hour period; daily

doldrums a region, between the equator and the tropics, of stormy weather caused by rising air. Prevailing winds tend to be non-existent (calm) here because air movement is upward as opposed to along the surface

doline an erosional feature of karst topography formed when a cave collapses, forming a sink-hole

Doppler radar electronic sensors that record velocity by measuring the distance between the receiver and individual particles in the atmosphere; used to track storm clouds and tornadoes

drainage pattern the way in which water runs over the earth's surface

drift an archaic term for glacial deposits that originates from the previous misconception that glacial deposits were formed from the great Biblical flood

drumlin depositional glacial features resembling oval hills with the long axis parallel to the direction of flow

dry adiabatic heating the process that occurs when dry, cool air warms as it descends a mountain; also called Chinook Wind

dry adiabatic lapse rate the rate at which the temperature of a pocket of ascending air will cool—about 10°C per 1000 m

dust bowl a region that has been greatly eroded by winds and flash flooding due to the loss of ground cover after a drought

dynamic metamorphic rocks rocks that change because they are compressed by rock layers and tectonic forces

E

eccentricity of orbit the fluctuation of the earth's orbit from a circle to an ellipse

ecotourism the activity of visiting a country to enjoy the natural environment

eddies swirling bits of matter much like a whirlpool in a stream

electromagnetic waves radiant energy that originates from the sun

element a natural substance that cannot be broken apart by chemical or physical means

elevation altitude above sea level

elliptical oval-shaped such that the length of one chord is longer than the chord which is perpendicular to it

emergent coastlines shorelines that form either when sea level drops or coastal land rebounds to maintain isostatic equilibrium

emergents trees that grow above the forest canopy in tropical rainforests

environmental lapse rate the gradual decrease in temperature that occurs as one ascends a mountain— about 6.4° C per 1000 m

epicenter the location below the earth's surface where two plates rupture causing an earthquake

epiphytes plants that grow on other plants without taking nutrients from them (as parasites do)

equinox literally "equal night"; the date when the sun is directly over the equator (around March 20 and September 20) giving all places on earth 12 hours of night and 12 hours of daylight

erg desert with shifting sand dunes

erosion the wearing down and transport of weathered material—see also gradational processes, transport, deposition and weathering

erratic a depositional feature created by glaciers carrying large boulders from one place to another

esker a depositional feature formed when glacial meltwater flows through, under, or over a glacier. When the ice melts, a deposit of sorted sediments is left as a meandering hill

estuary the flooded mouth of a river valley usually in a submerged coastline

evapo-transpiration a term used to describe the combined processes of the evaporation of surface water and the transpiration of water from plants

exfoliation the peeling of off rock layers as surface pressure is reduced—see mechanical weathering

exposure the influence of wind on temperature and humidity

extension faults regions in the earth's crust where plates move apart—see also faults

extirpated a plant or animal that no longer lives in a region that was once part of its range; like extinct, but only in one region

extractive reserve a region set aside in a wilderness area where residents are allowed to harvest forest products without interfering with natural systems

extrusive igneous rocks rocks formed when volcanoes erupt or from extrusive volcanism

extrusive volcanism volcanic structures that occur above the earth's surface

F

fault plane the surface of a crustal plate that is exposed when one plate rides over another

faulting the geological process in which one rock mass displaces or deforms another along a fracture in the earth's surface

fens wetlands that are drained by rivers

fetch the distance wind blows over a body of water to produce waves

field verification see ground truthing

finger lakes erosional features caused by glaciers carving deep grooves in less resistant underlying rock layers

fire storm incredibly intense fires that create convectional updrafts and affect local weather systems

firn ice pellets that form from multi-year snow and provide the building blocks from which glaciers are made

fjords erosional features formed when glaciated valleys flood with sea water to form steep-walled, deep inlets

flood plains the part of a river valley that regularly floods

flux change

fold mountains mountains created through the process of folding

folding the geological process in which layers of the earth's surface are deformed into "folds" due to lateral pressure exerted from opposing sides

foliation the banding of structures found in metamorphic rocks

food chain the sequence of producers and consumers that are dependent upon each other in an ecosystem

food pyramid a diagram that shows a vertical stack of horizontal bars with each bar showing the number of plant or animals needed to support the layer above. The number of plants and animals decreases from the bottom to the top so the chart has a pyramid shape

food web several food chains joined together—see also food chain and food pyramid

fossil correlation the principle that like fossils are the same age no matter where they are discovered. Fossil correlation is useful in the dating (in relative time) of sediments and other geological deposits found in different locations where like fossils are found

fossil fuels natural materials that have been converted—through natural processes—into materials that can be burned to generate heat and light; Examples include coal, oil and natural gas

front the line where two air masses meet

frontal depression a trough of low pressure that results when warm air rises over cooler air along a front

Fujita scale a system whereby tornadoes can be rated based on the damage done

G

galaxy the term used to describe a collective number of stars, solar systems, and other objects that are concentrated in one part of the universe. The galaxy our solar system is found in is called the Milky Way

GCMs see General Circulation Model

general circulation model a sophisticated computer program that seeks to replicate weather patterns using complex mathematical algorithms

generation the formation of a tsunami resulting from a seafloor disturbance

geological time scale the measurement of time that is divided into abstract terms and subdivides rocks into geological terms, calibrated in millennia from when the earth began

geologist a person who studies geology

geology the study of the lithosphere, rocks, minerals, and all the other earth materials that relate to these objects

georeference to determine that exact position of a place on the earth's surface

geostationary referring to satellites that orbit the earth at the same speed the earth rotates so that the satellite is always over the same earth location

geotechnologies procedures and/or equipment such as computers, sensors, and other advanced devices used to measure earth processes from areas remote from the region being studied

geothermal energy power that is derived directly from forces in the lithosphere—volcanic heating, for example

glacial surge an unusually rapid glacial advance

glaciologist a person who studies glaciers

global positioning system a geotechnology that utilizes computers, satellites, and sensors to determine the exact location of the sender on the earth's surface

gräben a long depression in the earth's surface formed from the sinking of the surface through two parallel faults

gradational processes geological forces that wear down and erode surfaces and deposit sediments—see also erosion, deposition, weathering

Great Rift Valley a long depression in East Africa formed from the sinking of the surface through two parallel faults

ground truthing the use of field observations to determine statistical values derived from remotely sensed images; once values are known, it is assumed that the same values found elsewhere will represent the same surface features

Gutenberg Discontinuity the dividing line between the solid mantle and the liquid core of the earth

gyres generalized circular movements of ocean currents due to the coriolis effect, prevailing winds, and the shape of continents

H

half-life the length of time it takes a radioactive element to degrade into an isotope

hanging valleys U-shaped valleys formed as alpine glaciers erode the steep slopes of V-shaped tributary river valleys; these formations hang above the valleys where the main stream flowed

harmattan a dry desert wind found in North Africa

Hawaiian volcano a volcano type characterized by extremely fluid basaltic lava flows

headlands shorelines that project into the ocean

herbivore a consumer that eats only plants

hoarfrost frozen dew formed when nights are particularly cold and the ground is relatively warm

horizon pertaining to the layers of soil devleopment

horn an erosional feature formed in alpine glaciation when three or more cirques form a steep-sided peak

horst a long ridge formed in the earth's surface from the uplift of the surface through two parallel faults

Hubble's law the scientific law that contends that galaxies move proportionally faster as they move out from the center of a universe

human time scale the measurement of time as it relates to the length of a human life as calibrated in hours and years

humus the accumulated organic material found in soils

hurricanes severe cyclones found in the western hemisphere; called typhoons in Asia, and cyclones in Australia

hybrid a plant or animal that has been bred either naturally or through selective breeding to produce a new species

hydrocarbons compounds that contain hydrogen and carbon and are commonly used as fuels, i.e. oil, coal, natural gas

hydrolysis a form of chemical weathering in which ions of silicate are replaced with ions of water, rendering a rock into fragments

hydrosphere that part of the earth that is made up of water in all its forms

hypertemporal satellite remote-sensed data information that is derived from sensors employed on satellites and which shows differences over time

hypothesis a creative idea as to how a scientific event or entity came to be, based on a number of logical assumptions

I

igneous intrusions structures formed when molten rock filled cracks in the earth's crust

igneous rocks combinations of various minerals that were formed from volcanism

impermeable pertaining to rocks and other features that do not allow water to percolate through

insolation the amount of solar radiation a place receives based on the amount of daylight and the angle at which the sun's rays hit the earth's surface

intensity the term used to describe the amount of solar energy a place receives based on the angle of the sun, i.e. how direct the sun's rays are

interfluve the land located between two tributaries of a river

interglacial period: a climatic period between ice ages

interlobate moraine a moraine that forms between two or more lobes of a glacier, e.g. the Oak Ridges Moraine

intertropical convergence zone see thermal equator

intrusive igneous rocks rocks formed when magma solidifies underground; rocks formed from intrusive volcanism

intrusive structures volcanic structures that occur below the earth's surface

inundation flooding that occurs as a result of a tsunami, for example

ionosphere the layer of the atmosphere that starts about 80 km above the earth's surface

iso map a map that uses lines to show places with equal values, such as in contours, temperature, air pressure

isobar lines on maps that join places with equal air pressure

isohyet lines on maps that join places with equal precipitation

isostasy the movement of surface features up or down in response to the plasticity of the asthenosphere. If a great mass is removed from the earth's surface, as in the melting of a continental glacier or the drying up of an ocean, the earth's surface rebounds or rises up in response to the decreased pressure on the asthenosphere

isotherm lines on maps that join places with equal temperatures

isotope the name given to a radioactive element that has started to degrade or lose its radioactivity

J

jet stream air currents in the stratosphere that influence the movement of storms

K

kames hills formed in moraines when large amounts of load accumulate in one part of a glacier and are left in situ when the glacier melts

karst a limestone landscape where there is little surface water but abundant caves and underground river features

kettles hollows, often lakes and wetlands, formed in moraines when large amounts of ice accumulate in one part of a glacier and are left behind when the glacier retreats

kinetic energy the energy of movement

L

lacoliths intrusive features created when magma fills a hollow or cavern within a geological structure

lacustrine pertaining to lakes as in lacustrine deposits or lacustrine plains

lacustrine plain depositional feature formed from deposits laid down in a glacial ponding

landscape systems dynamic places in nature where energy flows through the different elements of the lithosphere, hydrosphere, atmosphere, and biosphere

lateral moraines moraines that form along the sides of alpine glaciers

leached a term to describe soils that have had their water-soluble minerals washed away

leaching the washing away of water-soluble minerals from soils; also, the precipitation of harmful chemicals and other forms of anthropogenic contamination into aquifers levees: depositional features that result from river sediment being deposited along river banks. In rivers of old age, levees can create a river channel above the flood plain

light year the distance light travels in one year (approximately 9.5 x 109 km)

lithosphere that part of the earth that is made up of rocks and minerals

load the material carried by gradational agents such as rivers, glaciers, and waves

longitudinal dunes depositional features found in deserts made up of hills of sand that run parallel to the prevailing winds

longshore drift a depositional feature formed when wave action drags sand along the shoreline as waves break at angles on the beach

M

magma chamber a pocket of molten rock within a volcano

magma conduit the tube through which magma flows

magma molten rock that flows beneath the earth's surface; it is often confused with lava, molten rock that flows on the earth's surface

magnetopause the dividing line between the atmosphere and space

magnetosphere the part of the atmosphere that has a magnetic field produced by the movement of the liquid core of the earth

mantle the layers of the earth found between the core and the crust

maritime air mass air masses that develop over oceans

maritime climate a set of atmospheric conditions (relatively mild winters and relatively cool summers) that results from proximity to a large body of water

maritime winds bodies of air that move from the sea in over the land in the daytime and from the land out to sea at night. These winds are caused by convection currents

marshes wetlands that form along the edges of lakes or in potholes

mass wasting a gradational process that results from weathered material sliding down a slope because of the force of gravity

mean the average—add the numbers and divide the sum by the number of members in the sample

meander scar an oxbow lake that has dried up leaving a dry hollow where the river channel had once been

meander a sinuous back and forth sweep of a river in old age

mechanical weathering the wearing down of the earth's surface through the friction of erosive forces such as running water and wind

medial moraine a lateral moraine that ends up between two alpine glaciers as they converge

median the middle number when the members of a sample are listed numerically

mesopause the boundary in the layers of the atmosphere between the mesosphere and the ionosphere

mesosphere the layer of the atmosphere that starts about 55 km above the earth's surface and extends to about 80 km from the earth's surface

mineral an inorganic compound of one or more elements found naturally in the lithosphere

mixed forest a stand of trees made up of coniferous and deciduous trees

mode the most common number in a sample population

moraine a depositional feature associated with glaciation that occurs when glaciers retreat or melt and consequently drop their load

moratorium a halt in the harvesting of a natural resource to allow stocks to replenish

muskeg a wetland created when the active layer of the permafrost melts

mutant an individual with characteristics that are different from their ancestors; evolution occurs when a mutant is better adapted to current environmental conditions than other members of the species

N

natural selection the process whereby a species evolves to adapt to a particular environment or fails to survive

neap tide unusually low tides because the sun's gravitational pull is partially negating the gravitational pull of the moon

negative correlation a relationship between two variables in which one set of statistics increases while the other decreases

niche a place in a food web where there is little competition, so a species with specific adaptations has a competitive advantage over other species (e.g., giraffes are able to reach leaves on trees too tall for other herbivores to reach)

nimbostratus clouds low altitude clouds associated with frontal precipitation

nuclear energy the power created when an atom is split either naturally or artificially through the process of nuclear fission

nuée ardente a glowing cloud of poisonous, volcanic gases that may occur during an eruption and suffocate victims

O

occluded front a front in which the cold air dominates the weather on ground but a warm mass is present aloft

ocean currents rivers of water flowing through the oceans; cold currents flow from the poles while warm currents flow from the equator

omnivore a consumer that eats plants and animals

orographic precipitation rainfall, snow etc. that occurs because the dew point is reached as winds are forced to rise up over landforms such as mountains

outwash fan a depositional feature, the same as an alluvial fan or delta, formed from glacial meltwater

oxbow lake an area of poor drainage that occurs when a meander is cut off from the main river channel thus forming a lake or slough

oxidation the process whereby rocks oxidize

oxidize the process whereby elements in rock are combined chemically with oxygen

ozone layer the layer in the stratosphere where there are concentrations of ozone (O_3)

ozone a form of oxygen (made up of three oxygen atoms) that is created by strong electro-magnetic currents such as radiant solar energy passing through atmospheric oxygen (O_2)

P

parabolic dunes depositional features made of hills of sand that are stabilized by vegetation at each end

parallel drainage pattern a drainage pattern in which the tributaries join the main river at (more or less) right angles

parasites organisms that grow on other living organisms and take nutrients from them

parent material see regolith

peat an organic mat formed from slowly rotting vegetation in a wetland

pedestal rock an erosional feature formed from the differential weathering of underlying rock layers so a relatively large rock layer is balanced on top of a relatively narrow column

pedologist one who studies soils

perennial legume a plant that lives for more than one year and that fixes nitrogen directly from the air in the soil through bacteria that live symbiotically on its roots. As a result, it naturally improves soil fertility

perennial a plant that lives for more than one year

peridotite a rock which is formed in the mantle and is rarely found on the earth's surface

periglacial pertaining to landscapes that were recently glaciated (in geological time, i.e. 10000 ybp)

permafrost permanently frozen ground

permeable referring to rock or soil that allows water to flow straight through, like sand or limestone

photosynthesis the process whereby plants convert sunlight, nutrients, carbon dioxide, and water into plant material. Oxygen is given off as a by-product of this process

pingo a periglacial feature caused from the freezing of former wetlands

pioneer plants producers that colonize a region that has little or no vegetative cover due to natural or human causes

pioneer species any species that colonizes a region that has no or little vegetative cover for one reason or another

pirated river a river that has been captured by another river

pitcher plant a carnivorous plant found in areas having nutrient-poor soils, such as Newfoundland

pixels the tiny squares into which computer monitor screens are divided. Statistically each has a different numeric value that can be manipulated to show earth relationships

placer deposits sedimentary deposits of marketable minerals that are found in rivers downstream from mineral veins

placosols fertile red clay soils formed from red sandstone and shale and found in Atlantic Canada, for example

plates sections of crust that float on the upper mantle or asthenosphere

polar easterlies prevailing winds blowing from east to west between the North Pole and the Arctic Circle and the South Pole and the Antarctic Circle

ponding a depositional feature formed when glacial meltwater is trapped either by ice or moraines and forms a temporary lake where lacustrine deposits are laid down

positive correlation in statistical analysis, the relationship between two variables in which both sets of statistics increase

precession of the equinoxes the annual shifting of the equinox (about 8 metres each year) north and south due to the changing tilt of the earth. It is believed to be partially responsible for causing the ice ages

precipitate the depositing of a mineral because the solution in which it was dissolved has become saturated

prescribed burn fires that are purposely set to reduce accumulated brush and forest litter so that a major forest fire will not occur and destroy tree crowns

prevailing winds bodies of air that tend to flow in one direction because of convectional flows and the coriolis effect

primary consumer see herbivore

process of sedimentation the gradual filling in of lakes and other depressions with layers of silt, dust, and other materials that float freely in the air

processes of gradation geological forces that wear down and erode surfaces and deposit sediments on them

producer a life form that creates living matter from the sun through the process of photosynthesis, i.e. plants

profile the cross-sectional view of a portion of a contour map created through the use of contour lines

propagation pertaining to the way in which tsunamis increase in size

protoplanet a lump of matter that will eventually form into a planet

proximity of water bodies the climatic factor which brings milder winter temperatures and cooler summer temperatures to the area bordering the water body

R

radial drainage pattern a drainage pattern that forms around a cone-shaped hill or mountain, such as a volcano

radiometric dating the use of radioactive isotopes to date the age of a rock based on the principle that radioactive elements degrade over set times

radiosondes weather balloons with attached instruments

rain shadow the leeward side of a mountain valley where descending air is dried by the adiabatic lapse rate and is abnormally dry when compared to the windward side of the mountain

recharge the filling of aquifers naturally from wetlands, lakes, and other water repositories

region an area of the earth's surface having similar characteristics

regolith the weathered bedrock from which soils are formed

rejuvenation the "rebirth" of a river as the base level is readjusted downward due to an isostatic adjustment or change in sea level

relative time changes that are measured in relation to other events. For example, a river valley may have been created after a period of continental glaciation but before a flood

relief: the degree to which a surface is flat or rough. A terrain with low relief is relatively flat while a region with high relief is rugged

remote sensing the use of sensors to study objects that are physically inaccessible

resolution the number of pixels contained on a computer screen. High resolution means there are many pixels, while low resolution means there are few pixels

Richter scale a measurement system used to determine the relative strength of earthquakes. It is a logarithmic scale, so a reading of 7 is 10 times the power of a level 6 earthquake

rift valley a long depression in the earth's surface formed from the sinking of the surface through two parallel faults

ring of fire the almost continuous line of volcanoes and tectonically active regions that circle the Pacific ocean

riparian zone an ecosystem running along a water course dominated by water-loving plants and animals

river capture see also pirated river

S

salt pans deposits of salt formed from the evaporation of subsurface water. As the water disappears, the mineral salts held in suspension are left on the surface

saltation part of a river's load that is dragged and bounced along the river bottom because the particles are so large that they are neither suspended or dissolved in the water that carries it

saturated zone the layer where ground water accumulates under the earth's surface

sclerophyll a scrub vegetation type found in regions of low summer rainfall (mediterranean ecoregion)

scree slope a hill formed at the base of a cliff from weathered material deposited by mass wasting

secondary consumer see carnivore

sedimentary rocks combinations of various minerals that were formed as sediments became cemented together

sedimentation the filling in of wetlands and lakes by layers of deposited silt and other materials

seigneural system a land settlement pattern that allowed many people access to the river by dividing the land along it into very long, narrow lots, with the narrow side fronting the river. It is common in Quebec

seismic analysis the examination of waves formed from earth vibrations; often used to prospect for oil and natural gas

seismograph a chart that shows the vibrations that occur when shock waves travel through geological structures

seismology the study of vibrations. By studying sound waves as they travel through a geological formation, seismologists are able to determine the characteristics of these formations. Seismology has many applications including earthquake and volcano prediction as well as the prospecting for hydrocarbons

selective cutting the forestry technique used in which only selected, marketable trees are harvested and other species are left undisturbed

sheeting see exfoliation

shoaling the action that occurs when a tsunami reaches a shoreline

sial the part of the earth's crust that lies beneath the continents and is made up primarily of silicon and aluminum

sills intrusive structures created when magma fills a horizontal crack within a geological structure

sima the part of the earth's crust that lies beneath the oceans and is made up primarily of silicon and magnesium

skerries terminal moraines that form at the mouths of fjords as a series of islands

slag the left-over, solid-waste product formed from smelting

slash and burn agriculture the subsistence farming practice in which a portion of the forest is cleared for temporary gardens, which may last two to five or more years depending on soil fertility. Once the soil becomes infertile, the plot is abandoned and the forest naturally replenishes the degraded soil

slope failure the inability of a slope to maintain its shape due to such factors as tectonic instability, moisture, or lack of vegetation

smelters industrial plants that remove impurities (especially sulphur) from ore through the use of heat

smelting the process of removing impurities from ore

snow line the line seen on air photos that indicates the point past which the snow never melts

soil creep the movement of soil down a slope

soil horizons the layers which make up soil; the A horizon contains humus and litter; the B horizon is a mixture of regolith and organic matter; the C horizon is mainly regolith

soil respiration the process whereby soil gives off carbon dioxide

solar wind streams of radioactive particles sent to the earth from the sun

solifluction a form of mass wasting that occurs when water-soaked soil causes slope failure on unusually shallow grades because frozen subsoil reduces subsurface drainage

solstice literally "sun stop"; the date when the sun is directly over the Tropic of Cancer (around June 20) or the Tropic of Capricorn (December 20). The winter solstice occurs in December in the Northern Hemisphere and the summer solstice occurs in June in the Northern Hemisphere

solution sediment that is dissolved in the water that carries it

sorted sediment deposits laid down in flowing water that gradually decrease in size from large particles to gradually smaller ones as the flow velocity decreases

source region the place over which an air mass develops

spelunking the act of exploring caves

spillways erosional features in the form of giant river valleys that are created as massive volumes of meltwater flow out from glaciers

spodosols acidic soils found where drainage is poor and coniferous trees dominate

spring tide an unusually high tide due to the fact that the sun's gravitational pull is in line with the gravitational pull of the moon

stalactite a depositional feature created from the discharged load of calcium-rich water dripping from cave ceilings

stalagmite a depositional feature created from the discharged load of calcium-rich water dripping onto cave floor

star dune a sand that resemble a star because the wind direction is variable

stratopause the layer of the atmosphere that lies between the stratosphere and the mesosphere

stratosphere the layer of the atmosphere that starts about 21 km above the earth's surface and extends to about 55 km from the earth's surface

stratus clouds gray, poorly defined clouds associated with frontal precipitation

strike slip fault: the lateral movement of one plate past another

stromatolite rock formations created from the accumulation of blue-green algae and sediments over millions of years

subducting the process whereby one fault slides under another

subduction fault regions in the earth's crust where one plate slides under another submerged coastline: shorelines that form either when sea level rises or coastal land subsides

sun-synchronous a term describing a satellite orbit that moves at the same speed as the sun so that the satellite is always in daylight

superposition the principle that sediments increase in age as one digs down into the earth's surface; logically new sediments are deposited on top of older. Exceptions occur when folding and other geological processes disrupt normal geological processes

surface runoff the water that drains off the land after a storm

surface tension the tension or elastic membrane formed by water or any liquid, which causes the surface to bulge up without spilling over

suspension in river dynamics that part of the load that is carried by water without touching the streambed

sustainable resource management an approach to harvesting raw materials that allows the resource to grow back or reproduce faster than it is being extracted from nature

swamps wetlands where trees grow

symbiotic relationship an associations that exist among species that allow for each to prosper because of the actions of the other

synclines valleys formed through the folding process

T

taiga an ecological belt of stunted coniferous forests and wetlands that girdles the earth in the Northern Hemisphere between 55° and 60° latitude. It is a transition between the boreal forest and the tundra

tectonic stability the degree to which the crust is permanent or unmoved by earthquakes, or isostasy

temperature inversion a situation that exists when the air is warmer some distance above the earth's surface as compared to air directly above the surface. It often occurs in valleys where cold air sinks into the valley

temporary base level a base level that is achieved when an outlet to the ocean is cut off so that an inland sea or salt lake is formed

terminal moraine moraines that form at the end of alpine glaciers

terraces features found along emergent shorelines indicating where the former shoreline had been when the land was relatively lower than sea level

theory an idea that results when a hypothesis is supported by observation and scientific inquiry

thermal equator the parallel of latitude (between the Tropic of Cancer and the Tropic of Capricorn) over which the sun is directly located on any given day of the year

thermal expansion the breaking up of rocks due to heating and cooling

thermo-haline currents ocean flows that occur because of differences in the salt content of sea water

thermosphere see ionosphere

tornado warning a bulletin issued by the weather office when a tornado has been spotted

tornado watch a warning issued by the weather office when conditions are right for the formation of tornadoes

tornado an intense cyclone common in the spring an early summer as cold fronts pass through air masses that have strong convectional flows

trade winds air movement across the surface of the earth from east to west between the Tropic of Cancer and the equator, and the Tropic of Capricorn and the equator

translucent allowing light to pass through without being transparent

transport the movement of weathered material from one place to another

transverse dune a giant ripple-like sand dune formed at a right angle to the direction of the prevailing wind

trellis drainage a drainage pattern in which tributaries join the main river at right angles, creating a structure resembling a garden trellis

tremors vibrations in the earth's surface

tributaries smaller rivers that flow into larger rivers

tropical depression a region of low pressure caused by convectional flows over heated water bodies in the low latitudes

tropical storm a tropical depression that has wind speeds under 63 km/hr

tropopause the layer of atmosphere that lies between the troposphere and the stratosphere

troposphere the layer of the atmosphere closest to the earth's surface

trough in meteorology a line of low air pressure; or, the low point of a sea wave in trowel see occluded front 1a giant wave caused from tectonic instability on the sea floor

twilight zone the transition between day and night seen on the circle of illumination

U

uniformitarianism the principle that assumes that natural forces that occur on earth are universal and do not change no matter where else in the universe they occur or when they have occurred in the geological time scale

unsaturated zone the layer of the earth that has no water or a further capacity to hold water

upwind against the direction of the wind

V

variation in tilt the gradual change in the earth's tilt on its axis between 23.5° and 24.4°

vesuvian volcano a highly explosive volcano formed when a volcanic plug prevents the release of built up gasses in the magma chamber and magma conduit

viticulture the growing of grapes for the purpose of making wine

volcanic plug the solidified structure that seals a vesuvian volcano, thus rendering the volcano extremely explosive as gasses build within the magma conduit and magma chamber

volcanism the geological process in which layers of the earth's surface are changed because of up-wellings of magma and other materials either beneath the earth's surface or on top of the earth's surface

W

wadi a dry river bed found in an aeolian landscape

water table the level between the saturated zone and the unsaturated zone

wave refraction the bending of waves around headlands

wave trains the organized procession of waves as they come ashore

weathering the wearing down of the earth's surface

wind chill how much colder a temperature actually feels to humans because of the wind

wind duration the length of time air flows in the same direction over a surface

wind gaps dry valleys that result from a river capture

wind shear the movement of wind—usually from the southwest—that occurs when a tornado is formed

wind velocity the speed with which air moves over the earth's surface

X

xerophytic pertaining to plants adapted to dry climates

Y

yazoo stream a tributary that runs parallel to the main stream because it is unable to cut through the levee

Z

zero tillage an agricultural method in which the ground is not turned over or "tilled" between crops

zone of ablation the part of a glacier where snow accumulates

zoogeographers scientists that study the geographic range of animals

Text and Illustration Credits

4 Adapted from 'Japan volcano erupts, 15,000 flee billowing ash' by Toshiyuki Aizawa, Reuters News Service, 3 April 2000.

9 Adapted from *Canadian Oxford School Atlas*, 7th Edition, by Quentin Stanford (Toronto: Oxford University Press, 1998). Reprinted by permission.

19 MAURICIO ANTON/NGS Image Collection

40 Selcan Hacaoglu, 'Out of rubble from Turkey earthquake comes 'a miracle'', The Associated Press, 23 August 1999. Reprinted with permission of The Associated Press.

45 Adapted from *The World Book Encyclopedia* © 2001 World Book, Inc., by permission of the publisher. www.worldbook.com

57 ROB WOOD/NGS Image Collection

73 NGS CARTOGRAPHIC (MAP ONLY)/NGS Image Collection

73 ROB WOOD/NGS Image Collection

112 Adaptation from 'Venezuelan officials try to clear their consciences in claims that millions of poor have illegally invaded the mountainsides' from Vheadline.com. Reprinted by permission.

140 Map of Gros Morne National Park (Parks Canada) adapted with the permission of the Minister of Public Works and Government Services Canada, 2001.

141-42 Figures from *Rocks Adrift*, Second Edition, Michael Burzynski, (Rocky Harbour, NF: Gros Morne Co-operating Association, 1995), pp. 20, 21, 25, 26, 28, 32, and 33   Public Works and Government Services Canada

150 Adapted from 'Searching for Answers' by John Nicol with Cheryl Hawkes, *Maclean's*, 12 June 2000. Reprinted by permission of Maclean's Magazine.

163 Adapted from Environment Canada, 'Groundwater Flow,' Groundwater--Nature's Hidden Treasure. Freshwater Series A-5. Reproduced with permission, 2001. Available on Environment Canada's Freshwater Website at: http://www.ec.gc.ca/water/en/nature/grdwtr/e_gdwtr.htm

208 Adaptation of map of Permafrost regions of Canada from Environment Canada Website, Geological Survey of Canada

218 Adapted from 'Effects of global warming clear in Canadian Arctic' by David Ljunggren, Reuters News Service, 20 April 2000.

315 'Global warming seen doubling heat deaths by 2020', Reuters News Service, 22 November 2000

317 'Scientists say Europe's growing season lengthening', Reuters News Service, 26 February 1999

318 Adaptation of map, 'The Weather - The Facts', from *New Internationalist*, Issue 319, December 1999, reprinted with permission.

322 Comparison of local temperatures and atmospheric concentrations of methane and carbon dioxide in Antarctica over the past 160,000 years from *Understanding Atmospheric Change*, (Ottawa: Environment Canada, State of the Environment: 1991), SOE Report 91-2 Public Works and Government Services Canada

325 Projected and Observed 20th Century Temperature Trends; Solar Radiation 1900-2000; Mean Summer and Winter Temperature Changes for 2050; Precipitation % Change 2010-2030, 2040-2060, and 2080-2100; Temperature Change °C 2010-2030, 2040-2060, 2080-2100: Adapted from *Projections for Canada's Climate Future*, Henry G. Hengeveld, Meteorological Service of Canada, Catalogue En57-2000-01E (Environment Canada, 2000) with the permission of the Minister of Public Works and Government Services Canada 2001.

334 'In Logged Forests, Hunting of Wildlife Becomes Deadly 'Second Harvest'' from Science Daily

340 Adapted from *Fundamentals of Physical Geography* by David Briggs, Peter Smithson, Timothy Ball (Toronto: Copp Clark Pitman, 1989). Reprinted by permission of Pearson Education Canada Inc.

348 Adapted by permission of Dr H. Seino, National Institute of Agro-Environmental Sciences.

367 Adapted from *Fundamentals of Physical Geography* by David Briggs, Peter Smithson, Timothy Ball (Toronto: Copp Clark Pitman, 1989). Reprinted by permission of Pearson Education Canada Inc.

396 Illustration of Airborne Laser Terrain Mapping Adapted by permission of TopScan GmBH.

426 Adaptation of illustration of how satellites work from Satellite Atlas of the World, (Washington, DC: National Geographic Society, 1998), p. 12

50-386 Figures 4.9, 4.13, 5.9, 5.14, 7.15, 8.13, 11.5, 19.5, 22.15 include images customized from Mountain High Maps® copyright© 1993 Digital Wisdom, Inc.

Every reasonable effort has been made to trace the original source of text material, illustrations, and photographs contained in this book. Where the attempt has been unsuccessful, the publisher would be pleased to hear from copyright holders to rectify any omissions.

Photo Credits

1 Koji Saschara; 6 NASA; 7 NASA; 10 NASA; 11 Corbis/Magma; 13 NASA; 17 Rob Norman; Ken Lucas/Visuals Unlimited; 23 Al Harvey; 24 A. J. Copley/Visuals Unlimited; 28 NASA; 33 Ron Chasmer; 37 Mark Epstein/Visuals Unlimited; 39 Tim Haifu/Visuals Unlimited; 41 Eyal Warshaysky/Visuals Unlimited; 42 Walt Anderson/Visuals Unlimited; Science VU/Visuals Unlimited; 43 (t) NASA, (m) Dick Hemingway, (m) NASA, (m) Robert E. Barber/Visuals Unlimited, (b) George Herben/Visuals Unlimited; 46 (tl) Norm Piluke/Ivy Images, (bl) Roger Wifney/Ivy Images, (tr) V. Last/Geographical Visual Aids, (br) Rob & Ann Simpson/Visuals Unlimited; 56 Enric Marti/AP; 68 US Geoglogical Survey; 70 Canada Map Company; 74 Bettmann/Corbis; 75 US Geological Survey; 78 Corbis/Magma; 85 Arthur R. Hill/Visuals Unlimited; 86 V. Last/Geographical Visual Aids; Ron Chasmer; 87 V. Last/Geographical Visual Aids; 88 Pamela Gore; 90 J.A. Wilkinson/VALAN; 91 (t) Bolstad/Panos, (b) Smith/Panos; 94 Ekati Mine; 95 Ekati Mine; 104 Ron Chasmer; 105 Ron Chasmer; 106 Ron Chasmer; V. Last/Geographical Visual Aids; 107 Ron Chasmer; 108 Paul Chiasson/CP Archive; 109 NASA; 111 Ken Lucas/Visuals Unlimited; 113 Silvia Inquierdo/AP; 121 NASA; 122 John Gerlach/Visuals Unlimited; 124 Ron Chasmer; 126 Ottmar Bierwagen/Ivy Images; 127 NASA; 129 Pavel Rahman/AP; 133 Ron Chasmer; 136 Canada Map Company; 138 Al Harvey; 139 Al Harvey; 140 Gros Morne National Park; 143 Gros Morne National Park; 144 Gros Morne National Park; 149 Mark Gibson/Visuals Unlimited; 150 Kevin Frayer/CP Archive; 152 Fred Banyendum/Spectrum Stock/Ivy Images; 153 (t) NASA, (m) Dick Hemingway, (m) NASA, (m) Robert E. Barber/Visuals Unlimited, (b) George Herben/Visuals Unlimited; 157 Bill Ivy/Ivy Images; 159 NASA; 161 Jeff J. Daly/Visuals Unlimited; 164 Bob Sacha Photography; 170 Kim Heacox/Ivy Images; 177 Laurie Grace; 179 NASA; 180 Ottmar Bierwagen/Ivy Images; 182 Ron Chasmer; 185 Canada In Stock/Ivy Images; 186 NASA; 187 NASA; 190 Glenn Oliver/Visuals Unlimited, Ottmar Bierwagen/Canada In Stock/Ivy Images; 191 Jacques Boissinot/CP Archive; 197 Ron Chasmer; 199 John Mahler/Toronto Star; 200 Bill Ivy/Ivy Images; 204 Patrick McClosky/Ivy Images; 205 Armstrong, R. 2001 "State of the Cryosphere." National Snow and Ice Data Center. [cited 31 January 2001]; 206 Meterological Service of Canada; 207 Armstrong, R. 2001 "State of the Cryosphere." National Snow and Ice Data Center. [cited 31 January 2001]; 219 Steve McCutcheon/Visuals Unlimited; 220 Mark Schneider/Visuals Unlimited; 221 (t) NASA, (m) Dick Hemingway, (m) NASA, (m) Robert E. Barber/Visuals Unlimited, (b) George Herben/Visuals Unlimited; 226 NASA; 233 Ron Chasmer; 241 Dick Hemingway; 243 Paul Orser/Ivy Images; 244 Ivy Images; 248 Paul Orser/Ivy Images; 252 Dick Hemingway; Rob & Ann Simpson/Visuals Unlimited; 254 Craig Robertson/CP Archive; 255 NASA; 262 James W. Richardson/Visuals Unlimited; 266 NASA; 269 Canadian Geographic; 269 NOAA-14 Image of the 20th of July 1996. Received and digitally processed by the Satellite Receiving Station (STARIMSAT) and Remote Sensing Laboratory, Universite du Quebec a Chicoutimi; 272 NASA; 274 Corbis/Magma; 278 Adrian Wyld/CP Archive; 287 Environment Canada; 291 NASA; 292 Environment Canada; 297 © Jim Unger. Laughingstock Licensing Inc. All rights reserved; 301 Ottmar Bierwagen/Ivy Images; 302 Corbis/Magma; 307 Corbis/Magma; 308 Bachmann/Ivy Images; 316 Greg Baker/CP Archive, Kevin Frayer/CP Archive; 335 Nancy Stone/Chicago Tribune; 336 Stone; 337 (t) NASA, (m) Dick Hemingway, (m) NASA, (m) Robert E. Barber/Visuals Unlimited, (b) George Herben/Visuals Unlimited; 339 Fritz Polking/Visuals Unlimited; 343 Jerome Wexler/Visuals Unlimited; 345 NASA; 346 Science VU/Visuals Unlimited; 349 NASA; 360 (tl) Inga Spence/Visuals Unlimited, (tr) Steve McCutcheon/Visuals Unlimited, (m) Steve McCutcheon/Visuals Unlimited, (bl) Jane Thomas/Visuals Unlimited, (br) Cheyenne Rouse/Visuals Unlimited; 366 David Sieren/Visuals Unlimited; 368 David Sieren/Visuals Unlimited; 369 Ivy Images; 370 Robin Karpan/Visuals Unlimited; 379 Inga Spence/Visuals Unlimited; 380 (tl) David Wrobel/Visuals Unlimited, (tr) Glenn M. Oliver/Visuals Unlimited, (bl) Jeff Greenberg/Visuals Unlimited; 385 (tl) Ken Lucas/Visuals Unlimited, (m) Gerald & Buff Corsi/Visuals Unlimited, (b) Joe McDonald/Visuals Unlimited; 386 (tl) Ken Lucas/Visuals Unlimited, (tr) Thomas Gula/Visuals Unlimited, (br) Joe McDonald/Visuals Unlimited; 389 Doug Bryant Photography; 392 Corbis/Magma; 394 G. Prance/Visuals Unlimited; 395 Corbis/Magma; 397 Ivy Images; 401 Steve McCutcheon/Visuals Unlimited; 404 Martin G. Miller/Visuals Unlimited; 406 James Alan Brown/Visuals Unlimited; 408 Corbis/Magma; 409 Jon Turk/Visuals Unlimited; 414 (tl) Steve McCutcheon/Visuals Unlimited, (tr) A. J. Cunningham/Visuals Unlimited; 415 (l) John Sohlden/Vis uals Unlimited, (r) Steve McCutcheon/Visuals Unlimited; 416 CP Archive; 417 Ivy Images; 424 (l) Jeff Greenberg/Visuals Unlimited, (r) Ivy Images; 425 NASA; 427 NASA; 428 Brian Rogers/Visuals Unlimited; 430 Jeff Greenberg/Visuals Unlimited; 432 Robin Karpan/Visuals Unlimited; 432 National Archives of Canada C-114467; 433 National Archives of Canada 1366-8; 435 National Archives of Canada PA-139647; 439 Tom Uhlman/Visuals Unlimited; 441 Inga Spence/Visuals Unlimited

Index